A Journey into Bioethics: Complete with Classic Cases

Custom Edition

Ronald Munson

CENGAGE
Learning·

Australia • Brazil • Japan • Korea • Mexico • Singapore • Spain • United Kingdom • United States

CENGAGE
Learning·

A Journey into Bioethics: Complete with Classic Cases Custom Edition

Intervention and Reflection: Basic Issues in Bioethics, Ninth Edition
Ronald Munson
© 2012, 2008, 2004 Cengage Learning. All rights reserved.

Senior Manager, Student Engagement:
Linda deStefano
Janey Moeller

Manager, Student Engagement:
Julie Diering

Marketing Manager:
Rachel Kloos

Manager, Production Editorial:
Kim Fry

Manager, Intellectual Property Project Manager:

Brian Methe

Senior Manager, Production and Manufacturing:

Donna M. Brown

Manager, Production:

Terri Dailey

For product information and technology assistance, contact us at
Cengage Learning Customer & Sales Support, 1-800-354-9706

For permission to use material from this text or product,
submit all requests online at **cengage.com/permissions**
Further permissions questions can be emailed to
permissionrequest@cengage.com

This book contains select works from existing Cengage Learning resources and was produced by Cengage Learning Custom Solutions for collegiate use. As such, those adopting and/or contributing to this work are responsible for editorial content accuracy, continuity and completeness.

Compilation © 2014 Cengage Learning

ISBN-13: 978-1-305-00368-2

ISBN-10: 1-305-00368-3

WCN: 01-100-101

Cengage Learning

5191 Natorp Boulevard
Mason, Ohio 45040
USA

Cengage Learning is a leading provider of customized learning solutions with office locations around the globe, including Singapore, the United Kingdom, Australia, Mexico, Brazil, and Japan. Locate your local office at: **international.cengage.com/region.**
Cengage Learning products are represented in Canada by Nelson Education, Ltd.
For your lifelong learning solutions, visit **www.cengage.com /custom.**
Visit our corporate website at **www.cengage.com.**

Printed in the United States of America

Brief Contents

Preface

In shaping the ninth edition of this book, I have tried to capture both the intellectual excitement and the great seriousness that surround bioethics. I've done my best, in particular, to convey these aspects to those new to the field. By emphasizing cases and presenting relevant medical, scientific, and social information, I introduce readers to the basic issues and make them active participants in the enterprise of deliberation and problem solving.

I believe that everyone at every level of knowledge or intellectual sophistication will find this a useful and engaging book.

Topics

The topics are all fundamental ones in bioethics. They reflect the range and variety of the problems we now confront and involve ethical and social issues that have excited the most immediate concern. But more than this, the problems raised are so profoundly serious that they lead people to turn hopefully to philosophical consideration in search of satisfactory resolutions.

Readings

The readings present current thinking about the topics and show that such consideration can be worthwhile. All are readable and nontechnical, and many reveal bioethics at its best. Although philosophers are strongly represented, the authors also include jurists, scientists, clinical researchers, social critics, and practicing physicians. The moral problems of medicine always have scientific, social, legal, and economic aspects, and to deal with them sensibly and thoroughly, we need the knowledge and perceptions of people from a variety of disciplines.

I have also opted for diversity in another way: by trying to see to it that opposing viewpoints are presented for major topics.

Part of the intellectual excitement of bioethics is generated by the searing controversies surrounding its issues, and to ignore these conflicts would be misleading. Even worse, it would deny readers the opportunity of dealing directly with proposals and arguments incompatible with their own views. Hence, I've felt an obligation to raise issues that some would prefer to ignore and to present proposals to resolve them that others reject as wrong or even immoral. I hold, along with most reasonable people, that we must face our problems and consider all proposed solutions seriously. Otherwise, rational inquiry evaporates and power and prejudice take its place.

Chapter Structure

Each chapter for the first five Parts of this book is like a sandwich with several layers. Each opens with a set of Case Presentations and Social Contexts (the number and variety vary by chapter), which are followed by the chapter's Briefing Session. The Readings appear next, and after them the Decision Scenarios.

Case Presentations

In the Case Presentations, I sketch out important cases in bioethics in narrative accounts. These are the Cases that have faced us with crucial issues and shaped our thinking about what we believe is morally legitimate in various areas of clinical practice and medical and biological research.

Some of the people at the focus of the cases are familiar. Nearly everyone has heard of Nadya Suleman ("the Octomom"),

Terry Schiavo, Karen Quinlan, Jack Kevorkian, and Dax Cowart. The most important aspect of the Case Presentations, in my view, is that they remind us that, in dealing with bioethical questions, we are not engaged in some purely intellectual abstract game. Real lives are often at stake, and real people may suffer or die.

Social Contexts

The Social Context sections provide information relevant to understanding the current social, political, or biomedical situation in which issues are being debated. They offer a broader and deeper view of problems like distributing health care under the new Affordable Care Act, dealing with the AIDS pandemic, and regulating the practice of fertility clinics.

If we hope to raise the level of public discussion of an issue and genuinely inform the life of our society, we must understand and consider the social situation in which the issue arises.

Briefing Sessions

In the Briefing Session in each chapter, I discuss some of the specific moral problems that occur in medical and biological practice, research, and policymaking. In addition, I present whatever factual information is needed to understand how such problems arise. Finally, I suggest the ways moral theories or principles might be used to resolve some problems. My suggestions, in any event, are offered only as starting points in the search for satisfactory answers.

Readings

The Readings make up the next, and perhaps most important, layer of a chapter sandwich. They provide the variety of basic arguments and viewpoints relevant to the problems addressed by the chapter. While each selection stands alone, I have tried to present opposing positions together to give a fair and even-handed view of the questions involved. The

multiplicity of topics addressed in the book means, however, that I could not always represent the varieties and strengths of a general point of view. The arguments are offered to prompt inquiry, not to make it unnecessary.

Decision Scenarios

The Decision Scenarios constitute the final component of each chapter. These are brief, dramatic presentations of situations in which moral questions are crucial or in which ethical or social-policy decisions have to be made. The scenarios are followed by questions asking the reader to decide what the problems are and how they might best be dealt with. Thus, the Decision Scenarios are really exercises in bioethics that can direct and structure reflection and discussion.

Foundations of Bioethics

For some readers, the most important feature of this book may be Part VI, "Foundations of Bioethics." In the first section here, I sketch the basics of five major ethical theories and indicate how they might be used to answer particular moral questions in medicine and research. In the second section, I present and illustrate several major moral principles. These principles are endorsed (or at least expressed in practice) by virtually all ethical theories. Even so, I do not try to demonstrate how the principles follow from or are consistent with particular theories. In the third section, I present the fundamental ideas of three ethical theories usually framed as not involving principles: virtue ethics, care ethics, and feminist ethics.

The main purpose in these sections is to give those without a background in ethics the information they need to frame and evaluate moral arguments about the issues in bioethics.

Tables of Contents

To make it easier to navigate the book, in addition to the main Table of Contents, I have included a Contents section at the beginning of each chapter. The chapter contents section lists the Case Presentations and Social Contexts in the chapter and also spells out the major subheadings of the Briefing Sessions. The Contents pages are designed to reveal all the topics covered in the chapter at a glance and prevent readers from getting lost in the thicket of cases and discussions.

Notes and References

The Section on Notes and References section lists sources for materials used in the Cases, Briefing Sessions, Social Contexts, and Decision Scenarios. For space reasons, however, the section will not be included in the printed copy of the book. It will, instead, be posted on the book's website.

Website for This Book

Wadsworth Publishing Company, the publisher of this book, maintains the Wadsworth Philosophy Shoppe site at http://philosophy. wadsworth.com. This book has a Web page at that site, and it is there that supplemental materials and any needed corrections will be posted.

Additional Resources

Websites such as those of the National Library of Medicine, the National Institutes of Health, and the Centers for Disease Control provide access to Medline, the National Library of Medicine's bibliographic database, making it possible to carry out extensive research on almost any bioethical, clinical, or biomedical topic. Addresses of other medically related websites are easily located by any search engine. Medline indexes not only medical journals, but journals in bioethics.

Those interested in diseases like diabetes, Huntington's, or breast cancer or in therapies such as stem-cell rescue or heart transplants can readily acquire a great deal of up-to-the-minute information by consulting relevant websites. Those maintained by research institutions (e.g., Johns Hopkins and the Mayo Clinic) and disease advocacy group resource centers (e.g., the American Cancer Society and the March of Dimes Birth Defects Foundation) are generally the most up-to-date and most trustworthy.

Content Changes in the Ninth Edition

Alterations of importance have been made throughout the book in response to the impact that changes in social circumstances, court decisions, scientific understanding, government regulations, and clinical practice have had on moral issues in medicine. Here is a sample of issues freshly discussed:

- Autism and vaccinations: Is there a duty to vaccinate?
- New cases of withholding medical care from children on religious grounds: Can the practice be justified?
- HPV vaccine: Should it be required?
- New studies show effectiveness of placebos: Must patients always be told the truth?
- Medical tourism: When people return with problems, do doctors have a duty to care for them?
- Obesity epidemic: Should society step in?
- Complete face transplant: Is it worth the risk?
- Abigail Burroughs: Do the dying have a right to experimental drugs?
- Prisoners as test subjects: Do the new rules protect them enough?
- Genae Girard: Should genes be patented?
- Direct-to-consumer genetic testing: Should it be permitted?

- Personal genome and disease: The next stage of the Human Genome Project

- GINA (Genetic Information Non-Discrimination Act): What it does and does not do

- FDA-approved gene therapy: The beginning of a new era?

- Embryonic stem cells from skin cells: Is the ethical problem solved?

- The "Octomom" case: Do fertility clinics need regulating?

- Buying donor eggs: Do donors need protection?

- Sperm shopping: How much should the children know?

- New statistical profile of abortion in the U.S.: Attitudes have shifted

- New legislation on late-term abortion: Does it go too far?

- Ellen: A new emergency-contraception pill and an old controversy

- Extreme-prematurity update: Multiples still pose serious problems

- Diagnostic criteria for death: Two sets of criteria for the same condition

- Elizabeth Bouvia's demand to starve: Would it be assisted suicide?

- Oregon and assisted suicide: Other states may follow its example

- Steve Jobs' liver transplant: Did he cheat?

- Prisoners and health care: Should prisoners be equally entitled?

- Affordable Health Care Act: How is the new law supposed to work?

- Background to health care reform: Why something needed to be done

- Angela Carder is given a c-section: Can a hospital decide to act to save a fetus without the consent of the mother?

- New study of the effectiveness of mammograms in preventing deaths from breast cancer: Should evidence dictate policy?

- Update on race-effective drugs: Should race be used in clinical trials?

- African Americans and health disparities: Why the gap?

- Darren Chicchia and AIDS: Was this athlete guilty of a crime, or was he [ok] the victim of a bad law?

- Update on the AIDS pandemic: The disease has spread worldwide and threatens developed nations

- HIV-vaccine search continues: Even one 50% effective would be valuable

The Briefing Sessions have been revised in dozens of ways, and the new Case Presentations include those of Steve Jobs, Abigail Burroughs, Darren Chicchia, Genae Gerard, Angela Carder, Elizabeth Bouvia, and Nadya Suleman. The Social Contexts present information about the numerous controversies presented in the preceding list. The list is not intended to be exhaustive, but it is long enough to indicate that the new material in this edition is considerable. Despite this addition of material, I think it is important to keep in mind that most of the issues in the previous edition remain subjects of serious discussion. New information, however, is crucial for keeping the debates relevant.

Each chapter includes from five to ten Decision Scenarios, and a fair number are new to this edition. The new ones often represent recent cases or issues not presented elsewhere in the text. The Decision Scenarios have now been given titles, and I hope that this will help reveal their content and thus make them more accessible.

The Readings in this edition maintain the broad scope and wide variety of those in the last. Thirty-five readings are completely new, including one on clinical research written especially for this edition. Included are selections by (without attempting to be systematic or exhaustive) Onoro O'Neil, Robert Northcott, Peter Singer, Brian Martin, Aki Tsuchiya and Alan Williams, Howard Minkoff and Jeffrey Ecker, Don Marquis, Mark T. Brown, Robert F. Card, H. T. Engelhardt, Jr., Julian Savulescu, Allison Davis, Ezekiel Emanuel and Alan Wertheimer, Kai Nielson, Norman Daniels, and Gopal Sreenivassan.

The new Readings represent some of the latest or best thinking on the many complicated issues that medical practice and research have faced us with. The arguments presented in the selections are worth careful consideration.

Envoi

I have tried to be helpful without being too intrusive. Anyone who teaches bioethics wants enough flexibility to arrange a course in the way she or he sees fit. I have attempted to offer that flexibility, while at the same time supplying readers with the kind of information and support they need.

This book, with its Case Presentations, Briefing Sessions, Social Context sections, Decision Scenarios, and "Foundations of Bioethics" section, is more ambitious than any similar work. I've been pleased by responses from my colleagues to the earlier editions. Even their criticisms were tempered by a sympathetic understanding of the difficulty of producing a book of this scope that attempts to do so many things.

Thanks to the help of many people who took the trouble to write to me, I was able to correct errors in this edition that I missed in the last. I am under no illusion that the book has achieved perfection, and I would still appreciate comments or suggestions from those who use the book and discover ways it needs to be corrected or can be improved. Communications may be e-mailed to me or sent to my university address (Department of Philosophy, University of Missouri–St. Louis, St. Louis, MO 63121).

I owe so many intellectual debts that I must declare bankruptcy. This means that those who invested their help in the project have to settle for an acknowledgment that is less than they are rightly owed. My greatest debt is to those authors who allowed their work to be printed here. I hope they will find no grounds for objecting to the way I have dealt with them. I am also grateful to the following reviewers for their criticisms and recommendations: Kim Amer, DePaul University; Chris Campolo, Hendrix College; Stephen S. Hanson, University of Louisville; Fabrice Jotterand, UT Southwestern Medical School; Tim Madigan, Saint John Fisher College; David P. Schenck, University of South Florida; and Kristen Tym, University of Wisconsin–Milwaukee.

I'm grateful to Joann Kozyrev for her faith in this book and for her unstinting support during the time of its completion and production. I would have faced many more difficulties in completing it without her intervention and good judgment.

Miriam Munson's name deserves to appear on the title page as an indication of how grateful I am to her for her hard work and keen judgment. Her quick eye and sharp intelligence kept me from making many errors, large and small. The book is better because of her.

I have not always listened to those who have taken the trouble to warn and advise me, and this is reason enough for me to claim the errors here as my own.

Ronald Munson
University of Missouri–St. Louis, 2010
munson@umsl.edu

Part VI

Foundations of Bioethics: Ethical Theories, Moral Principles, and Medical Decisions

Foundations of Bioethics: Ethical Theories, Moral Principles, and Medical Decisions

"He's stopped breathing, Doctor," the nurse said. She sounded calm and not at all hysterical. By the time Dr. Sarah Cunningham had reached Mr. Sabatini's bedside, the nurse was already providing mouth-to-mouth resuscitation. But Mr. Sabatini still had the purplish blue color of cyanosis, caused by a lack of oxygen in his blood.

Dr. Cunningham knew that, if Mr. Sabatini was to survive, he would have to be given oxygen fast and placed on a respirator. But should she order this done?

Mr. Sabatini was an old man, almost ninety. So far as anyone knew, he was alone in the world and would hardly be missed when he died. His health was poor. He had congestive heart disease and was dying slowly and painfully from intestinal cancer.

Wouldn't it be a kindness to Mr. Sabatini to allow him this quick and painless death? Why condemn him to lingering on for a few extra hours or weeks?

The decision that Sarah Cunningham faces is a moral one. She has to decide whether she should take the steps that might prolong Mr. Sabatini's life or not take them and accept the consequence that he will almost surely die within minutes. She knows the medical procedures that can be employed, but she has to decide whether she should employ them.

This kind of case rivets our attention because of its immediacy and drama. But there are many other situations that arise in the context of medical practice and research that present problems that require moral decisions. Some are equal in drama to the problem facing Dr. Cunningham, while others are not so dramatic but are of at least equal seriousness. There are far too many to catalog, but consider this sample: Is it right for a woman to have an abortion for any reason? Should children with serious birth defects be put to death? Do people have a right to die? Does everyone have a right to medical care? Should physicians ever lie to their patients? Should people suffering from a genetic disease be allowed to have children? Can parents agree to allow their children to be used as experimental subjects?

Most of us have little tolerance for questions like these. They seem so cold and abstract. Our attitude changes, however, when we find ourselves in a position in which we are the decision makers. It changes, too, when we are in a position in which we must advise those who make the decisions. Or when we are on the receiving end of the decisions.

But whether we view the problems abstractly or concretely, we are inclined to ask the same question: Are there any rules, standards, or principles that we can use as guides when we are faced with moral decisions? If there are, then Dr. Cunningham need not be wholly unprepared to decide whether she should order steps taken to save Mr. Sabatini. Nor need we be unprepared to decide issues like those in the questions above.

The branch of philosophy concerned with principles that allow us to make decisions about what is right and wrong is called *ethics* or *moral philosophy*. *Bioethics* is specifically concerned with moral principles and decisions in the context of medical practice, policy, and research. Moral difficulties connected with medicine are so complex and important that they require special attention. Medical ethics gives them this attention, but it remains a part of the discipline of ethics. Thus, if we are to answer our question as to whether there are any rules or principles to use when making moral decisions in the medical context, we must turn to general ethical theories and to a consideration of moral principles that have been proposed to hold in all contexts of human action.

In the first section, we will discuss five major ethical theories that have been put forward by philosophers. Each of these theories represents an attempt to supply basic principles we can rely on in making moral decisions. We'll consider these theories and examine how they might be applied to moral issues in the medical context. We will discuss the reasons that have been offered to persuade us to accept each theory, but we will also point out some of the difficulties each theory presents.

In the second section, we will examine and illustrate several moral principles that are of special relevance to medical research and practice. These principles are frequently appealed to in discussions of practical ethical problems and are sufficiently uncontroversial to be endorsed in a general way by any of the ethical theories mentioned in the first section. (Those who defend theories without principles do not, of course, endorse them as principles.)

In the third and last section, we will consider the basic concepts of three ethical theories usually offered as theories that are free of principles: virtue ethics, care ethics, and feminist ethics. We will consider how these theories might be used in making moral decisions, but we will also call attention to some of the criticisms urged against each of them.

The three sections are not dependent on one another, and it is possible to profit from one without reading the others. (The price for this independence is a small amount of repetition.) Nevertheless, reading all three sections is recommended. The Case Presentations and Social Contexts presented in the majority of this book can most easily be followed by someone who has at least some familiarity with basic moral theories.

Also, some points in discussions turn upon questions about the applicability of certain familiar moral principles or whether it is possible to operate without any principles. Being acquainted with those principles makes it easier to understand and evaluate such discussions.

BASIC ETHICAL THEORIES

Ethical theories attempt to articulate and justify principles that can be employed as guides for making moral decisions and as standards for the evaluation of actions and policies. In effect, such theories define what it means to act morally, and in doing so, they stipulate in a general fashion the duties or obligations that fall upon us.

Ethical theories also offer a means to explain and justify actions. If our actions are guided by a particular theory, then we can explain them by demonstrating that the principles of the theory required us to act as we did. In such cases, the explanation also constitutes a justification. We justify our actions by showing that, according to the theory, we had an obligation to do what we did. (In some cases, we may justify our actions by showing that the theory *permitted* our actions—that is, didn't require them, but didn't rule them out as wrong.)

Advocates of a particular ethical theory present what they consider to be good reasons and relevant evidence in its support. Their general aim is to show that the theory is one that any reasonable individual would find persuasive or would endorse as correct. Accordingly, appeals to religion, faith, or nonnatural factors are not considered to be either necessary or legitimate to justify the theory. Rational persuasion alone is regarded as the basis of justification.

In this section, we will briefly consider four general ethical theories and one theory of justice that has an essential ethical component. In each case, we will begin by examining the basic principles of the theory and the grounds offered for its acceptance. We will then explore some of the possibilities of applying the theory to problems that arise within the medical context. Finally, we will mention some of the practical consequences and conceptual difficulties that raise questions about the theory's adequacy or correctness.

Utilitarianism

The ethical theory known as utilitarianism was given its most influential formulation in the nineteenth century by the British philosophers Jeremy Bentham (1748–1832) and John Stuart Mill (1806–1873). Bentham and Mill did not produce identical theories, but both of their versions have come to be spoken of as "classical utilitarianism." Subsequent elaborations and qualifications of utilitarianism are inevitably based on the formulations of Bentham and Mill, so their theories are worth careful examination.

The Principle of Utility

The foundation of utilitarianism is a single apparently simple principle. Mill calls it the "principle of utility" and states it this way: *Actions are right in proportion as they tend to promote happiness, wrong as they tend to produce the reverse of happiness.*

The principle focuses attention on the *consequences* of actions, rather than upon some feature of the actions themselves. The "utility" or "usefulness" of an action is determined by the extent to which it produces happiness. Thus, no action is *in itself* right or wrong. Nor is an action right or wrong by virtue of the actor's hopes, intentions, or past actions. Consequences alone are important. Breaking a promise, lying, causing pain, or even killing a person may, under certain circumstances, be the right action to take. Under other circumstances, the action might be wrong.

We need not think of the principle as applying to just one action that we are considering. It supplies the basis for a kind of cost–benefit analysis to employ in a situation in which several lines of action are possible. Using the principle, we are supposed to consider the possible results of each action. Then we are to choose the one that produces the most benefit (happiness) at the least cost (unhappiness). The action we take may produce some unhappiness, but it

is a balance of happiness over unhappiness that the principle tells us to seek.

Suppose, for example, that a woman in a large hospital is near death: she is in a coma, an EEG shows only minimal brain function, and a respirator is required to keep her breathing. Another patient has just been brought to the hospital from the scene of an automobile accident. His kidneys have been severely damaged, and he is in need of an immediate transplant. There is a good tissue match with the woman's kidneys. Is it right to hasten her death by removing a kidney?

The principle of utility would probably consider the removal justified. The woman is virtually dead, while the man has a good chance of surviving. It is true that the woman's life is threatened even more by the surgery. It may in fact kill her. But, on balance, the kidney transplant seems likely to produce more happiness than unhappiness. In fact, it seems better than the alternative of doing nothing. For in that case, both patients are likely to die.

The principle of utility is also called the "greatest happiness principle" by Bentham and Mill. The reason for this name is clear when the principle is stated in this way: *Those actions are right which produce the greatest happiness for the greatest number of people.* This alternative formulation makes it obvious that, in deciding how to act, it is not just my happiness or the happiness of a particular person or group that must be considered. According to utilitarianism, every person is to count just as much as any other person. That is, when we are considering how we should act, everyone's interest must be considered. The right action, then, will be the one that produces the most happiness for the largest number of people.

Mill is particularly anxious that utilitarianism not be construed as no more than a sophisticated justification for crude self-interest. He stresses that, in making a moral decision, we must look at the situation in an objective way. We must, he says, be a "benevolent spectator" and then act in a way that will bring about the best results for all concerned. This view is summarized in a famous passage:

> *The happiness which forms the utilitarian standard of what is right in conduct is not the agent's own happiness, but that of all concerned. As between his own happiness and that of others, utilitarianism requires him to be as strictly impartial as a disinterested and benevolent spectator. In the golden rule of Jesus of Nazareth, we read the complete spirit of the ethics of utility. To do as you would be done by, and to love your neighbor as yourself, constitute the ideal perfection of utilitarian morality.*

The key concept in both formulations of the principle of utility is "happiness." Bentham simply identifies happiness with pleasure—pleasure of any kind. The aim of ethics, then, is to increase the amount of pleasure in the world to the greatest possible extent. In furtherance of this aim, Bentham recommends the use of a "calculus of pleasure and pain," in which characteristics of pleasure such as intensity, duration, and number of people affected are measured and assigned numerical values. To determine which of several possible actions is the right one, we need only determine which one receives the highest numerical score. Unfortunately, Bentham does not tell us what units to use or how to make the measurements.

Mill also identifies happiness with pleasure, but he differs from Bentham in a major respect. Unlike Bentham, he insists that some pleasures are "higher" than others. Thus, pleasures of the intellect are superior to, say, purely sensual pleasures. This difference in the concept of pleasure can become significant in a medical context. For example, in the choice of using limited resources to save the life of a lathe operator or of an art historian, Mill's view might assign more value to the life of the art historian. That person, Mill might say, is capable of "higher pleasures" than the lathe operator. (Of course, other factors would be relevant here for Mill.)

Both Mill and Bentham regard happiness as an intrinsic good. That is, it is something good in itself or for its own sake. Actions, by contrast, are good only to the extent to which they tend to promote happiness. Therefore, they are only instrumentally good. Since utilitarianism determines the rightness of actions in terms of their tendency to promote the greatest happiness for the greatest number, it is considered to be a *teleological* ethical theory. (*Teleological* comes from the Greek word *telos*, which means "end" or "goal.") A teleological ethical theory judges the rightness of an action in terms of an external goal or purpose—"general happiness" or utility for utilitarianism. However, utilitarianism is also a *consequentialist* theory, for the outcomes or consequences of actions are the only considerations relevant to determining their moral rightness. Not all teleological theories are consequentialist.

Some more recent formulations of utilitarianism have rejected the notion that happiness, no matter how defined, is the sole intrinsic good that actions or policies must promote. Critics of the classical view have argued that the list of things we recognize as valuable in themselves should be increased to include ones such as knowledge, beauty, love, friendship, liberty, and health. According to this *pluralistic* view, in applying the principle of utility we must consider the entire range of intrinsic goods that an action is likely to promote. Thus, the right action is the one that can be expected to produce the greatest sum of intrinsic goods. In most of the discussion that follows, we will speak of the greatest happiness or benefit, but it is easy enough to see how the same points can be made from a pluralistic perspective.

Act and Rule Utilitarianism

All utilitarians accept the principle of utility as the standard for determining the rightness of actions. But they divide into two groups over the matter of the application of the principle.

Act utilitarianism holds that the principle should be applied to particular acts in particular circumstances. *Rule utilitarianism* maintains that the principle should be used to test rules, which can in turn be used to decide the rightness of particular acts. Let's consider each of these views and see how it works in practice.

Act utilitarianism holds that an act is right if, and only if, no other act could have been performed that would produce a higher utility. Suppose a child is born with severe impairments. The child has an open spine, severe brain damage, and dysfunctional kidneys. What should be done? (We will leave open the question of who should decide.)

The act utilitarian holds that we must attempt to determine the consequences of the various actions that are open to us. We should consider, for example, these possibilities: (1) Give the child only the ordinary treatment that would be given to a normal child; (2) give the child special treatment for its problems; (3) give the child no treatment—allow it to die; (4) put the child to death in a painless way.

According to act utilitarianism, we must explore the potential results of each possibility. We must realize, for example, that when such a child is given only ordinary treatment, it will be worse off, if it survives, than if it had been given special treatment. Also, a child left alone and allowed to die is likely to suffer more pain than one killed by a lethal injection. Furthermore, a child treated aggressively will have to undergo numerous surgical procedures of limited effectiveness. We must also consider the family of the child and judge the emotional and financial effects that each of the possible actions will have on them. Then, too, we must take into account such matters as the "quality of life" of a child with severe brain damage and multiple defects, the effect on physicians and nurses in killing the child or allowing it to die, and the financial costs to society in providing long-term care.

After these considerations, we should then choose the action that has the greatest utility. We should act in the way that will produce the most benefit for all concerned. Which of the possibilities we select will depend on the precise features of the situation: how impaired the child is, how good its chances are for living an acceptable life, the character and financial status of the family, and so on. The great strength of act utilitarianism is that it invites us to deal with each case as unique. When the circumstances of another case are different, we might, without being inconsistent, choose another of the possible actions.

Act utilitarianism shows a sensitivity to specific cases, but it is not free from difficulties. Some philosophers have pointed out that there is no way that we can be sure that we have made the right choice of actions. We are sure to be ignorant of much relevant information. Besides, we can't know with much certainty what the results of our actions will really be. There is no way to be sure, for example, that even a severely impaired infant will not recover enough to live a better life than we predict.

The act utilitarian can reply that acting morally doesn't mean being omniscient. We need to make a reasonable effort to get relevant information, and we can usually predict the probable consequences of our actions. Acting morally doesn't require any more than this.

Another objection to act utilitarianism is more serious. According to the doctrine, we are obligated to keep a promise only if keeping it will produce more utility than some other action. If some other action will produce the same utility, then keeping the promise is permissible but not obligatory. Suppose a surgeon promises a patient that only he will perform an operation, then allows a well-qualified resident to perform part of it. Suppose all goes well and the patient never discovers that the promise was not kept. The outcome for the patient is exactly the same as if the surgeon had kept the promise. From the point of view of act utilitarianism, there is nothing wrong with the surgeon's failure to keep it. Yet critics charge that there is something wrong—that, in making the promise, the surgeon took on an obligation. Act utilitarianism is unable to account for obligations engendered by such actions as promising and pledging, critics say, for such actions involve something other than consequences.

A third objection to act utilitarianism arises in situations in which virtually everyone must follow the same rules in order to achieve a high level of utility, but even greater utility can be achieved if a few people do not follow the rules. Consider the relationship between physicians and the Medicaid program. The program pays physicians for services provided to those poor enough to qualify for the program. The program would collapse if nearly all physicians were not honest in billing Medicaid for their services. Not only would many poor people suffer, but physicians themselves would lose a source of income.

Suppose a particular physician believes that the requirements to qualify for Medicaid are too restrictive and that many who urgently need medical care cannot afford it. As an act utilitarian, she reasons that it is right for her to get money to open a free clinic under the program. She intends to bill for services she does not provide, then use that money to treat those not covered by Medicaid. Her claims will be small compared to the entire Medicaid budget, so it is unlikely that anyone who qualifies for Medicaid will go without treatment. Since she will tell no one what she is doing, others are not likely to be influenced by her example and make false claims for similar or less worthy purposes. The money she is paid will bring substantial benefit to those in need of health care. Thus, she concludes, by violating the rules of the program, her actions will produce greater utility than would be produced by following the rules.

The physician's action would be morally right, according to act utilitarians. Yet, critics say, we expect an action that is morally right to

be one that is right for everyone in similar circumstances. If every physician in the Medicaid program acted in this way, however, the program would be destroyed and thus produce no utility at all. Furthermore, according to critics, the physician's action produces unfairness. Although it is true that the patients she treats at her free clinic gain a benefit they would not otherwise have, similar patients must go without treatment. The Medicaid policy, whatever its flaws, is at least prima facie fair in providing benefits to all who meet its requirements. Once again, then, according to critics, more seems to be involved in judging the moral worth of an action than can be accounted for by act utilitarianism.

In connection with such objections, some critics have gone so far as to claim that it is impossible to see how a society in which everyone was an act utilitarian could function. We could not count on promises being kept nor take for granted that people were telling us the truth. Social policies would be no more than general guides to action, and we could never be sure that people would regard themselves as obligated to adhere to the provisions of those policies. Decisions made by individuals about each individual action would not obviously lead to the promotion of the highest degree of utility. Indeed, some critics say, such a society might collapse, for communication among individuals would be difficult, if not impossible, social cohesion would be weakened, and general policies and regulations would have very uncertain effects.

The critics are not necessarily right, of course, and defenders of act utilitarianism have made substantial efforts to answer the criticisms we have presented. Some have denied that the theory has those implications and argued that some of our generally accepted moral perceptions should be changed. In connection with this last point, Carl Wellman provides an insight into the sort of conflict between moral feelings and rational judgment that the acceptance of act utilitarianism can produce. Concerning euthanasia, Wellman writes,

> Try as I may, I honestly cannot discover great hidden disutilities in the act of killing an elderly person suffering greatly from an incurable illness, provided that certain safeguards like a written medical opinion by at least two doctors and a request by the patient are preserved. In this case I cannot find any way to reconcile my theory with my moral judgment. What I do in this case is to hold fast to act-utilitarianism and distrust my moral sense. I claim that my condemnation of such acts is an irrational disapproval, a condemnation that will change upon further reasoning about the act. . . . That I feel wrongness is clear, but I cannot state to myself any rational justification for my feeling. Hence, I discount this particular judgment as irrational.

Rule utilitarianism maintains that an action is right if it conforms to a rule of conduct that has been validated by the principle of utility as one that will produce at least as much utility as any other rule applicable to the situation. A rule like "Provide only ordinary care for severely brain damaged newborns with multiple impairments," if it were established, would allow us to decide about the course of action to follow in situations like that of our earlier example.

The rule utilitarian is concerned with assessing the utility not of individual actions, but of particular rules. In practice, then, we do not have to go through the calculations involved in determining in each case whether a specific action will increase utility. All that we have to establish is that following a certain rule will in general result in a situation in which utility is maximized. Once rules are established, they can be relied on to determine whether a particular action is right.

The basic idea behind rule utilitarianism is that having a set of rules that are always observed produces the greatest social utility. Having everyone follow the same rule in each case of the same kind yields more utility for everybody in the long run. An act utilitarian can agree that having rules may produce more social utility than not having them. But the act utilitarian insists that the rules be regarded as no more than general guides to action, as "rules of thumb." Thus, for act utilitarianism it is perfectly legitimate to violate a rule if doing so will maximize utility in that instance. By contrast, the rule utilitarian holds that rules must generally be followed, even though following them may produce less net utility (more unhappiness than happiness) in a particular case.

Rule utilitarianism can endorse rules like "Keep your promises." Thus, unlike act utilitarianism, it can account for the general sense that, in making promises, we are placing ourselves under an obligation that cannot be set aside for the sake of increasing utility. If "Keep your promises" is accepted as a rule, then the surgeon who fails to perform all of an operation himself when he has promised his patient he would do so has not done the right thing, even if the patient never learns the truth.

Rule utilitarians recognize that circumstances can arise in which it would be disastrous to follow a general rule, even when it is true that, *in general*, greater happiness would result from following the rule all the time. Clearly, we should not keep a promise to meet someone for lunch when we have to choose between keeping the promise and rushing a heart-attack victim to the hospital. It is consistent with the theory to formulate rules that include appropriate escape clauses. For example, "Keep your promises, unless breaking them is required to save a life" and "Keep your promises, unless keeping them would lead to a disastrous result unforeseen at the time the promise was made" are rules that a rule utilitarian might regard as more likely to lead to greater utility than "Always keep your promises no matter what the consequences may be." What a rule utilitarian cannot endorse is a rule like "Keep your promises, except when breaking a promise would produce more utility." This would in effect transform the rule utilitarian into an act utilitarian.

Of course, rule utilitarians are not committed to endorsing general rules only. It is compatible with the view to offer quite specific rules, and in fact there is no constraint on just how specific a rule may be. A rule utilitarian might, for example, establish a rule such as "If an infant is born with an open spine, severe brain damage, and dysfunctional kidneys, then the infant should receive no life-sustaining treatment."

The possibility of formulating a large number of rules and establishing them separately opens this basic version of rule utilitarianism to two objections. First, some rules are likely to conflict when they are applicable to the same case and basic rule utilitarianism offers no way to resolve such conflicts. What should a physician do when faced both with a rule like that above and with another that directs him to "Provide life-sustaining care to all who require it"? Rules that, when considered individually, pass the test of promoting utility, may express contradictory demands when taken together. A further objection to basic rule utilitarianism is that establishing rules to cover many different circumstances and situations results in such an abundance of rules that employing the rules to make moral decisions becomes virtually impossible in practice.

Partly because of such difficulties, rule utilitarians have taken the approach of establishing the utility of a set of rules or an entire moral code. The set can include rules for resolving possible conflicts, and an effort can be made to keep the rules few and simple to minimize the practical difficulty of employing them. Once again, as with individual actions or rules, the principle of utility is employed to determine which set of rules, out of the various sets considered, ought to be accepted.

In this more sophisticated form, rule utilitarianism can be characterized as the theory

that an action is right when it conforms to a set of rules that has been determined to produce at least as much overall utility as any other set. It is possible to accept the present forms of social and economic institutions, such as private property and a market economy, as constraints and then argue for the set of rules that will yield the most utility under those conditions. However, it is also possible to be more radical and argue for a particular set of rules that would lead to the greatest possible utility, quite apart from present social forms. Indeed, such a set of rules might be proposed and defended in an effort to bring about changes in present society that are needed to increase the overall level of utility. Utilitarianism, whether act or rule, is not restricted to being a theory about individual moral obligation. It is also a social and political theory.

We have already seen that rule utilitarianism, unlike act utilitarianism, makes possible the sort of obligation we associate with making a promise. But how might rule utilitarianism deal with the case of the physician who files false Medicaid claims to raise money to operate a free clinic? An obvious answer, although certainly not the only one possible, is that any set of rules likely to be adopted by a rule utilitarian will contain at least one rule making fraud morally wrong. Without a rule forbidding fraud, no social program that requires the cooperation of its participants is likely to achieve its aim. Such a rule protects the program from miscalculations of utility that individuals may make for self-serving reasons, keeps the program focused on its goal, and prevents it from becoming fragmented. Even if some few individuals commit fraud, the rule against it is crucial in discouraging as many as possible. Otherwise, as we pointed out earlier, such a program would collapse. By requiring that the program operate as it was designed, rule utilitarianism also preserves prima facie fairness, because only those who qualify receive benefits.

The most telling objection to rule utilitarianism, according to some philosophers, is that it is inconsistent. The justification of a set of moral rules is that the rules maximize utility. If rules are to maximize utility, then it seems obvious that they may require that an act produce more utility than any other possible act in a particular situation. Otherwise, the maximum amount of utility would not result. But if the rules satisfy this demand, then they will justify exactly the same actions as act utilitarianism. Thus, the rules will consider it right to break promises, make fraudulent claims, and so on. When rule utilitarianism moves to block these possibilities by requiring that rules produce only the most utility overall, it becomes inconsistent: the set of rules is said to maximize utility, but the rules will require actions that do not maximize utility. Thus, rule utilitarianism seems both to accept and reject the principle of utility as the ultimate moral standard.

Preference Utilitarianism

Some philosophers have called into question the idea of using happiness or any other intrinsic value (e.g., knowledge or health) as a criterion of the rightness of an action. The notion of an intrinsic value, they have argued, is too imprecise to be used as a practical guide. Furthermore, it is not at all clear that people share the same values, and even if they do, they are not committed to them to the same degree. Someone may value knowledge more than health, whereas someone else may value physical pleasure over knowledge or health. As a result, there can be no clear-cut procedure for determining what action is likely to produce the best outcome for an individual or group.

The attempt to develop explicit techniques (such as those of decision theory) to help resolve questions about choosing the best action or policy has led some thinkers to replace considerations of intrinsic value with considerations of actual preferences. What someone wants, desires, or prefers can be determined, in principle, in an objective way by consulting the person directly. In addition,

people are often able to do more than merely express a preference. Sometimes they can rank their preferences from that which is most desired to that which is least desired.

Such a ranking is of special importance in situations involving risk, for people can be asked to decide how much risk they are willing to take to attempt to realize a given preference. A young woman with a hip injury who is otherwise in good health may be willing to accept the risk of surgery to increase her chances of being restored to many years of active life. By contrast, an elderly woman in frail health may prefer to avoid surgery and accept the limitations that the injury imposes on her physical activities. For the elderly woman, not only are the risks of surgery greater because of her poor health, but even if the surgery is successful, she also will have fewer years to benefit from it.

By contrast, the older woman may place such a premium on physical activity that she is willing to take the risk of surgery to improve her chances of securing even a few more years of it. Only she can say what is important to her and how willing she is to take the risk required to secure it.

These considerations about personal preferences can also be raised about social preferences. Statistical information about what people desire and what they are willing to forgo to see their desires satisfied becomes relevant to institutional and legislative deliberations about what policies to adopt. For example, a crucial question facing our own society is whether we are willing to provide everyone with at least a basic minimum of health care, even if this requires increasing taxes or reducing our support for other social goods, such as education and defense.

Employing the satisfaction of preferences as the criterion of the rightness of an action or policy makes it possible to measure some of the relevant factors in some situations. The life expectancy of infants with particular impairments at birth can be estimated by statistics; a given surgical procedure has a certain success rate and a certain mortality rate. Similarly, a particular social policy has a certain financial cost, and if implemented, the policy is likely to mean the loss of other possible benefits and opportunities.

Ideally, information of this kind should allow a rational decision maker to calculate the best course of action for an individual or group. The best action will be the one that best combines the satisfaction of preferences with other conditions (e.g., financial costs and risks) that are at least minimally acceptable. To use the jargon of the theorists, the best action is the one that maximizes the utilities of the person or group.

A utilitarianism that employs preferences has the advantage of suggesting more explicit methods of analysis and rules for decision making than the classical formulation. It also has the potential for being more sensitive to the expressed desires of individuals. However, preference utilitarianism is not free from specific difficulties.

Most prominent is the problem posed by preferences that we would generally regard as unacceptable. What are we to say about those who prefer mass murder, child abuse, or torturing animals? Obviously, subjective preferences cannot be treated equally, and we must have a way to distinguish acceptable from unacceptable ones. Whether this can be done by relying on the principle of utility alone is doubtful. In the view of some commentators, some other moral principle (or principles) is needed. (See the discussion of justice immediately following.)

Difficulties with Utilitarianism

Classical utilitarianism is open to a variety of objections. We will concentrate on only one, however, for it seems to reveal a fatal flaw in the structure of the entire theory. This most serious of all objections is that the principle of utility appears to justify the imposition of great suffering on a few people for the benefit of many people.

Certain kinds of human experimentation forcefully illustrate this possibility. Suppose an investigator is concerned with acquiring a better understanding of brain functions. She could learn a great deal by systematically destroying the brain of one person and carefully noting the results. Such a study would offer many more opportunities for increasing our knowledge of the brain than those studies which use as subjects people who have damage to their brains in accidental ways. We may suppose that the experimenter chooses as her subject a person without education or training, without family or friends, who cannot be regarded as making much of a contribution to society. The subject will die from the experiment, but it is not unreasonable to suppose that the knowledge of the human brain gained from the experiment will improve the lives of countless numbers of people.

The principle of utility seems to make such experiments legitimate because the outcome is a greater amount of good than harm. One or a few have suffered immensely, but the many have profited to an extent that far outweighs that suffering.

Clearly, what is missing from utilitarianism is the concept of *justice*. It cannot be right to increase the general happiness at the expense of one person or group. There must be some way of distributing happiness and unhappiness and avoiding exploitation.

Mill was aware that utilitarianism needs a principle of justice, but most contemporary philosophers do not believe that such a principle can be derived from the principle of utility. In their opinion, utilitarianism as an ethical theory suffers severely from this defect. Yet some philosophers, while acknowledging the defect, have still held that utilitarianism is the best substantive moral theory available.

Kant's Ethics

For utilitarianism, the rightness of an action depends upon its consequences. In stark contrast to this view is the ethical theory formulated by the German philosopher Immanuel Kant (1724–1804) in his book *Fundamental Principles of the Metaphysics of Morals*. For Kant, the consequences of an action are morally irrelevant. Rather, an action is right when it is in accordance with a rule that satisfies a principle he calls the "categorical imperative." Since this is the basic principle of Kant's ethics, we can begin our discussion with it.

The Categorical Imperative

If you decide to have an abortion and go through with it, it is possible to view your action as involving a rule. You can be thought of as endorsing a rule to the effect "Whenever I am in circumstances like these, then I will have an abortion." Kant calls such a rule a "maxim." In his view, all reasoned and considered actions can be regarded as involving maxims.

The maxims in such cases are personal or subjective, but they can be thought of as being candidates for moral rules. If they pass the test imposed by the categorical imperative, then we can say that such actions are right. Furthermore, in passing the test, the maxims cease to be merely personal and subjective. They gain the status of objective rules of morality that hold for everyone.

Kant formulates the categorical imperative in this way: *Act only on that maxim which you can will to be a universal law.* Kant calls the principle "categorical" to distinguish it from "hypothetical" imperatives. These tell us what to do if we want to bring about certain consequences—such as happiness. A categorical imperative prescribes what we ought to do without reference to any consequences. The principle is an "imperative" because it is a command.

The test imposed on maxims by the categorical imperative is one of generalization or "universalizability." The central idea of the test is that a moral maxim is one that can be generalized to apply to all cases of the same kind. That is, you must be willing to see your rule

adopted as a maxim by everyone who is in a situation similar to yours. You must be willing to see your maxim universalized, even though it may turn out on some other occasion to work to your disadvantage.

For a maxim to satisfy the categorical imperative, it is not necessary that we be agreeable in some psychological sense to seeing it made into a universal law. Rather, the test is one that requires us to avoid inconsistency or conflict in what we will as a universal rule.

Suppose, for example, that I am a physician and I tell a patient that he has a serious illness, although I know that he doesn't. This may be to my immediate advantage, for the treatment and the supposed cure will increase my income and reputation. The maxim of my action might be phrased as, "Whenever I have a healthy patient, I will lie to him and say that he has an illness."

Now suppose that I try to generalize my maxim. In doing so, I will discover that I am willing the existence of a practice that has contradictory properties. If "Whenever any physician has a healthy patient, she will lie to him and say he has an illness" is made a universal law, then every patient will be told that he has an illness. Trust in the diagnostic pronouncements of physicians will be destroyed, while my scheme depends on my patients' trusting me and accepting the truth of my lying diagnosis.

It is as if I were saying, "Let there be a rule of truth telling such that people can assume that others are telling them the truth, but let there also be a rule that physicians may lie to their patients when it is in the interest of the physician to do so." In willing both rules, I am willing something contradictory. Thus, I can will my action in a particular case, but I can't will that my action be universal without generating a logical conflict.

Kant claims that such considerations show that it is always wrong to lie. Lying produces a contradiction in what we will. On one hand, we will that people believe what we say—that they accept our assurances and promises. On the other hand, we will that people be free to give false assurances and make false promises. Lying thus produces a self-defeating situation, for, when the maxim involved is generalized, the very framework required for lying collapses.

Similarly, consider the egoist who seeks only his self-interest and so makes "Never show love or compassion for others" the maxim of his actions. When universalized, this maxim results in the same kind of self-defeating situation that lying does. Since the egoist will sometimes find himself in need of love and compassion, if he wills the maxim of his action to be a universal law, then he will be depriving himself of something that is in his self-interest. Thus, in willing the abolition of love and compassion out of self-interest, he creates a logical contradiction in what he wills.

Another Formulation

According to Kant, there is only one categorical imperative, but it can be stated in three different ways. Each is intended to reveal a different aspect of the principle. The second formulation, the only other we will consider, can be stated in this way: *Always act so as to treat humanity, either yourself or others, always as an end and never as only a means.*

This version illustrates Kant's notion that every rational creature has a worth in itself. This worth is not conferred by being born into a society with a certain political structure, nor even by belonging to a certain biological species. The worth is inherent in the sheer possession of rationality. Rational creatures possess what Kant calls an "autonomous, self-legislating will." That is, they are able to consider the consequences of their actions, make rules for themselves, and direct their actions by those self-imposed rules. Thus, rationality confers upon everyone an intrinsic worth and dignity.

This formulation of the categorical imperative perhaps rules out some of the standards that are sometimes used to determine who is selected to receive certain medical resources (such as kidney machines) when the demand is greater than the supply. Standards that make a person's education, accomplishments, or social position relevant seem contrary to this version of the categorical imperative. They violate the basic notion that each person has an inherent worth equal to that of any other person. Unlike dogs or horses, people cannot be judged on "show points."

For Kant, all of morality has its ultimate source in rationality. The categorical imperative, in any formulation, is an expression of rationality, and it is the principle that would be followed in practice by any purely rational being. Moral rules are not mere arbitrary conventions or subjective standards. They are objective truths that have their source in the rational nature of human beings.

Duty

Utilitarianism identifies the good with happiness or pleasure and makes the production of happiness the supreme principle of morality. But, for Kant, happiness is at best a conditional or qualified good. In his view, there is only one thing that can be said to be good in itself: a good will.

Will is what directs our actions and guides our conduct. But what makes a will a "good will"? Kant's answer is that a will becomes good when it acts purely for the sake of duty.

We act for the sake of duty (or from duty) when we act on maxims that satisfy the categorical imperative. This means, then, that it is the motive force behind our actions—the character of our will—that determines their moral character. Morality does not rest on results—such as the production of happiness—but neither does it rest on our feelings, impulses, or inclinations. An action is right, for Kant, only when it is done for the sake of duty.

Suppose that I decide to donate one of my kidneys for transplanting. If my hope is to gain approval or praise, or even if I am moved by pity and a genuine wish to reduce suffering, and there is no other consideration behind my action, then, although I have done the morally right thing, my action has no inner moral worth. I may have acted *in accordance with duty* (done the same thing as duty would have required), but I did not act *from duty.*

This view of duty and its connection with morality captures attitudes we frequently express. Consider a nurse who gives special care to a severely ill patient. Suppose you learned that the nurse was providing such extraordinary care only because he hoped that the patient or her family would reward him with a special bonus. Knowing this, you would be unlikely to say that the nurse was acting in a morally outstanding way. We might even think the nurse was being greedy or cynical, and we would say that he was doing the right thing for the wrong reasons.

Kant distinguishes between two types of duties: perfect and imperfect. (The distinction corresponds to the two ways in which maxims can be self-defeating when tested by the categorical imperative.) A *perfect duty* is one we must always observe; an *imperfect duty* is one that we must observe only on some occasions. I have a perfect duty not to injure another person, but I have only an imperfect duty to show love and compassion. I must sometimes show it, but when I show it and which people I select to receive it are entirely up to me.

My duties determine what others can legitimately claim from me as a right. Some rights can be claimed as perfect rights, while others cannot. Everyone can demand of me that I do him or her no injury. But no one can tell me that I must make him or her the recipient of my love and compassion. In deciding how to discharge my imperfect duties, I am free to follow my emotions and inclinations.

For utilitarianism, an action is right when it produces something that is intrinsically valuable (happiness). Because actions are judged by their contributions to achieving a goal, utilitarianism is a teleological theory. By contrast, Kant's ethics holds that an action has features in itself that make it right or in accordance with duty. These features are distinct from the action's consequences. Such a theory is called *deontological,* a term derived from the Greek word for "duty" or "obligation."

Kant's Ethics in the Medical Context

Four features of Kant's ethics are of particular importance in dealing with issues in medical treatment and research:

1. No matter what the consequences may be, it is always wrong to lie.

2. We must always treat people (including ourselves) as ends and not as means only.

3. An action is right when it satisfies the categorical imperative.

4. Perfect and imperfect duties give a basis for claims that certain rights should be recognized.

We can present only two brief examples of how these features can be instrumental in resolving medical ethical issues, but these are suggestive of other possibilities.

Our first application of Kant's ethics bears on medical research. The task of medical investigators would be easier if they did not have to tell patients that they were going to be made part of a research program. Patients would then become subjects without even knowing it, and more often than not their risk would be negligible. Even though no overt lying would be involved, on Kantian principles this procedure would be wrong. It would require treating people as a means only and not as an end.

Likewise, it would never be right for an experimenter to deceive a potential experimental subject. If an experimenter told a patient, "We would like to use this new drug on you because it might help you" and this were not really so, the experimenter would be performing a wrong action. Lying is always wrong.

Nor could the experimenter justify this deception by telling herself that the research is of such importance that it is legitimate to lie to the patient. On Kant's principles, good results never make an action morally right. Thus, a patient must give voluntary and informed consent to become a subject of medical experimentation. Otherwise, the patient is being deprived of autonomy and treated as a means only.

We may volunteer because we expect the research to bring direct benefits to us. But we may also volunteer even though no direct personal benefits can be expected. We may see participation in the research as an occasion for fulfilling an imperfect duty to improve human welfare.

But, just as Kant's principles place restrictions on the researcher, they place limits on us as potential subjects. We have a duty to treat ourselves as ends and act so as to preserve our dignity and worth as humans. Therefore, it would not be right for us to volunteer for an experiment that threatened our lives or threatened to destroy our ability to function as autonomous rational beings without first satisfying ourselves that the experiment was legitimate and necessary.

Our second application of Kant's ethics in a medical context bears on the relationship between people as patients and those who accept responsibility for caring for them. A physician, for example, has only an imperfect duty to accept me as a patient. He has a duty to make use of his skills and talents to treat the sick, but I cannot legitimately insist on being the beneficiary. How he discharges his duty is his decision.

If, however, I am accepted as a patient, then I can make some legitimate claims. I can demand that nothing be done to cause me pointless harm, because it is never right to injure a person. Furthermore, I can demand that I never be lied to or deceived. Suppose, for example, I am given a placebo (a harmless but inactive substance) and told that it is a powerful and effective medication. Or suppose that

a biopsy shows that I have an inoperable form of cancer, but my physician tells me, "There's nothing seriously wrong with you." In both cases, the physician may suppose that he is deceiving me "for my own good": the placebo may be psychologically effective and make me feel better, and the lie about cancer may save me from useless worry. Yet, by being deceived, I am being denied the dignity inherent in my status as a rational being. Lying is wrong in general, and in such cases as these it also deprives me of my autonomy, of my power to make decisions and form my own opinions. As a result, such deception dehumanizes me.

As an autonomous rational being, a person is entitled to control over his or her own body. This means that medical procedures can be performed on me only with my permission. It would be wrong even if the medication were needed for my "own good." I may voluntarily put myself under the care of a physician and submit to all that I am asked to, but the decision belongs to me alone.

In exercising control over my body, however, I also have a duty to myself. Suppose, for example, that I refuse to allow surgery to be performed on me, although I have been told it is necessary to preserve my life. Since I have a duty to preserve my life, as does every person, my refusal is morally unjustifiable. Even here, however, it is not legitimate for others to force me to "do my duty." In fact, in Kantian ethics it is impossible to force another to do his or her duty because it is not the action, but the maxim involved, that determines whether or not one's duty has been done.

It is obvious even from our sketchy examples that Kantian ethics is a fruitful source of principles and ideas for working out some of the specific moral difficulties of medical experimentation and practice. The absolute requirements imposed by the categorical imperative can be a source of strength and even of comfort. By contrast, utilitarianism requires us to weigh alternative courses of actions by anticipating their consequences and deciding whether what we are considering doing can be justified by those results. Kant's ethics saves us from this kind of doubt and indecision: we know we must never lie, no matter what good may come of it. Furthermore, the lack of a principle of justice that is the most severe defect of utilitarianism is met by Kant's categorical imperative. When every person is to be treated as an end and never as only a means, the possibility of legitimately exploiting some for the benefit of others is wholly eliminated.

Difficulties with Kantian Ethics

Kant's ethical theory is complex and controversial. It has problems of a theoretical sort that manifest themselves in practice and lead us to doubt whether the absolute rules determined by the categorical imperative can always provide a straightforward solution to our moral difficulties. We will limit ourselves to discussing just three problems.

First, Kant's principles may produce resolutions to cases in which there is a conflict of duties that seems intuitively wrong. I have a duty to keep my promises, and I also have a duty to help those in need. Suppose, then, that I am a physician and I have promised a colleague to attend a staff conference. Right before the conference starts, I am talking with a patient who lapses into an insulin coma. If I get involved in treating the patient, I'll have to break my promise to attend the conference. What should I do?

The answer is obvious: I should treat the patient. Our moral intuition tells us this. But for Kant, keeping promises is a perfect duty, while helping others is an imperfect one. This suggests, then, that according to Kantian principles, I should abandon my patient and rush off to keep my appointment. Something is apparently wrong with a view that holds that a promise should never be broken—even when the promise concerns a relatively trivial matter and the consequences of keeping it are disastrous.

Another difficulty with the categorical imperative arises because we are free to choose how we formulate a maxim for testing. In all likelihood, none of us would approve a maxim such as "Lie when it is convenient for you." But what about one like "Lie when telling the truth is likely to cause harm to another"? We would be more inclined to make this a universal law. Now consider the maxim "Whenever a physician has good reason to believe that a patient's life will be seriously threatened if she is told the truth about her condition, then the physician should lie." Virtually everyone would be willing to see this made into a universal law.

Yet these three maxims could apply to the same situation. Since Kant does not tell us how to formulate our maxims, it is clear that we can act virtually any way we choose if we are willing to describe the situation in detail. We might be willing to have everyone act just as we are inclined to act whenever they find themselves in exactly this kind of situation. The categorical imperative, then, does not seem to solve our moral problems quite so neatly as it first appears to.

A final problem arises from Kant's notion that we have duties to rational beings or persons. Ordinarily, we have little difficulty with this commitment to persons, yet there are circumstances, particularly in the medical context, in which serious problems arise. Consider, for example, a fetus developing in its mother's womb. Is the fetus to be considered a person? The way this question is answered makes all the difference in deciding about the rightness or wrongness of abortion.

A similar difficulty is present when we consider how we are to deal with an infant with serious birth defects. Is it our duty to care for this infant and do all we can to see that it lives? If the infant is not a person, then perhaps we do not owe him the sort of treatment it would be our duty to provide a similarly afflicted adult. It's clear from these two cases that the notion of a person as an autonomous rational being is both too restrictive and arbitrary. It begs important moral questions.

Another difficulty connected with Kant's concept of a rational person is the notion of an "autonomous self-regulating will." Under what conditions can we assume that an individual possesses such a will? Does a child, a mentally retarded person, or someone in prison? Without such a will, in Kant's view, such an individual cannot legitimately consent to be the subject of an experiment or even give permission for necessary medical treatment. This notion is very much in need of development before Kant's principles can be relied on to resolve ethical questions in medicine.

The difficulties that we have discussed require serious consideration. This does not mean, of course, that they cannot be resolved or that, because of them, Kant's theory is worthless. As with utilitarianism, there are some philosophers who believe the theory is the best available, despite its shortcomings. That it captures many of our intuitive beliefs about what is right (not to lie, to treat people with dignity, to act benevolently) and supplies us with a test for determining our duties (the categorical imperative) recommends it strongly as an ethical theory.

Ross's Ethics

The English philosopher W. D. Ross (1877–1971) presented an ethical theory in his book *The Right and the Good* that can be seen as an attempt to incorporate aspects of utilitarianism and aspects of Kantianism. Ross rejected the utilitarian notion that an action is made right by its consequences alone, but he was also troubled by Kant's absolute rules. He saw not only that such rules fail to show sensitivity to the complexities of actual situations, but also that they sometimes conflict with one another. Like Kant, Ross is a deontologist, but with an important difference: Ross believes that it is necessary to consider consequences in making

a moral choice, even though he believes that it is not the results of an action taken alone that make it right.

Moral Properties and Rules

For Ross, there is an unbridgeable distinction between moral and nonmoral properties. There are only two moral properties—rightness and goodness—and these cannot be replaced by, or explained in terms of, other properties. Thus, to say that an action is right is not at all the same as saying that it causes pleasure or increases happiness, as utilitarianism claims.

At the same time, however, Ross does not deny that there is a connection between moral properties and nonmoral ones. What he denies is the possibility of establishing an identity between them. Thus, it may be right to relieve the suffering of someone, but right is not identical with relieving suffering. (More exactly put, the rightness of the action is not identical with the action's being a case of relieving suffering.)

Ross also makes clear that we must often know many nonmoral facts about a situation before we can legitimately make a moral judgment. If I see a physician injecting someone, I cannot say whether she is acting rightly without determining what she is injecting, why she is doing it, and so on. Thus, rightness is a property that depends partly on the nonmoral properties that characterize a situation. I cannot determine whether the physician is doing the right thing or the wrong thing until I determine what the nonmoral properties are.

Ross believes that there are cases in which we have no genuine doubt about whether the property of rightness or goodness is present. The world abounds with examples of cruelty, lying, and selfishness, and in these cases we are immediately aware of the absence of rightness or goodness. But the world also abounds with examples of compassion, reliability, and generosity in which rightness and goodness are clearly present. Ross claims that our experience with such cases puts us in a position to come to know rightness and goodness with the same degree of certainty as when we grasp the mathematical truth that a triangle has three angles.

Furthermore, according to Ross, our experience of many individual cases puts us in a position to recognize the validity of a general statement like "It is wrong to cause needless pain." We come to see such rules in much the same way that we come to recognize the letter A after having seen it written or printed in a variety of handwritings or typefaces.

Thus, our moral intuitions can supply us with moral rules of a general kind. But Ross refuses to acknowledge these rules as absolute. For him, they can serve only as guides to assist us in deciding what we should do. Ultimately, in any particular case we must rely not only on the rules but also on reason and our understanding of the situation.

Thus, even with rules, we may not recognize what the right thing to do is in a given situation. We recognize, he suggests, that there is always some right thing to do, but what it is may be far from obvious. In fact, doubt about what is the right way of acting may arise just because we have rules to guide us. We become aware of the fact that there are several possible courses of action, and all of them seem to be right.

Consider the problem of whether to lie to a terminally ill patient about his condition. Let us suppose that, if we lie to him, we can avoid causing him at least some useless anguish. But then aren't we violating his trust in us to act morally and to speak the truth?

In such cases, we seem to have a conflict in our duties. It is because of such familiar kinds of conflicts that Ross rejects the possibility of discovering absolute, invariant moral rules like "Always tell the truth" and "Always eliminate needless suffering." In cases like the one above, we cannot hold that both rules are absolute without contradicting ourselves. Ross says that we have to recognize that every rule

has exceptions and must in some situations be overridden.

Actual Duties and Prima Facie Duties

If rules like "Always tell the truth" cannot be absolute, then what status can they have? When our rules come into conflict in particular situations, how are we to decide which rule applies? Ross answers this question by making use of a distinction between what is actually right and what is prima facie right. Since we have a duty to do what is right, this distinction can be expressed as one between *actual duty* and *prima facie duty*.

An actual duty is simply what my real duty is in a situation. It is the action that, out of the various possibilities, I ought to perform. More often than not, however, I may not know what my actual duty is. In fact, for Ross, the whole problem of ethics might be said to be the problem of knowing what my actual duty is in any given situation.

Prima facie literally means "at first sight," but Ross uses the phrase to mean something like "other things being equal." Accordingly, a prima facie duty is one that dictates what I should do when other relevant factors in a situation are not considered. If I promised to meet you for lunch, then I have a prima facie duty to meet you. But suppose I am a physician, and just as I am about to leave for an appointment, the patient I am with suffers cardiac arrest. In such circumstances, according to Ross's view, I should break my promise and render aid to the patient. My prima facie duty to keep my promise doesn't make that fact obligatory. It constitutes a moral reason for meeting you, but there is also a moral reason for not meeting you. I also have a prima facie duty to aid my patient, and this is a reason that outweighs the first one. Thus, aiding the patient is both a prima facie duty and, in this situation, my actual duty.

The notion of a prima facie duty permits Ross to offer a set of moral rules stated in such a way that they are both universal and free from exceptions. For Ross, for example, lying is always wrong, but it is wrong prima facie. It may be that in a particular situation my actual duty requires that I lie. Even though what I have done is prima facie wrong, it is the morally right thing to do if some other prima facie duty that requires lying in the case is more stringent than the prima facie duty to tell the truth. (Perhaps only by lying am I able to prevent a terrorist from blowing up an airplane.) I must be able to explain and justify my failure to tell the truth, and it is of course possible that I may not be able to do so. It may be that I was confused and misunderstood the situation or failed to consider other alternatives. I may have been wrong to believe that my actual duty required me to lie. However, even if I was correct in my belief, that I lied is still prima facie wrong. It is this fact (and for Ross it is a fact) that requires me to explain and justify my action.

We have considered only a few simple examples of prima facie duties, but Ross is more thorough and systematic than our examples might suggest. He offers a list of duties that he considers binding on all moral agents. Here they are in summary form:

1. *Duties of fidelity:* telling the truth, keeping actual and implicit promises, and not representing fiction as history

2. *Duties of reparation:* righting the wrongs we have done to others

3. *Duties of gratitude:* recognizing the services others have done for us

4. *Duties of justice:* preventing a distribution of pleasure or happiness that is not in keeping with the merit of the people involved

5. *Duties of beneficence:* helping to better the condition of other beings with respect to virtue, intelligence, or pleasure

6. *Duties of self-improvement:* bettering ourselves with respect to virtue or intelligence

7. *Duties of nonmaleficence:* avoiding or preventing an injury to others

Ross doesn't claim that this is a complete list of the prima facie duties that we recognize. However, he does believe that the duties on the list are all ones that we acknowledge and are willing to accept as legitimate and binding without argument. He believes that if we simply reflect on these prima facie duties, we will see that they may be truly asserted. As he puts the matter:

I . . . am claiming that we know them to be true. To me it seems as self-evident as anything could be, that to make a promise, for instance, is to create a moral claim on us in someone else. Many readers will perhaps say that they do not know this to be true. If so I certainly cannot prove it to them. I can only ask them to reflect again, in the hope that they will ultimately agree that they also know it to be true.

Notice that Ross explicitly rejects the possibility of providing us with reasons or arguments to convince us to accept his list of prima facie duties. We are merely invited to reflect on certain kinds of cases, like keeping promises, and Ross is convinced that this reflection will bring us to accept his claim that these are true duties. Ross, like other intuitionists, tries to get us to agree with his moral perceptions in much the same way as we might try to get people to agree with us about our color perceptions. We might, for example, show a paint sample to a friend and say, "Don't you think that looks blue? It does to me. Think about it for a minute."

We introduced the distinction between actual and prima facie duties to deal with those situations in which duties seem to conflict. The problem, as we can now state it, is this: What are we to do in a situation in which we recognize more than one prima facie duty and it is not possible for us to act in a way that will fulfill them? We know, of course, that we should act in a way that satisfies our actual duty. But that is just our problem. What, after all, is our actual duty when our prima facie duties are in conflict?

Ross offers us two principles to deal with cases of conflicting duty. The first principle is designed to handle situations in which just two prima facie duties are in conflict: *That act is one's duty which is in accord with the more stringent prima facie obligation.* The second principle is intended to deal with cases in which several prima facie duties are in conflict: *That act is one's duty which has the greatest balance of prima facie rightness over prima facie wrongness.*

Unfortunately, both these principles present problems in application. Ross does not tell us how we are to determine when an obligation is "more stringent" than another. Nor does he give us a rule for determining the "balance" of prima facie rightness over wrongness. Ultimately, according to Ross, we must simply rely upon our perceptions of the situation. There is no automatic or mechanical procedure that can be followed. If we learn the facts in the case, consider the consequences of our possible actions, and reflect on our prima facie duties, we should be able to arrive at a conclusion as to the best course of action—in Ross's view, something that we as moral agents must and can do.

To return to specific cases, perhaps there is no direct way to answer the abstract question, Is the duty not to lie to a patient more stringent than the duty not to cause needless suffering? So much depends on the character and condition of the individual patient that an abstract determination of our duty based on balance or stringency is useless. However, knowing the patient, we should be able to perceive what the right course of action is.

Ross further believes that there are situations in which there are no particular difficulties about resolving the conflict between prima facie duties. For example, most of us would agree that, if we can save someone from serious injury by lying, then we have more of an obligation to save someone from injury than we do to tell the truth.

Ross's Ethics in the Medical Context

Ross's moral rules are not absolute in the sense that Kant's are; consequently, as with utilitarianism, it is not possible to say what someone's duty would be in an actual concrete situation. We can discuss in general, however, the advantages that Ross's theory brings to medical–moral issues. We will mention only two for illustration.

First and most important is Ross's list of prima facie duties. The list of duties can serve an important function in the moral education of physicians, researchers, and other medical personnel. The list encourages each person who is responsible for patient care to reflect on the prima facie obligations that the person has toward those people and to set aside one of those obligations only when morally certain that another obligation takes precedence.

The specific duties imposed in a prima facie way are numerous and can be expressed in terms relevant to the medical context: do not injure patients; do not distribute scarce resources in a way that fails to recognize individual worth; do not lie to patients; show patients kindness and understanding; educate patients in ways useful to them; do not hold out false hopes to patients; and so on.

Second, like utilitarianism, Ross's ethics encourages us to show sensitivity to the unique features of situations before acting. Like Kant's ethics, however, Ross's also insists that we look at the world from a particular moral perspective. In arriving at decisions about what is right, we must learn the facts of the case and explore the possible consequences of our actions. Ultimately, however, we must guide our actions by what is right, rather than by what is useful, what will produce happiness, or anything of the kind.

Since, for Ross, actions are not always justified in terms of their results, we cannot say unequivocally, "It's right to trick this person into becoming a research subject because the experiment may benefit thousands." Yet, we cannot say that it is always wrong for a researcher to trick a person into volunteering. An action is right or wrong regardless of what we think about it, but in a particular case circumstances might justify an experimenter in allowing some other duty to take precedence over the duty of fidelity.

Fundamentally, then, Ross's ethics offers us the possibility of gaining the advantages of utilitarianism without ignoring the fact that there seem to be duties with an undeniable moral force behind them that cannot be accounted for by utilitarianism. Ross's ethics accommodates not only our intuition that certain actions should be performed just because they are right but also our inclination to pay attention to the results of actions and not just the motives behind them.

Difficulties with Ross's Moral Rules

The advantages Ross's ethics offers over both utilitarianism and Kantianism are offset by some serious difficulties. To begin with, it seems false that we all grasp the same principles. We are well aware that people's beliefs about what is right and about what their duties are result from the kind of education and experience that they have had. The ability to perceive what is good or right does not appear to be universally shared. Ross does say that the principles are the convictions of "the moral consciousness of the best people." In any ordinary sense of "best," there is reason to say that such people don't always agree on moral principles. If "best" means "morally best," then Ross is close to being circular: the best people are those who acknowledge the same prima facie obligations, and those who recognize the same prima facie obligations are the best people.

Some have objected that Ross's list of prima facie duties seems incomplete. For example, Ross does not explicitly say that we have a prima facie obligation not to steal, but most people would hold that if we have any prima facie duties at all, the duty not to steal must surely be counted among them. Of course, it is possible to say that stealing is covered by some other obligation—the duty of fidelity, perhaps, since stealing may violate a trust. Nevertheless, from a theory based on intuition, the omission of such duties leaves Ross's list peculiarly incomplete.

Further, some critics have claimed that it is not clear that there is always even a prima facie obligation to do some of the things Ross lists. Suppose that I promise to lie about a friend's physical condition so that she can continue to collect insurance payments. Some would say that I have no obligation at all to keep such an unwise promise. In such a case, there would be no conflict of duties, because I don't have even a prima facie duty to keep such a promise.

Finally, Ross's theory, some have charged, seems to be false to the facts of moral disagreements. When we disagree with someone about an ethical matter, we consider reasons for and against some position. Sometimes the discussion results in agreement. But, according to Ross's view, this should not be possible. Although we may discuss circumstances and consequences and agree about the prima facie duties involved, ultimately I arrive at my judgment about the duty that is most stringent or has the greatest degree of prima facie rightness, and you arrive at yours. At this point, it seems, there can be no further discussion, even though the two judgments are incompatible. Thus, a choice between the two judgments about what act should be performed becomes arbitrary.

Few contemporary philosophers would be willing to endorse Ross's ethical theory without serious qualifications. The need for a special kind of moral perception (or "intuition") marks the theory as unacceptable for most philosophers. Yet many would acknowledge that the theory has great value in illuminating such aspects of our moral experience as reaching decisions when we feel the pull of conflicting obligations. Furthermore, at least some would acknowledge Ross's prima facie duties as constituting an adequate set of moral principles.

Rawls's Theory of Justice

In 1971, the Harvard philosopher John Rawls (1921–2002) published a book called *A Theory of Justice*. The work continues to attract a considerable amount of attention and has been described by some as the most important book in moral and social philosophy of the twentieth century.

One commentator, R. P. Wolfe, points out that Rawls attempts to develop a theory that combines the strengths of utilitarianism with those of the deontological position of Kant and Ross, while avoiding the weaknesses of each view. Utilitarianism claims outright that happiness is fundamental and suggests a direct procedure for answering ethical–social questions. But it is flawed by its lack of a principle of justice. Kant and Ross make rightness a fundamental moral notion and stress the ultimate dignity of human beings. Yet neither provides a workable method for solving problems of social morality. Clearly, Rawls's theory promises much if it can succeed in uniting the two ethical traditions we have discussed.

The Original Position and the Principles of Justice

For Rawls, the central task of government is to preserve and promote the liberty and welfare of individuals. Thus, principles of justice are needed to serve as standards for designing and evaluating social institutions and practices. They provide a way of resolving conflicts among the competing claims that individuals make and a means of protecting the legitimate interests of individuals. In a sense, the principles of justice constitute a blueprint for the development of a just society.

But how are we to formulate principles of justice? Rawls makes use of a hypothetical device he calls "the original position." Imagine a group of people like those who make up our society. These people display the ordinary range of intelligence, talents, ambitions, convictions, and social and economic advantages. They include both sexes and members of various racial and ethnic groups.

Furthermore, suppose that this group is placed behind what Rawls calls "a veil of ignorance." Assume that each person is made ignorant of his or her sex, race, natural endowments, social position, economic condition, and so on. Furthermore, assume that these people are capable of cooperating with one another, that they follow the principles of rational decision making, and that they are capable of a sense of justice and will adhere to principles they agree to adopt. Finally, assume that they all desire what Rawls calls "primary goods": the rights, opportunities, powers, wealth, and such that are both worth possessing in themselves and are necessary to securing the more specific goods an individual may want.

Rawls argues that the principles of justice chosen by such a group will be just if the conditions under which they are selected and the procedures for agreeing on them are fair. The original position, with its veil of ignorance, characterizes a state in which alternative notions of justice can be discussed freely by all. Since the ignorance of the participants means that individuals cannot gain advantage for themselves by choosing principles that favor their own circumstances, the eventual choices of the participants will be fair. Since the participants are assumed to be rational, they will be persuaded by the same reasons and arguments. These features of the original position lead Rawls to characterize his view as "justice as fairness."

We might imagine at first that some people in the original position would gamble and argue for principles that would introduce gross inequalities in their society. For example, some might argue for slavery. If these people should turn out to be masters after the veil of ignorance is stripped away, they would gain immensely. But if they turn out to be slaves, then they would lose immensely. However, since the veil of ignorance keeps them from knowing their actual positions in society, it would not be rational for them to endorse a principle that might condemn them to the bottom of the social order.

Given the uncertainties of the original situation, there is a better strategy that these rational people would choose. In the economic discipline known as game theory, this strategy is called "maximin," or maximizing the minimum. When we choose in uncertain situations, the maximin strategy directs us to select, from all the alternatives, the one whose worst possible outcome is better than the worst possible outcome of the other alternatives. (If you don't know whether you're going to be a slave, you shouldn't approve a set of principles that permits slavery when you have other options.)

Acting in accordance with this strategy, Rawls argues that people in the original position would agree on the following two principles of justice:

1. Each person is to have an equal right to the most extensive total system of equal basic liberties compatible with a similar system of liberty for all.

2. Social and economic inequalities are to be arranged so that they are both (a) to the greatest benefit of the least advantaged... and (b) attached to offices and positions open to all under conditions of fair equality of opportunity.

For Rawls, these two principles are taken to govern the distribution of all social goods: liberty, property, wealth, and social privilege. The first principle has priority. It guarantees a system of equal liberty for all. Furthermore, because of its priority, it explicitly prohibits

the bartering away of liberty for social or economic benefits. (For example, a society cannot withhold the right to vote from its members on the grounds that voting rights damage the economy.)

The second principle governs the distribution of social goods other than liberty. Although society could organize itself in a way that would eliminate differences in wealth and abolish the advantages that attach to different social positions, Rawls argues that those in the original position would not choose this form of egalitarianism. Instead, they would opt for the second principle of justice. This means that, in a just society, differences in wealth and social position can be tolerated only when they can be shown to benefit everyone and to benefit, in particular, those who have the fewest advantages. A just society is not one in which everyone is equal, but one in which inequalities must be demonstrated to be legitimate. Furthermore, there must be a genuine opportunity for acquiring membership in a group that enjoys special benefits. Those not qualified to enter medical schools because of past discrimination in education, for example, can claim a right for special preparation to qualify them. (Of course, in a Rawlsian society, there would be no discrimination to be compensated for.)

Rawls argues that these two principles are required to establish a just society. Furthermore, in distributing liberty and social goods, the principles guarantee the worth and self-respect of the individual. People are free to pursue their own conception of the good and fashion their own lives. Ultimately, the only constraints placed on them as members of society are those expressed in the principles of justice.

Yet Rawls also acknowledges that those in the original position would recognize that we have duties both to ourselves and to others. They would, for example, want to take measures to see that their interests are protected if they should meet with disabling accidents, become seriously mentally disturbed, and so on. Thus, Rawls approves a form of paternalism: others should act for us when we are unable to act for ourselves. When our preferences are known to them, those acting for us should attempt to follow what we would wish. Otherwise, they should act for us as they would act for themselves if they were viewing our situation from the standpoint of the original position. Paternalism is thus a duty to ourselves that would be recognized by those in the original position.

Rawls is also aware of the need for principles that bind and guide individuals as moral decision makers. He claims that those in the original position would reach agreement on principles for such notions as fairness in our dealings with others, fidelity, respect for persons, and beneficence. From these principles, we gain some of our obligations to one another.

But, Rawls claims, there are also "natural duties" that would be recognized by those in the original position. Among those Rawls mentions are (1) the duty of justice—supporting and complying with just institutions; (2) the duty of helping others in need or jeopardy; (3) the duty not to harm or injure another; and (4) the duty to keep our promises.

For the most part, these are duties that hold between or among people. They are only some of the duties that would be offered by those in the original position as unconditional duties.

Thus, Rawls in effect endorses virtually the same duties as those that Ross presents as prima facie duties. Rawls realizes that the problem of conflicts of duty was left unsolved by Ross and so perceives the need for assigning priorities to duties—ranking them as higher and lower. Rawls believes that a full system of principles worked out from the original position would include rules for ranking duties. Rawls's primary concern, however, is with justice in social institutions, and he does not attempt to establish any rules for ranking.

Rawls's Theory of Justice in the Medical Context

Rawls's "natural duties" are virtually the same as Ross's prima facie duties. Consequently, most of what we said earlier about prima facie duties and moral decision making applies to Rawls.

Rawls endorses the legitimacy of paternalism, although he does not attempt to specify detailed principles to justify individual cases. He does tell us that we should consider the preferences of others when they are known to us and when we are in a situation in which we must act for them because they are unable to act for themselves. For example, suppose we know that a person approves of electroconvulsive therapy (shock treatments, or ECT) for the treatment of severe depression. If that person should become so depressed as to be unable to reach a decision about his own treatment, then we would be justified in seeing to it that he received ECT.

To take a similar case, suppose you are a surgeon and have a patient who has expressed to you her wish to avoid numerous operations that may prolong her life six months or so but will be unable to restore her to health. If, in operating, you learned that she has a form of uterine cancer that had spread through her lower extremities and if, in your best judgment, nothing could be done to restore her to health, then it would be your duty to her to allow her to die as she chooses. Repeated operations would be contrary to her concept of her own good.

The most important question in exploring Rawls's theory is how the two principles of justice might apply to the social institutions and practices of medical care and research. Most obviously, Rawls's principles repair utilitarianism's flaw with respect to human experimentation. It would never be right, in Rawls's view, to exploit one group of people or even one person for the benefit of others. Thus, experiments in which people are forced to be subjects or are tricked into participating are ruled out. They involve a violation of basic liberties of individuals and of the absolute respect for persons that the principles of justice require.

A person has a right to decide what risks she is willing to take with her own life and health. Thus, voluntary consent is required before someone can legitimately become a research subject. However, society might decide to reward research volunteers with money, honors, or social privileges to encourage participation in research. Provided that the overall structure of society already conforms to the two principles of justice, this is a perfectly legitimate practice, so long as it brings benefits (ideally) to everyone and the possibility of gaining the rewards of participation is open to all.

Regarding the allocation of social resources in the training of medical personnel (physicians, nurses, therapists, and so on), one may conclude that such investments are justified only if the withdrawal of the support would work to the disadvantage of those already most disadvantaged. Public money may be spent in the form of scholarships and institutional grants to educate individuals who may then derive great social and economic benefits from their education. But, for Rawls, the inequality that is produced is not necessarily unjust. Society can invest its resources in this way if it brings benefits to those most in need of them.

The implication of this position seems to be that everyone is entitled to health care. First, it could be argued that health is among the "primary goods" that Rawls's principles are designed to protect and promote. After all, without health, an individual is hardly in a position to pursue other, more specific goods, and those in the original position might be imagined to be aware of this fact and to endorse only those principles of justice that would require providing at least basic health care to those in the society. Furthermore, it could be argued that the inequalities of the health care system can be justified only if those in most need can benefit from them. Since this is not obviously the case with the present

system, Rawls's principles seem to call for a reform that would provide health care to those who are unable to pay.

However, it is important to point out that it is not at all obvious that a demand to reform our health care system follows from Rawls's position. For one thing, it is not clear that Rawls's principles are intended to be directly applied to our society as it is. Our society includes among its members people with serious disabilities and people with both acute and chronic diseases. If Rawls's principles are intended to apply only to people with normal physical and psychological abilities and needs, as he sometimes suggests, then it is not clear that those who are ill can be regarded as appropriate candidates. If they are considered appropriate, then the results may be unacceptable. The principles of justice may require that we devote vast amounts of social resources to making only marginal improvements in the lives of those who are ill.

Furthermore, Rawls does not explicitly mention the promotion of health as one of the primary goods. It may seem reasonable to include it among them, given the significance of health as a condition for additional pursuits, but this is a point that requires support. Norman Daniels argues considering health a primary good seems the most promising position to take if Rawls's principles are to be used as a basis for evaluating our current health policies and practices.

It seems reasonable to hold that Rawls's principles, particularly the second, can be used to restrict access to certain kinds of health care. In general, individuals may spend their money in any way they wish to seek their notions of what is good. Thus, if someone wants cosmetic surgery to change the shape of his chin and has the money to pay a surgeon, then he may have it done. But if medical facilities or personnel should become overburdened and unable to provide needed care for the most seriously afflicted, then the society would be obligated to forbid cosmetic surgery. By doing this, it would then increase the net access to needed health care by all members of society. The rich who desired cosmetic surgery would not be permitted to exploit the poor who needed basic health care.

These are just a few of the possible implications that Rawls's theory has for medical research and practice. It seems likely that more and more applications of the theory will be worked out in detail in the future.

Difficulties with Rawls's Theory

Rawls's theory is currently the subject of much discussion in philosophy. The debate is often highly technical, and a great number of objections have been raised. At present, however, there are no objections that would be acknowledged as legitimate by all critics. Rather than attempt to summarize the debate, we will simply point to two aspects of Rawls's theory that have been acknowledged as difficulties.

One criticism concerns the original position and its veil of ignorance. Rawls does not permit those in the original position to know anything of their own purposes, plans, or interests—of their conception of the good. They do not know whether they prefer tennis to Tennyson, pleasures of mind over pleasures of the body. They are allowed to consider only those goods—self-respect, wealth, social position—which Rawls puts before them. Thus, critics have said, Rawls has excluded morally relevant knowledge. It is impossible to see how people could agree on principles to regulate their lives when they are so ignorant of their desires and purposes. Rawls seems to have biased the original position in his favor, and this calls into question his claim that the original position is a fair and reasonable way of arriving at principles of justice.

A second criticism focuses on whether Rawls's theory is really as different from utilitarianism as it appears to be. Rawls's theory may well permit inequalities of treatment under certain conditions in the same way

that the principle of utility permits them. The principles of justice that were stated earlier apply, Rawls says, only when liberty can be effectively established and maintained. Rawls is very unclear about when a situation may be regarded as one of this kind. When it is not, his principles of justice are ones of a "general conception." Under this conception, liberties of individuals can be restricted, provided that the restrictions are for the benefit of all. It is possible to imagine, then, circumstances in which we might force individuals to become experimental subjects both for their own benefit and for that of others. We might, for example, require that all cigarette smokers participate in experiments intended to acquire knowledge about lung and heart damage. Since everyone would benefit, directly or indirectly, from such knowledge, forcing their participation would be legitimate. Thus, under the general conception of justice, the difference between Rawls's principles and the principle of utility may in practice become vanishingly small.

Natural Law Ethics and Moral Theology

The general view that the rightness of actions is something determined by nature itself, rather than by the laws and customs of societies or the preferences of individuals, is called *natural law theory*. Moral principles are thus regarded as objective truths that can be discovered in the nature of things by reason and reflection. The basic idea of the theory was expressed succinctly by the Roman philosopher Cicero (103–43 B.C.): "Law is the highest reason, implanted in Nature, which commands what ought to be done and forbids the opposite. This reason, when firmly fixed and fully developed in the human mind, is Law." The natural law theory originated in classical Greek and Roman philosophy and has immensely influenced the development of moral and political theories. Indeed, all the ethical theories we have discussed are indebted to the natural law tradition. The reliance upon reason as a means of settling upon or establishing ethical principles and the emphasis on the need to reckon with the natural abilities and inclinations of human nature are just two of the threads that are woven into the theories that we have discussed.

Purposes, Reason, and the Moral Law as Interpreted by Roman Catholicism

The natural law theory of Roman Catholicism was given its most influential formulation in the thirteenth century by St. Thomas Aquinas (1225–1274). Contemporary versions of the theory are mostly elaborations and interpretations of Aquinas's basic statement. Thus, an understanding of Aquinas's views is important for grasping the philosophical principles that underlie the Roman Catholic position on such issues as abortion.

Aquinas was writing at a time in which a great number of the texts of Aristotle (384–322 B.C.) were becoming available in the West, and Aquinas's philosophical theories incorporated many of Aristotle's principles. A fundamental notion borrowed by Aquinas is the view that the universe is organized in a teleological way. That is, the universe is structured in such a way that each thing in it has a goal or purpose. Thus, when conditions are right, a tadpole will develop into a frog. In its growth and change, the tadpole is following "the law of its nature." It is achieving its goal.

Humans have a material nature, just as a tadpole does, and in their own growth and development they, too, follow a law of their material nature. But Aquinas also stresses that humans possess a trait that no other creature does: reason. Thus, the full development of human potentialities—the fulfillment of human purpose—requires that we follow the direction of the law of reason, as well as being subjected to the laws of material human nature.

The development of reason is one of our ends as human beings, but we also rely upon reason to determine what our ends are and how we can achieve them. It is this function of reason that leads Aquinas to identify reason as the source of the moral law. Reason is practical in its operation, for it directs our actions so that we can bring about certain results. In giving us directions, reason imposes an obligation on us, the obligation to bring about the results that it specifies. But Aquinas says that reason cannot arbitrarily set goals for us. Reason directs us toward our good as the goal of our action, and what that good is, is discoverable within our nature. Thus, reason recognizes the basic principle "Good is to be done and evil avoided."

But this principle is purely formal, or empty of content. To make it a practical principle, we must consider what the human good is. According to Aquinas, the human good is that which is suitable or proper to human nature. It is what is "built into" human nature in the way that, in a sense, a frog is already "built into" a tadpole. Thus, the good is that to which we are directed by our natural inclinations as both physical and rational creatures.

Like other creatures, we have a natural inclination to preserve our lives; consequently, reason imposes on us an obligation to care for our health, not to kill ourselves, and not to put ourselves in positions in which we might be killed. We realize through reason that others have a rational nature like ours, and we see that we are bound to treat them with the same dignity and respect that we accord ourselves. Furthermore, when we see that humans require a society to make their full development possible, we realize that we have an obligation to support laws and practices that make society possible.

For example, as we have a natural inclination to propagate our species (viewed as a "natural" good), reason places on us an obligation not to thwart or pervert that inclination. As a consequence, to fulfill this obligation within society, reason supports the institution of marriage.

Reason also finds in our nature grounds for procedural principles. For example, because everyone has an inclination to preserve his life and well-being, no one should be forced to testify against himself. Similarly, because all individuals are self-interested, no one should be permitted to be a judge in his own case.

Physical inclinations, under the direction of reason, point us toward our natural good. But, according to Aquinas, reason itself can also be a source of inclinations. For example, Aquinas says that reason is the source of our natural inclination to seek the truth, particularly the truth about the existence and nature of God.

Just from the few examples we have considered, it should be clear how Aquinas believed it was possible to discover natural goods in human nature. Relying upon these as goals or purposes to be achieved, reason would then work out the practical way of achieving them. Thus, through the subtle application of reason, it should be possible to establish a body of moral principles and rules. These are the doctrines of natural law.

Because natural law is founded on human nature, which is regarded as unchangeable, Aquinas regards natural law itself as unchangeable. Moreover, it is seen as the same for all people, at all times, and in all societies. Even those without knowledge of God can, through the operation of reason, recognize their natural obligations.

For Aquinas and for Roman Catholicism, this view of natural law is just one aspect of a broader theological framework. The teleological organization of the universe is attributed to the planning of a creator: goals or purposes are ordained by God. Furthermore, although natural law is discoverable in the universe, its ultimate source is divine wisdom and God's eternal law. Everyone who is rational is capable of grasping natural law. But because passions and irrational inclinations may corrupt human nature and because some people lack the abilities or time

to work out the demands of natural law, God also chose to reveal our duties to us in explicit ways. The major source of revelation, of course, is taken to be the biblical scriptures.

Natural law, scriptural revelation, the interpretation of the Scriptures by the Church, Church tradition, and the teachings of the Church are regarded in Roman Catholicism as the sources of moral ideals and principles. By guiding one's life by them, one can develop the rational and moral part of one's nature and move toward the goal of achieving the sort of perfection that is suitable for humans.

This general moral–theological point of view is the source for particular Roman Catholic doctrines that have special relevance to medicine. We will consider just two of the most important principles.

The Principle of Double Effect. A particular kind of moral conflict arises when the performance of an action will produce both good and bad effects. On the basis of the good effect, it seems it is our duty to perform the action; but on the basis of the bad effect, it seems our duty not to perform it.

Let's assume that the death of a fetus is in itself a bad effect and consider a case like the following: A woman who is three months pregnant is found to have a cancerous uterus. If the woman's life is to be saved, the uterus must be removed at once. But if the uterus is removed, then the life of the unborn child will be lost. Should the operation be performed?

The principle of double effect is intended to help in the resolution of these kinds of conflicts. The principle holds that such an action should be performed only if the intention is to bring about the good effect and the bad effect will be an unintended or indirect consequence. More specifically, four conditions must be satisfied:

1. The action itself must be morally indifferent or morally good.

2. The bad effect must not be the means by which the good effect is achieved.

3. The motive must be the achievement of the good effect only.

4. The good effect must be at least equivalent in importance to the bad effect.

Are these conditions satisfied in the case that we mentioned? The operation itself, if this is considered to be the action, is at least morally indifferent. That is, in itself it is neither good nor bad. That takes care of the first condition. If the mother's life is to be saved, it will not be *by means of* killing the fetus. It will be by means of removing the cancerous uterus. Thus, the second condition is met. The motive of the surgeon, we may suppose, is not the death of the fetus but saving the life of the woman. If so, then the third condition is satisfied. Finally, since two lives are at stake, the good effect (saving the life of the woman) is at least equal to the bad effect (the death of the fetus). The fourth condition is thus met. Under ordinary conditions, then, these conditions would be considered satisfied, and such an operation would be morally justified.

The principle of double effect is most often mentioned in a medical context in cases of abortion. But, in fact, it has a much wider range of application in medical ethics. It bears on cases of contraception, sterilization, organ transplants, and the use of extraordinary measures to maintain life.

The Principle of Totality. The principle of totality can be expressed in this way: an individual has a right to dispose of his or her organs or to destroy their capacity to function only to the extent that the general well-being of the whole body demands it. Thus, it is clear that we have a natural obligation to preserve our lives, but, by the Roman Catholic view, we also have a duty to preserve the integrity of our bodies. This duty is based on the belief that each of our organs was designed by God to play a role in maintaining the functional integrity of our bodies—that each has a place in the divine plan. As we are the custodians of our bodies, not their owners, it is our duty to care for them as a trust.

The principle of totality has implications for a great number of medical procedures. Strictly speaking, even cosmetic surgery is morally right only when it is required to maintain or ensure the normal functioning of the rest of the body. More important, procedures that are typically employed for contraceptive purposes—vasectomies and tubal ligations—are ruled out. After all, such procedures involve "mutilation" and the destruction of the capacity of the organs of reproduction to function properly. The principle of totality thus also forbids the sterilization of the mentally retarded.

As an ethical theory, natural law theory is sometimes described as teleological. In endorsing the principle "Good is to be done and evil avoided," the theory identifies a goal with respect to which the rightness of an action is to be judged. As the principle of double effect illustrates, the intention of the individual who acts is crucial to determining whether the goal is sought. In a sense, the intention of the action—what the individual wills—defines the action. Thus, "performing an abortion" and "saving a woman's life" are not necessarily the same action, even in those instances in which their external features are the same. Unlike utilitarianism, which is also a teleological theory, natural law theory is not consequentialist: the outcome of an action is not the sole feature to consider in determining the moral character of the action.

Applications of Roman Catholic Moral–Theological Viewpoints in the Medical Context

Roman Catholic ethicists and moral theologians have written and developed a body of widely accepted doctrine. We will consider only four topics.

First, the application of the principle of double effect and the principle of totality have definite consequences in the area of medical experimentation. Since we hold our bodies in trust, we are responsible for assessing the degree of risk present in an experiment in which we are asked to be a subject. Thus, we need to be fully informed of the nature of the experiment and the risks that it holds for us. If, after obtaining this knowledge, we decide to give our consent, it must be given freely and not as the result of deception or coercion.

Because human experimentation carries with it the possibility of injury and death, the principle of double effect and its four strictures apply. If scientific evidence indicates that a sick person may benefit from participating in an experiment, then the experiment is morally justifiable. If, however, the evidence indicates that the chances of helping that person are slight and he or she may die or be gravely injured, then the experiment is not justified. In general, the likelihood of a person's benefiting from the experiment must exceed the danger of that person's suffering greater losses.

A person who is incurably ill may volunteer to be an experimental subject, even though she or he cannot reasonably expect personal gain in the form of improved health. The good that is hoped for is good for others, in the form of increased medical knowledge. Even here, however, there are constraints imposed by the principle of double effect. There must be no likelihood that the experiment will seriously injure anyone, and the probable value of the knowledge expected to result must balance the risk run by the patient. Not even the incurably ill can be made subjects of trivial experiments.

The good sought by healthy volunteers is also the good of others. The same restrictions mentioned in connection with the incurably ill apply to experimenting on healthy people. In addition, the principle of totality places constraints on what a person may volunteer to do with his or her body. No healthy person may submit to an experiment that involves the probability of serious injury, impaired health, mutilation, or death.

A second medical topic addressed by Roman Catholic theologians is whether "ordinary" or "extraordinary" measures are to be taken in the preservation of human life. While

it is believed that natural law and divine law impose on us a moral obligation to preserve our lives, Catholic moralists have interpreted this obligation as requiring that we rely upon only ordinary means. In the medical profession, the phrase "ordinary means" is used to refer to medical procedures that are standard or orthodox, in contrast with those that are untried or experimental. But from the viewpoint of Catholic ethics, "ordinary" used in the medical context applies to "all medicines, treatments, and operations which offer a reasonable hope of benefit for the patient and which can be obtained and used without excessive expense, pain, or other inconvenience." Thus, by contrast, extraordinary means are those which offer the patient no reasonable hope or whose use causes serious hardship for the patient or others.

Medical measures that would save the life of a patient but subject her to years of pain or produce in her severe physical or mental incapacities are considered extraordinary. A patient or her family are under no obligation to choose such measures, and physicians are under a positive obligation not to encourage their choice.

The third medical topic for consideration is euthanasia. In the Roman Catholic ethical view, euthanasia in any form is considered immoral. It is presumed to be a direct violation of God's dominion over creation and the human obligation to preserve life. The Ethical Directives for Catholic Hospitals is explicit on the matter of taking a life:

> *The direct killing of any innocent person, even at his own request, is always morally wrong. Any procedure whose sole immediate effect is the death of a human being is a direct killing. . . . Euthanasia ("mercy killing") in all its forms is forbidden. . . . The failure to supply the ordinary means of preserving life is equivalent to euthanasia.*

According to this view, it is wrong to allow babies suffering from serious birth defects to die. If they can be saved by ordinary means, there is an obligation to do so. It is also wrong to act to terminate the lives of those hopelessly ill, either by taking steps to bring about their deaths or by failing to take steps to maintain their lives by ordinary means.

It is never permissible to hasten the death of a person as a direct intention. It is, however, permissible to administer drugs that alleviate pain. The principle of double effect suggests that giving such drugs is a morally justifiable action even though the drugs may indirectly hasten the death of a person.

Last, we may inquire how Roman Catholicism views abortion. According to the Roman Catholic view, from the moment of conception, the conceptus (later, the fetus) is considered to be a person with all the rights of a person. For this reason, direct abortion at any stage of pregnancy is regarded as morally wrong. Abortion is "direct" when it results from a procedure "whose sole immediate effect is the termination of pregnancy." This means that what is generally referred to as therapeutic abortion, in which an abortion is performed to safeguard the life or health of the woman, is considered wrong. For example, a woman with serious heart disease who becomes pregnant cannot morally justify an abortion on the grounds that the pregnancy is a serious threat to her life. Even when the ultimate aim is to save the life of the woman, direct abortion is wrong.

We have already seen, however, that the principle of double effect permits the performance of an action that may result in the death of an unborn child if the action satisfies the four criteria for applying the principle. Thus, *indirect* abortion is considered to be morally permissible. That is, the abortion must be the outcome of some action (for example, removal of a cancerous uterus) that is performed for the direct and total purpose of treating a pathological condition affecting the woman. The end sought in direct abortion is the destruction of life, but the end sought in indirect abortion is the preservation of life.

Difficulties with Natural Law Ethics and Moral Theology

Our discussion has centered on the natural law theory of ethics as it has been interpreted in Roman Catholic theology. Thus, there are two possible types of difficulties: those associated with natural law ethics in its own right and those associated with its incorporation into theology. The theological difficulties go beyond the scope of our aims and interests. We will restrict ourselves to considering the basic difficulty that faces natural law theory as formulated by Aquinas. Since it is this formulation that has been used in Roman Catholic moral theology, we shall be raising a problem for it in an indirect way.

The fundamental difficulty with Aquinas's argument for natural law is caused by the assumption, borrowed from Aristotle, that the universe is organized in a teleological fashion. (This is the assumption that every kind of thing has a goal or purpose.) This assumption is essential to Aquinas's ethical theory, for he identifies the good of a thing with its natural mode of operation. Without the assumption, we are faced with the great diversity and moral indifference of nature. Inclinations, even when shared by all humans, are no more than inclinations. There are no grounds for considering them "goods," and they have no moral status. The universe is bereft of natural values.

Yet, there are many reasons to consider this assumption false. Physics surrendered the notion of a teleological organization in the world as long ago as the seventeenth century: the rejection of Aristotle's physics also entailed the rejection of Aristotle's teleological view of the world. This left biology as the major source of arguments in favor of teleology. But contemporary evolutionary theory shows that the apparent purposive character of evolutionary change can be accounted for by the operation of natural selection on random mutations. Also, the development and growth of organisms can be explained by the presence of genetic information that controls the processes. The tadpole develops into a frog because evolution has produced a genetic program that directs the sequence of complicated chemical changes. Thus, no adequate grounds seem to exist for asserting that the teleological organization of nature is anything more than apparent.

Science and "reason alone" do not support teleology. It can be endorsed only if one is willing to assume that any apparent teleological organization is the product of a divine plan. Yet, because all apparent teleology can be explained in nonteleological ways, this assumption seems neither necessary nor legitimate.

Without its foundation of teleology, Aquinas's theory of natural law ethics seems to collapse. This is not to say, of course, that some other natural law theory—one not requiring the assumption of teleology—might not be persuasively defended.

MAJOR MORAL PRINCIPLES

Making moral decisions is always a difficult and stressful task. Abstract discussions of issues never quite capture the feelings of uncertainty and self-doubt we characteristically experience when called upon to decide what ought to be done or to judge whether someone did the right thing. There are no mechanical processes or algorithms we can apply in a situation of moral doubt. There are no computer programs to supply us with the proper decision when given the relevant data.

In a very real sense, we are on our own when it comes to making ethical decisions. This does not mean that we are without resources and must decide blindly or even naively. When we have the luxury of time, when the need to make a decision is not pressing, we may attempt to work out an answer to a moral question by relying upon a general ethical theory like those discussed earlier. However, in ordinary life we rarely have the opportunity or time to engage in an elaborate process of reasoning and analysis.

A more practical approach is to employ moral principles that have been derived from and justified by a moral theory. A principle such as "Avoid causing needless harm" can serve as a more direct guide to action and decision making than, say, Kant's categorical imperative can. With such a principle in mind, we realize that if we are acting as a physician, then we have a duty to use our knowledge and skills to protect our patients from injury. For example, we should not expose a patient to the needless risk of a diagnostic test that does not promise to yield useful information.

In this section, we will present and illustrate five moral principles. All are ones of special relevance to dealing with the ethical issues presented by decisions concerning medical care. The principles have their limitations. For one thing, they are in no sense complete. Moral issues arise, even in the context of medicine, for which they can supply no direct guidance. In other situations, the principles themselves may come into conflict and point toward incompatible solutions. (How can we both avoid causing harm and allow a terminally ill patient to die?) The principles themselves indicate no way such conflicts can be resolved, for, even taken together, they do not constitute a coherent moral theory. To resolve conflicts, it may be necessary to employ the more basic principles of such a theory.

It is fair to say that each of the five basic moral theories we have discussed endorses the legitimacy of these principles. Not all would formulate them in the same way, and not all would give them the same moral weight. Nevertheless, each theory would accept them as expressing appropriate guidelines for moral decision making.

Indeed, the best way to think about the principles is as guidelines. They are in no way rules that can be applied automatically. Rather, they express standards to be consulted in attempting to arrive at a justified decision. As such, they provide a basis for evaluating actions or policies as well as for making individual moral decisions.

The principles help guarantee that our decisions are made in accordance with them and not according to our whims or prejudices. By following the principles, we are more likely to reach decisions that are reasoned, consistent, and applicable to similar cases.

The Principle of Nonmaleficence

"Above all, do no harm" is perhaps the most famous and most quoted of all moral maxims in medicine. It captures in a succinct way what is universally considered to be an overriding duty of anyone who undertakes the care of a patient. We believe that, in treating a patient, a physician should not by carelessness, malice, inadvertence, or avoidable ignorance do anything that will cause injury to the patient.

The maxim is one expression of what is sometimes called in ethics the principle of nonmaleficence. The principle can be formulated in various ways, but here is one relatively uncontroversial way of stating it: *We ought to act in ways that do not cause needless harm or injury to others.* Stated in a positive fashion, the principle tells us that we have a duty to avoid maleficence—that is, to avoid harming or injuring other people.

In the most obvious case, we violate the principle of nonmaleficence when we intentionally do something we know will cause someone harm. For example, suppose that, during the course of an operation, a surgeon deliberately severs a muscle, knowing that, by doing so, he will cripple the patient. Then the surgeon is guilty of maleficence and is morally (as well as legally) blameworthy for his action.

The principle may also be violated when no malice or intention to do harm is involved. A nurse who carelessly gives a patient the wrong medication and causes the patient to suffer irreversible brain damage may have had no intention of causing the patient any injury. However, the nurse was negligent in his actions and failed to exercise due care in

discharging his responsibilities. His actions resulted in an avoidable injury to his patient. Hence, he failed to meet his obligation of nonmaleficence.

The duty imposed by the principle of nonmaleficence is not a demand to accomplish the impossible. We realize that we cannot reasonably expect perfection in the practice of medicine. We know that the results of treatments are often uncertain and may cause more harm than good. We know that the knowledge we have of diseases is only partial and that decisions about diagnosis and therapy typically involve the exercise of judgment, with no guarantee of correctness. We know that an uncertainty is built into the very nature of things and that our power to control the outcome of natural processes is limited. Consequently, we realize that we cannot hold physicians and other health professionals accountable for every instance of death and injury involving patients under their care.

Nevertheless, we can demand that physicians and others live up to reasonable standards of performance. In the conduct of their professions, we can expect them to be cautious and diligent, patient and thoughtful. We can expect them to pay attention to what they are doing and to deliberate about whether a particular procedure should be done. In addition, we can expect them to possess the knowledge and skills relevant to the proper discharge of their duties.

These features and others like them make up the standards of performance that define what we have a right to expect from physicians and other health professionals. In the language of the law, these are the standards of "due care," and it is by reference to them that we evaluate the medical care given to patients. Failure to meet the standards opens practitioners (physicians, nurses, dentists, therapists) to the charge of moral or legal maleficence.

In our society, we have attempted to guarantee that at least some of the due-care standards are met by relying upon such measures as degree programs, licensing laws, certifying boards, and hospital credentials committees. Such an approach offers a way of ensuring that physicians and others have acquired at least a minimum level of knowledge, skill, and experience before undertaking the responsibilities attached to their roles. The approach also encourages such values as diligence, prudence, and caution, but there is of course no way of guaranteeing that in a particular case a physician will exhibit those virtues. Haste, carelessness, and inattention are always possible, and the potential that a patient will suffer an injury from them is always present.

The standards of due care are connected in some respects with such factual matters as the current state of medical knowledge and training and the immediate circumstances in which a physician provides care. For example, in the 1920s and 1930s, it was not at all unusual for a general practitioner to perform relatively complicated surgery, particularly in rural areas. In performing surgery, he would be acting in a reasonable and expected fashion and could not legitimately be charged with violating the principle of nonmaleficence.

However, the change in medicine from that earlier time to the present has also altered our beliefs about what is reasonable and expected. Today, a general practitioner who has had no special training and is not board certified and yet performs surgery on her patients may be legitimately criticized for maleficence. The standards of due care in surgery are now higher and more exacting than they once were, and the general practitioner who undertakes to perform most forms of surgery causes her patients to undergo an unusual and unnecessary risk literally at her hands. Their interest

would be better served if their surgery were performed by a trained and qualified surgeon.

Such a case also illustrates the idea that no actual harm or injury must occur for someone to be acting in violation of the principle of nonmaleficence. The general practitioner performing surgery may not cause any injury to his patients, but he puts them in a position in which the possibility of harm to them is greater than it needs to be. It is in this respect that he is not exercising due care in his treatment and so can be charged with maleficence. He has subjected his patients to *unnecessary risk*—risk greater than they would be subject to in the hands of a trained surgeon.

It is important to stress that the principle of nonmaleficence does not require that a physician subject a patient to no risks at all. Virtually every form of diagnostic testing and medical treatment involves some degree of risk to the patient, and to provide medical care at all, a physician must often act in ways that involve a possible injury to the patient. For example, a physician who takes a thorough medical history, performs a physical examination, and then treats a patient with an antibiotic for bacterial infection cannot be held morally responsible if the patient suffers a severe drug reaction. That such a thing might happen is a possibility that cannot be foreseen in an individual case.

Similarly, a serious medical problem may justify subjecting the patient to a serious risk. (Gaining the consent of the patient is an obvious consideration, however.) A life-threatening condition, such as an occluded right coronary artery, may warrant coronary-bypass surgery with all its attendant dangers.

In effect, the principle of nonmaleficence tells us to avoid needless risk and, when risk is an inevitable aspect of an appropriate diagnostic test or treatment, to minimize the risk as much as is reasonably possible. A physician who orders a lumbar puncture for a patient who complains of occasional headaches is acting inappropriately, given the nature of the complaint, and is subjecting his patient to needless risk. By contrast, a physician who orders such a test after examining a patient who has severe and recurring headaches, a fever, pain and stiffness in his neck, and additional key clinical signs is acting appropriately. The risk to the patient from the lumbar puncture is the same in both cases, but the risk is warranted in the second case and not in the first. A failure to act with due care violates the principle of nonmaleficence, even if no harm results, whereas acting with due care does not violate the principle, even if harm does result.

The Principle of Beneficence

"As to diseases, make a habit of two things— to help or at least to do no harm." This directive from the Hippocratic writings stresses that the physician has two duties. The second of them ("at least to do no harm") we discussed in connection with the principle of nonmaleficence. The first of them ("to help") we will consider here in connection with the principle of beneficence.

Like the previous principle, the principle of beneficence can be stated in various and different ways. Here is one formulation: *We should act in ways that promote the welfare of other people.* That is, we should help other people when we are able to do so.

Some philosophers have expressed doubt that we have an actual duty to help others. We certainly have a duty not to harm other people, but it has seemed to some that there are no grounds for saying that we have a duty to promote their welfare. We would deserve praise if we did, but we would not deserve blame if we did not. From this point of view, being beneficent is beyond the scope of duty.

We need not consider whether this view is correct in general. For our purposes, it is enough to realize that the nature of the relationship between a physician and a patient does impose the duty of acting in the patient's welfare. That is, the duty of beneficence is inherent in the role of physician. A physician who was not acting for the sake of the patient's good would, in a very real sense, not be acting as a physician.

That we recognize the principle of beneficence as a duty appropriate to the physician's role is seen most clearly in cases in which the physician is also a researcher and her patient is also an experimental subject. In such instances, there is a possibility of a role conflict, for the researcher's aim of acquiring knowledge is not always compatible with the physician's aim of helping the patient. (See Chapter 1 for a discussion of this problem.)

The duty required by the principle of beneficence is inherent in the role not only of physicians but of all health professionals. Nurses, therapists, clinical psychologists, social workers, and others accept the duty of promoting the welfare of their patients or clients as an appropriate part of their responsibilities. We expect nurses and others to do good for us, and it is this expectation that leads us to designate them as belonging to what are often called "the helping professions."

The extent to which beneficence is required as a duty for physicians and others is not a matter easily resolved. In practice, we recognize that limits exist to what can be expected from even those who have chosen to make a career of helping others. We do not expect physicians to sacrifice completely their self-interest and welfare on behalf of their patients. We do not think their duty demands that they be totally selfless. If some do, we may praise them as secular saints or moral heroes, but that is because they go beyond the demands of duty. At the same time, we would have little good to say of a physician who always put his interest above that of his patients, who never made a personal sacrifice to service their interests.

Just as there are standards of due care that explicitly and implicitly define what we consider to be right conduct in protecting patients from harm, so there seem to be implicit standards of beneficence. We obviously expect physicians to help patients by providing them with appropriate treatment. More than this, we expect physicians to be prepared to make *reasonable* sacrifices for the sake of their patients. Even in the age of "health care teams," a single physician assumes responsibility for a particular patient when the patient is hospitalized or treated for a serious illness. It is this physician who is expected to make the crucial medical decisions, and we expect her to realize that discharging that responsibility may involve an interruption of private plans and activities. A surgeon who is informed that her postoperative patient has started to bleed can be expected to cancel her plan to attend a concert. Doing so is a reasonable duty imposed by the principle of beneficence. If she failed to discharge the duty, then, in the absence of mitigating circumstances, she would become the object of disapproval by her patient and by her medical colleagues.

It would be very difficult to spell out exactly what duties are required by the principle of beneficence. Even if we limit ourselves to the medical context, there are so many ways of promoting someone's welfare and so many different circumstances to consider that it would be virtually impossible to provide anything like a catalog of appropriate actions. However, such a catalog is hardly necessary. Most people most often have a sense of what is reasonable and what is not, and it is this sense that we rely on in making judgments about whether physicians and others are fulfilling the duty of beneficence in their actions.

The principles of nonmaleficence and beneficence impose social duties also. In the most general terms, we look to society to take measures to promote the health and safety of its citizens. The great advances made in public health during the nineteenth century were made because the society recognized a responsibility to attempt to prevent the spread of disease. Water treatment plants, immunization programs, and quarantine as restrictions were all in recognition of society's duty of nonmaleficence.

These and similar programs have been continued and augmented, and our society has also recognized a duty of beneficence in connection with health care. The Medicaid program for the poor and Medicare for the elderly are major efforts to see to at least some of the health needs of a large segment of the population. Prenatal programs for expectant mothers and public clinics are among the other social responses we have made to promote the health of citizens.

Less obvious than programs that provide direct medical care are ones that support medical research and basic science. Directly or indirectly, such programs contribute to meeting the health needs of our society. Much basic research is relevant to acquiring an understanding of the processes involved in both health and disease, and much medical research is specifically aimed at the development of effective diagnostic and therapeutic measures.

In principle, social beneficence has no limits, but in practice it must. Social resources like tax revenues are in restricted supply, and the society must decide how they are to be spent. Housing and food for the poor, education, defense, the arts, and the humanities are just some of the areas demanding support in the name of social beneficence. Medical care is one among many claimants, and we must decide as a society what proportion of our social resources we want to commit to it. Are we prepared to guarantee to all whatever medical care they need? Are we willing to endorse only a basic level of care? Do we want to say that what is available to some (the rich or well insured) must be available to all (the poor and uninsured)? Just how beneficent we wish to be—and can afford to be—is a matter still under discussion. (See Chapter 8.)

The Principle of Utility

The principle of utility can be formulated in this way: *We should act in such a way as to bring about the greatest benefit and the least harm.* As we discussed earlier, the principle is the very foundation of the moral theory of utilitarianism. However, the principle need not be regarded as unique to utilitarianism. It can be thought of as one moral principle among others that present us with a prima facie duty, and, as such, it need not be regarded as always taking precedence over others. In particular, we would never think it was justified to deprive someone of a right, even if by doing so we could bring benefit to many others.

We need not repeat the discussion of the principle of utility presented earlier, but it may be useful to consider here how the principle relates to the principles of nonmaleficence and beneficence. When we consider the problem of distributing social resources, it becomes clear that acting in accordance with the principles of nonmaleficence and beneficence usually involves trade-offs. To use our earlier example, as a society we are concerned with providing for the health care needs of our citizens. To accomplish this end, we support various programs—Medicare, Medicaid, hospital-building programs, medical research, and so on.

However, there are limits to what we can do. Medical care is not the only concern of our society. We are interested in protecting people from harm and in promoting their interests, but there are many forms of harm and many kinds of interest to be promoted. With finite resources at our disposal, the more money we spend on health care, the less we can spend on education, the arts, the humanities, and so on.

Even if we decided to spend more money on health care than we are currently spending, there would come a point at which we would receive only a marginal return for our money. General health would eventually reach such a level that it would be difficult to raise it still higher. To save even one additional life, we would have to spend a vast sum of money. By contrast, at the start of a health care program, relatively little money can make a relatively big difference. Furthermore, money spent for marginal improvements would be directed away from other needs that had become even more crucial because of underfunding. Thus, we could not spend all our resources on health care without ignoring other social needs.

The aim of social planning is to balance the competing needs of the society. Taken alone, the principles of nonmaleficence and beneficence are of no help in resolving the conflicts among social needs. The principle of utility must come into play to establish and rank needs and to serve as a guide for determining to what extent it is possible to satisfy one social need in comparison with others. In effect, the principle imposes a social duty on us all to use our resources to do as much good as possible. That is, we must do the most good *overall*, even when this means we are not able to meet all needs in a particular area.

The application of the principle of utility is not limited to large-scale social issues, such as how to divide our resources among medical care, defense, education, and so on. We may also rely on the principle when we are deliberating about the choice of alternative means of accomplishing an aim. For example, we might decide to institute a mandatory screening program to detect infants with PKU but decide against a program to detect those with Tay–Sachs. PKU can often be treated successfully if discovered early enough, whereas early detection of Tay–Sachs makes little or no difference in the outcome of the disease. Furthermore, PKU is distributed in the general population, whereas Tay–Sachs occurs mostly in a special segment of the population. In general, then, the additional money spent on screening for Tay–Sachs would not be justified by the results. The money could do more good, produce more benefits, were it spent some other way.

The principle of utility is also relevant to making decisions about the diagnosis and treatment of individuals. For example, as we mentioned earlier, no diagnostic test can be justified if it causes the patient more risk than the information likely to be gained is worth. Invasive procedures are associated with a certain rate of injury and death (morbidity and mortality). It would make no sense to subject a patient to a kidney biopsy if the findings were not likely to affect the course of treatment or if the risk from the biopsy were greater than the risk of the suspected disease itself. Attempts are well under way in medicine to employ the formal theories of decision analysis to assist physicians in determining whether a particular mode of diagnosis, therapy, or surgery can be justified in individual cases. Underlying the details of formal analysis is the principle of utility, which directs us to act in a way that will bring about the greatest benefit and the least harm.

Principles of Distributive Justice

We expect (and can demand) to be treated justly in our dealings with other people and with institutions. If our insurance policy covers up to thirty days of hospitalization, then we expect a claim against the policy for that amount of time to be honored. If we arrive in an emergency room with a broken arm before the arrival of someone else with a broken arm, we expect to be attended to before that person.

We do not always expect that being treated justly will work to our direct advantage. Although we would prefer to keep all the money we earn, we realize that we must pay our share of taxes. If a profusely bleeding person arrives in the emergency room after we do, we recognize that he is in need of immediate treatment and should be attended to before we are.

Justice has at least two major aspects. Seeing to it that people receive that to which they are entitled, that their rights are recognized and protected, falls under the general heading of *noncomparative justice*. By contrast, *comparative justice* is concerned with the application of laws and rules and with the distribution of burdens and benefits.

The concern of comparative justice that is most significant to the medical context is *distributive justice*. As the name suggests, distributive justice concerns the distribution of such social benefits and burdens as medical services, welfare payments, public offices, taxes, and military service. In general, the distribution of income has been the focus of recent discussions of distributive justice. In medical ethics, the focus has been the distribution of health care. Are all in the society entitled to receive health care benefits, whether or not they can pay for them? If so, then is everyone entitled to the same amount of health care? (See Chapter 8 for a discussion of this issue.)

Philosophical theories of justice attempt to resolve questions of distributive justice by providing a detailed account of the features of individuals and society that will justify our making distinctions in the ways we distribute benefits and burdens. If some people are to be rich and others poor, if some are to rule and others serve, then there must be some rational and moral basis for such distinctions. We look to theories of justice to provide us with such a basis. (See the earlier discussion of John Rawls's theory for an outstanding recent example.)

Theories of justice differ significantly, but at the core of all of them is the basic principle that "Similar cases ought to be treated in similar ways." The principle expresses the notion that justice involves fairness of treatment. For example, it is manifestly unfair to award two different grades to two people who score the same on a multiple-choice exam. If two cases are the same, then it is arbitrary or irrational to treat them differently. To justify different treatment, we would have to show that the cases are also dissimilar in some relevant respect.

This fairness principle is known as the *formal* principle of justice. It is called "formal" because, like a sentence with blanks, it must be filled in with information. Specifically, we must be told what factors or features are to be considered *relevant* in deciding whether two cases are similar. If two cases differ in relevant respects, we may be justified in treating them differently. We may do so without being either irrational or arbitrary.

Theories of distributive justice present us with *substantive* (or *material*) principles of justice. The theories present us with arguments to show why certain features or factors should be considered relevant in deciding whether cases are similar. The substantive principles can then be referred to in determining whether particular laws, practices, or public policies can be considered just. Further, the substantive principles can be employed as guidelines for framing laws and policies and for developing a just society.

Arguments in favor of particular theories of justice are too lengthy to present here. However, it is useful to consider briefly four substantive principles that have been offered by various theorists as ones worthy of acceptance. To a considerable extent, differences among these principles help explain present disagreements in our society about the ways in which such social "goods" as income, education, and health care should be distributed. Although the principles themselves direct the distribution of burdens (taxation, public service, and so on) as well as benefits, we will focus on benefits. The basic question answered by each principle is "Who is entitled to what proportion of society's goods?"

The Principle of Equality

According to the principle of equality, all benefits and burdens are to be distributed equally. Everyone is entitled to the same sized slice of the pie, and everyone must bear an equal part of the social load. The principle, strictly interpreted, requires a radical egalitarianism: everyone is to be treated the same in all respects.

The principle is most plausible for a society not too far above the margin of production. When there is enough to go around but not much more, then it is manifestly unfair for some to have more than they need and for others to have less than they need. When a society is more affluent, the principle may lose some of its persuasiveness. When greater efforts by a few produce more goods than the efforts of the ordinary person, it may be unfair not

to recognize the accomplishments of a few by greater rewards. Rawls's theory remains an egalitarian one, while providing a way to resolve this apparent conflict. According to Rawls, any departure from equality is arbitrary, unless it can be shown that the inequality will work out to *everyone's* advantage.

The Principle of Need

The principle of need is an extension of the egalitarian principle of equal distribution. If goods are parceled out according to individual need, those who have greater needs will receive a greater share. However, the outcome will be one of equality. Since the basic needs of everyone will be met, everyone will end up at the same level. The treatment of individuals will be equal, in this respect, even though the proportion of goods they receive will not be.

What is to count as a need is a significant question that cannot be answered by a principle of distribution alone. Obviously, basic biological needs (food, clothing, shelter) must be included, but what about psychological or intellectual needs? The difficulty of resolving the question of needs is seen in the fact that— even in our affluent society, the richest in the history of the world—we are still debating the question of whether health care should be available to all.

The Principle of Contribution

According to the principle of contribution, people should get back that proportion of social goods that is the result of their productive labor. If two people work to grow potatoes and the first works twice as long or twice as hard as the second, then the first should be entitled to twice as large a share of the harvest.

The difficulty with this principle in an industrialized, capitalistic society is that contributions to production can take forms other than time and labor. Some people risk their money in investments needed to make production possible, and others contribute crucial ideas or inventions. How are comparisons to be made? Furthermore, in highly industrialized societies it is the functioning of the entire system, rather than the work of any particular individual, that creates the goods to be distributed. A single individual's claim on the outcome of the whole system may be very small.

Nonetheless, it is individuals who make the system work, so it does seem just that individuals should benefit from their contributions. If it is true that it is the system of social organization itself that is most responsible for creating the goods, then this is an argument for supporting the system through taxation and other means. If individual contributions count for relatively little (although for something), there may be no real grounds for attempting to distinguish among them in distributing social benefits.

The Principle of Effort

According to the principle of effort, the degree of effort made by the individual should determine the proportion of goods received by the individual. Thus, the file clerk who works just as hard as the president of a company should receive the same proportion of social goods as the president. Those who are lazy and refuse to exert themselves will receive proportionally less than those who work hard.

The advantage of the principle is that it captures our sense of what is fair—that those who do their best should be similarly rewarded, while those who do less than their best should be less well rewarded. The principle assumes that people have equal opportunities to do their best and that if they do not, it is their own fault. One difficulty with this assumption is that, even if the society presents equal opportunities, nature does not. Some people are born with disabilities or meet with accidents, and their misfortunes may make it difficult for them to want to do their best, even when they are given the opportunity.

Each principle has its shortcomings, but this does not mean that adjustments cannot be made to correct their weaknesses. A complete

theory of justice need not be limited in the number of principles that it accepts, and it is doubtful that any theory can be shown to be both fair and plausible if it restricts itself to only one principle. Although all theories require adjustment, theories fall into types in accordance with the principles they emphasize. For example, Marxist theories select need as basic, whereas libertarian theories stress personal contribution as the grounds for distribution. Utilitarian theories employ that combination of principles which promises to maximize both private and public interests.

Joel Feinberg, to whom the preceding discussion is indebted, may be mentioned as an example of a careful theorist who recommends the adoption of a combination of principles. Feinberg sees the principle of equality based on needs as the basic determination of distributive justice. After basic needs have been satisfied, the principles of contribution and effort should be given the most weight.

According to Feinberg, when there is economic abundance, the claim to "minimally decent conditions" can reasonably be made for every person in the society. To have one's basic needs satisfied under such conditions amounts to a fundamental right. However, when everyone's basic needs are taken care of and society produces a surplus of goods, considerations of contribution and effort become relevant. Those who contribute most to the increase in goods or those who work the hardest to produce it (or some combination) can legitimately lay claim to a greater share.

The principles of justice we have discussed may seem at first to be intolerably abstract and so irrelevant to the practical business of society. However, it is important to keep in mind that it is by referring to such principles that we criticize our society and its laws and practices. The claim that society is failing to meet some basic need of all of its citizens and that this is unfair or unjust is a powerful charge. It can be a call to action in the service of justice. If the claim can be demonstrated, it has more than rhetorical power. It imposes upon us all an obligation to eliminate the source of the injustice.

Similarly, in framing laws and formulating policies, we expect those who occupy the offices of power and influence to make their decisions in accordance with principles. Prominent among these must be principles of justice. It may be impossible in the conduct of daily business to apply any principle directly or exclusively, for we can hardly remake our society overnight. Yet if we are committed to a just society, then the principles of justice can at least serve as guidelines when policy decisions are made. They remind us that it is not always fair for the race to go to the swift.

The Principle of Autonomy

The principle of autonomy can be stated this way: *Rational individuals should be permitted to be self-determining*. According to this formulation, we act autonomously when our actions are the result of our own choices and decisions. Thus, autonomy and self-determination are equivalent.

Autonomy is associated with the status we ascribe to rational beings as persons in the morally relevant sense. We are committed to the notion that persons are by their very nature uniquely qualified to decide what is in their own best interest. This is because, to use Kant's terms, persons are ends in themselves, not means to some other ends. As such, they have an inherent worth, and it is the duty of others to respect that worth and avoid treating them as though they were just ordinary parts of the world to be manipulated according to the will of someone else. A recognition of autonomy is a recognition of that inherent worth, and a violation of autonomy is a violation of our concept of what it is to be a person. To deny someone autonomy is to treat that individual as something less than a person.

This view of the nature of autonomy and its connection with our recognition of what is involved in being a person is shared by several significant moral theories. At the core of each theory is the concept of the rational individual as a moral agent who, along with other moral agents, possesses an unconditional worth. Moral responsibility itself is based on the assumption that such agents are free to determine their own actions and pursue their own aims.

Autonomy is significant not only because it is a condition for moral responsibility, but because it is through the exercise of autonomy that individuals shape their lives. We might not approve of what people do with their lives. It is sad to see talent wasted and opportunities for personal development rejected. Nevertheless, as we sometimes say, "It's his life." We recognize that people are entitled to attempt to make their lives what they want them to be and that it would be wrong for us to take control of their lives and dictate their actions, even if we could. We recognize that a person must "walk to heaven or hell" by her own freely chosen path.

Simply put, to act autonomously is to decide for oneself what to do. Of course, decisions are never made outside of a context, and the world and the people in it exert influence, impose constraints, and restrict opportunities. It is useful to call attention to three interrelated aspects of autonomy in order to get a better understanding of the ways in which autonomy can be exercised, denied, and restricted. We will look at autonomy in the contexts of actions, options, and decision making.

Autonomy and Actions

Consider the following situations: A police officer shoves a demonstrator off the sidewalk during an abortion protest. An attendant in a psychiatric ward warns a patient to stay in bed or be strapped down. A corrections officer warns a prison inmate that if he does not donate blood he will not be allowed out of his cell to eat dinner. A state law requires that anyone admitted to a hospital be screened for the HIV antibody.

In each of these situations, either actual force, the threat of force, or potential penalties are employed to direct the actions of an individual toward some end. All involve some form of coercion, and the coercion is used to restrict the freedom of individuals to act as they might choose. Under such circumstances, the individual ceases to be the agent who initiates the action as a result of his or her choice. The individual's initiative is set aside, wholly or partially, in favor of someone else's.

Autonomy is violated in such cases even if the individual intends to act in the way that is imposed or demanded. Perhaps the prison inmate would have donated blood anyway, and surely some people would have wanted to be screened for HIV. However, the use of coercion makes the wishes or intentions of the individual partly or totally irrelevant to whether the act is performed.

Autonomy as the initiation of action through one's own intervention and choice can clearly be restricted to a greater or lesser degree. Someone who is physically forced to become a subject in a medical experiment, as in a Nazi concentration camp, is totally deprived of autonomy. The same is true of someone tricked into becoming a subject without knowing it. In the infamous Tuskegee syphilis studies, some participants were led to believe they were receiving appropriate medical treatment when in fact they were part of a control group in the experiment. The situation is somewhat different for someone who agrees to become a subject in order to receive needed medical care. Such a person is acting under strong coercion, but the loss of autonomy is not complete. It is at least possible to refuse to participate, even if the cost of doing so may be extremely high.

In situations more typical than these, autonomy may be compromised rather than denied. For example, someone who is by nature nonassertive or someone who is poor and uneducated may find it very difficult to preserve his power of self-determination when he becomes a patient in a hospital. Medical authority, represented by physicians and the hospital staff, may be so intimidating to such a person that he does not feel free to exercise his autonomy. In such a case, although no one may be deliberately attempting to infringe on the patient's autonomy, social and psychological factors may constitute a force so coercive that the patient feels he has no choice but to do what he is told.

Autonomy and Options

Autonomy involves more than freedom from duress in making decisions. There must be genuine possibilities to decide among. A forced option is no option at all, and anyone who is in the position of having to take what he can get can hardly be regarded as self-determining or as exercising free choice.

In our society, economic and social conditions frequently limit the options available in medical care. As a rule, the poor simply do not have the same choices available to them as the rich. Someone properly insured or financially well off who might be helped by a heart transplant can decide whether or not to undergo the risk of having one. That is an option not generally available to someone who is uninsured and poor.

Similarly, a woman who depends on Medicaid and lives in a state in which Medicaid funds cannot be used to pay for abortions may not have the option of having an abortion. Her choice is not a genuine one, for she lacks the means to implement it. The situation is quite different for a middle-class woman faced with the same question. She may decide against having an abortion, but whatever she decides, the choice is real. She is autonomous in a way that the poor woman is not.

Those who believe that one of the goals of our society is to promote and protect the autonomy of individuals have frequently argued that we must do more to offer all individuals the same range of health care options. If we do not, they have suggested, then our society cannot be one in which everyone has an equal degree of autonomy. In a very real sense, those who are rich will have greater freedom of action than those who are poor.

Autonomy and Decision Making

More is involved in decision making than merely saying yes or no. In particular, relevant information is an essential condition for genuine decision making. We are exercising our autonomy in the fullest sense only when we are making *informed* decisions.

It is pointless to have options if we are not aware of them; we can hardly be said to be directing the course of our lives if our decisions must be made in ignorance of information that is available and relevant to our choices. These are the reasons that lying and other forms of deception are so destructive of autonomy. If someone with a progressive and ordinarily fatal disease is not told about it by her physician, then she is in no position to decide how to shape what remains of her life. The lack of a crucial piece of information—that she is dying—is likely to lead her to make decisions different from the ones she would make were she in possession of the information.

Information is the key to protecting and preserving autonomy in most medical situations. A patient who is not informed of alternative forms of treatment and their associated risks is denied the opportunity to make his own wishes and values count for something in his own life. For example, someone with coronary artery disease who is not told of the relative merits of medical treatment with drugs but is told only that he is a candidate for coronary-artery bypass surgery is in no position to decide what risks he wishes to take and what ordeals he is prepared to undergo. A physician who does not supply the patient with the information the patient needs is restricting the patient's autonomy. The principle of autonomy requires *informed* consent, for consent alone does not involve genuine self-determination.

Making decisions for "the good" of others (paternalism), without consulting their wishes, deprives them of their status as autonomous agents. For example, some people at the final stages of a terminal illness might prefer to be allowed to die without heroic intervention, while others might prefer to prolong their lives as long as medical skills and technological powers make possible. If a physician or family undertakes to make a decision in this matter on behalf of the patient, then no matter what their motive, they are denying to the patient the power of self-determination.

Because autonomy is so bound up with informed consent and decision making, special problems arise in the case of those unable to give consent and make decisions. Patients who are comatose, severely brain damaged, psychotic, or seriously mentally impaired are not capable of making decisions on their own behalf. The nature of their condition has already deprived them of their autonomy. Of course, this does not mean that they have no status as moral persons or that they have no interests. It falls to others to see that their interests are served.

The situation is similar for those, such as infants and young children, who are incapable of understanding. Any consent that is given must be given by others. But what are the limits of consent that can legitimately be given for some other person? Consenting to needed medical care seems legitimate, but what about rejecting needed medical care? What about consenting to becoming a subject in a research program? These questions are as crucial as they are difficult to resolve.

Restrictions on Autonomy

Autonomy is not an absolute or unconditional value. We would regard it as absurd for someone to claim that she was justified in committing a murder because she was only exercising her power of self-determination. Such a defense would be morally ludicrous.

However, we do value autonomy and recognize a general duty to respect it and even to promote its exercise. We demand compelling reasons to justify restricting the power of individuals to make their own choices and direct their own lives.

We will briefly examine four principles that are frequently appealed to in justifying restrictions on autonomy. The principles have been discussed most in the context of social and legal theory, for it is through laws and penalties that a society most directly regulates the conduct of its citizens. However, the principles can also be appealed to in justifying policies and practices of institutions (such as hospitals) and the actions of individuals that affect other people.

Appealing to a principle can provide, at best, only a prima facie justification. Even if a principle can be shown to apply to a particular case in which freedom of action is restricted, we may value the lost freedom more than what is gained by restricting it. Reasons suggested by the principle may not be adequately persuasive. Furthermore, the principles themselves are frequently the subjects of controversy, and, with the exception of the harm principle, it is doubtful that any of the principles would be universally endorsed by philosophers and legal theorists.

The Harm Principle. According to the harm principle, we may restrict the freedom of people to act if the restriction is necessary to prevent harm to others. In the most obvious case, we may take action to prevent violence like rape, robbery, killing, or assault. We may act to protect someone who is at apparent risk of harm from the action of someone else. The risk of harm need not be the result of the intention to harm. Thus, we might take steps to see that a surgeon whose skills and judgment have been impaired through drug use is not permitted to operate. The risk that he poses to his patients warrants the effort to keep him from acting as he wishes.

The harm principle may also be used to justify laws that exert coercive force and so restrict freedom of action. Laws against homicide and assault are clear examples, but the principle extends also to the regulation of institutions and practices. People may be robbed at the point of a pen, as well as at the point of a knife, and the harm produced by fraud may be as great as that produced by outright theft. Careless or deceptive medical practitioners may cause direct harm to their patients, and laws that regulate the standards of medical practice restrict the freedom of practitioners for the protection of patients.

The Principle of Paternalism. In its weak version, the principle of paternalism is no more than the harm principle applied to the individual himself. According to the principle, we are justified in restricting someone's freedom to act if doing so is necessary to prevent him from harming himself. Thus, we might force an alcoholic into a treatment program and justify our action by claiming that we did so to prevent him from continuing to harm himself by his drinking.

In its strong version, the principle of paternalism justifies restricting someone's autonomy if by doing so we can benefit her. In such a case, our concern is not only with preventing the person from harming herself, but also with promoting her good in a positive way. The principle might be appealed to even in cases in which our actions go against the other's known wishes. For example, a physician might decide to treat a patient with a placebo (an inactive drug), even if she has asked to be told the truth about her medical condition and her therapy. He might attempt to justify his action by claiming that if the patient knew she was receiving a placebo, then the placebo would be less likely to be effective. Since taking the placebo while believing that it is an active drug makes her feel better, the physician may claim that by deceiving her he is doing something to help her.

Paternalism may be expressed in laws and public policies, as well as in private actions. Some have suggested the drug laws as a prime example of governmental paternalism. By making certain drugs illegal and inaccessible and by placing other drugs under the control of physicians, the laws aim to protect people from themselves. Self-medication is virtually eliminated, and the so-called recreational use of drugs is prohibited. The price for such laws is a restriction on individual autonomy. Some have argued that the price is too high and that the most the government should do is warn and educate the individual about the consequences of using certain drugs.

The Principle of Legal Moralism. The principle of legal moralism holds that a legitimate function of the law is to enforce morality by turning the immoral into the illegal. Hence, the legal restrictions placed on actions are justified by the presumed fact that the actions are immoral and so ought not to be performed.

To a considerable extent, laws express the values of a society and the society's judgments about what is morally right. In our society, homicide and theft are recognized as crimes, and those who commit them are guilty of legal, as well as moral, wrongdoing. Society attempts to prevent such crimes and to punish offenders.

The degree to which the law should embody moral judgments is a hard question. It is particularly difficult to answer in a pluralistic society like ours, in which there may be sharp differences of opinion about the moral legitimacy of some actions. Until quite recently, for example, materials considered obscene could not be freely purchased, birth-control literature could not be freely distributed nor contraceptives legally prescribed in some states, and the conditions of divorce were generally stringent and punitive. Even now, many states outlaw homosexual solicitation and acts, and prostitution is generally illegal. The foundation for such laws is the belief by many that the practices proscribed are morally wrong.

The current heated debate over abortion reflects, in some of its aspects, the conflict between those who favor strong legal moralism and those who oppose it. Many who consider abortion morally wrong would also like to see it made illegal once more. Others, even though they may oppose abortion, believe that it is a private moral matter and that the attempt to regulate it by law is an unwarranted intrusion of state power.

The Welfare Principle. The welfare principle holds that it is justifiable to restrict individual autonomy if doing so will result in providing benefits to others. Those who endorse this principle are not inclined to think that it demands a serious self-sacrifice for the welfare of others. Rather, in their view, an ideal application of the principle would be the case in which we give up just a little autonomy to bring about a great deal of benefit to others.

For example, transplant organs are in short supply at the moment because their availability depends mostly on their being freely donated. The situation could be dramatically changed by a law requiring that organs from the recently dead be salvaged and made available for use as transplants.

Such a law would end the present system of voluntary donation, and by doing so it would restrict our freedom to decide what is to be done with our bodies after death. However, it would be easy to argue that the tremendous value that others might gain from such a law easily outweighs the slight restriction on autonomy that it would involve.

These four principles are not the only ones that offer grounds for abridging the autonomy of individuals, but they are the most relevant to decision making and policy planning in medicine. It is important to keep in mind that merely appealing to a principle is not enough to warrant a limit on autonomy. A principle points in the direction of an argument, but it is no substitute for one. The high value we place on autonomy gives its preservation a high priority, and compelling considerations are required to justify compromising it. In the view of some philosophers who endorse the position taken by Mill, only the harm principle can serve as grounds for legitimately restricting autonomy. Other theorists find persuasive reasons to do so in other principles.

THEORIES WITHOUT PRINCIPLES

Most of traditional Western ethics is based on the assumption that ethical beliefs are best represented by a set of rules or abstract principles. Kant's categorical imperative, Mill's principle of utility, and Ross's list of prima facie duties attempt to supply guides for moral action and decision making that apply in all circumstances.

Moral decisions thus typically involve bringing a case under a rule, in much the same way that law courts apply statutory laws to cases brought before them. Much ethical dispute, like much legal dispute, is over whether an abstract rule does or does not apply in a concrete case.

In recent decades, some ethical theorists have turned away from the principle-governed, legalistic approach to ethics in favor of another approach from the Western tradition. Some of the new theorists have emphasized the importance of character as the source of moral action, whereas others have stressed the central role of shared concerns and the crucial importance of social practices and institutions in shaping our moral lives.

We will present brief sketches of ethical theories that (according to their proponents) cannot be reduced to sets of abstract principles. Although moral theorists debate such questions as whether the virtue of being a truthful person (a character trait) isn't ultimately derived from the duty to tell the truth (a principle), we will steer clear of these issues. Rather, as with theories based on principles, we will restrict ourselves to a general statement of each theory, indicate how it might be applied in a medical context, and then discuss some of the difficulties it faces as a moral theory.

The three theories discussed here have been presented by their proponents in a variety of versions, some of them quite elaborate and philosophically sophisticated. Keep in mind that we are presenting only sketches.

Virtue Ethics

J. D. Salinger's character Holden Caulfield dislikes "phonies" and dreams of standing in a field and keeping little kids from running off the edge of the cliff beyond. He wants to be a "catcher in the rye."

Millions of us who have read *The Catcher in the Rye* have admired Holden and wanted to be like him in some ways. We, too, would like to avoid phoniness, particularly in ourselves, and we would like to do something to make the world a better place, particularly for children. Holden isn't a perfect person, but even so, he's a moral hero, a sort of icon or example of what we wish we could be in some respects.

Every culture is populated by real and fictional characters representing the sort of people we should try to become. Some characters are seen as perfect, while others are people who, despite their flaws, show what they were capable of in confronting life's problems and struggles. To name only a few historically important people, consider Socrates, Jesus, Gautama Buddha, Moses, Florence Nightingale, Confucius, Martin Luther King, Susan B. Anthony, Anne Frank, Gandhi, and Mother Teresa. It would be easy to make an even longer list of fictional characters who evoke our admiration and make us feel that we would be better people if we could be more like them.

Virtue ethics is ethics based on character. Its fundamental idea is that a person who has acquired the proper set of dispositions will do what is right when faced with a situation involving a moral choice. Thus, virtue ethics doesn't involve invoking principles or rules to guide actions.

The virtuous person is both the basic concept and the goal of virtue ethics. The virtuous person is one who acts right, because she is just that sort of person. Right actions flow out of character, and the virtuous person has a disposition to do the right thing. Rules need not be consulted, calculations need not be performed, abstract duties need not be considered.

People become virtuous in the way they become good swimmers. Upbringing, education, the example of others, reflection, personal effort, and experience all play a role. As with swimming, some people may be more naturally inclined to become virtuous than others. Those who are naturally patient, reflective, and slow to anger may find it easier than those who are impatient, impulsive, and possessed of a fiery temper.

Families and social institutions—like schools, clubs, and athletic teams, as well as religious institutions—play a role in shaping our moral character. They tell us how we should behave when we lose a school election or win a softball game. They teach us what we should do when we have a chance to take money without anyone's finding out, when we witness a case of discrimination, when we ourselves are treated unfairly.

Quite apart from explicit teachings or doctrines, the lives of historical figures like Jesus, Mohammed, and Buddha have served as examples of what it is possible for a person to become. Perhaps no one believes that he can achieve the level of moral perfection such people represent, but they offer us models for fashioning ourselves. In the way a swimmer may study the backstroke, we can study the way moral heroes have dealt with the moral questions that face us.

When a Christian asks, "What would Jesus do?" it is not typically an attempt to call on divine guidance. Rather, it is an occasion for reflection, of attempting to imagine what someone trying to live a life like Jesus's would do. We try to improve our character by becoming more like those who are admirable. Hence, in addition to education and social influences, we must engage in self-criticism and make deliberate efforts to improve.

The Virtues

The virtuous person is disposed to demonstrate virtues through behavior. *Virtue* is a translation of the Greek word *arete*, which also has much the same meaning as *excellence*. (Virtue ethics is also called *aretaic ethics*.) The excellent tennis player demonstrates in playing tennis that he possesses characteristics needed to play the game well. Similarly, the virtuous person demonstrates through living that she possesses the appropriate range of excellences.

Virtues have traditionally been divided into moral and practical, or nonmoral, virtues:

Moral virtues: *benevolence, compassion, honesty, charity, sincerity, sympathy, respect, consideration, kindness, thoughtfulness, loyalty, fairness, and so on*

Nonmoral virtues: *rationality (or intelligence), tenacity, capability, patience, prudence, skillfulness, staunchness, shrewdness, proficiency, and so on*

The distinction between moral and nonmoral virtues is far from clear, but the rough idea is that those in one set are associated with living a good (moral) life, whereas those in the other are associated with the practical aspects of living. A thief can be patient (a nonmoral virtue), but not honest (a moral one). By contrast, an honest (moral virtue) person may lack patience. (How to classify *courage* has always been a problem. A courageous thief may be more successful than a cowardly one, but a benevolent person lacking the courage to put his views into practice will be ineffective.)

Virtue Ethics in the Medical Context

Consider Dr. Charles Holmes, an emergency-room trauma surgeon who chose his specialty because the money is good and the hours reasonable. He treats the patients, and then he goes home. Holmes is technically expert, but he lacks compassion for his patients and is not interested in their worries or fears. He shows no tact in dealing with patients and barely acknowledges that they are people.

Dr. Holmes is far removed from our notion of what a physician as a compassionate healer should be. In treating his patients as broken machines, he may help them in important ways, but his skills as a physician are deficient. Holmes, we might say, lacks the disposition necessary to be a good physician.

From at least the time of the ancient Greeks, the Western tradition has expected physicians to be virtuous, and more recently we have broadened that expectation to include nurses, medical technicians, and all who care for patients. The tradition is resplendent with stories of those who behaved in ways that make them moral examples for all who commit themselves to providing patient care. Scores of European physicians at the time of the Black Death (the bubonic plague) in the fourteenth century tended to their patients, even though they knew they risked infection themselves. The eighteenth-century American physician Benjamin Rush did his best to help cholera sufferers, although he knew that he was likely to get the disease. Florence Nightingale, braving harsh conditions and the risk of sickness, helped care for British troops during the Crimean War and fought to establish nursing as a profession.

Virtue ethics calls attention to the strength of medicine at its moral (and practical) best. Courage, loyalty, integrity, compassion, and benevolence, along with determination and intelligence, are virtues associated with physicians and others who provide what we consider the right sort of care for their patients. We expect everyone involved in patient care to display in their behavior a similar constellation of virtues. Virtue ethics, with its emphasis on character and behavioral dispositions, comes closer to capturing our concept of the ideal health professional than does a rule-based view of moral decision making such as Kant's ethics or utilitarianism.

Difficulties with Virtue Ethics

A fundamental difficulty with virtue ethics is that it provides us with no explicit guidance in deciding how to act in particular circumstances. Suppose someone is terminally ill, in great pain, and asking for assistance in dying. Should we agree to help? We may ask, "What would Jesus do?" and the answer may be "I don't know." If we have been brought up to be virtuous, perhaps we should have no need to ask such questions. But how are we to know who among us has been properly brought up, and for those of us who aren't sure, what should we do?

Medicine is repeatedly faced with the problem of deciding about what actions ought to be taken, but virtue ethics is about character and dispositions. However, even a benevolent person (one disposed to act benevolently) may not know how to distribute organs that are in scarce supply. Further, virtue ethics does not supply any clear way to resolve moral conflicts. What if Assiz thinks it would be wrong to abort a fetus twenty-four weeks after conception, but Puzo does not. How can they go about resolving their dispute? The answer is not clear.

Also, virtues, like duties, can be incompatible when they are translated into action. If I am a transplant coordinator and try to express my gratitude to my physics teacher by allowing her to jump to the head of the waiting list for a new liver, this will conflict with my commitment to fairness. But if virtues are not ranked, how do I decide what to do in such a case? Surely we don't think it would be right for me to put my teacher at the head of the list, but on what grounds can virtue ethics say that it would be wrong?

Part I

Rights

Chapter 1

Physicians, Patients, and Others: Autonomy, Truth Telling, and Confidentiality

CASES AND CONTEXTS

Donald (Dax) Cowart Rejects Treatment—and Is Ignored

The man stretched out on the steel platform of the sling with his knees drawn up is thin to the point of emaciation. His face and numerous patches of bare, raw flesh are slathered with layers of thick white salve. A pad covers one eye, and the eyelid of the other is sewn shut. Bandages wrapped around his legs and torso give him the look of a mummy in a low-budget horror movie.

In obvious pain, he writhes on the platform. With rock music playing in the background, white-uniformed attendants in gauze masks raise the sling and lower him into a steel tank of clear liquid.

The real horror began for Donald Cowart in July of 1973. The previous May he had left active duty in the Air Force after three years of service, including a tour of duty in Vietnam, to take a slot in the Air Force Reserve. He returned to his family home in east Texas to wait for an opening as a commercial airline pilot. He was twenty-five years old, a college graduate, unmarried, and in excellent health and top physical condition. A high school athlete who had played football and basketball and run track, he had stayed athletic. He played golf, surfed when he could, and rodeoed. As a pilot for a large airline, he'd be busy, but not too busy to continue the active life he was used to. But in 1973 the airlines weren't looking for new pilots,

and while Don waited for them to start hiring again, he decided to join his father as a real estate broker. The two had always been close, so working together was a pleasure for both of them.

And then everything changed forever.

One hot Wednesday afternoon in July, Don and his father drove out to the country to take a look at a piece of land Don thought might be a good buy. They parked the car in a shady, cool spot at a low place in the road beside a bridge. They took a walking tour of the land, but when they returned to the car, it wouldn't start.

Mr. Cowart got out, raised the hood, and tinkered with the carburetor. Don, in the driver's seat, turned the key repeatedly, grinding the engine around so much, he got afraid he would run down the battery. Then after three or four minutes of trying, a blue flame suddenly shot from the carburetor, and a tremendous explosion rocked the car, throwing Don sideways onto the passenger seat. A huge ball of live fire enveloped the car.

Don managed to get the door open; then, still surrounded by fire, he ran three steps toward the woods, the only place that wasn't on fire. But seeing that the undergrowth was so thick that he was likely to get trapped in it and burn to death, he turned away and ran straight down the road. He hurtled through three thick walls of fire, and when he cleared the last one, he threw himself to the ground and rolled to smother the flames.

Getting to his feet, he ran again, shouting for help. He noticed his vision was blurred, as if he were looking at everything from under water, and he realized his eyes had been seared by the fire. *This can't be happening,* he thought as he ran. But the pain assured him that it was. He heard a voice shouting, "I'm coming!" and only then did he stop running and lie down beside the road.

He thought at the time that the car's gas tank had exploded, and only after he had been in a hospital for several days did he learn that the blast and fire were caused by a leak in a propane gas transmission line. Seeping from the line, the gas had collected in the hollow by the bridge, saturating the air to such an extent that the car wouldn't start because the engine couldn't get enough oxygen. The spark from the starter had ignited the gas.

When the farmer who had heard Don's shouts arrived, he said, "Oh, my God." Then Don knew for the first time that he was burned more badly than he had thought. After the farmer came back from looking for Mr. Cowart, Don asked him to get him a gun. "Why?" the man asked.

"Can't you see I'm a dead man?" Don told him. "I'm going to die anyway."

"I can't do that," the farmer said gently.

When the first ambulance arrived, Don sent it to pick up his father. When the second came, he didn't want to go to the hospital. "All I wanted to do was die and to die as quickly as possible," he recalled nine years later. Despite his protest, the attendants put him in the ambulance. He asked them to pick him up by his belt, because his burns were so excruciating he couldn't bear to be touched.

Don and his father were taken to a small nearby hospital, but because of the extent of their injuries, they were soon transported to the burn unit of Parkland Hospital in Dallas, 140 miles away. "I'm sorry, Donny boy," his father told him as they were placed in the ambulance. Mr. Cowart died on the way to Parkland. Don continued to insist that he be allowed to die.

Charles Baxter, Don's attending physician, estimated that Don had extremely deep burns over about sixty-five percent of his body. His face, upper arms, torso, and legs had suffered severe third-degree burns, and both ears were virtually destroyed. His eyes were so damaged that his left eye had to be surgically removed, and he eventually lost the vision in his right eye. His fingers were burned off down to the second joint, making it impossible for him to pick up anything. The pain was tremendous, and even though he was given substantial doses of narcotics, it remained unbearable for more than a year.

Don's mother had heard about an accidental explosion on the radio, but she learned her husband and son were involved only when the police called her out of an evening church service to tell her. After rushing to Dallas to be with Don, she was approached by his physicians to sign consent forms for surgery and treatment. Knowing nothing about burn therapies, she took the advice offered to her by the physicians. She knew of Don's protest against being treated, but she expected his wish to be allowed to die to pass as soon as he began to recover.

Rex Houston, the family's attorney and close friend, filed a lawsuit with the owners of the propane transmission line for damages resulting from the explosion. He was concerned with going to trial as soon as possible. Don was unmarried and had nobody depending on him, so if he died before the case was heard, the lawsuit would be likely to produce little money. But with Don as a living plaintiff and a young man who had lost the use of both hands and both eyes, the suit had the potential to be of tremendous value. "I had to have a living plaintiff," Houston said years later. Dr. Baxter later said he had discussed the legal and moral aspects of Don's treatment with Mr. Houston.

Don continued to want to die. He asked a nurse with whom he had developed a rapport to give him a drug that would kill him or at least to help him do something to take his own life. As sympathetic as she was, she was forced to refuse his request. Don also asked a family friend to get a gun for him, but then, even while he was asking, he observed that getting him a gun would be pointless, because he had no fingers to pull the trigger.

Dr. Baxter's initial response to Don's request to die was dismissive: "Oh, you don't want to do that," he would say. For a while, though, Don convinced Dr. Baxter he was serious and not simply reacting out of the immediate pain and shock. But eventually Dr. Baxter decided Don talked about wanting to die only to manipulate the people around him and gain control over his environment. Don later rejected this interpretation.

Mrs. Cowart considered her son's medical condition too serious to allow him to make decisions about accepting or rejecting treatment. "Everything was discussed with her in detail," Dr. Baxter recalled. "She was most co-operative and most helpful. We approached the problem of his desire to die very openly." Also, Dr. Baxter remembered, "Even the possibility that it could be allowed was discussed with her. She was never in favor of it, because basically she thought he did not have this desire."

When his burns had healed enough that he was out of danger, Don was moved to the Texas Institute of Rehabilitation in Houston. He agreed to give the program a try, but after about three weeks, he began to refuse treatment again. He had learned that rehabilitation would take years of pain and suffering. The doctors at the Institute honored his request that he not be treated, and in a few days, the burns on his legs became infected again, and the grafted skin peeled away. He came near death.

Dr. Robert Meier, a rehabilitation specialist responsible for Don's care, called a meeting with Don's mother and attorney. They decided that because Don's burns had become infected again due to his refusal to have his dressings changed, he should be hospitalized in an acute care center again.

Don was transferred to the University of Texas Medical Branch at Galveston in April of 1974. Once there, he again refused treatment. Psychiatrist Robert B. White was called in by the surgeons in charge of Don's case, because they thought Don's refusal might be the result of clinical depression or some form of mental illness. If he were found incompetent, a legal guardian could be appointed to give permission for the additional surgery he needed. After examining Don and with the concurrence of a second psychiatrist, Dr. White concluded that Don was fully competent and not suffering from any kind of mental illness. He was, moreover, intelligent, self-aware, and highly articulate.

To control the many infected areas on his body, Don had to be submerged daily in a tank of highly chlorinated water to destroy the microorganisms breeding on the surface of his wounds. The experience was excruciatingly painful, and despite Don's protests and refusals, the "tankings" were carried out anyway. He refused to give his permission for surgery on his hands, which had become more clawlike due to scarring and contracture. Eventually, he consented, with his surgeon's assurance that he would give Don enough drugs to control the pain.

Don wanted to leave the hospital so he could go home and die. But he couldn't leave without help, and neither his physicians nor his mother would agree to

help. His mother wanted him taken care of, and moving him home to die of massive infection was more than she could accept. Don accused her of being responsible for prolonging his hopeless condition.

Surgeon Duane Larson was puzzled by Don's ongoing insistence that he wanted to die. Don wasn't on the verge of death and would surely recover some degree of normalcy. He would find new ways to enjoy life. "In essence he was asking people to participate in his death," Dr. Larson recalled.

One alternative Dr. Larson mentioned to Don was for him to be treated until he was well enough to leave the hospital; then he could kill himself, if he still wanted to. Another alternative was to get Don to see that new things could be done to lessen his pain and make him more comfortable. But Dr. Larson also thought Don might be brought to see that some of his outbursts were merely angry "little boy feelings" anyone would experience after going through such a terrible ordeal.

The tankings were by far the worst treatments. "It was like pouring alcohol on an open wound," Don remembered. Being lifted out of the tank was even worse, because the room was freezing, and every nerve in the damaged parts of his body produced agony. "All I could do was scream at the top of my lungs until I would finally pass out with exhaustion. The tankings took place seven days a week—week after week after week."

"Don't ask us to let you die," Dr. Meier had told Don at the rehabilitation center, "because in a sense what that means is we're killing you. If you want to die, then let me fix your hands, operate on them and open them up so at least you can do something with them, and if you want to commit suicide then, you can. But don't ask us to stand here and literally kill you."

"The argument that not treating a patient is the same as killing borders on the ridiculous," Don said years later. "If letting the patient die is characterized as playing God, then treating the patient to save his life has to be as well. In the final analysis, I was nothing but a hostage to the current state of medical technology." Just a few years earlier he would have died, but the management of burns had advanced sufficiently to keep him alive. He was, he said, "forced to receive treatment," because he was "too weak to resist and unable to walk out on my own." Ironically, as Don later saw the situation, what was happening to him was taking place when the country was emphasizing the importance of individual liberties and freedom of choice by the individual.

Don was treated for ten months. He lost all ten fingers, was blind, and terribly scarred and disfigured. He had to have help with everything and was unable to take care of even his most basic bodily needs. His pain was still constant and he couldn't walk.

Discharged from the hospital, he took up residence in his mother's house. At first he was relieved to be out of the hospital, but in a few weeks he fell into a deep depression. Frustration built up as he experienced his loss of independence, grew bored, and worried about what he was going to do with the rest of his life. Marriage seemed at best a remote possibility.

Because of his disfigurement, he thought about never going out in public, but eventually he began to go to stores and restaurants, protected by his blindness from the stares and reactions of others. Money from the court settlement gave him the financial independence to do what he wanted and was able to do.

Starting law school, he lived with a married couple and learned to do some things for himself. But in the spring of that year, beset by a sleep disturbance and upset by the breakdown of a personal relationship, he tried to kill himself with an overdose of sleeping pills and tranquilizers. He was found in time for him to be taken to the hospital and have his stomach pumped. Despite what Dr. Larson and others had told him while his burns were being treated, he wasn't going to be allowed to kill himself. Don was rehospitalized for depression and insomnia for about a month and eventually returned to law school.

After graduating, Don—who was now called Dax—set up a practice in Corpus Christi. He married Karen, someone he had known in high school, in 1983.

His mother is sure she made the right decision in signing the consent forms for treatment, particularly now that her son's life is filled with the satisfactions of marriage and a job he likes. She wishes she had asked the doctors to give him more pain medication, though. They hadn't told her it was possible.

Dax doesn't blame his mother for her decisions. He blames his doctors for putting her in the position of having to make them. *He* should have been the one asked. "The individual freedom of a competent adult should never be restricted," he says, "except when it conflicts with the freedom of some other individual." For him the individual should be able to decide what minimum quality of life is acceptable to him or her. This is not a decision that should be made by physicians or anyone else on behalf of another person.

Now that Donald Cowart is living a satisfactory life, is he glad his physicians and his mother continued his treatment against his wishes? "I'm enjoying life now, and I'm glad to be alive," Cowart says. "But I still think it was wrong to force me to undergo what I had to, to be alive."

Nor would the assurance of pulling through be enough to make him change his mind. "If the same thing were to occur tomorrow, knowing I could reach this same point, I still would not want to undergo the pain and agony that I had to undergo to be alive now. I should want that choice to lie entirely with myself and not others."

SOCIAL CONTEXT
Autism and Vaccination

Autism spectrum disorders (ASDs) are a group of developmental disabilities. The disorders involve difficulties (often severe) in learning language and in communicating and interacting with others.

Spectrum

The spectrum of disorders is wide, and the behaviors of the people who fall within it can range from withdrawn and passive to highly agitated, violent, and potentially self-destructive. ASDs are often accompanied by abnormalities in cognitive abilities, learning, attention, and sensory processing.

The behavioral symptoms typically appear before a child turns three. Parents may watch their baby develop in expected ways for a period of months or even years, then notice that the child stops making eye contact and seems to lose interest in them and in the surrounding world. These changes in behavior may be signs that the child is no longer following the path of normal development and needs to be evaluated.

The term *spectrum* indicates that a range and variety of behaviors can be considered autistic. Disorders within the spectrum are given specific diagnoses by experts who test the child, observe the child's behavior, and compare it with what might be expected given the child's age. Included in the spectrum are *autistic disorder* (autism), *Asperger syndrome*, and *pervasive developmental disorder—not otherwise specified* (PDD-NOS).

People with Asperger disorder or PDD-NOS have fewer symptoms compared with people with autism, and in terms of language, intelligence, and social skills, they are usually only mildly impaired. In the discussion here, however, unless there is a reason to be more specific, we will use **autism** to refer to the entire autistic disorders spectrum.

Numbers and Facts

The Centers for Disease Control estimates that an average of one out of every 110 children has autism. Given that four million children are born every year in the U.S., about 36,500 a year will be diagnosed with the disorder. If the prevalence has been the same over the last twenty years, about 730,000 people ages 21 or younger can be considered autistic. This means that about thirteen percent of the children in the U.S. have a developmental disability that ranges from mild (language problems) to severe (cognitive difficulties, cerebral palsy, and severe autism).

Generally accepted facts about autism also include the following:

- Males are three to four times more likely than females to be autistic.

- Autism occurs in all races and in all parts of the world.

- A sibling of someone with autism is twenty-five times more likely to be autistic than someone in the general population.

- If one identical twin has autism, the other twin has autism sixty to ninety percent of the time. If one fraternal twin has autism, the other has autism up to twenty-four percent of the time.

- Parents who have a child with autism have a two to eight percent chance of having a second child with autism.

- Families with an autistic child are more likely to have a family member with a neurological disorder or a chromosomal disorder than families in the general population.

- About ten percent of children with autism have an identifiable genetic, neurological, or metabolic disorder. As more is learned about autism, this number is likely to increase.

- About forty-one percent of children with autistic spectrum disorders have an intellectual disability (defined as an IQ of 70 or lower).

- About forty percent of children with autistic spectrum disorders do not talk at all. About thirty percent acquire a few words at age twelve to eighteen months, then lose them.

- Autism is a lifelong disorder that cannot be "cured."

- Lifetime costs to care for a person with autism are $3.2 million.

Causes

The causes of autism are unknown. The disorder almost certainly has a genetic component, but it is not a genetic disease in the way that sickle cell anemia or cystic fibrosis are genetic diseases. Autism, instead of being produced by a single inherited gene, may result from the interaction of a group of genes. Even if this is so, however, some genetically predisposed infants may not develop the disorder, because they don't encounter some unknown environmental factor that acts as a trigger. It may also be possible that there is not "a cause" of autism, but that different sets of conditions may result in behavior that falls within the autism spectrum.

During the 1950s and 1960s, a favorite theory was that autism is the result of psycho-dynamic processes in the individual. Mothers who are cold and rejecting, those Bruno Bettle-heim called "refrigerator mothers," were held to be responsible for producing children who lacked language and empathy and withdrew from the world. No one accepts such a view today.

Increase In Autism?

Before the 1980s, the term *autism* was used in a rigorous way to diagnose behavior now considered limited to the *autistic disorder* part of the ASD spectrum. The disorder was a rare diagnosis, and only 0.5 percent of children (10 in 2,000) received it.

Autism is now only one of three disorders in the ASD spectrum. Applying the diagnostic criteria in use since the 1990s, 0.7 percent of children (7 in 1000) are estimated to have an autism spectrum disorder. These estimates are about ten times higher than those relying on the older diagnostic criteria.

Some recent evidence based on studies of particular populations shows that more than 1 percent of the children in the U.S., Japan, Sweden, and the United Kingdom have one of the disorders in the spectrum. (A study in Norway found that 2.7 percent of the children in the population had symptoms of autism.)

Most scientists don't think the increase in the number of *reported cases* of autism represents a genuine increase in the number of *actual cases* of autism. Rather, the change in diagnostic criteria and social factors may account for the amazing increase in the number of reported cases. For example, (1) once we might have considered a child a little odd, but now we classify him as autistic; (2) the old criteria classified only "low-functioning" children as autistic, but now "high-functioning" children are also included in the category; (3) physicians are now sensitive to the need to look for early signs of autism, so overdiagnose it; (4) parents are more attentive to their children and more medically

sophisticated, and to satisfy them, pediatricians diagnose as autism cases they would not have a decade earlier; (5) the rise in special-education and social-benefit programs gives parents and school districts an incentive to pressure pediatricians to give children with difficulties a diagnosis of autism.

All these factors may be responsible for some of the increase in the number of *reports* of autism. No one doubts that autism is a real disorder, or that cases of autism are picked up now that once would have been missed. Nor does anyone doubt the need to find ways to reduce the occurrence of autism. It seems doubtful, however, that the occurrence of autism is on the rise. That is, the disorder does not appear to have increased in frequency in the population.

Vaccines and Autism: First Shot

A crucial assumption of those who believe that vaccines cause autism is that the rise in the number of reported cases represents the rise in actual cases. An increase in the use of vaccines has been paralleled by an increase in cases of autism, so proponents of this view argue that the vaccines are responsible for the autism.

The debate started in 1998 with observations about the MMR vaccine—a combination of vaccines to protect children against the viral diseases measles, mumps, and rubella (German measles)—and autistic symptoms.

Pediatrician Andrew Wakefield and his collaborators published a paper that year in *The Lancet* in which they reported that a dozen children in London's Royal Free Hospital who had intestinal symptoms (pain, bloating, and inflammation) also displayed autism-like symptoms. Furthermore, eight of the twelve had started displaying autistic symptoms within days of being injected with the MMR vaccine.

The paper did not claim that the MMR vaccine was the cause of autism. The authors suggested, however, that the exposure to the measles virus in the vaccine might have been a contributing factor. Later, Wakefield, speaking only for himself, expressed the view that the virus in the vaccine might cause inflammation in the gut and the inflammation might affect brain development. Thus, the MMR vaccine would be the initiating event in the causal chain leading to autism.

Thimerosal

As writer Alice Park points out, parents of autistic children had already been primed to suspect vaccines might cause autism. Beginning in the 1930s, a mercury compound called thimerosal was used in vaccines as a preservative to keep molds and bacteria from growing in them. That mercury and other heavy metals can cause brain damage was already a familiar fact. It was also understood that children are particularly susceptible to damage from heavy metals because their brains are still undergoing development.

It made intuitive sense to many people that thimerosal was responsible for autism. Not only was the substance known to destroy brain tissue, but the timing was right. Children are given several vaccines by their second year, and it is around this time that the first symptoms of autism typically appear. Thus, it seems that a vaccine causes brain damage, which produces the symptoms of autism.

As obvious as this conclusion may appear, it is the result of fallacious post-hoc reasoning. That the symptoms of autism appear after vaccinations does not prove that vaccines cause the symptoms. (After you put on your winter coat, the geese fly south, but putting on your coat doesn't make them fly south.) Evidence of a different kind is needed.

This evidence seemed to be at hand in 2001 when the FDA released the results of a study showing that six-month-old children who received all five of their recommended vaccinations were being given twice the amount of mercury the Environmental Protection Agency considered safe for people who eat fish as a regular part of their diet. Prompted by this startling finding, the FDA and vaccine makers went into overdrive, and by the end of 2001,

thimerosal-free versions of all five vaccines were available for use. These included DPT (diphtheria, pertussis, and tetanus), hepatitis-B, and HiB (*Haemophilus influenzae*, type B). The thimerosal content dropped from a total of 187.5 micrograms to no more than trace amounts. Thus, six-month-old babies who received all five of the recommended vaccinations would have virtually no exposure to thimerosal.

Proponents of what had become known as the "vaccine hypothesis" expected the rates of autism to drop dramatically: no thimerosal, no autism. But the opposite happened. The rate of autism has *increased* since thimerosal was removed from vaccines, so that its occurrence among eight-year-olds (those vaccinated after 2001) is one in 150.

In 2003, the Centers for Disease Control and the National Institutes of Health assembled a panel to review and evaluate the scientific literature concerning the connection between thimerosal and autistic symptoms. The panel concluded that there was no evidence to support such a link. Furthermore, the panel noted that it did not consider the use of more resources to investigate the possibility of such a link a wise investment. Instead, the panel held, the money should be spent on investigating the genetics and developmental biology of the disease.

The National Institute of Medicine also conducted a scientific review of the potential connection between thimerosal and autism. Its conclusion was that "The evidence favors rejection of a causal relationship between thimerosal-containing vaccines and autism." The CDC endorsed this conclusion.

MMR Vaccine

What about the claim made by Wakefield and his collaborators that the MMR vaccine may be responsible for triggering inflammatory processes in the gut that result in autism? In 2004, ten of Wakefield's thirteen collaborators published a retraction of their paper in *The*

Lancet, stating that their evidence was not adequate to support such a claim.

Wakefield himself was said to have an undisclosed conflict of interest connected with his plans to market another measles vaccine, something he could not do with much hope of success so long as the MMR vaccine was standard. A 1993 paper by Wakefield on the role of the measles virus in causing autism reported results that could not be reproduced, and a 2002 study on the same topic has been criticized as being poorly designed.

In 2010, after years of investigation, the British General Medical Council concluded that in gathering data used in the original 1998 *Lancet* paper, Wakefield violated ethical principles. He had subjected eleven children to invasive tests such as lumbar punctures and colonoscopies that were irrelevant to their treatment, and he performed these tests without informed consent. Wakefield had shown, the panel said, a "callous disregard" for the suffering of the children involved in his research. After the release of the panel's report, *The Lancet* retracted the 1998 paper that had connected vaccines with autism.

Since the initial suggestion was made in the 1998 Wakefield paper, at least twenty-five studies have been conducted to explore the connection between the MMR vaccine and the development of autism. None of the studies, all published in peer-reviewed scientific journals, has established such a link. The scientific community has rejected the MMR vaccine as a causal factor responsible for autism just as decisively as it has rejected the link between thimerosal and autism.

Court Rulings

The scientific findings have formed the basis for court decisions involving vaccines and claims of harm. In 2002, the U.S. Court of Federal Claims combined the cases of 5,000 families with autistic children seeking compensation from the federal Vaccine Injury Compensation Trust Fund. The fund, which is supported by a 75-cent tax on vaccines, was established to deal with death and injury claims alleged to be connected with vaccines administered after October 1, 1988. Families with children who can be shown to have died or been injured by the vaccines receive compensation from the fund, in exchange for surrendering their right to sue the vaccine manufacturers.

The Omnibus Autism Proceedings began in 2002 with a court composed of three judges acting as Special Masters. (Special Masters are civil court officers appointed because of their expertise in areas relevant to issues about which the courts must decide.) The court heard nine cases based on three different theories about the causes of autism.

In three separate cases decided in March 2010, the Masters all ruled that thimerosal did not cause autism in the children whose families made claims for compensation. One Master found it "extremely unlikely" that vaccines caused autism in the cases under consideration, and another expressed the view that many parents "relied upon practitioners and researchers who peddled hope, not opinions grounded in science and medicine." In three earlier cases decided in February 2009, the Special Masters had made the same rulings, and their decisions had been upheld on appeal.

The Coalition for Vaccine Safety, an organization that claims to represent 75,000 families, was scornful of the decisions. "The deck is stacked against families in vaccine court," said a member of the group's steering committee. "Government attorneys defend a government program using government-funded science before government judges. Where's the justice in that?"

The opposite view was expressed by Paul Offit, who developed a rotavirus vaccine from which he receives royalties. The hypothesis that vaccines cause autism "has already had its day in scientific court," he said. "But in America we like to have our day in literal court. Fortunately, we now have these rulings."

"Vaccines Weaken the Immune System"

Perhaps because the rise in the number of reported cases of autism has been paralleled by an increase in the number of vaccinations children receive, some parents cannot believe vaccines are not in some way responsible for the disorder.

The idea behind any vaccine is that injected antigens (proteins) will trigger the immune response. The immune system will turn out antibodies against the antigen, and should the immune system encounter the antigen again (be exposed to a virus, for example), the pre-existing antibodies will respond immediately. Vaccines build up the body's immunity to the antigens.

The most recent form of the vaccine hypothesis is that the proteins in vaccines damage the immune system. Current recommendations are that babies be inoculated against as many as fifteen diseases and get twenty-eight vaccinations before they are six months old. Thus, vaccine critics claim, the number of antigens in the vaccines overwhelm the child's immune system, and this results in whatever brain changes may be responsible for autism.

This hypothesis is supported by no more evidence than that the number of vaccines given to infants has increased. This is, again, an instance of post-hoc reasoning. Besides, the idea of an immune-system overload is not one with any scientific validity. Indeed, its very meaning is unclear.

Perhaps the more important flaw in the hypothesis is that it rests on the mistaken assumption that the increase in the number of vaccines has meant an increase in the number of antigens to which an infant is exposed. The original smallpox vaccine given to people now ages 30 years or older when they were infants contained 200 different antigens, and it did not cause a rise in autism cases. By contrast with the smallpox vaccine the total number of antigens in all fifteen of the standard vaccines is only 150. Scientists are now able to identify just those proteins (antigens) that trigger the immune response and provide immunity from the disease.

Finally, critics of the protein-overload hypothesis point out that infants are exposed to thousands of new proteins every day. They eat new foods, breathe in dust, and are exposed to pollen, dirt, and cat dander. There is no obvious reason why exposing them to additional antigens should trigger some process leading to autism.

Vaccines Can Harm

Human biology is amazingly complex, and individuals vary widely in multiple subtle ways. Some infants are born with a genetic predisposition to react badly to gluten in their diet, but gluten allergies are comparatively rare. It should be no surprise, though, that some infants may have a genetic predisposition to react badly to some of the substances in vaccines.

In 2008 a Georgia girl with a preexisting cellular disease developed a severe allergic reaction to the vaccines she received as an infant and later developed autism-like symptoms. She is the first, and so far the only, case in which it is plausible to say that the vaccines caused autism.

The case shows that in rare instances vaccines can cause harm of the sort that defenders of the vaccine hypothesis fear. Rare cases are important for prompting additional scientific inquiry, but they don't prove that all or even a significant number of cases of autism can be ascribed to vaccines. Rare cases should certainly not become the basis for rewriting public health policies.

Protection

The traditional childhood diseases of diphtheria, whooping cough (pertussis), polio, measles, rubella, and mumps are now rare in developed countries. Yet, hardly more than a generation ago these diseases, which now seem as exotic to most people as the bubonic plague, were common in almost every American household. All are serious diseases that cause not only suffering, but death, among infants and children.

(To get a sense of how dangerous the diseases still are, consider that in 2008 (the most recent figures), 164,000 people died—eighteen every hour—from measles alone. Nearly all deaths were in children under five in countries in which children are not routinely vaccinated.)

The importance of immunization to individuals is obvious, but having such a high percentage immunized has a general benefit as well. Newborn infants and people (including children) who have compromised immune systems because of certain illnesses (e.g., HIV infection) or treatments (e.g., chemotherapy) cannot be vaccinated because of the harm it would cause them. They depend on the immunity of those around them to protect them.

The greater the percentage of people in a population who are immunized against a given disease, the less likely it is that an infectious agent will establish itself within the population and threaten the lives of those who are most vulnerable. This phenomenon is known to immunologists as *herd immunity.*

Herd Immunity

Herd immunity serves as a barrier to protect a population from the ravages of infectious diseases. The higher the percentage of people inoculated, the stronger the barrier. When the percentage starts to decline, the barrier grows weaker and more porous. Those who are most susceptible to the disease have a greater likelihood of becoming its victims.

The story of what happened with polio in Nigeria in 2001–2007 is a prime example of what occurs when the barrier weakens. In 2001, some sixty-six people in Nigeria died most likely because of the live (although weakened) virus they received in the oral polio vaccine during a vaccination campaign. These deaths convinced the country's Muslim and political leaders that the planned campaign to eradicate polio in Nigeria was actually a Western

attempt to sterilize Muslims. The campaign was cancelled, and Nigerian children were unprotected against the virus.

The rate of polio infection in Nigeria afterward increased by a factor of 30. Because viruses don't recognize political boundaries, the outbreak of polio in Nigeria spread to a dozen other countries. Some had previously been free of the disease. The breakdown of Nigeria's herd immunity led to a significant loss of life, an increase in suffering, and lifelong disability for thousands of people.

Public health officials in the U.S. have long recognized the importance of herd immunity to the well-being of the country, and it has not been left to voluntary decisions by individuals. All states have laws requiring that children be vaccinated before they are enrolled in school, and more than seventy-seven percent of children are immunized by their first day. The rewards are obvious. The CDC estimates that vaccinating all U.S. children born in a given year from birth to adolescence saves 33,000 lives, prevents fourteen million infections, and saves $10 billion in medical costs.

The laws requiring vaccination are not ironclad, however. Physicians can issue waivers for children with compromised immune systems, and in forty-eight states, when parents object to vaccination on religious grounds, those states grant their children waivers. At least twenty states permit parents to seek waivers on personal philosophical grounds. In all, about six percent of U.S. children enter school unvaccinated on a waiver of some sort: one percent medical and five percent religious or "philosophical."

Parents who believe that vaccines are likely to cause harm to their children are responsible for the decline in the inoculation rate during recent years. Quite often, their fear is based on the belief that vaccines are responsible for an increase in autism. (They are not persuaded that only the *reports* of autism have increased, not actual cases.) Hence, they believe their children should not be vaccinated and that other parents should not be required to vaccinate their children either.

Parents who decide not to vaccinate their child must depend on herd immunity for their child's protection. Sometimes, however, this defense fails disastrously. Alice Park reported in *Time* (May 21, 2008) the case of Kelly Lacek, who decided to stop vaccinating her two-month-old son Matthew when her chiropractor expressed doubts about the safety of thimerosal vaccines.

All was well until Matthew turned three. Lacek returned home to find him suffering from a high fever and gasping for breath. Physicians at the ER were puzzled, until one experienced physician asked Lacek if Matthew had been fully vaccinated.

Matthew was infected with *Haemophilius-b*, a bacterium that produces fever and a swelling of the tissues of the throat, which makes breathing difficult. Hib also causes meningitis, a brain infection that, untreated, can lead to death. Matthew survived, and his mother made sure that he and his siblings received all recommended immunizations.

Parents' Perception of Best Interest

Parents, with rare exceptions, want to do what is in the best interest of their child. We have no reason to believe that parents who refuse to vaccinate their children on the basis of their beliefs about the risk posed by vaccines or their religious beliefs are acting in bad faith. They believe they are entitled to make decisions about the welfare of their child and that it is violation of their right for the state to order them to take measures they believe are wrong.

This is a view ordinarily supported by the society. We leave it up to parents to decide how much time their children spend online, whether they get the shoes they want, and whether they have to eat their spinach. We expect parents to follow the "best interest" principle in making decisions about children, and we usually allow parents to exercise their judgment about what counts as their child's best interest.

The view becomes problematic, however, when the beliefs of the parents conflict with standards generally accepted within the society. If parents believe, for example, that their child will not die if they recite a certain incantation while plunging a knife into his chest, we try to prevent that from happening. The parents may not be mentally ill, but their beliefs cannot be justified in terms of accepted standards of evidence, and the society has an obligation to protect the child.

The situation becomes especially vexed when the religious beliefs of the parents are shared by a significant number of people, yet those beliefs are at odds with what society believes to be in the best interest of the child. These conflicts occur, for the most part, with respect to not seeking medical treatment for an ailing child. Although we support religious freedom, we also support the view that a child's best interest should be served according to society's accepted standards. Hence, such conflicts will continue to arise in our society, unless we decide that one should always take precedence over the other. The issue has been long debated, but it is not yet resolved.

Another sort of problem arises when the decisions of parents affect the welfare of the society. This is what happens when parents refuse to have their children immunized. The drop in the rate of immunizations, as in the example of Nigeria, weakens herd immunity and, as a consequence, the barrier between infectious diseases and the most vulnerable population in the society—the youngest, the oldest, and many of the sickest. Not having one's child immunized thus has a consequence for others, as well as for the child.

Various outbreaks of infectious diseases in the U.S. in recent years can be attributed to the lack of immunization. Four states have already experienced measles outbreaks that can be traced to unvaccinated children. The more parents refuse to vaccinate their children, the more likely it is that there will be an increase in the number of cases of infectious diseases. This means more death, suffering, and disability that could have been avoided.

Whose Choice?

Should parents be free to decide whether vaccinations are in the best interest of their children? This may be a case in which parents who reject vaccination for their children are not acting in their child's best interest, judged by the accepted standards (scientific and medical) of society. Further, such parents are not only putting their own child at risk; they are also putting others in the society at risk.

In 1905, the U.S. Supreme Court, in *Jacobson vs. Massachusetts*, addressed the issue of whether the state's requirement that everyone be vaccinated for smallpox violated Jacobson's "inherent right" to "care for his own body and health in such way as seems to him best." The Court pointed out that, in general, the state has the right to impose burdens and restraints on citizens for the good of all. Jacobson, the Court ruled, could not expect to enjoy the benefits of living in a community in which people have been vaccinated without accepting the risks of vaccination himself. What's more, even if some scientists questioned the efficacy of vaccination, the legislature had the right to adopt and enforce one of the competing scientific views.

With respect to beliefs about vaccination and autism, we are in a situation similar to that in the Jacobson case: If we prize the right of parents to make decisions about their child on the basis of their beliefs about the child's best interest, then we must pay a double price. We must accept that, on the basis of the knowledge we have, the child will run a serious risk of dying from an infectious disease that could have been prevented. We must also accept that the herd immunity protecting us from a number of diseases will be reduced. Thus, other people are also likely to die.

* * *

On March 1, 2010, the journal *Pediatrics* reported the results of a survey of 1500 parents of children ages 17 or younger. Despite all evidence to the contrary, one out of four parents say they think some vaccines cause autism in healthy children. Nearly one in eight have refused at least one recommended vaccination.

The controversy over vaccination will continue, but the debate will not be over science. The scientific evidence is now sufficient to show that there is no causal link between autism and vaccinations. The debate will be about how we as a society should deal with parents who believe that the causal link is real and don't want their child to be vaccinated.

CASE PRESENTATION
Suffer the Little Children?

Eleven-year-old Kara Neumann began to feel tired and sick, then became progressively weaker. She lost her ability to walk, and eventually she could no longer speak. "Kara laid down and was unable to move her mouth," the police report later said, " and merely made moaning sounds and moved her eyes back and forth."

Kara's parents, Lelani and Dale Neumann, were worried about their daughter and prayed for her recovery. They did not call a doctor or take Kara to a hospital ER for treatment, though. The Neumanns were adherents of the doctrines of an online faith outreach organization called Unleavened Bread Ministries. The group's website presents stories of healing through faith and prayer alone. According to the testimonies, all diseases, whether of people or animals, can be cured by prayer and divine intervention. "Jesus never sent anyone to a doctor or hospital," says an essay by "Pastor Bob" posted on the site and quoted by reporter Dirk Johnson. "Jesus offered healing by one means only! Healing was by faith."

Kara's aunt in California did not share the Neumann's belief that faith and prayer could cure their daughter. When she learned from them how sick Kara was and that they intended to do no more than pray for her, she phoned the sheriff's department in Kara's hometown of

Wenton, Wisconsin, and implored them to intervene and save Kara's life. The department dispatched an ambulance to the Neumanns' house, and Kara was rushed to the nearest hospital. Kara was pronounced DOA—dead on arrival.

She died from ketoacidosis, the result of her undiagnosed and untreated Type I (juvenile-onset) diabetes. The islet cells in her pancreas had failed to produce the hormone insulin in sufficient quantities, and as a result, glucose couldn't enter muscle cells to be converted into energy. Needing energy, her body then began to break down fats, producing toxic fatty acids known as ketones. Ketoacidosis is characterized by severe dehydration and nausea, followed by the impairment of muscle, lung, and heart function. The last stage is irreversible coma and death.

Thousands of children each year are diagnosed with Type I diabetes, and the overwhelming majority are successfully treated with diet, exercise, and insulin injections. Kara was examined by a doctor when she was three, but that had been her last visit. Her death could have been prevented by appropriate medical care.

Number of Cases

Rita Swan, director of Children's Health Care is a Legal Duty, estimates that in the last twenty-five years about 300 children have died because their parents refused to get medical treatment for them for religious reasons. (Swan's own sixteen-month-old son died after she failed to take him to be treated for what turned out to be meningitis. This led her to renounce her Christian Science religion and become an advocate for children's health care.) Nearly all states, forty-four by some estimates, thirty according to Swan's group, have laws that permit parents who believe in healing by faith or in the unreality of disease to withhold medical treatment from their children.

No year passes without a case in which a child dies or is put at serious risk of death because parents reject standard medical treatments in favor of prayer or some religious ceremony based on faith. In May of 2009, for example, Colleen Hauser fled her home in New Ulm, Minnesota, with her son Daniel so that Daniel wouldn't have to submit to court-ordered chemotherapy for Hodgkin's lymphoma. Daniel had a cancerous tumor in his chest likely to be fatal without the standard treatment, but Colleen Hauser and her husband wanted Daniel to have natural healing treatments based on American Indian

traditions. A warrant was issued for Ms. Hauser's arrest, but she eventually returned home and agreed to allow Daniel to be treated at a Minneapolis hospital.

In 2008, two sets of parents in Oregon refused to get medical care for their children on religious grounds, and both children died. One couple was charged with manslaughter in the death of their fifteen-month-old daughter who died of pneumonia. The other couple was charged with criminally negligent homicide when their fifteen-year-old son died a painful death from a urinary tract infection. Both children had diseases that were easily treated, and both most likely would have made a full recovery.

Each time a child dies because of the parent's religious beliefs and the case becomes public, lawyers, physicians, and ethicists talk about the need to change the laws to protect children. This has not happened yet, but it seemed most likely to happen as a response to events in the case of Robyn Twitchell. The Twitchells were educated and middle class, unlike many of the parents whose religious beliefs lead them to avoid getting medical help for their children.

The Death of Robyn Twitchell

Two-year-old Robyn Twitchell ate very little for dinner on April 3. Then, shortly after eating, he began to cry. The crying was soon replaced by vomiting and screaming. Robyn lived in Boston, the city where the Christian Science religion was founded, and both his parents, David and Ginger Twitchell, were devout Christian Scientists. The tenets of the religion hold that disease has no physical being or reality but, rather, is the absence of being. Because God is complete being, disease is an indication of the absence of God, of being away from God. Healing must be mental and spiritual, for it consists in bringing someone back to God, of breaking down the fears, misperceptions, and disordered thinking that stand in the way of having the proper relationship with God. When someone is ill, the person may need help getting to the root cause of the estrangement from God. The role of a Christian Science practitioner is to employ teaching, discussion, and prayer to assist someone suffering from an illness to discover its spiritual source.

Acting on the basis of their beliefs, the Twitchells called in Nancy Calkins, a Christian Science practitioner, to help Robyn. She prayed for Robyn and sang hymns, and, although she visited him three times during the next five days, he showed no signs of getting better. A Christian Scientist nurse was brought in to help feed and bathe Robyn, and on her chart she described him as "listless at times, rejecting all food, and moaning in pain" and "vomiting." On April 8, 1986, Robyn began to have spasms, and his eyes rolled up into his head. He finally lost consciousness, and that evening he died.

Robyn was found to have died of a bowel obstruction that could have been treated by medicine and surgery. Medical experts were sure that he wouldn't have died had his parents sought medical attention for him.

Manslaughter Charges

David and Ginger Twitchell were charged with involuntary manslaughter. In a trial lasting two months, the prosecution and defense both claimed rights had been violated. The Twitchells' attorneys appealed, in particular, to the First Amendment guarantee of the free exercise of religion and claimed that the state was attempting to deny it to them.

Prosecutors responded by pointing out that courts have repeatedly held that not all religious practices are protected. Laws against polygamy and laws requiring vaccinations or blood transfusions for minors, for example, have all been held to be constitutional.

The prosecutors also claimed that Robyn's rights had been violated by his parents' failure to seek care for him as required by law. They also cited the 1923 Supreme Court ruling in *Prince v. Massachusetts,* which held that "Parents may be free to become martyrs of themselves, but it does not follow they are free to make martyrs of their children."

Guilty

The Jury found the Twitchells guilty of the charge, and the judge sentenced them to ten years' probation. John Kiernan, the prosecutor, had not recommended a jail sentence. "The intent of our recommendation was to protect the other Twitchell children." Judge Sandra Hamlin instructed the Twitchells that they must seek medical care for their three children if they showed signs of needing it, and they must take the children to a physician for regular checkups.

"This has been a prosecution against our faith," David Twitchell said. Although, speaking of Robyn, at one point he also said, most sadly, "If medicine could have saved him, I wish I had turned to it."

The prosecutor called the decision "a victory for children." However, Stephen Lyons, one of the defense attorneys, said it was wrong to "substitute the imperfect and flawed judgment of medicine for the judgment of a parent." A spokesman for the Christian Science church said it was not possible to combine spiritual and medical healing as the ruling required. "They're trying to prosecute out of existence this method of treatment," he said.

During the last several years a number of children have died because religious beliefs kept their parents from getting them necessary medical care. Christian Science parents have been convicted of involuntary manslaughter, felony child abuse, or child endangerment in California, Arizona, and Florida.

The Twitchell case was one of several initially successful prosecutions. The case directly challenged the First Church of Christ Scientist (the official name of the church) in the city where it was founded and has its headquarters, and the church recognized the challenge and helped in providing leading attorneys to defend the case. "The message has been sent," John Kiernan said after the Twitchells were sentenced. "Every parent of whatever religious belief or persuasion is obligated to include medical care in taking care of his child."

Appeal

The Twitchells' attorneys immediately announced they would appeal the decision on the grounds that the ruling rested on the judge's misinterpretation of a Massachusetts child-neglect law, which explicitly exempts those who believe in spiritual healing. Because of this, legal authorities considered it possible that the Twitchell decision would be overturned on appeal.

A spiritual-healing exemption is found in similar laws in almost all states. Such exclusions make it difficult to successfully prosecute Christian Scientists or others on the grounds of child neglect. The American Academy of Pediatrics is one of several groups that have campaigned to eliminate the exceptions from child-protection laws, but so far only South Dakota has actually changed its laws.

Despite legal exemptions, parents belonging to religious groups like the Church of the First Born, Faith Assembly, and True Followers of Christ have been convicted and imprisoned for failing to provide their children with medical care. However, so far no Christian Scientist has gone to jail. When a Christian Scientist has been convicted, the sentence has been suspended or has involved probation or community service and the promise to seek medical care for their children in the future.

Critics claim Christian Scientists have been treated more leniently than members of more fundamentalist groups, because a high proportion of church members are middle to upper-middle class and occupy influential positions in business, government, and the law. They also suggest that the legal exceptions for spiritual healing in child-protection laws are there because of the influence of the Christian Science church and its members.

Some legal observers initially believed that the Twitchell case would spur wider and more intense efforts to eliminate the spiritual-healing exception, and groups representing the rights of children consider such a change to be long overdue. However, the Twitchell conviction was overturned on appeal in 1993, and it did not turn out to have the impact on the law many hoped it would.

Neumann Sentences

Lelani and Dale Neumann were convicted of second-degree reckless homicide in August 2009. In October, they were ordered to do thirty days in jail each year for the next six years and were placed on ten years' probation. For the crime of which they were convicted, the Neumanns could have received a maximum prison term of twenty-five years. The prosecutor in their case had asked for a three-year sentence.

The Neumanns' attorney announced that he would appeal their conviction, on the grounds that the state law is not clear on the issue of using spiritual means to treat children. Perhaps the Neumanns, like the Twitchells, will have their convictions overturned.

If so, it will fall into a familiar pattern. Since 1982, at least fifty convictions have been handed down by courts in cases in which children have died because medical care was withheld for religious reasons. The convictions usually have been overturned on appeal. Almost no one has done jail time, and those who have are people who, like the Neumanns, belong to fringe religions groups.

In our society, except in exceptional cases, the religious beliefs of parents continue to take precedence over the medical welfare of their children.

SOCIAL CONTEXT
The HPV Vaccine: Hope or Hype?

HPV—human papillomavirus—is the world's most common sexually transmitted infection. Some twenty millions Americans are infected with HPV at any given time, and almost seven million new infections occur every year. Nearly eighty percent of all sexually active women and men are infected at some time during their lives.

HPV is transmitted through genital contact. Most often this is through vaginal and anal sex, but transmission through genital-to-genital contact or oral sex is also possible. The majority of HPV infections cause no symptoms, and the virus can be present and undetected for years. Most people who are infected don't know it, so they don't realize they are transmitting the virus to a sexual partner.

HPV infections are most often eventually eliminated by the body's immune system. More than 100 strains of the virus have been identified, and some of them cause genital warts in both males and females. At least sixteen strains cause cervical cancer, as well as cancers of the vulva, vagina, penis, anus, and head and neck (including the tongue, tonsils, and throat).

Cervical Cancer

Cervical cancer is the most common of the cancers caused by HPV. (The cervix is the opening at the end of the uterus.) Each year in the U.S., about 12,000 women are diagnosed with cervical cancer, and about 4000 die from the disease. However, this represents only a small fraction of women who are infected with HPV. Very little is known about the links between an HPV infection in a young woman and the development of cervical cancer decades later. No one can now predict which woman infected with HPV will develop cervical cancer or explain why some develop it and others do not.

Cervical cancer rates in the U.S. have decreased because of the widespread use of the Papanicolaou test ("Pap smear"). The test consists of a microscopic examination of cells from the cervix so that precancerous changes can be detected and surgery performed before the changed cells become cancerous and life threatening. Cervical cancer usually doesn't have symptoms until it is very advanced. Thus, in countries where the Pap test is not routinely performed, the death rate due to cervical cancer is considerably higher. According to the World Health Organization, 470,000 women are diagnosed each year with cervical cancer and 233,000 die from the disease.

Gardasil

Two strains of HPV (6 and 11) are known to cause seventy percent of all cervical cancers, and two other strains (16 and 18) are known to cause ninety percent of all genital warts. In March 2007 the pharmaceutical company Merck announced the availability of a new FDA-approved vaccine called Gardasil that is effective against these four strains. Gardasil doesn't work once someone becomes infected with the viruses, but the vaccine is highly effective in preventing infection.

The vaccine is produced by using recombinant techniques to splice the DNA that encodes L1 into the genetic material of yeast cells. L1 is the major protein forming the capsule around the virus. The yeast cells produce virus like particles that contain L1. The particles don't cause an HPV infection, but they trigger the immune system to produce antibodies against it.

Vaccination

Vaccinating women with Gardasil before they are infected with HPV would in theory,

eliminate up to seventy percent of the cases of cervical cancer. This would mean preventing as many as 84,000 cases a year and saving the lives of almost 3000 women. Cervical cancer caused by other strains of the HPV virus would not be prevented by vaccination, so even women who were vaccinated would need to continue to have a regular Pap test.

HPV is sexually transmitted, so the obvious way to reduce the incidence of infection and reduce the occurrence of cervical cancer would be to vaccinate girls and women before they are likely to become sexually active. This was the position taken by the Centers for Disease Control's Advisory Committee on Immunization Practices. Reviewing the research conducted to gain FDA approval, the committee concluded that, on the basis of the evidence available, Gardasil was safe for use in girls and women nine to twenty-six years old.

The committee recommended that girls be vaccinated between ages 11 and 12. Because Gardasil had just become available, the committee also recommended that females ages 13 to 26 be vaccinated. The reasoning was that, although older females may have been sexually active, they may have escaped infection by the HPV strains the vaccine can prevent. Thus, vaccination might benefit them.

The vaccine, to be effective, requires three injections given six-months apart. The costs amount to $300–$400, and the vaccine is considered to be effective for five to seven years. The side effects are ordinarily nothing more than temporary pain and soreness at the site of the injection (usually the arm), but some people experience headache, fever, nausea, dizziness, or vomiting. Some receiving the vaccine fainted. The number of serious adverse events reported from the clinical trails of the vaccine were not enough for the FDA to withhold its approval.

Require HPV Vaccination?

The advent of Gardasil was treated by the national media as a major medical story. The possibility of reducing the occurrence of a potentially deadly form of cancer by a significant percentage was regarded as important news, and medical experts and ethicists were interviewed about the impact the vaccine would likely have on the disease and society.

Vaccination with Gardasil to reduce the chance of HPV infection became the topic of a national debate. Should the CDC recommendation be followed and girls ages 11 to 12 vaccinated? Wouldn't it make more sense to wait until someone became sexually active? Should vaccination be required? Should boys be vaccinated also? Was the vaccine sufficiently safe? Shouldn't parents be the ones to make the decision about when their daughters are vaccinated?

The underlying theme of most discussions about the use of the vaccine was that, because it has the potential to prevent cancer, it should be used. Either parents ought to encourage their daughter to be vaccinated, or school systems ought to require vaccinations.

Governor Rick Perry of Texas was among the first officials to act. In April 2007, he issued an executive order requiring that sixth-grade girls be vaccinated with Gardasil by the start of the next school year. Parents, acting on behalf of their daughters, would be able to opt out of the vaccination program. "The governor believes we should protect as many young women as possible—rich and poor, insured and uninsured—while maintaining parent's rights to opt their daughters out of receiving the vaccine," a representative of Governor Perry said in a statement.

Texas would have become the first state to comply with the CDC recommendation, but the governor's order met with immediate criticism and eventual legislative action. In April 2007, in a 135–2 vote, the legislature barred the vaccination policy from going into effect until 2011. By then, it might be reviewed by the legislature and set aside.

Critics of Governor Perry claimed he had abused his executive authority in ordering the vaccinations. The legislative process should

have been followed and the issues debated and voted on. Moreover, Merck was represented in the state capital by the lobbyist Mike Toomey. Toomey had also been the chief of staff for Governor Perry from 2002 to 2004, so some legislators suspected that Perry's action may have been prompted by something more than the wish to protect the health of the women of Texas. This suspicion was reinforced by the fact that, at the time, Merck was lobbying state legislatures around the country to adopt policies requiring vaccinations with Gardasil.

Texas was not the only state with a governor who thought it was important to mandate that sixth-grade girls be vaccinated with Gardisil. Timothy M. Kaine of Virginia stated that he would sign the vaccination bill that had been submitted to him, and the state budget would include $4 million to help make sure that girls from low-income families got the vaccine. In addition, Governor Bill Richardson of New Mexico promised to sign the HPV-vaccine bill that had already been approved by the state legislature. The New Mexico legislation, like the Texas proposal, included a clause allowing parents to opt out on behalf of their children. Eventually, however, the governor vetoed the bill.

A number of other states considered implementing the CDC's Immunization Advisory Committee recommendation and mandating HPV vaccination for girls ages 12 to 13. So far, however, only Virginia has required such vaccinations. Other states have either made no decision or left the choice up to parents.

The New York Times, in a February 6, 2007, editorial, had congratulated Texas for "becoming the first state to mandate vaccinating young schoolgirls" against HPV and observed that "Other states would be wise to follow the same path."

Although it looked for a while as if many other states would, this point of view was far from universally shared. Some critics argued that requiring girls to be vaccinated would encourage sexual activity at an early age and increase promiscuity. Girls, starting in their early teens, would get the false impression that they would be protected from any harmful consequences associated with sex. Focus on the Family, a Christian advocacy group, expressed the view that women should avoid HIV infection by not having sex before marriage. (Opponents pointed out that this would require the partner also to have avoided sex before marriage, and that was not something a young woman ought to stake her health on.) The organization did not oppose voluntary HPV vaccination, however.

Other critics objected to any policy that would require girls to be vaccinated before they could attend school. Unlike diseases such as measles and mumps, they pointed out, HPV is not an infection that can be spread by casual contact. There is no justification, then, for requiring girls to be vaccinated in order to protect other people.

The choice should be left up to individuals and their famlies. Also, those questioning the safety of all vaccines said that number of childhood vaccinations is already too large and we should not add to it.

Some critics were struck by what they regarded as the unfairness of requiring that girls be vaccinated but not boys. Although only females develop cervical cancer, males are as much responsible for spreading HPV as females. Thus, they claimed, boys and men should be vaccinated also.

Merck and Marketing

Researchers Sheila and David Rothman, in a 2009 article in the *Journal of the American Medical Association (JAMA)* on the sales promotion of Gardasil by Merck, pointed out that Merck had taken a new approach in marketing a vaccine. Traditionally, a vaccine had been identified by the disease it prevented (e.g., the "measles vaccine") or by its developer (e.g., the "Salk vaccine"). Merck, however, named the HPV

vaccine Gardasil and promoted it to "guard against" cervical cancer, rather than reduce the risks of acquiring an HPV infection: Promoted in this way, Gardasil's worldwide sales from 2006–2008 were $1.4 billion. The trade publication *Pharmaceutical Executive* named Gardasil the 2006 "brand of the year" for generating a market "out of thin air."

Merck's marketing strategy required the company to promote Gardasil as if every girl and young woman in the country were at equal risk of developing cervical cancer. This meant concentrating marketing on major population cernters, rather than on areas of the country where the population density is lower, but the risks of cervical cancer are greater.

Black women in the south, Latino women in the southwest, and white women in Appalachia have much higher rates of cervical cancer than women in other parts of the country. Thus, the use of the vaccine in these areas might be expected eventually to reduce the number of deaths from the disease. The promotion of Gardasil in these areas would not be as cost effective, however, as promoting it in population centers.

The Rothmans call attention to the way that Merck provided grants to professional medical organizations to develop educational programs and speaker's bureaus to promote the use of Gardasil. The Rothmans observe that "much of the material [in the educational programs and preparations for speakers] did not address the full complexity of the issues surrounding the vaccine and did not provide balanced recommendations on risks and benefits." Merck not only overstressed both the benefits of the vaccine and the risks of cervical cancer, but succeeded in turning a large and influential segment of the medical establishment into Gardasil advocates.

Merck, as it had done in Texas, also lobbied heavily in state legislatures to get lawmakers to require that girls ages 11 to 12 be vaccinated with Gardasil. Once again, the major theme pressed by Merck in its marketing messages was that Gardasil is a vaccine against cervical cancer, and several professional medical groups (including the one performing biopsies for Pap tests) supported that message. Many state legislators were eager to show that they favored legislation that would benefit women in their state, so long as any vaccination requirements contained an opt-out provision.

Safety Concerns

In August 2009, three years after Gardasil was introduced, the CDC's Vaccine Adverse Event Reporting System listed more than 700 "very serious" adverse events associated with the use of the HPV vaccine. The adverse events included blood clots, neurological disorders such as Guillain-Barré syndrome, and death. Some twenty-three to twenty-five million doses of Gardasil had been distributed during the period covered by the reports. The total number of adverse events reported averaged about sixty per 100,000 doses of Gardasil, and 6.2 percent of the adverse events were classified as serious. They included thirty-two deaths.

What is not clear, experts agree, is whether the adverse events reported were caused by the HPV vaccine. Without knowing how many of the events would have occurred independently of the vaccine, it is not possible to conclude that the vaccine caused them. Would the person who was vaccinated and then died of a stroke caused by a blood clot have died anyway? Was the timing only accidental? A 2009 study, also published in *JAMA*, showed that ninety percent of those reporting problems with blood clots already had risk factors for developing blood clots (using birth-control pills or smoking) before getting the vaccine. How many other preexisting conditions were responsible for the adverse events reported? No one knows.

Futhermore, the adverse event reports themselves may not contain reliable data. The Vaccine Adverse Events Reporting System is voluntary, and the reports submitted are neither assessed for quality nor verified. Some of the adverse events are most likely real, yet no vaccine is 100 percent safe, and there is not

reason enough at present to claim that Gardasil is less safe than other widely used vaccines. "There are 732 serious problems identified in twenty-four million doses of the HPV vaccine," Keven Ault, professor of gynecology at Emory University, told a reporter. "I usually tell my patients that these serious events are tragic, rare, and likely unrelated to the vaccine."

This is not a view endorsed by all physicians. Dr. Jacques Moritz, director of gynecology at New York's St. Luke's–Roosevelt Hospital, told the same reporter that he saw no reason to offer Gardasil to patients, given the availability of good screening techniques like the Pap test and good treatments. He said he didn't plan to vaccinate his eleven-year-old daughter.

Dr. Charlotte Haug, in a *JAMA* editorial accompaning the articles mentioned earlier, is particularly critical of Gardasil. She points out that it was approved by the FDA on the basis of clinical trails that focused on whether it prevented HPV infections by the two strains, and it wasn't until almost a year later that the results of the Phase 3 trials were reported. These trials focused on the prevention of precancerous changes, and although the results were promising, no longer term results from the studies have been published since then. So far, the vaccine has not been proven to reduce cervical cancer.

Also, the adverse events that have been reported since the vaccine has come into use need to be investigated in a scientific fashion. The reports don't prove that the vaccine is unsafe, but we also can't conclude that the reports are groundless and that the vaccine is safe. We simply don't know enough to be sure in the absence of more systematic studies.

Whether a risk is worth taking depends on comparing the potential benefit and the potential risk. In Haug's view, the "net benefit to a woman of the HPV vaccine is uncertain." Even a woman who is infected with HPV for many years is unlikely to develop cancer if she has regular screening tests. Rationally, then, when it comes to the HPV vaccine, she should be willing to take only a small risk that it will cause her harm.

Hope or Hype?

The development of a new vaccine for an infectious disease is rare good news, and if the vaccine also protects against cancer, the news seems even better. It is no wonder that the announcement that Gardasil had been approved by the FDA for vaccinating girls and women was met with such enthusiasm. Even if the promotional efforts of Merck were instrumental in stirring up that enthusiasm and in encouraging states to consider requiring HPV vaccination for schoolgirls, this does not mean that Gardasil shouldn't be considered a potentially important weapon in the war against HPV and cervical cancer.

As more studies are done and data about the use of Gardasil accumulate, researchers will be able to make a more accurate assessment of its potential risks and benefits. Women will then be in a better position to decide whether they want to take the risks to get the benefits. It does not seem likely, however, that many states will pass legislation requiring that schoolgirls be vaccinated against HPV. Even if current doubts about the safety of the vaccine are resolved in its favor, people have come to realize that the great majority of women, even though infected for decades with HPV, will never develop cervical cancer and that they can ensure their safety by regular Pap tests. Because the vaccine protects against only two cancer-causing strains of HPV, even those who are vaccinated must still be regularly tested for precancerous changes in cervical cells. Thus, many people will see no compelling reason to subject themselves or their children to whatever slight risks the vaccine may pose. Finally, because the HPV virus is spread by sexual contact and not merely by closeness in a crowd, legislators are unlikely to believe that they have an obligation to require vaccination for the protection of others.

The HPV vaccine is far from being nothing but hype, but the hope that it offers seems less substantial than it did at first.

SOCIAL CONTEXT
Placebos and Transparency

Jane Hunter (as we will call her) was convinced that she had a serious, perhaps fatal, illness. She was constantly fatigued, and she felt so tired in the mornings that it was all she could do to get out of bed. Despite all her efforts, she seemed unable to get enough rest. She also ached all over, and various places on her body were extraordinarily tender. If she pressed a finger against the side of her neck, she would have to bite her lip to keep from crying. Points of pain were also located between her shoulder blades and behind her knees. Sometimes she seemed to hurt all over.

Jane didn't think of herself as a whiner and complainer, but she had been to see Dr. Jerrold Chang, her family doctor three times during the eight months she had been having problems. He had examined her and ordered a variety of tests to rule out diabetes, lupus, lung cancer, kidney disease, leukemia, and other sorts of blood disorders.

"I can't find anything wrong with you," Dr. Chang had told her. "I want you get a second opinion, though. So I'm going to ask you to see Dr. Ellen Deutch. She's a rheumatologist, and they specialize in diseases that involve inflammation. I think you probably have fibromyalgia."

"I've never heard of it." Jane felt a wave of panic pass through her. "How serious is it?"

"We're not sure it's a disease," Dr. Chang told her. "But it's what we call the group of symptoms like yours. About two percent of the population, mostly women, complain of constant fatigue, poor sleep, generalized aches and pains, and several painfully sensitive places on their bodies." Dr. Chang shrugged. "No one knows how to treat fibromyalgia or even if it's real."

"It seems real to me." Jane felt annoyed.

Jane's symptoms didn't improve during the four weeks she had to wait before she was able to get in to see Dr. Deutch. When she was finally able to tell her story, Dr. Deutch gave her another physical exam. She explained to Jane that she was checking in particular to see if Jane's thyroid had any nodules. Dr. Deutch then looked at the laboratory results from the numerous tests Dr. Chang had ordered.

"I agree with Dr. Chang that you most likely have fibromyalgia," Dr. Deutch told her. "I don't see a reason to perform any more tests at the moment, but I would like you to make an appointment to return in a month so I can check on your progress."

"You aren't going to give me any drugs or anything?" Jane felt her heart sink. She was both surprised and disappointed. She had convinced herself that her new doctor would be able to help her escape from the prison of fatigue and pain her life had become.

Dr. Deutch looked thoughtful a moment. "We can try something that might help. I'm going to give you some tablets that are a combination of dextrose and a small amount of sodium chloride. Some people with your condition have found them helpful." Dr. Deutch began writing on a prescription pad. "I want you to take two tablets three times a day, then let me know next time if you think they are helping."

Traditional Practice

Scenes like these are played out in the consulting rooms of physicians every day. Patients with vague complaints go to their doctors and ask them for help. Their doctors examine them thoroughly and give them a range of tests, but find nothing abnormal. Yet wanting to get their patients to feel better, the doctors prescribe something they hope will help.

The tablets Dr. Deutch prescribed for Jane are nothing but sugar mixed with a trace of table salt. They are essentially harmless, but they also cannot be considered to be an active drug. Jane would probably get similar amounts of the contents of the tablets by eating a small candy bar. Dr. Deutch has prescribed a placebo to treat Jane's condition.

The word *placebo* is Latin for "I shall please." Over the centuries, people who feel ill have consulted physicians with the expectation that their doctors will give them something to make them feel better. Doctors have always tried to oblige. Before the current era, this might have meant prescribing a particular diet, letting the patient's blood, administering enemas, or giving drugs to cause vomiting. But these procedures were part of legitimate medical practice based on accepted theory. (The theory dominant for about two thousand years was that disease results from an imbalance in the four humors—blood, phlegm, black bile, and yellow bile—so the aim of treatment was to restore the balance.)

Even if a doctor believed nothing was wrong with the patient, the patient still expected to be treated. Typically, this meant giving the patient some sort of medicine. Thus, the doctor might prescribe an emetic like nux vomica or a laxative like syrup of figs just to satisfy the patient. Such substances have definite and unpleasant effects, however, so the doctor might prefer to give the patient a box of pills made from sugar or bread dough. These pills would be harmless, produce no side effects, and assure the patient that his doctor was taking his medical complaint seriously and treating it appropriately.

Every traditional doctor learned during his apprenticeship that placebos were often successful in treating patients with vague complaints. Hence, prescribing placebos in such cases became a standard part of medical practice. Even in the current era, the patient dismissively described as "LOL-NAD" ("a little old lady in no apparent distress") who showed up in an emergency department or a doctor's office would often, after examination, be sent away with a prescription for a two-week course of sugar pills. So, too, would a patient who seemed to be a hypochondriac or mildly to moderately depressed. Just receiving medical attention might be all the patient needed to begin to feel better.

Tradition Challenged

During the 1960s and the 1970s, many of the customary practices of physicians were called into question. In particular, the paternalism prevalent in the medical community was severely criticized. Until the 1960s, for example, it was common for a doctor not to tell a patient that he had cancer. But, critics charged, what gave the doctor the right to withhold such information? And why should the doctor decide whether the patient should be treated? That decision should be left up to the patient.

Informed consent was not a new idea in medical practice, but most often it was sought in only a formal fashion and used as a means to protect surgeons from lawsuits. During the 1960s and 1970s, however, in response to pressure from patient advocates and ethicists, the medical community began to acknowledge the importance of the autonomy of patients. This meant recognizing that informed consent is essential to protecting autonomy in cases in which a patient's interest is concerned. The doctor informs and advises, but it is the patient who makes the final decision about whether to accept a treatment.

The consequence of the recognition of autonomy and the incorporation of informed consent into medical practice was that physicians had to change many of their traditional patterns of behavior. Patients could no longer be kept in ignorance "for their own good." They had to be provided with information so that they could participate in making decisions directly affecting them.

Patients had to rely on their doctors to educate them and to tell them the truth. Doctors and patients were seen to be partners working together to do what was in the best interest of the patient. This requires transparency on the part of both patient and doctor. The patient shouldn't hide anything from her doctor, because the doctor needs reliable information to make a diagnosis and decide what to recommend as the best course of treatment. The doctor shouldn't hide anything from his patient, because the patient needs reliable information to exercise her autonomy and make a decision about what treatments she is willing to accept. Both effective medical practice and informed consent require trust and openness.

The transparency required by the doctor–patient relationship doesn't prima facie seem compatible with the use of placebos. Prescribing placebos can be viewed as engaging in a deceptive practice. The doctor is, in effect, telling the patient "You have a medical problem, and this is a drug I think will be effective in treating it." If the patient doesn't have a problem that fits into a recognized diagnostic category, doesn't the patient have a right to know this? If the patient's problem is like Jane's and fits into a category like fibromyalgia that isn't recognized as a disease and has no established treatment, shouldn't the patient be told this?

Placebos, in the view of many, are also relics of the time when medicine had available virtually no effective drugs. This time extended into the early part of the twentieth century. Hundreds—even thousands—of drugs and compounds were listed in the pharmacopoeia and prescribed by doctors, but almost none had been tested for effectiveness and safety. Now, however, we insist that drugs be shown to be safe and effective before they are prescribed. (By some estimates, however, only about twenty percent of drugs in use have been tested.) The use of placebos, critics say, undercuts our commitment to scientific medicine and is an implicit endorsement of a medical practice than can no longer be justified.

Placebos in Practice

Despite the new emphasis on transparency in the doctor–patient relationship, a recent survey of physicians in the specialties of internal medicine and rheumatology showed that about half (46–58%, depending on the phrasing of the question) regularly prescribe placebo treatments and most (62%) believe that the practice is ethically permissible. (The survey was about practices during the previous year, but it seems reasonable to assume that year was typical.)

Contemporary physicians don't usually prescribe such traditional placebos as sugar pills or saline (saltwater) solutions, however. (This may be because pharmacies no longer compound drugs to order.) Rather, most of them (41%) give their patient analgesics (aspirin or acetaminophen, for example) or vitamins (38%). A few (13%) prescribe antibiotics or sedatives. Whatever placebo they prescribe, most physicians (68%) accompany it by saying something like "This is a potentially beneficial medicine not typically used for your condition." Only rarely (5%) do doctors describe the treatment they prescribe as a placebo.

The practice of using placebos isn't confined to U.S. physicians. Another survey showed that 86% of general practitioners in Denmark use placebos, and surveys in Sweden, Israel, New Zealand, and the United Kingdom produced similar results.

The motivation of doctors who prescribe placebo treatments for their patients is most likely the desire to get their patients to feel better. Various studies have shown that a significant number of patients (perhaps as many as 12–20%) gain medical benefit from whatever treatment they receive. (It is for this reason that double-blind clinical trials with a large number of patients have become the standard for determining the effectiveness of a drug.) Thus, when a doctor gives a placebo to a patient with a vague complaint who shows no evidence of having a particular disease, the placebo has a reasonable chance of benefiting the patient.

The doctor who prescribes a placebo is not honoring the presumed commitment to transparency. However, the doctor may be benefiting the patient. If the primary duty of the physician is to benefit the patient—to relieve the patient's suffering—then the case can be made that the physician is sometimes justified in setting aside or violating the implicit commitment to being completely honest with the patient. Cases in which it is appropriate for a physician to prescribe a placebo may be ones in which paternalism can be justified.

Even if such a case can be made in general, it is harder to make the case for physicians who prescribe active placebos—that is, drugs given as placebos that have significant pharmacological consequences. Sugar pills are harmless, but people may have serious and potentially fatal allergic reactions to antibiotics. Similarly, sedatives may produce disturbed sleep, arrthymias, or life-threatening respiratory distress. A physician who prescribes an active placebo would most likely be hard pressed to come up with an adequate explanation for putting a patient at risk for what, by definition, has to be a situation in which the patient displays no signs of a disease for which an appropriate drug should be prescribed.

Bottom Line

The routine use of placebos in medical practice always raises ethical questions. Prescribing a placebo can be a physician's way of getting rid of a troublesome patient whose problem she can't solve. In the worst case, it can be a physician's way of shirking the responsibility for diagnosis or helping the patient understand that what is bothering him is not the symptom of a disease. In the best case, prescribing a placebo can be the physician's way of relieving a patient's worry and distress without causing harm.

Physicians prescribed placebos, in part, because they felt patients' expectations that their doctor will do something to help. Traditionally and even now, "doing something" has usually been construed to mean prescribing a drug. (This is one reason antibiotics have been overprescribed.) What patients should most appropriately expect from their physicians is

PLACEBO SURVEY

The following survey, mailed to 1200 internists and rheumatologists, elicited 679 responses: *Would you be willing to recommend a sugar pill if it proved to be better than no treatment for fibromyalgia?*

Very Likely: 24% Moderately likely: 34% Unlikely 31% Not likely: 10%

How many times a month do you recommend a therapy primarily because it will enhance the patient's expectations of getting better?

Never: 20% 1 or less: 34% 2–3: 28% More than 3: 18%

Is it appropriate to recommend a treatment primarily to enhance the patients' expectations?

Obligatory: 3% Permissible: 59% Rarely: 31% Never: 7%

Source: *Prescribing "Placebo Treatments": Results of National Survey of U.S. Internists and Rheumatologists.* **BMJ** 2008,337:a1189.

an informed judgment about their complaint and symptoms. Were patients able to accept the judgment that sometimes medicine has nothing to offer to make them feel better, then physicians would most likely not be so inclined to prescribe placebos.

SOCIAL CONTEXT
Health Cops: How Much Regulation Is Too Much?

Obesity is causally associated with these disorders: Type-2 diabetes, hypertension, heart disease, stroke, kidney failure blindness, and unhealing wounds leading to foot and leg amputations. Someone with a body-mass index (BMI) of 30 or more is, by definition, obese. (BMI is the ratio of height to weight. Thus, someone who is six feet tall is obese when he reaches 221 pounds; someone five feet, six inches, tall is obese when she reaches 186 pounds.) As the number of obese people in the population rises, the number of diseases caused by obesity also rises, and each disease is associated with high medical costs, disability, and death.

Longevity in Reverse

A 2005 *New England Journal of Medicine* study concludes that, because of obesity, for the first time in the nation's history life expectancy is growing shorter rather than longer. Current life expectancy for adults is seventy-seven years, but if deaths attributable to obesity were subtracted, an additional four to nine months would be added. However, the effect obesity has on life expectancy now is small compared to the effect it is likely to have as the current crop of children grows into adulthood. The adults of tomorrow may live from two to five years less than adults do now.

To put these figures in perspective, the four to nine months now lost to the effects of obesity mean that obesity is shortening the life span at a greater rate than the combined effects of accidents, homicides, and suicides. The effects on the children of today will to be to shorten their life spans to a greater extent than the *combined* effects of cancer and coronary artery disease.

Some experts estimate that 300,000–400,000 people die each year from obesity-related causes. The number of cases of disability and sickness associated with obesity is likely to be several times this number. Even so, as an author of the report, David Ludwig, observed, society is now in the lull before the real storm breaks. "There is an unprecedented increase in the prevalence of obesity at younger and younger ages without much public heath impact," he says. "But when they start developing heart attacks, stroke, kidney failure, amputations, blindness, and ultimately death at younger ages, then that could be a huge effect on life expectancy." When this starts happening, it will have a serious impact on health care costs, insurance, Social Security, and the productivity of the economy. Even if advances in medicine soften the blow obesity can be expected to deliver, the amount of suffering and sadness will rise as life expectancy falls and millions of individuals sicken and die.

Obesity Rates Level Off

During the period 2005–2010, Americans apparently reached the peak of obesity. The rates of obesity remained constant, but the rate was very high. Some thirty-four percent of adults are obese—double the 1980 percentage. During the same period, the percentage of obese children tripled, to reach seventeen percent.

Why did the rates level off? Some experts believe it is partly because women, who most often buy and prepare the food for families, became more aware of the need to feed their families a better diet. Also, the food served in schools improved, and children and the population in general were educated about the high-fat, high-salt, and high-calorie contents of fast food.

Not everyone is convinced that the halt in the increase is due to better eating habits or an increased awareness of the importance of a healthful diet. David Ludwig, the author of the 2005 report, thinks the plateau may be because the population has reached the biological limit of how obese it is possible to be. When people eat more, they gain weight, and an increasing number of calories go toward maintaining and

moving around the additional weight. "A population doesn't keep getting heavier and heavier indefinitely," Ludwig says. Also, "It could be that most of the people who are genetically susceptible or susceptible for psychological or behavioral reasons have already become obese."

The leveling off of obesity is a statistical feature of the population, but some groups within the population have not leveled off. From 1999 to 2008, boys who were the heaviest (mostly white) became even heavier. African-American adults have the highest obesity rates (37% of men, 50% of women), and 43% of Hispanic women count as obese. Weight in the general population has continued to increase, so 68% of adults and almost 75% of children are now overweight, defined as having a body-mass index of 25 or more.

Obesity rates have plateaued, but the problems posed by obesity are still with us. They will require considerable resources to deal with for decades to come. Even if the conveyor belt that has been moving people into the obese category were suddenly to stop, so many people are already obese that their problems will occupy at least another generation.

Soaring Costs

Type-2 diabetes, which most commonly results from obesity, is estimated to cost the nation $174 billion a year in medical bills, disability payments, and lost productivity. (Direct medical costs are $116 billion; $58 billion are for disability, work loss, and premature mortality.) Almost twenty-four million adults and children (nearly eight percent of the population) have diabetes, and almost two million new cases are diagnosed each year. Every 24 hours, 4100 people are diagnosed with the disease, and due to it, 55 people go blind, 120 develop end-stage kidney disease, and 230 amputations are performed. About ninety-five percent of diagnosed cases of diabetes are Type 2.

Genetic factors are now known to be involved in producing at least some cases of Type-2 diabetes. In January 2006, researchers at Decode Genetics announced that they had identified a variant gene that increases the risk of developing diabetes in those who inherit the gene. The variant, designated TCF7L2, is a regulatory gene that controls a metabolic pathway. It was found in the population of Iceland, and its existence was later confirmed in the populations of both Denmark and the United States. An estimate 38% of those possessing one copy (allele) of the variant gene have a 45% greater than usual risk of developing the disease, and the 7% of the population who possess two copies have a 141% greater risk.

The variant gene is responsible for 21% of all cases of diabetes in the U.S. population, and it is likely that other variant genes are involved in other cases. The immediate hope is that knowledge about TCF7L2 can be used to develop a genetic test to identify people who are at risk for developing the disease. They can then be encouraged to modify their lifestyle to avoid developing the disease. The longer term hope is that treatments can be found that act on the metabolic pathways influenced by the variant gene and thus prevent the development of the disease.

While a genetic predisposition is likely in every case of Type-2 diabetes even though not all the genes have been identified, obesity and a lack of physical activity appear to trigger the disease. People can show prediabetic conditions for seven to ten years before the disease is finally diagnosed, and by that time, significant damage may already be occurring in the patient's body. Numbness and tingling in the hands and feet may signal damage to the nervous system, bleeding in the retina can cause significant vision loss, poor circulation can lead to unhealing wounds that are prone to infection or to the death of tissues in the toes or feet, requiring amputation. (About seventy percent of limb amputations are due to diabetes.) High blood pressure caused by the disease can damage the kidneys, requiring dialysis or a transplant.

Obese people may face these problems one at a time, but often two, three, or even more problems occur in a cluster. Obesity triggers Type-2 diabetes, which raises blood pressure and causes a stroke, damages the kidneys so severely that they shut down, and causes blood vessels in the eye to leak blood and damage the retina. Hospitalization and lack of activity may slow circulation, causing tissues in the toes or feet to die, thus requiring amputation. The life of a diabetic is one of constant vigilance and relentless efforts to stave off the ravages of the disease.

The medical costs for caring for someone who develops Type-2 diabetes are staggering. Given that twenty-one million people are now being treated for diabetes, it is not surprising that the annual medical costs add up to $174 billion. Here are typical per-patient charges: stroke care, $40,200; limb amputation, $30,400; end-stage kidney disease, $37,000. With the rise of obesity causing an increase in the number of Type-2 diabetics, the annual cost of care for this group of patients can be expected to soar.

Public Health or Private Choice

If only we could keep people from being obese, the costs of health care would decrease and people would live longer and healthier lives. But what would we have to do to slow or perhaps halt the increase in overweight kids and adults? And how far are we as a society prepared to go in regulating the weight of our citizens? Should we even be thinking about intruding on this area of privacy and autonomy?

Researchers tend to regard obesity as a public health issue. They view it as a problem that, like smoking, should be addressed by using laws and public policies as tools to bring it under control. Obesity, like smoking, has a high economic cost attached to it, and that cost must be paid by society. The money spent on coping with Type-2 diabetes might be better spent on prenatal care, on providing health care for the poor or uninsured, or on education or scientific research. Type-2 diabetics typically develop the disease because they are significantly overweight, and the disease causes the problems discussed earlier, and treating these problems drives up the cost of medical care. Therefore, society is justified in taking measures to keep people from becoming obese.

West Virginia introduced a wellness program for Medicaid patients that asks them to sign a pledge to "do my best to stay healthy," to attend "health improvement programs as directed," to go for regularly scheduled checkups, to take the medicines that are prescribed, and to go to an emergency room only for an event like a heart attack, stroke, or seizure. West Virginia has some of the country's highest rates of smoking, obesity, diabetes, and heart disease. A state commissioner of health services said, "We want to reach people before they get chronic and debilitating diseases that will keep them on Medicaid for the rest of their lives."

Those who stick to the plan will receive such "enhanced benefits" as diabetes management, cardiac rehabilitation, mental health counseling, and prescription drugs and home-health visits from a nurse as needed. Those who do not sign up will receive only the benefits mandated by the federal government. (Medicaid is a joint federal–state program.) They will not be eligible for the advanced benefits, and their prescriptions will be limited to four a month.

Pressure has been building for years to provide children with school lunches that are nutritionally sound. Although steps have been taken in this direction, many state and local governments have decreased the amount of physical activity built into the school day. Recess has been eliminated or shortened to add extra classes, and athletic programs have been cut to reduce costs. A school without physical education (P.E.) doesn't require a P.E. teacher, and one without competitive teams doesn't require a coach.

Reversing the current practices of governments and schools could do much to prevent obesity and to promote children's health. Yet this would often require increasing the amount of funding that schools receive, and the public is generally not enthusiastic about increasing school taxes.

Some states have taken some tentative steps toward reducing the obesity crisis. The Arkansas State Board of Education now requires that schools send home with each child a weight report card along with the academic report card. The hope is that when the report is accompanied by nutritional education and advice, children, with the help of their parents, will be able to maintain their weight within limits compatible with good health. Local school districts in a number of states—California, Massachusetts, and Oregon among them—have initiated similar programs.

The federal government, after much pressure from consumer groups, now requires the labels on foods to provide more nutritional information than ever before. Labels display data about the calories, carbohydrates, fats, transfats, fiber, and vitamins in a specified serving of the food, to guide consumers in their decisions. Similarly, fast-food restaurants are required to make available to their customers nutritional information about the items they serve. Knowing that one bacon cheese double hamburger, fries, and a large milk shake can contain more than half the calories an average person should consume in a day ought to help people make sensible choices.

In 2010, the Food and Drug Administration proposed a new requirement for food manufacturers. They would have to start providing nutritional information about realistic serving sizes on the front of many packaged foods. Cereals, cookies, chips, and ice cream now print the information on the back or sides of packages, and the serving sizes manufacturers use do not reflect the amounts of the product that people typically consume as a serving. Frosted Flakes, for example, lists its serving size as ¾ cup (110 calories), but two cups (293 calories) is more likely to be an actual serving.

The FDA proposal is thus intended to give people a better sense of what they are eating. If people don't understand that "one serving" is a smaller amount than they are likely to eat, they won't understand how many calories and nutrients or how much fat they are consuming. Current serving sizes, the FDA contends, are often misleading. A fourteen-ounce bowl-shaped container of soup intended to be heated in a microwave looks as if constitutes a single serving, but the label says the bowl contains two servings. Thus, someone may be unknowingly consuming 680 mg of sodium, rather than 424 mg. The label on a small bag of potato chips says the chips are 100 calories per serving, but the bag is actually 132 calories. The difference may be small case by case, but the effects are cumulative.

How Far Is Too Far?

But just how far should the government go in the name of protecting the public health by preventing obesity and its consequences? Should all restaurants be required to put nutritional information about their dishes on their menus? Should unhealthful transfats like hydrogenated vegetable oils be outlawed as ingredients in food products? Should, as has been proposed in New York, limits be placed on the addition of salt to restaurant foods?

Is West Virginia justified in rewarding Medicaid beneficiaries to sign up for programs to control their weight and help them quit smoking? Should employers be required to provide nutritional and fitness programs for their employees? Should employees be required to maintain their weight within specified limits, or suffer a penalty, or even lose their jobs? Should the sale and consumption of high-fat or high-sugar products be licensed and regulated like liquor? Should the taxes on foods that contribute to obesity (e.g., soft drinks, high-sugar cereals) be treated like cigarettes, and should those foods be heavily taxed to discourage their consumption?

The fundamental question is, to what extent are we prepared to charge our government with the task of regulating our weight or our health in general? Some people may want a government agency to take over the difficult job of getting them to lose weight or, at the least, keeping them from gaining more. They may want a government-mandated exercise program. But are we ready to surrender some of our autonomy to gain the beneficial results that doing so offers?

Many people answer this question with a resounding no. In their view, what people eat, how much they eat, how much or how little they exercise, and how fat or thin they become is a purely private matter. Government is not justified in interfering with the nutritional aspect of their lives, anymore than it would be justified in interfering with the religious aspect. Providing information is acceptable, in a general way, but it may not be acceptable to require restaurants to inform people about the contents of their meals. People are smart enough to know that if they eat the grilled fish fillet and green salad, they are not going to be consuming as many calories as they would if they eat the double cheeseburger and fries.

Critics of proposals to involve the government in personal health insist that it certainly is not acceptable for the government to constrain or regulate people's behavior with the idea of keeping them from becoming obese. This is, they say, a direct violation of the autonomy of individuals, and what is more, such attempts are likely to increase the prejudice already shown toward overweight people in our society. Also, any talk of firing people or penalizing them for avoiding required exercise sessions or for being obese is a plan to violate individual rights. Besides, individuals vary in their genetic makeup, and we don't know enough about what predisposes people to becoming obese to hold those who do responsible for their condition.

A Medical Matter

Obesity is a problem with serious and expensive health consequences for the individual and for society. As more and more children become obese and as Type-2 diabetes and other obesity-related diseases increase, the society will face a public health crisis. The obesity epidemic will not be wholly unlike the HIV/AIDS epidemic of the 1980s and 1990s: relatively young people will face life-threatening, difficult-to-treat, and expensive medical problems, and so many will die that the longevity of the population will be significantly reduced for the first time since the advent of modern clinical medicine.

A major difference between the AIDS epidemic and the obesity epidemic is that we don't have to await some medical breakthrough in order to prevent or treat obesity. We know that, in almost every case, diet and exercise can bring weight under control. Even so, it is clear that many people have a complex and perhaps even addictive relationship with food, so that merely exhorting them to eat less and exercise more is not likely to help them achieve a normal weight. Obesity is better regarded as a medical problem than a moral one caused by a lack of willpower, but how to solve the problem is not well understood.

Without interfering with autonomy, government can help people acquire a better understanding of nutrition, and we can make it easier for people to seek medical advice about programs to reduce their weight. Most obese people aren't happy with their condition and would welcome appropriate help in changing it. They would not welcome being threatened with losing their jobs if they don't lose weight.

Even slight changes in our health-care system could do much to reduce the incidence of Type-2 diabetes. Most insurance plans pay little or nothing for preventive care of any sort, although they pay considerable amounts for expensive treatments. Hence, nutritional counseling, exercise programs, monitoring by a specialist in metabolic medicine, or care of the feet by a podiatric physician are not likely to be covered by most insurance policies. Yet these same policies may cover stroke care, laser therapy for retinal bleeding, and foot amputation—all treatments for conditions caused by diabetes. Mandating coverage for preventive care is a modest form of government intervention that might pay off for insurers as well as the insured.

SOCIAL CONTEXT
Medical Tourism

Jeju Island, South Korea, is not a travel destination as well known as Paris, London, or Rome, but for a certain kind of tourist, it has more to offer. These are tourists who are looking for a medical bargain: first-class medical care at rock-bottom prices.

Jeju is a resort island off the coast of South Korea where the government is building Health Care Town, a 370-acre medical complex of hospitals, clinics, and luxury apartments. The complex will be accompanied by an eighteen-hole golf course and shops filled with high-priced merchandise. The aim is to lure tourist patients from the U.S., Japan, Russia, and the Middle East.

Jeju is only the most recent destination for medical tourists. Other Asian nations are already in the business of trying to attract people with medical needs who are prepared to spend what counts as a great deal of money locally. Singapore, Thailand, and India are currently the most popular destinations for medical tourists, so South Korea will have to offer its visitor patients a lot if it expects to compete with those countries.

Mostly Surgery

The medical care sought at the more established tourist destinations is mostly surgery, and the list of surgeries available is almost as extensive as the menu of a Greek diner: face-lifts, tummy tucks, liposuction, eyelid and brow lifts, chin implants, nose jobs, dermabrasion, breast augmentation or reduction, stomach bypass, laparoscopic banding, knee and shoulder ligament repairs, spinal fusion, coronary-artery bypasses, and kidney and liver transplants. (Dentistry of all sorts is also available, the most popular being procedures like multiple dental implants and extensive reconstructions.)

When these operations are carried out at U.S. hospitals, they range in price from tens of thousands of dollars for cosmetic surgery to hundreds of thousands for kidney or liver transplants. These are prices that even people with insurance are often unable to pay. Either their policy doesn't cover the operation (almost always the case with cosmetic procedures and sometimes the case with transplants), or it pays only a small fraction of the costs. Operations performed at foreign centers are typically sixty to ninety percent lower in costs than those performed in U.S. hospitals. It is no mystery, then, why in recent years increasing numbers of Americans have sought medical care at foreign destinations.

One study indicates that in 2009 almost a million Americans traveled to another country to seek cheaper medical treatments. A report from the Deloite Center for Health Solutions suggests that in the next few years this number will increase to more than six million.

Appeal

Low price is not the only appeal of Asian medical centers. The physicians and surgeons have usually received at least part of their training at medical schools and hospitals in the U.S. or Western Europe, and everyone who deals with patients speaks English. The centers are also newly built modern complexes of steel and glass outfitted with the latest medical equipment—MRI machines, CAT and PET scanners, monitoring equipment, and operating microscopes. Patients' rooms are private and furnished like rooms in luxury hotels, with cable TV, broadband access, bathrooms, and often an extra bed so that a family member can stay with the patient. Meals are specially prepared, and patients may be able to convalesce in a resort-like setting, with swimming pools,

terraces, and gardens. Doctors and nurses are attentive and responsive, and the overall experience is reported by most patients as far better than that at even the best U.S. hospitals.

Some insurance companies have seen the advantage of allowing their clients to become medical tourists. If a company sees an opportunity to save money on expensive surgery such as a hip replacement or stomach-bypass surgery, it may agree to pay part of a patient's travel expenses, provided that the patient goes to a foreign hospital that is approved by the company.

Although some foreign hospitals that are tourist destinations are not rated by any agency, more than 200 of them are accredited by Joint Commission International, a branch of the organization that accredits American hospitals. Thus, these hospitals appear to meet the quality standards of most U.S. hospitals.

Duty to Treat?

So why shouldn't everyone who needs surgery and wants to save money, while being treated and convalescing in a resort setting, not become a medical tourist? The main difficulty for patients is not the surgery but the follow-up care after the surgery. Major surgery requires a recovery period of several weeks to several months, and during that time, it is usually necessary for a physician to fine-tune the recovery and determine the need for any additional treatment. For example, surgical wounds must be observed for infection, and hip and back function must be evaluated.

Physicians stress the importance of continuity of care—of examining the patient over time. But continuity of care is not possible when patients are treated overseas, then sent back home before they are fully healed.

Also, many American physicians and hospitals are reluctant to accept patients who have been operated on abroad. Some physicians claim that they should not be expected to take responsibility for patients with postoperative problems that may be the result of some other surgeon's negligence. In addition, some say, why should they risk being sued when they were not responsible for the original surgery. Some physicians maintain that they have no duty to treat such patients.

Critics of this view hold that physicians have a duty to treat the problems patients present, no matter what produced those problems. Besides, not every post-surgical complication is the result of negligence. Even the best surgeons can't guarantee a trouble-free result.

Critics also point out that in many cases patients sought offshore treatment because they couldn't get the treatment they needed under the American health-care system. Thus, the complications patients develop after they return home are, in effect, the price our society pays for not providing health care for all who need it. The debate over whether physicians have a duty to treat patients who were initially treated abroad is tied up with the concern of both physicians and hospitals with a patient's ability to pay. Someone who sought surgery abroad, then developed complications, is most likely not someone who has the financial resources required to cover any needed post-operative treatment in this country.

Who should pay for that treatment? Should such patients be turned away without treatment? Should the U.S. pass laws forbidding medical tourism? Some physicians and hospitals would answer the first question by saying that the patient needs to find someone who will pay for him if he has no resources. Some would also favor restricting traveling for the purpose of getting inexpensive surgery.

Turning away patients in need of care is not a practice that our society applauds. Even so, we do not require physicians or hospitals to provide patients with the medical care they need. We require only that they stabilize patients before discharging them.

But restricting medical tourism is not likely to happen. One reason is that the U.S. is itself a destination for medical tourists with substantial financial means. Many major medical centers welcome foreign nationals as patients because they are likely to be paying for their treatment in cash and at the nominal billing rate, not at the discounted rate that insurance companies establish by bargaining. Also, forbidding Americans to travel abroad for the purpose of taking advantage of a legal service offered in a foreign country would most likely be condemned as unconstitutional by the courts.

Unknown Risks, Uncertain Remedies

Not all hospitals that draw medical tourists are strictly monitored, so patients may be running risks that are hard to determine. Surgeons and other hospital personnel may not be as well qualified as they appear to be. Also, it is hard to be sure that the materials and medicines meet the highest standards. Hip implants come in a variety of grades, and a patient is typically not in a position to determine whether he is getting hardware of high quality. Similarly, even generic drugs may vary in quality, and once more, patients are rarely in a position to make sure that they are receiving products of the best quality. Physicians worry about whether they might be sued for treating a patient first operated on abroad, but for patients the risk is that they would have no substantial legal remedy for an operation gone wrong.

The most serious drawback for some unlucky patients is that if their surgery has a bad outcome, they may have little legal recourse, even if they believe the outcome was due to negligence. The laws in most Asian countries make it difficult to file lawsuits against physicians or to receive financial compensation. Malpractice suits and large monetary settlements for medical harm are an almost exclusively American phenomenon.

Comparative Results?

The natural question when comparing U.S. surgery with surgery performed at Asian hospitals catering to medical tourists is how the results of the surgery compare. Unfortunately, this is not a question that can be given a definitive answer. We don't have data about the surgical outcomes of the Asian hospitals, and even more surprising, we don't have data about the surgical outcomes at American hospitals either.

We don't know, for example, the complication rates for spinal-fusion surgery in Indian hospitals or Thai hospitals, so not only can we not compare hospitals in those countries, but we can't compare them with hospitals in our own. Indeed, we can't compare the outcomes at any two hospitals in the U.S. for most surgical procedures. Patients are thus in the position of having to rely on reputation and anecdotal information to make what might be one of the most important decisions in their lives.

Bad for the Countries?

Countries, like South Korea that promote medical tourism do it for financial reasons. The hospitals, operating rooms, examination and recovery rooms, rehabilitation suites, clinics, laboratories, pharmacies, cafeterias, restaurants, swimming pools, shops, and golf courses that are found in the new medical complexes employ hundreds of people and generate thousands of jobs in other sectors of the economy.

Some of those employed are highly educated physicians, surgeons, and nurses, but the majority are people with lower level skills. The medical center will need pharmacists, physical therapists, and operating-room technicians, but it will also require people to clean the rooms, do the laundry, and cook the meals. The medical

center will also buy some or most of its supplies from local or national manufacturers and producers. The medical center is supposed to generate income from foreign sources to benefit the overall economy in much the same way as a factory manufacturing computers for export is supposed to.

Because wages are comparatively low in countries that court medical tourists, they can provide high-quality care and luxurious accommodations at extremely low prices. The same economic principles that led clothing manufacturers to close their plants in New York and Los Angeles and open new ones in China and Honduras allow low-wage countries to offer medical care at bargain prices.

Critics of medical tourism charge that the analogy is a bad one. The countries that depend on medical tourism to improve their economies are typically comparatively poor, with populations that have limited access to health care. The medical centers catering to foreigners depend for their success on the expertise of some of the country's most highly educated citizens. This means, however, that the physicians who are employed to produce income for the country are not available to address the medical needs of the citizens. Physicians and surgeons represent a social investment for any society (e.g., they must be educated), and it is wrong (the argument goes) not to use that investment to benefit citizens in need of medical help. Medical tourism is thus seen as a practice in which poor countries subsidize the health-care costs of rich countries.

CASE PRESENTATION
Healing the Hmong

The Hmong are a Southeast Asian mountain people who were American allies during the Vietnam war. At the end of the war, whole families of Hmong were airlifted to the United States to protect them from reprisals. Most of the

Hmong settled in California, and more than 35,000 now live in or near Fresno.

The Hmong (pronounced "mung") brought their culture with them and have not abandoned it in favor of the general Western or American culture. This is unproblematic so far as matters like dress, food preferences, and modes of worship are concerned. But some Hmong practices have brought them into conflict with the law. Over the years, the Fresno police have been required to deal with complaints about the Hmong slaughtering pigs and other animals in their apartments. The police have also raided patches of ground where the Hmong were growing opium poppies. The police mounted an educational campaign to discourage Hmong men from engaging in their traditional practice of abducting teenage girls to be brides.

Hmong beliefs about illness, its causes, and its treatment have led to even more conflicts, with sometimes tragic results. Adhering to their traditional beliefs, the Hmong don't accept the view of the world depicted by Western science. They are animists who see the everyday world as a place shared with spirits, and they regard the interactions between spirits and humans as factors that shape the course of life. Spirits can be angered or seek revenge for insults or wrongs, and often the vengeful actions of the spirits are manifested as diseases. Propitiating the spirits may involve praying, performing healing rituals, burning incense, or carrying out animal sacrifices.

Hmong and Western cultures come into sharp conflict over the treatment of sick children. Hmong parents of a child with clubfeet, an observer reported, avoided getting the child treated, because they thought the child's feet were deformed as punishment for an ancestor's wrongdoing. To try to correct the problem might result in another family member's becoming sick.

Other Hmong parents have refused to have surgery for their child, because they believe surgery maims the body and makes it impossible for the child to be reincarnated. But two cases of conflict between Hmong cultural beliefs and the Western notion of the legal and moral responsibility to provide children with appropriate medical care have been at the focus of concern and debate.

Lee Lor

Lee Lor, a fifteen-year-old girl, was admitted to Valley Children's Hospital in late September of 1994 with a complaint of severe abdominal pains. Her physicians made a diagnosis of acute appendicitis and operated on her immediately. During the operation, however, the surgeon discovered that Lee Lor had a cancerous abdominal tumor. To remove the tumor, he also had to take out an ovary and part of one of her fallopian tubes. Her family later claimed that it wasn't until three days afterward that

they were told about the cancer and the surgery to remove it. A hospital spokesman said they were told, but he suggested that they may have not have understood what they were told because of problems with the translation.

Chemo

Failing to get permission from Lee Lor's family to initiate chemotherapy, the hospital notified the Fresno County Department of Social Services of the situation. The agency obtained a court order requiring Lee Lor to submit to chemotherapy. The police, facing a barrage of stones hurled by a group of Hmong, removed Lee Lor from her home, strapped to a stretcher. Her father was so upset that a police officer had to wrestle a knife out of his hand to keep him from killing himself. A guard was posted outside Lee's room in the hospital.

To protest Lee Lor's forced treatment, several hundred Hmong marched through the city twice. At a town meeting, they accused the county and the hospital of racism.

Lee Lor was given chemotherapy for a week, then allowed to return home. On the day of her discharge, a court hearing was initiated to determine whether she should be placed in a foster home until the completion of her course of chemotherapy. Her physicians estimated that with treatment she had an eighty percent chance of survival, but without it her chances dropped to ten percent.

Lee Lor made her own decision by running away from home on October 28. Her parents saw her sleeping on a couch with her eight siblings, but the next morning she was gone. She left with little or no money, but she took with her a supply of herbal medicines. Her parents notified the police, but they also called in the family shaman. The shaman reported that she had a vision of Lee Lor out in the open and well.

Some two months later, Lee Lor returned home. She had spent the time wandering around the state and was apparently no worse for the wear. While she was gone, the Department of Social Services had dropped its efforts to get a court order to continue her chemotherapy. In one sense, Lee Lor and her parents and the Hmong community had won their battle against Western medicine.

Lia Lee

Anne Fadiman, in *The Spirit Catches You and You Fall Down*, follows the experiences of a Hmong family, the Lees, in Merced, California, as they encounter the people and institutions of Western medicine in seeking help for their infant daughter Lia.

At the county medical center, Lia was diagnosed with a severe seizure disorder. The Lee family, in accordance with Hmong tradition, believed it was caused by spirits call *dabs* catching hold of Lia and throwing her down, then holding her there, despite her struggles to get up. The only remedy, the Lees thought, was to sacrifice animals and persuade the *dabs* to turn her soul loose. Once they did, she would be free of seizures forever.

Lia's physicians at the hospital where she was evaluated prescribed a drug regimen to bring her seizures under control. Her family, however, believing her seizures had nothing to do with anything that could be helped by medications, refused to give her the drugs.

Brain Damage

Uncontrolled by medications, Lia's seizures became worse over time. Lia eventually suffered irreversible brain damage caused by the seizures. Her physicians attributed her worsened condition to her parent's failure to give her the drugs that could have helped her, while her parents attributed it to the drugs her physicians gave her during several hospital stays.

"You can't tell them somebody is diabetic because their pancreas doesn't work," said one of her physicians. "They don't have a word for pancreas. They don't have an *idea* for pancreas." Two conceptual worlds were in collision.

Are Good Intentions Enough?

The Lees were devoted to their daughter, but like the parents of Lee Lor, they were caught within the conceptual framework of the Hmong culture. They found the conceptual framework of Western scientific medicine unintelligible and came to distrust it and the doctors who represented it.

Both sets of parents did what they believed best for their children. Even so, the practices and treatments of Western medicine are more effective in dealing with cancer and seizure disorders than are those based on the Hmong's animistic view of the world.

If parents are doing what they think best for their child, does a respect for the beliefs of others require us to refrain from interfering when a sick child is given a treatment we consider ineffective? Or, instead, does our knowledge of what is more likely to be effective require us to intervene to make sure that the child receives the treatment we think will benefit her—even if this means acting against the wishes of her parents?

These questions are not prompted just by "alien" cultures like that of the Hmong. We need only to think of Jehovah's Witnesses or Christian Scientists (see the Case Presentation "Suffer the Little Children") to realize that even in our own culture, when the best treatment for a child's illness is at issue, the beliefs of parents can come into conflict with the beliefs of scientific medicine.

Our society is committed to both individual autonomy and recognizing the responsibility of parents in caring for their children. Hence, we are ambivalent about setting aside parental decisions. When the beliefs of an entire culture like that of the Hmong are concerned, we become even more ambivalent. No one wants to be thought guilty of cultural chauvinism or arrogance.

We recognize, however, that allowing a competent adult to choose a treatment with little or no chance of success is quite different from allowing an adult to make that choice for a child. Children are dependent on their parents and are expected to submit to whatever their parents decide is best for them.

Does society, recognizing this difference, have a duty to intervene when parents make what is generally acknowledged to be the wrong choice about their child's medical treatment? Were California officials right to try to protect the welfare of Lee Lor and Lia Lee, the two Hmong girls, by making sure that they got what we consider proper medical care?

CASE PRESENTATION
The Vegan Baby

Joseph and Silva Swinton's daughter Ilce (pronounced "ice") Swinton was born on July 21, 2000, in Queens, New York. She was delivered in a house shared with relatives, without a doctor, nurse, or midwife in attendance. Ilce was three months premature, weighed three pounds (less than half that of the average baby), and suffered from respiratory problems due to underdeveloped lungs. She received no medical attention for her breathing difficulties.

Silva Swinton, who was 32 at the time of Ilce's birth, had once weighed more than 300 pounds. She had dropped to a normal weight by sticking to a strict vegan diet—no meat, fish, milk, or cheese—nothing but vegetables, grains, fruits, and nuts. She and her husband, who was the same age, had followed their vegan diet for several years, and both believed it had improved their health and helped prevent the various chronic ailments Silva had suffered from when she was so overweight.

Silva decided not to breast feed Ilce. Instead, she and Joseph agreed that the baby should be fed the same diet that they followed. This meant no milk or milk-based infant formula. They gave her pureed organic vegetables, ground nuts, fruit juices, and vitamins. Silva read labels on jars of baby food and tried to match the contents while avoiding any additives. Although Ilce did not do well on the diet she was fed, her parents stuck to it. For whatever reason, they didn't give her the soy-based baby formula favored by strict vegetarians.

When Ilce was fifteen months old, an anonymous caller tipped off the Administration for Children's Services that the baby wasn't being properly cared for. The agency intervened, and Ilce was taken to a hospital on November 16, 2001. When the physicians examined her, they found that her body was wasted from severe malnourishment, and she weighed only ten pounds, half as much as a baby her age should weigh. Also, her teeth had not started to grow, and she suffered from rickets, a bone disorder due to a vitamin D deficiency that is rarely seen in developed countries. Ilce's bones were soft and brittle from a lack of calcification, and some were broken. Her internal organs had also failed to develop as they should.

Ilce was kept in the hospital for four months and fed a medically prescribed diet, including doses of vitamin D. She was eventually released into the care of Silva Swinton's aunt. The aunt was already taking care of the Swintons' second child, Ini Free Swinton, who was born in 2003. Both children were fed a vegetarian diet approved by physicians, and Ms. Swinton was allowed supervised visits twice a week.

The Queens District Attorney's office charged both Swintons with first-degree assault, claiming that they either knew or should have known that the strict diet would endanger their child's life. Prosecutors in court also claimed that the Swintons had failed to seek medical care for Ilce, even though it was obvious that she was starving to death, failing to grow, and displaying symptoms of poor health.

Ms. Swinton's lawyer, Christopher Shella, argued that Ilce's premature birth was the cause of most of her medical problems and that her parents were trying to do their best for her. Their treatment of their child, he claimed, was not due to malice, and they should not be found guilty of a criminal offense and sent to prison. They were not sufficiently knowledgeable about infant nutrition to know that they were endangering their child.

Mr. Swinton's lawyer, Rona Gordon-Galcus, described the Swintons as "loving and attentive" parents who "did nothing knowingly to harm their child." She moved that the case be dismissed because there was no evidence of criminal intention. The motion was denied.

On April 4, 2003, a jury of the New York State Supreme Count found Silva and Joseph Swinton guilty of first-degree assault and the lesser charges of first-degree reckless endangerment and endangering the welfare of a child. They were immediately taken into police custody and faced with prison terms of five to twenty-five years.

"I don't see any justice here," Ms. Swinton's lawyer said. "That they made the wrong choice doesn't make it depraved, given how much they cared about their child." To be guilty of first-degree assault, the law requires that a perpetrator display "depraved intentions."

"We were brand-new parents trying to do everything we could for her," Ms. Swinton said at the end of the trial.

Nutritionists had testified during the trial that both breast feeding and the feeding of soy baby formula are permitted in the usual vegan diet. Had Ilce been fed either, the chances were good that she would not have become malnourished.

"This community spoke through the jury and indicated that the weakest will be protected," prosecutor Eric Rosenbaum said. "The law protects children."

By the time Ilce was three years old, she was round faced and well nourished. She was beginning to develop more normally, even though her doctors feared she would always suffer from some neurological deficits. Permanent neurological damage can result from either prematurity or malnutrition. Ilce had experienced both.

BRIEFING SESSION

Consider the following cases:

1. A state decides to require that all behavioral therapists (that is, all who make use of psychological conditioning techniques to alter behavior patterns) be either licensed psychologists or psychiatrists.

2. A member of the Jehovah's Witnesses religion, which is opposed to the transfusion of blood and blood products, refuses to consent to a needed appendectomy. But when his appendix ruptures and he lapses into unconsciousness, the surgical resident operates and saves his life.

3. A physician decides not to tell the parents of an infant who died shortly after birth that the cause of death was an unpredictable birth defect, because he does not wish to influence their desire to have another child.

4. A janitor employed in an elementary school consults a psychiatrist retained by the school board and tells her that he has molested young children on two occasions. The psychiatrist decides that it is her duty to inform the school board.

5. A six-year-old develops a high fever accompanied by violent vomiting and convulsions while at school. The child is rushed to a nearby hospital. The attending physician makes a diagnosis of meningitis and telephones the parents for permission to initiate treatment. Both parents are Christian Scientists, and they insist that no medical treatment be given to her. The physician initiates treatment anyway, and the parents later sue the physician and the hospital.

6. A thirty-year-old woman who is twenty-four-weeks pregnant is involved in an automobile accident that leaves her with a spinal cord injury. Her physician tells her that she would have a greater chance of recovery if she were not pregnant. She then requests an abortion. The hospital disagrees with her decision and gets a court order forbidding the abortion.

There is perhaps no single moral issue that is present in all these cases. Rather, there is a complex of related issues. Each case involves acting on the behalf of someone else—another individual, the public at large, or a special group. And each action comes into conflict with the autonomy, wishes, or expectations of some person or persons. Even though the issues are related, it is most fruitful to discuss them under separate headings. We will begin with a brief account of autonomy, then turn to a discussion of paternalism and imposed restrictions on autonomy.

Autonomy

We are said to act autonomously when our actions are the outcome of our deliberations and choices. To be autonomous is to be self-determining. Hence, autonomy is violated when we are coerced to act by actual force or by explicit and implicit threats or when we act under misapprehension or under the influence of factors that impair our judgment.

We associate autonomy with the status we ascribe to rational agents as persons in the moral sense. Moral theories are committed to the idea that persons are, by their nature, uniquely qualified to decide what is in their own best interest. This is because they are ends in themselves, not means to some other end. As such, persons have inherent worth, rather than instrumental worth. Others have a duty to recognize this worth and to avoid treating persons as though they were only instruments to be employed to achieve a goal chosen by someone else. To treat someone as if she lacks autonomy is thus to treat her as less than a person.

All the cases previously listed may be viewed as involving violations of the autonomy of the individuals concerned. (1) Laws requiring a license to provide therapy restrict the actions of individuals who do not qualify for a license. (2) The Jehovah's Witness is given blood he does not want. (3) Information crucial to decision making is withheld from the parents of the child with the genetic disease, so their future decision cannot be a properly informed one. (4) By breaking confidentiality, the psychiatrist is usurping the prerogative of the janitor to keep secret information that may harm him. (5) By treating the girl with meningitis, the physician is violating the generally recognized right of parents to make decisions concerning their child's welfare. (6) By refusing the woman's request for an abortion, the hospital and the court are forcing her to remain pregnant against her will.

The high value we place on autonomy is based on the realization that without it we can make very little of our lives. In its absence, we become the creatures of others, and our lives assume the forms others choose for us. Without being able to act in ways that shape our own destiny by pursuing our aims and making our own decisions, we are not realizing the potential we have as rational agents. Autonomy permits us the opportunity to make decisions ourselves; even if we are dissatisfied with the result, we have the satisfaction of knowing that the mistakes were our own. We at least acted as rational agents.

One of the traditional problems of social organization is to structure society in such a way that the autonomy of individuals will be preserved and promoted. However, autonomy is not an absolute or unconditional value, but just one among others. For example, few would wish to live in a society in which you could do what you wanted only if you had enough physical power to get your way. Because one person's exercise of autonomy is likely to come into conflict with another's, we are willing to accept some restrictions to preserve as much of our own freedom as possible. We value our own safety, the opportunity to carry out our plans in peace, the lives of other rational beings, and perhaps even their welfare.

Because autonomy is so basic to us, we usually view it as not requiring any justification. However, this predisposition in favor of autonomy means that to violate someone's autonomy, to set aside that person's wishes and render impotent her power of action, requires that we offer a strong justification. Various principles have been proposed to justify conditions under which we are warranted in restricting autonomy.

The most relevant principle in discussing the relationships among physicians, patients, and society is that of paternalism. The connection of paternalism with the physician–patient relationship and with truth telling and confidentiality in the medical and social context is discussed in the next section. (For a fuller account of autonomy, as well as the principles invoked to justify restricting its exercise, see Part V, "Foundations of Bioethics." The harm principle is of particular relevance to the topics presented here.)

Paternalism

Exactly what paternalism is, is itself a matter of dispute. Roughly speaking, we can say that paternalism consists in acting in a way that is believed to protect or advance the interest of a person, even if acting in this way goes against the person's own immediate desires or limits the person's freedom of choice. Oversimplifying, paternalism is the view that "Father knows best." (The word "parentalism" is now sometimes preferred to "paternalism" because of the latter's gender association. See Part V for the distinction between the weak and strong versions of the principle of paternalism.) Thus, the first three cases presented on page 38 are instances of paternalistic behavior.

It is useful to distinguish what we can call "state paternalism" from "personal paternalism." State paternalism, as the name suggests, is the control exerted by a legislature, agency, or other governmental body over particular kinds of practices or procedures. Such control is typically exercised through laws, licensing requirements, technical specifications, and operational guidelines and regulations. (The first case listed is an example of state paternalism.)

By contrast, personal paternalism consists in an individual's deciding, on the basis of his own principles or values, that he knows what is best for another person. The individual then acts in a way that deprives the other person of genuine and effective choice. (Cases 2 and 3 are examples of this.) Paternalism is personal when it is not a matter of public or semipublic policy but is a result of private, moral decision making.

The line between public and private paternalism is often blurred. For example, suppose a physician on the staff of a hospital believes a pregnant patient should have surgery to improve the chances for the normal development of the fetus. The physician presents his view to the hospital's attorney, and, agreeing with him, the attorney goes to court to request a court order for the surgery. The judge is persuaded and issues the order. Although the order is based on arguments that certain laws are applicable in the case, the order itself is neither a personal decision nor a matter of public policy. The order reflects the judgment of a physician who has succeeded in getting others to agree.

Despite the sometimes blurred distinction between state and personal paternalism, the distinction is useful. Most important, it permits us to separate issues associated with decisions about public policies affecting classes of individuals (for example, people needing medication) from issues associated with decisions by particular people affecting specific individuals (for example, a Dr. Latvia explaining treatment options to a Mr. Zonda).

State Paternalism in Medical and Health Care

At first sight, state paternalism seems wholly unobjectionable in the medical context. We are

all certain to feel more confident in consulting a physician when we know that she or he has had to meet standards of education, competency, and character set by a state licensing board and medical society. We feel relatively sure that we aren't putting ourselves in the hands of an incompetent quack.

Indeed, that we can feel such assurance can be regarded as one of the marks of the social advancement of medicine. As late as the early twentieth century in the United States, the standards for physicians were low, and licensing laws were either nonexistent or poorly enforced. It was possible to qualify as a physician with as little as four months' formal schooling and a two-year apprenticeship.

Rigorous standards and strictly enforced laws have undoubtedly done much to improve medical care in this country. At the very least, they have made it less dangerous to consult a physician. At the same time, however, they have also placed close restrictions on individual freedom of choice. In the nineteenth century, a person could choose among a wide variety of medical viewpoints. That is no longer so today.

We now recognize that some medical viewpoints are simply wrong and, if implemented, may endanger a patient. At the least, people treated by those who espouse such views run the risk of not getting the best kind of medical care available. Unlike people in the nineteenth century, we are confident that we know (within limits) what kinds of medical therapies are effective and what kinds are useless or harmful. The scientific character of contemporary medicine gives us this assurance.

Secure in these beliefs, our society generally endorses paternalism by the state in the regulation of medical practice. We believe it is important to protect sick people from quacks and charlatans, from those who raise false hopes and take advantage of human suffering. We generally accept, then, that the range of choice of health therapy ought to be limited to what we consider to be legitimate and scientific.

This point of view is not one that everyone is pleased to endorse. In particular, those seeking treatment for cancer have sometimes wanted to try drugs rumored to be effective but not approved by the Food and Drug Administration. Such drugs cannot be legally prescribed in the United States, and those wishing to gain access to them must travel to foreign clinics, often at considerable discomfort and expense. Some have claimed that FDA regulations make it impossible for them to choose the therapy they wish and that this is an unwarranted restriction of their rights. It should be enough, they claim, for the government to issue a warning if it thinks one is called for. But after that, people should be free to act as they choose.

The debate about unapproved therapies raises a more general question: To what extent is it legitimate for a government to restrict the actions and choices of its citizens for their own good? It is perhaps not possible to give a wholly satisfactory general answer to this question. People don't object that they are not permitted to drink polluted water from the city water supply or that they are not able to buy candy bars contaminated with insect parts. Yet some do object if they have to drink water that contains fluorides or if they cannot buy candy bars that contain saccharine. But all such limitations result from governmental attempts to protect the health of citizens. Seeing to the well-being of its citizens certainly must be recognized as one of the legitimate aims of a government. And this aim may easily include seeing to their physical health. State paternalism with respect to health seems, in general, to be justifiable. Yet the laws and regulations through which the paternal concern is expressed are certain to come into conflict with the exercise of individual liberties. Perhaps the only way in which such conflicts can be resolved is on an issue-by-issue basis. Later, we will discuss some of the limitations that moral theories place on state paternalism.

State paternalism in medical and health-care matters may be more pervasive than it seems at first sight. Laws regulating medical practice, the licensing of physicians and medical personnel, regulations governing the licensing and testing of drugs, and guidelines that must be followed in scientific research are some of the more obvious expressions of paternalism. Less obvious is the fact that government research funds can be expended only in prescribed ways and that only certain approved forms of medical care and therapy will be paid for under government-sponsored health programs. For example, it was a political and social triumph for chiropractors and Christian Science readers when some of their services were included under Medicare coverage. Thus, government money, as well as laws and regulations, can be used in paternalistic ways.

Personal Paternalism in Medical and Health Care

That patients occupy a dependent role with respect to their physicians seems to be true historically, sociologically, and psychologically. The patient is sick; the physician is well. The patient is in need of the knowledge and skills of the physician, but the physician does not need those of the patient. The patient seeks out the physician to ask for help, but the physician does not seek out the patient. The patient is a single individual, while the physician represents the institution of medicine with its hospitals, nurses, technicians, consultants, and so on. In his dependence on the physician, the patient willingly surrenders some of his autonomy. Explicitly or implicitly, he agrees to allow the physician to make certain decisions for him that he would ordinarily make for himself.

The physician tells him what to eat and drink and what to avoid, what medicine he should take and when to take it, how much exercise he should get and what kind it should be. The patient consents to run at least part of his life by "doctor's orders" in the hope that he will regain his health or at least improve his condition.

The physician acquires a great amount of power in this relationship. But she also acquires a great responsibility. It has been recognized at least since the time of Hippocrates that the physician has an obligation to act in the best interest of the patient. The patient is willing to transfer part of his autonomy because he is confident that the physician will act in that way. If this analysis of the present form of the physician–patient relationship is roughly correct, two questions are appropriate.

First, should the relationship be one in which the patient is so dependent on the pateralism of the physician? Perhaps it would be better if patients did not think of themselves as transferring any of their autonomy to physicians. Physicians might better be thought of as people offering advice rather than as ones issuing orders. Thus, patients, free to accept or reject advice, would retain fully their power to govern their own lives. If this is a desirable goal, it is clear that the present nature of the physician–patient relationship needs to be drastically altered.

The problem with this point of view is that the patient is ordinarily not in a position to judge the advice that is offered. The reason for consulting a physician in the first place is to gain the advantage of her knowledge and judgment. Moreover, courses of medical therapy are often complicated ones involving many interdependent steps. A patient could not expect the best treatment if he insisted on accepting some of the steps and rejecting others. As a practical matter, a patient who expects good medical care must to a considerable extent put himself in the hands of his physician.

For this reason, the second question is perhaps based on a more realistic assessment of the nature of medical care: How much autonomy must be given up by the patient? The power of the physician over the patient cannot be absolute. The patient cannot become the slave or creature of the physician—this is not what a patient consents to when he agrees to place himself under the care of a physician. What,

then, are the limits of the paternalism that can be legitimately exercised by the physician?

Informed Consent and Medical Treatment

Traditionally, many physicians believed they could do almost anything to a patient so long as it was in the patient's best interest. Indeed, many thought they could act even against the patient's wishes because they considered themselves to know the patient's interest better than the patient himself and thought that eventually the patient would thank them for taking charge and making hard decisions about treatment. (See the Dax Cowart Case Presentation that begins this chapter for what has become the standard example of this way of thinking.)

Although some physicians may still wish to press treatments on patients for the patients' own good, patients need not choose to do as they are advised. Some people refuse to take needed medications, change their diets, quit smoking, exercise more, or undergo surgical procedures that promise to improve the quality of their lives, if not lengthen them. Valuing autonomy, we now realize, requires recognizing that people do not always do what is good for them in a medical way, and accepting this outcome as a consequence of the exercise of autonomy.

People may even choose to reject treatment necessary to save their lives. Over the past two decades, the courts have recognized repeatedly and explicitly that the right to refuse or discontinue medical treatment has a basis in the Constitution and in common law. To receive medical treatment, people must first give their consent, and if they wish to reject treatment, even after it has been started, they are legally and morally entitled to do so.

Free and Informed Consent

Both ethicists and the courts have understood *consent* (in the context of agreeing to treatment) to mean that several specific conditions must be fulfilled. For consent to be morally and legally meaningful, individuals must be (1) competent to understand what they are told about their condition and capable of exercising judgment; (2) provided with relevant information about their illness and the proposed treatment for it in an understandable form and allowed the opportunity to ask questions; (3) given information about alternative treatments, including no treatment at all; and (4) allowed the freedom to make a decision about their treatment without coercion. (For a fuller discussion of consent in the context of becoming an experimental subject, see the Orientation in the next chapter.)

Most public, legal, and philosophical attention on the topic of refusing treatment has focused on cases in which terminally ill patients wished to have respirators disconnected or the guardians of patients in chronic vegetative states wanted nutrition and hydration to be discontinued. The issues have concerned the rights of patients themselves, and in this respect the questions were more or less straightforward. (See Chapter 11, "Euthanasia and Physician-Assisted Suicide," for detailed discussions.)

The matter of refusing treatment becomes more complicated when the interest of someone other than or in addition to the patient is involved. Two sorts of cases, in particular, present difficulties: cases in which parents' beliefs cause them to deny their children necessary medical attention and cases in which a pregnant woman's behavior results in damage to her fetus.

Parents and Children

First is the situation in which parents, acting on the basis of their beliefs, refuse to authorize needed medical treatment for their child. The duty of the physician is to provide the child the best medical care possible. The duty of the parent is to protect and promote the welfare of the child. Ordinarily, in the medical context, these two duties are convergent with respect to the line of action they lead to. The parents ask the physician to "do what is best" for their child,

and the physician discusses the options and risks with the parents and secures their consent on behalf of the child. (See the earlier discussion of informed consent and children for details.)

However, this convergence of duties leading to agreement about action is dependent on physicians and parents sharing some fundamental beliefs about the nature of disease and the efficacy of medical therapy in controlling it. When these beliefs are not shared, the outcome is a divergence of opinion about what should be done in the best interest of the child. The actions favored by the physician will be incompatible with the actions favored by the parents.

As in the Case Presentation "Suffer the Little Children" and example 5 in the Briefing Session, some parents are adherents of religions like Christian Science that teach that disease has no reality but is a manifestation of incorrect or disordered thinking. Adherents of other religions endorse the idea that prayer alone has healing powers. People with such beliefs thus think that the appropriate response to illness is to seek spiritual healing rather than to employ medical modalities.

What about the children of those with such beliefs? Their parents can legitimately claim that by refusing to seek or accept medical treatment for their children, they are doing what they consider best. It is a recognized principle that parents should decide the best interest of their children except in very special circumstances. We don't think, for example, that a psychotic or clinically depressed parent should be allowed to decide a child's welfare. Should Christian Scientists and others with similar beliefs be put into the category of incompetent parents and forced to act against their beliefs and seek medical care for their children?

A strong case can be made for answering yes. If mentally competent adults wish to avoid or reject medical treatment for themselves, the principle of autonomy supports a public policy permitting this. However, when the interest of someone who lacks the abilities to deliberate and decide for himself is concerned, it is reasonable to favor a policy that will protect that person from harm. This is particularly so when matters as basic as the person's health and safety are at stake.

Hence, to justify restricting the generally recognized right of parents to see to the welfare of their children, we can appeal to the harm principle. We might say that if a parent's action or failure to take action tends to result in harm to a child, then we are justified in restricting his or her freedom to make decisions on behalf of the child. We could then look to someone else—a court or an appointed guardian—to represent the child's best interest.

In general, we consider a legitimate function of the state to be the protection of its citizens. When parents fail to take reasonable steps to secure the welfare of their children, doing so becomes a matter of interest to the state.

Pregnancy and Autonomy

The second kind of case is one that involves an actual or potential conflict between the actions of a pregnant woman and the interest of the fetus she is carrying. (This kind of case is illustrated in example 6 on page 38.)

An obvious way of dealing with an alleged conflict between what a pregnant woman wants or does and the interest of her fetus is to deny that conflict is possible. If one holds that the fetus, at every developmental stage, is a part of the woman's body and that she is free to do with her body as she pleases, then there can be no conflict. The woman is simply deciding for herself, and it would be an unjustifiable violation of her autonomy to regulate her actions in ways that the actions of men or nonpregnant women are not regulated.

However, a number of difficulties are associated with this position. The most significant one is that as a fetus continues to develop, it becomes increasingly implausible to hold that it is no different from any other "part" of a woman's body. The problem of when the fetus is a person in the moral sense is one that plagues

the abortion dispute (see Chapter 9), and it is no less relevant to this issue.

Furthermore, even if one is not prepared to say that the fetus has the status of a person, particularly at the very early stages of pregnancy, it seems prima facie wrong to act as if the fetus (barring miscarriage or abortion) were not going to develop into a child.

Suppose a woman knows that she is pregnant and knows that continuing to drink alcohol even moderately is likely to cause the child who will be born to suffer from birth defects. Most people would consider it wrong for her to disregard the consequences of her actions. Once she has decided against (or failed to secure) an abortion, it seems she must accept the responsibility that goes with carrying a child to term. For even a moderate view, this would imply avoiding behavior she knows will be likely to cause birth defects.

However, another aspect of the question of whether a pregnant woman has any responsibility to protect the welfare of the fetus is to what extent, if any, we are justified in regulating the woman's actions. Should a pregnant woman retain her autonomy intact? Or is it legitimate for us to require her, by virtue of being pregnant, to follow a set of rules or laws not applicable to other people?

Once again, the status of the fetus as a person makes such a question hard to answer. Should we regard cases of "fetal neglect" or "fetal abuse" as no different from cases of child neglect or abuse? If the answer is yes, then the pregnant woman does not differ from the parent of a minor child. In the same way the state might order a Christian Science parent to seek medical help for a sick child, we might consider ourselves justified in insisting that a pregnant woman get prenatal care and avoid drugs and alcohol. Just as parents are subject to laws and rules that don't apply to other people, so then are pregnant women.

Assuming this answer is accepted, the question becomes one of how far we should go in prescribing behavior for a pregnant woman.

Should we require a basic minimum, or should we establish an obtainable ideal? Even the basic questions surrounding the issue of pregnancy and responsibility remain unanswered by our society. We have yet to develop a social policy to reduce the incidence of fetal alcohol syndrome and drug-damaged babies while also protecting the autonomy of pregnant women.

Truth Telling in Medicine

The question of the limits of paternalism arises most forcefully when physicians deceive patients. When, if ever, is it justifiable for a physician to deceive his patient?

The paternalistic answer is that deception by the physician is justified when it is in the best interest of the patient. Suppose, for example, that a transplant surgeon detects signs of tissue rejection in a patient who has just received a donor kidney. The surgeon is virtually certain that within a week the kidney will have to be surgically removed and the patient put on dialysis again. Although in no immediate clinical danger, the patient is suffering from postoperative depression. It is altogether possible that if the patient is told at this time that the transplant appears to be a failure, his depression will become more severe. This, in turn, might lead to a worsening of the patient's physical condition, perhaps even to a life-threatening extent.

Eventually the patient will have to be told of the need for another operation. But by the time that need arises, his psychological condition may have improved. Is the surgeon justified in avoiding giving a direct and honest answer to the patient when he asks about his condition? In the surgeon's assessment of the situation, the answer is likely to do the patient harm. His duty as a physician, then, seems to require that he deceive the patient, either by lying to him (an act of commission) or by allowing him to believe that his condition is satisfactory and the transplant was successful (an act of omission).

Yet doesn't the patient have a right to know the truth from his physician? After all, it is his life that is being threatened. Should he not be told how things stand with him so that he will be in a position to make decisions that affect his own future? Is the surgeon not exceeding the bounds of the powers granted to him by the patient? The patient surely had no intention of completely turning over his autonomy to the surgeon.

The issue is one of truth telling. Does the physician always owe it to the patient to tell the truth? Some writers make a distinction between lying to the patient and merely being nonresponsive or evasive. But is this really a morally relevant distinction? In either case, the truth is being kept from the patient. Both are instances of medical paternalism.

Some insight into the attitudes of physicians and patients with respect to disturbing medical information can be gathered from a 2005 study by the Rand Corporation and Harvard Medical School. Researchers asked 509 oncologists how candid they were in giving a prognosis to cancer patients whom they expected to die in six to twelve months. Some ninety-eight percent said they told these patients that their cancer would eventually kill them, but only five percent gave their patients an estimate of their remaining time. Yet seventy-five percent of these oncologists said that they themselves would want an estimate. This might be viewed prima facie as the expression of a paternalistic attitude toward their patients by the oncologists.

Placebos

The use of placebos (from the Latin *placebo*, meaning "I shall please") in medical therapy is another issue that raises questions about the legitimate limits of paternalism in medicine. The "placebo effect" is a well-documented psychological phenomenon: even patients who are seriously ill will sometimes show improvement when they are given any kind of medication (a sugar pill, for example) or treatment. This can happen even when the medication or treatment is irrelevant to their condition.

The placebo effect can be exploited by physicians for the (apparent) good of their patients.

Many patients cannot accept a physician's well-considered judgments. When they come to a physician with a complaint and are told that there is nothing organically wrong with them, that no treatment or medication is called for, they continue to ail. They may then lose confidence in their physician or be less inclined to seek medical advice for more serious complaints.

One way to avoid these consequences is for the physician to prescribe a placebo for the patient. Since the patient (we can assume) suffers from no organic disease, he is not in need of any genuine medication. And because of the placebo effect, he may actually find himself relieved of the symptoms that caused him to seek medical help. Moreover, the patient feels satisfied that he has been treated, and his confidence in his physician and in medicine in general remains intact.

Since the placebo effect is not likely to be produced if the patient knows he is being given an ineffective medication, the physician cannot be candid about the "treatment" prescribed. She must either be silent, say something indefinite like "I think this might help your condition," or lie. Since the placebo effect is more likely to be achieved if the medication is touted as being amazingly effective against complaints like those of the patient, there is a reason for the physician to lie outright. Because the patient may stand to gain a considerable amount of good from placebo therapy, the physician may think of herself as acting in the best interest of her patient.

Despite its apparent advantages, placebo therapy may be open to two ethical criticisms. First, we can ask whether giving placebos is really in the best interest of a patient. It encourages many patients in their belief that drugs can solve their problems. Patients with vague and general complaints may need some kind of psychological counseling, and giving them placebos merely discourages them from coming to grips with their genuine problems. Also, not all placebos are harmless (see the discussion in the Social Context on page 22). Some contain active chemicals that produce side effects (something likely to enhance the placebo effect),

so the physician who prescribes placebos may be subjecting her patient to some degree of risk.

Second, by deceiving her patient the physician is depriving him of the chance to make genuine decisions about his own life. Because the person is not genuinely sick, it does not seem legitimate to regard him as having deputized his physician to act in his behalf or as having transferred any of his power or autonomy to the physician. In Kant's terms, the physician is not acknowledging the patient's status as an autonomous rational agent. She is not according him the dignity that he possesses simply by virtue of being human. (A utilitarian who wished to claim that telling the truth to patients is a policy that will produce the best overall benefits could offer essentially the same criticism.)

Some of the traditional ethical problems about using placebos as a form of treatment rest, in part, on the assumption that placebos can be an effective form of therapy. At least one recent study analyzing investigations employing placebos as part of the experimental design casts doubt on the so-called placebo effect. Yet, even assuming the result is correct, we still must deal with the issue of whether it is ever morally legitimate to mislead a patient by giving her an inactive substance in the guise of an effective medication.

Dignity and Consent

Deception is not the only issue raised by the general question of the legitimacy of medical paternalism. Another of some importance is difficult to state precisely, but it has to do with the attitude and behavior of physicians toward their patients. Patients often feel that physicians deal with them in a way that is literally paternalistic—that physicians treat them like children.

The physician, like the magician or shaman, is often seen as a figure of power and mystery, one who controls the forces of nature and, by doing so, relieves suffering and restores health. Some physicians like this role and act in accordance with it. They resent having their authority questioned and fail to treat their patients with dignity and respect.

For example, many physicians call their patients by their first names, while expecting patients to refer to them as "Dr. X." In our society, women in particular have been most critical of such condescending attitudes displayed by physicians.

More serious is the fact that many physicians do not make a genuine effort to educate patients about the state of their health, the significance of laboratory findings, or the reasons that medication or other therapy is being prescribed. Patients are not only expected to follow orders but to do so without questioning them. Patients are, in effect, denied an opportunity to refuse treatment; consent is taken for granted.

The amount of time that it takes to help a patient understand his medical condition and the reason for the prescribed therapy is, particularly in this era of managed care, one reason that physicians do not attempt to provide such information. A busy physician in an office practice may see thirty or forty patients a day, and it is difficult to give each of them the necessary amount of attention. Also, patients without a medical background obviously can find it hard to understand medical explanations—particularly in the ways in which they are often given.

The result, for whatever reasons, is a situation in which physicians make decisions about patients without allowing patients to know the basis for them. Explanations are not given, physicians sometimes say, because patients "wouldn't understand" or "might draw the wrong conclusions about their illness" or "might worry needlessly." Patients thus not only are not provided information but are also discouraged from asking questions or revealing their doubts.

The moral questions here concern the responsibility of the physician. Is it ultimately useful for patients that physicians should play the role of a distant and mysterious figure of power? Do patients have a right to ask that physicians treat them with the same dignity as physicians treat one another? Should a physician attempt to educate her patients about their illnesses? Or is a physician's only real responsibility to provide patients with needed medical treatment?

Furthermore, is it always obvious that the physician knows what will count as the all-around best treatment for a patient? Patients, being human, have values of their own, and they may well not rank their best chance for effective medical treatment above all else. A woman with breast cancer, for example, may wish to avoid having a breast surgically removed (mastectomy) and so prefer another mode of treatment, even though her physician may consider it less effective. Can her physician legitimately withhold from her knowledge of alternative modes of treatment and so allow her no choice? Can he make the decision about treatment himself on the grounds that it is a purely medical matter, one about which the patient has no expert knowledge?

If patients have a right to decide about their treatment, physicians have an obligation to provide them with an account of their options and with the information they need to make a reasonable choice. Thus, treating patients with dignity requires recognizing their status as autonomous agents and securing their free and informed consent.

Confidentiality (Privacy)

"Whatever I see or hear, professionally or privately, which ought not be divulged, I will keep it secret and tell no one," runs one of the pledges in the Hippocratic Oath.

The tradition of medical practice in the West has taken this injunction very seriously. That it has done so is not entirely due to the high moral character of physicians, for the pledge to secrecy also serves an important practical function. Physicians need to have information of an intimate and highly personal sort to make diagnoses and prescribe therapies. If physicians were known to reveal such personal information, then patients would be reluctant to cooperate, and the practice of medicine would be adversely affected.

Furthermore, because psychological factors play a role in medical therapy, the chances of success in medical treatment are improved when patients can place trust and confidence in their physicians. This aspect of the physician–patient relationship actually forms a part of medical therapy. It is particularly so for the "talking cures" characteristic of some forms of psychiatry and psychotherapy.

Breaching Confidentiality

A number of states recognize the need for "privileged communication" between physician and patient and have laws to protect physicians from being compelled to testify about their patients in court. Yet physicians are also members of a society, and the society must attempt to protect the general interest. This sometimes places the physician in the middle of a conflict between the interest of the individual and the interest of society.

For example, physicians are often required by law to act in ways that force them to reveal certain information about their patients. The clearest instance of this is the legal obligation to report to health departments the names of those patients who are carriers of such communicable diseases as syphilis and tuberculosis. This permits health authorities to warn those with whom the carriers have come into contact and to guard against the spread of the diseases. Thus, the interest of society is given precedence over physician–patient confidentiality.

Confidentiality may also be breached in cases when the interest of the patient is at stake. Thus, a woman seeking medical attention for trauma resulting from abuse by a husband or boyfriend may have no choice about whether the police are notified. State laws may give the physician no choice about whether to report a suspected case of assault.

Similarly, physicians usually have no discretion about whether to report cases of suspected child abuse. Although the parents of the child may deny responsibility for the child's injuries, if the physician suspects the parents of abuse, she must make a report notifying police of her suspicions.

Few people question society's right to demand that physicians violate a patient's confidence when protecting the health of great numbers of people is at stake. More open to question are laws that require physicians to report gunshot wounds or other injuries that might be connected with criminal actions. (In some states, before abortion became legal, physicians were required to report cases of attempted abortion.) Furthermore, as citizens, physicians have a legal duty to report any information they may have about crime unless they are protected by a privileged-communication law.

Thus, the physician can be placed in a position of conflict. If he acts to protect the patients' confidences, then he runs the risk of acting illegally. If he acts in accordance with the law, then he must violate the confidence of his patients. What needs to be decided from a moral point of view is to what extent the laws that place a physician in such a situation are justified.

The physician who is not in private practice but is employed by a government agency or a business organization also encounters similar conflicts. Her obligations run in two directions: to her patients and to her employer.

Should a physician who works for a government agency, for example, tell her superiors that an employee has confided in her that he is a drug addict? If she does not, the employee may be subject to blackmail or bribery. If she does, then she must violate the patient's confidence.

Or what if a psychiatrist retained by a company decides one of its employees is so psychologically disturbed that she cannot function effectively in her job? Should the psychiatrist inform the employer, even if it means going against the wishes of the patient? (Consider also the fourth case cited on page 38.)

Duty to Warn?

Even more serious problems arise in psychiatry. Suppose that a patient expresses to his psychiatrist feelings of great anger against someone and even announces that he intends to go out and kill that person. What should the psychiatrist do? Should he report the threat to the police? Does he have an obligation to warn the person being threatened?

This is the fundamental issue dealt with by the California Supreme Court in the *Tarasoff* case. The court ruled that therapists at the student health service of the University of California, Berkeley, were negligent in their duty to warn Tatiana Tarasoff that Prosenjit Poddar, one of their patients, had threatened her life. The therapists reported the threat orally to the police, but they did not warn Tarasoff. Two months later, after her return from a trip to Brazil, she was murdered by Poddar.

Poddar was tried and convicted of second-degree murder. The conviction was overturned on appeal, on the grounds that the jury had not been properly instructed. The state decided against a second trial, and Poddar was released on condition that he return to India.

The parents of Tatiana Tarasoff sued the university for damages and eventually won a favorable judgment in the California Supreme Court. The court ruled that not only were the therapists justified in breaking the confidentiality of a patient, but they had a duty to warn her that her life was in danger. Since this ruling many psychiatrists and other therapists have argued that the court went too far in its demands.

Managed Care

A worrying trend with the rise of managed care is the availability of intimate information about patients that the patients provided to their physicians on the assumption that it would remain confidential. For patients to have their medical bills paid, their physicians may have to reveal to the insurer information concerning such matters as a patient's sexual history and practices, drug use, and troubling psychological problems. Most observers now believe that the assumption that what one tells one's physician will remain private no longer holds. The result is that patients are becoming less willing to

tell their physicians anything that might cause them harm if it were known to their spouse, employer, or insurance company.

HIPA Regulations

On April 14, 2003, the first comprehensive federal rules governing medical privacy went into effect. The Health Insurance Portability and Accountability Act of 1996 (HIPA) was originally conceived to protect information about patients as it is transferred from one computer database to another when a patient changes insurers or physicians.

The proposed legislation required patients to give written consent before physicians and hospitals released any information about them. When the proposed rules were made public, however, insurers, hospitals, and some medical organizations condemned the proposals as unrealistic and unworkable.

Critics claimed that a physician wouldn't even be able to question a patient about her symptoms without first securing her written consent and that pharmacies wouldn't be able to fill a called-in prescription. The health-care industry said the rules would impose an unrealistically heavy burden of paperwork on it and that this, in turn, would cause the cost of medical care to soar.

The written-consent requirement was dropped, and HIPA rules now require only that health-care providers notify patients of their legally acknowledged rights with respect to privacy and make a "good-faith effort" to obtain from patients a written acknowledgment that they have been notified.

The rights and policies acknowledged by HIPA, even in its modified form, include a number of important ones:

* Patients have a right to examine their medical records, secure copies, and correct errors.

* Medical information from a patient's records cannot be disclosed to an employer without the patient's explicit authorization.

- Researchers may use medical records for epidemiological studies, but they must remove all uniquely identifying information such as names, addresses, and Social Security numbers.

- Pharmacists are forbidden to use data about a patient for marketing purposes (e.g., selling prescription information to a pharmaceutical company that may try to get patients to ask their doctors to switch them from drugs produced by a rival company).

- The rules guarantee that parents will have "appropriate access" to the medical records of their minor children, including information about abortion, psychotherapy, and drug use.

- Hospital staff and those involved in treating a patient are restricted to knowing the minimum amount of personal information necessary to performing their tasks.

- Medical consultants, laboratories, lawyers, and business associates connected with the care of patients must sign contracts agreeing to protect the patients' confidentiality.

The law doesn't require that physicians secure the consent of patients before releasing information about them, so long as the release is for a medical purpose. Thus, a physician can solicit an opinion from another physician, tell a physical therapist why the patient needs treatment, or call in a prescription to a pharmacy.

HIPA has imposed some additional costs on hospitals and forced them to abandon longstanding practices. Even a moderate-sized hospital may have to negotiate confidentiality contracts with 400–500 business associates. Also, people can no longer be listed as patients in the hospital without their permission. Thus, hospitals may not be able to tell family members who call that their mother was taken to the emergency room with a stroke, was stabilized, and is now unconscious in the ICU.

Defenders of the HIPA rules as originally proposed claim that without the written-consent requirement, the rules are inadequate to protect patients from the breaches of privacy made possible by computers and the electronic storage of information. Even if this is true, HIPA has undeniably done a great deal to protect and promote the medical privacy of individuals. It has made everyone involved in health care, including patients, aware of the importance of confidentiality and the legitimacy of demanding it.

A 2005 ruling by the U.S. Department of Justice, however, raises a doubt about whether HIPA rules will protect privacy. The Justice Department decided that the HIPA law applies only to such "covered entities" as physicians, hospitals, and medical laboratories, and not to people who work for these "entities." This seems to mean that a physician may be fined as much as $250,000 or sent to prison for up to ten years for selling a mailing list of her patients who take drugs for heart problems, but her insurance clerk who does the same thing is not liable to prosecution.

The basic question about confidentiality concerns the extent to which we are willing to go to protect it. It is doubtful that anyone would want to assert that confidentiality should be absolutely guaranteed. But, if not, then under what conditions is it better to violate it than to preserve it?

Ethical Theories: Autonomy, Truth Telling, Confidentiality

What we have called state paternalism and personal paternalism are compatible with utilitarian ethical theory. But whether they are justifiable is a matter of controversy. According to the principle of utility, if governmental laws, policies, practices, or regulations serve the general interest, then they are justified. It can be argued that they are justified even if they restrict the individual's freedom of choice or action, because, for utilitarianism, autonomy has no absolute value. Personal paternalism is justified in a similar way. If a physician believes that she can protect her patient from unnecessary suffering or relieve his pain by keeping him in ignorance, by lying to him, by giving him placebos, or by otherwise deceiving him, these actions are morally legitimate.

However, John Stuart Mill did not take this view of paternalism. Mill argued that freedom of choice (autonomy) is of such importance that it can be justifiably restricted only when it can be shown that unregulated choice would cause harm to other people. Mill claimed that compelling people to act in certain ways "for their own good" is never legitimate. This position, Mill argued, is one that is justified by the principle of utility. Ordinarily, then, people have the freedom to decide what is going to be done to them, so free and informed consent is a prerequisite for medical treatment. Clearly, utilitarianism does not offer a straightforward answer to the question of the legitimacy of paternalism.

What we have said about paternalism applies also to confidentiality. Generally speaking, if violating confidentiality seems necessary to produce a state of affairs in which happiness is increased, then the violation is justified. This might be the case when, for example, someone's life is in danger or someone is being tried for a serious crime and the testimony of a physician is needed to help establish her innocence. Yet it also might be argued from the point of view of rule utilitarianism that confidentiality is such a basic ingredient in the physician–patient relationship that, in the long run, more good will be produced if confidentiality is never violated.

The Kantian view of paternalism, truth telling and confidentiality is more clearcut. Every person is a rational and autonomous agent. As such, he is entitled to make decisions that affect his own life. This means that a person is entitled to receive information relevant to making such decisions and is entitled to the truth,

no matter how painful it might be. Thus, for treatment to be justified, the informed consent of the individual is required.

The use of placebos or any other kind of deception in medicine is morally illegitimate in a Kantian view, because this would involve denying a person the respect and dignity to which she is entitled. The categorical imperative also rules out lying for the maxim involved in such an action produces a contradiction. (There are special difficulties in applying the categorical imperative that are discussed in Part V, "Foundations of Bioethics." When these are taken into account, Kant's view is perhaps not quite so straightforward and definite as it first appears.)

It can be argued that Kant's principles also establish that confidentiality should be regarded as absolute. When a person becomes a patient, she does so with the expectation that with regard to what she tells her physician, there is an implicit promise of confidentiality. The physician implicitly promises that he will not reveal any information about his patient, either what he has been told or what he has learned for himself. If this analysis is correct, then the physician is under an obligation to preserve confidentiality, because keeping promises is an absolute duty. Here, as in the case of lying, there are difficulties connected with the way a maxim is stated. (See Part V, "Foundations of Bioethics," for a discussion.)

Ross's principles recognize that everyone has a moral right to be treated as an autonomous agent who is entitled to make decisions affecting his own life. Thus, free and informed consent to medical treatment is required. Also, everyone is entitled to know the truth and to be educated in helpful ways. Similarly, if confidentiality is a form of promise keeping, everyone is entitled to expect that it will be maintained. Thus, paternalism, lying, and violation of confidence are prima facie morally objectionable.

But, of course, it is possible to imagine circumstances in which they would be justified. The right course of action that a physician must follow is one that can be determined only on the basis of the physician's knowledge of the patient, the patient's problem, and the general situation. Thus, Ross's principles rule out paternalism, deception, and violations of confidence as general policies, but they do not make them morally illegitimate in an absolute way.

Rawls's theory of social and political morality is compatible with state paternalism of a restricted kind. No laws, practices, or policies can legitimately violate the rights of individuals. At the same time, however, a society, viewing arrangements from the original position, might decide to institute a set of practices that would promote what they agreed to be their interests. If, for example, health is agreed to be an interest, then they might be willing to grant to the state the power to regulate a large range of matters connected with the promotion of health. Establishing standards for physicians would be an example of such regulation.

But they might also go so far as to give the state power to decide (on the advice of experts) what medical treatments are legitimate, what drugs are safe and effective to use, what substances should be controlled or prohibited, and so on. So long as the principles of justice are not violated and so long as the society can be regarded as imposing these regulations on itself for the promotion of its own good, then such paternalistic practices are unobjectionable.

With respect to personal paternalism, consent, deception, and confidentiality, Rawl's general theory offers no specific answers. But since Rawls endorses Ross's account of prima facie duties (while rejecting Ross's intuitionism), it seems reasonable to believe that Rawls's view on these matters would be the same as Ross's.

The natural law doctrine of Roman Catholicism suggests that paternalism in both its forms is legitimate. If the state is organized to bring about such "natural goods" as health, then laws and practices that promote those

goods are morally right. Individuals do have a worth in themselves and should be free to direct and organize their own lives. Thus, they generally should be informed and should make their own medical decisions. Yet at the same time, individuals may be ignorant of sufficient relevant information, lack the intellectual capacities to determine what is really in their best interest, or be moved by momentary passions and circumstances. For these reasons, the state may act so that people are protected from their own shortcomings, and yet their genuine desire—their "natural ends"—are satisfied.

Thus, natural law doctrine concludes that because each individual has an inherent worth, she is entitled to be told the truth in medical situations (and others) and not deceived. But it reasons, too, that because a physician has superior knowledge, he may often perceive the interest of the patient better than the patient herself. Accordingly, natural law doctrine indicates that although the physician should avoid lying, he is still under an obligation to act for the best interest of his patient. That may mean allowing the patient to believe something that is not so (as in placebo therapy) or withholding information from the patient. In order for this to be morally legitimate, however, the physician's motive must always be that of advancing the welfare of the patient.

In the matter of confidentiality, the natural law doctrine recognizes that the relationship between physician and patient is one of trust, and a physician has a duty not to betray the confidences of her patients. But the relationship is not sacrosanct and the duty is not absolute. When the physician finds herself in a situation in which a greater wrong will be done if she does not reveal a confidence entrusted to her by a patient, she has a duty to reveal the confidence. If, for example, the physician possesses knowledge that would save someone from death or unmerited suffering, then it is her duty to make this knowledge available, even if by doing so she violates a patient's trust.

We have only sketched an outline of the possible ways in which ethical theories might deal with the issues involved in paternalism, consent to treatment, truth telling, and confidentiality. Some of the views presented are open to challenge, and none has been worked out in a completely useful way. That is one of the tasks that remains to be performed.

Autonomy, paternalism, truth telling, and confidentiality are bound together in a complicated web of moral issues. We have not identified all the strands of the web, nor have we traced out their connections with one another.

We have, however, mentioned enough difficulties to reveal the seriousness of the issues.

As the cases and contexts that follow illustrate, some of the issues are social ones and require that we decide about the moral legitimacy of certain kinds of laws, practices, and policies. Others are matters of personal morality that concern our obligations to society and to other people. Our ethical theories, we can hope, will provide us with the means of arriving at workable and justifiable resolutions of the issues. But before this point is reached, much intellectual effort and ingenuity will have to be invested.

Decision in the *Tarasoff* Case

Supreme Court of California

This ruling of the California Supreme Court has been of particular concern to psychiatrists and psychotherapists. The court ruled that therapists at the student health center of the University of California, Berkeley, were negligent in their duty to warn Tatiana Tarasoff that Prosenjit Poddar, one of their patients, had threatened her life. Although the therapists reported the threat to the police, Tarasoff herself was not warned, and she was murdered by Poddar.

The ruling and dissenting opinions in this case address the issue of balancing the state's interest in protecting its citizens from injury against the interest of patients and therapists in preserving confidentiality. Does a therapist have a duty to warn at all? Should a patient be informed that not everything he tells his therapist will be held in confidence? Is a therapist obliged to seek a court order committing a patient involuntarily to an institution if the patient poses a threat the therapist deems to be seriously motivated?

In the majority opinion, Justice Matthew Tobriner argues that a therapist whose patient poses a serious danger to someone has a legal obligation to use "reasonable care" to protect the intended victim. This may involve warning the person, but if it is reasonable to believe that a warning is not enough, then the therapist has a duty to seek to have the patient involuntarily institutionalized.

In the dissenting opinion, Justice William Clark argues that the law should not interfere with the confidentiality between therapist and patient for three reasons: (1) Without the guarantee of confidentiality, those needing treatment may not seek it; (2) violence may increase, because those needing treatment were deterred from getting it; and (3) therapists, to protect their interest, will seek more involuntary commitments, thus violating the rights of their patients and undermining the trust needed for effective treatment.

Poddar was convicted of second-degree murder. The conviction was overturned on appeal, on the grounds that the jury had not been properly instructed. The state decided against a second trial, and Poddar was released on the condition that he return to India. Although Poddar escaped punishment for his actions, the issues of confidentiality raised by the case have yet to be satisfactorily resolved.

Justice Matthew O. Tobriner; Majority Opinion

On October 27, 1969, Prosenjit Poddar killed Tatiana Tarasoff. Plaintiffs, Tatiana's parents, allege that two months earlier Poddar confided his intention to kill Tatiana to Dr. Lawrence Moore, a psychologist employed

From California Supreme Court, Tarasoff v. Regents of the University of California, 131 *California Reporter*, 14 (July 1, 1976).

by the Cowell Memorial Hospital at the University of California at Berkeley. They allege that on Moore's request, the campus police briefly detained Poddar, but released him when he appeared rational. They further claim that Dr. Harvey Powelson, Moore's superior, then directed that no further action be taken to detain Poddar. No one warned plaintiffs of Tatiana's peril....

We shall explain that defendant therapists cannot escape liability merely because Tatiana herself was not their patient. When a therapist determines, or pursuant to the standards of his profession should determine, that his patient presents a serious danger of violence to another, he incurs an obligation to use reasonable care to protect the intended victim against such danger. The discharge of this duty may require the therapist to take one or more of various steps, depending upon the nature of the case. Thus it may call for him to warn the intended victim or others likely to apprise the victim of the danger, to notify the police, or to take whatever other steps are reasonably necessary under the circumstances. . . .

1. Plaintiff's Complaints

. . . Plaintiffs' first cause of action, entitled "Failure to Detain a Dangerous Patient," alleges that on August 20, 1969, Poddar was a voluntary outpatient receiving therapy at Cowell Memorial Hospital. Poddar informed Moore, his therapist, that he was going to kill an unnamed girl, readily identifiable as Tatiana, when she returned home from spending the summer in Brazil. Moore, with the concurrence of Dr. Gold, who had initially examined Poddar, and Dr. Yandell, assistant to the director of the department of psychiatry, decided that Poddar should be committed for observation in a mental hospital. Moore orally notified Officers Atkinson and Teel of the campus police that he would request commitment. He then sent a letter to Police Chief William Beall requesting the assistance of the police department in securing Poddar's confinement.

Officers Atkinson, Brownrigg, and Halleran took Poddar into custody, but, satisfied that Poddar was rational, released him on his promise to stay away from Tatiana. Powelson, director of the department of psychiatry at Cowell Memorial Hospital, then asked the police to return Moore's letter, directed that all copies of the letter and notes that Moore had taken as therapist be destroyed, and "ordered no action to place Prosenjit Poddar in 72-hour treatment and evaluation facility."

Plaintiffs' second cause of action, entitled "Failure to Warn on a Dangerous Patient," incorporates the allegations of the first cause of action, but adds the assertion that defendants negligently permitted Poddar to be released from police custody without "notifying the parents of Tatiana Tarasoff that their daughter was in grave danger from Prosenjit Poddar." Poddar persuaded Tatiana's brother to share an apartment with him near Tatiana's residence; shortly after her return from Brazil, Poddar went to her residence and killed her. . . .

2. Plaintiffs Can State a Cause of Action Against Defendant Therapists for Negligent Failure to Protect Tatiana

The second cause of action can be amended to allege 'that Tatiana's death proximately resulted from defendants' negligent failure to warn Tatiana or others likely to apprise her of her danger. Plaintiffs contend that as amended, such allegations of negligence and proximate causation, with resulting damages, establish a cause of action. Defendants, however, contend that in the circumstances of the present case they owed no duty of care to Tatiana or her parents and that, in the absence of such duty, they were free to act in careless disregard of Tatiana's life and safety.

. . . In analyzing this issue, we bear in mind that legal duties are not discoverable facts of nature, but merely conclusory expressions that, in cases of a particular type, liability should be imposed for damage done. As stated in *Dillon* v. *Legg* (1968): . . . "The assertion that liability must . . . be denied because defendant bears no 'duty' to plaintiff begs the essential question—whether the plaintiff's interests are entitled to legal protection against the defendant's conduct. . . . [Duty] is not sacrosanct in itself, but only an expression of the sum total of those considerations of policy which lead the law to say that the particular plaintiff is entitled to protection." . . .

In the landmark case of *Rowland* v. *Christian* (1968), . . . Justice Peters recognized that liability should be imposed "for an injury occasioned to another by his want of ordinary care or skill" as expressed in section 1714 of the Civil Code. Thus, Justice Peters, quoting from *Heaven* v. *Pender* (1883) . . . stated: " 'whenever one person is by circumstances placed in such a position with regard to another . . . that if he did not use ordinary care and skill in his own conduct . . . he would cause danger of injury to the person or property of the other, a duty arises to use ordinary care and skill to avoid such danger.' "

. . . We depart from "this fundamental principle" only upon the "balancing of a number of considerations"; major ones "are the foreseeability of harm to the plaintiff, the degree of certainty that the plaintiff suffered injury, the closeness of the connection between the defendant's conduct and the injury suffered, the moral blame attached to the defendant's conduct, the policy of preventing future harm, the extent of the burden to the defendant and consequences to the community of imposing a duty to exercise care with resulting liability for breach, and the availability, cost and prevalence of insurance for the risk involved."

The most important of these considerations in establishing duty is foreseeability. As a general principle, a "defendant owes a duty of care to all persons who are foreseeably endangered by his conduct, with respect to all risks which make the conduct unreasonably dangerous." As we shall explain, however, when the avoidance of foreseeable harm requires a defendant to control the conduct of another person, or to warn of such conduct, the common law has traditionally imposed liability only if the defendant bears some special relationship to the dangerous person or to the potential victim. Since the relationship between a therapist and his patient satisfies this requirement, we need not here decide whether foreseeability alone is sufficient to create a duty to exercise reasonable care to protect a potential victim of another's conduct. . . .

Although plaintiffs' pleadings assert no special relation between Tatiana and defendant therapists, they establish as between Poddar and defendant therapists the special relation that arises between a patient and his doctor or psychotherapist. Such a relationship may support affirmative duties for the benefit of third persons. Thus, for example, a hospital must exercise reasonable care to control the behavior of a patient which may endanger other persons. A doctor must also warn a patient if the patient's condition or medication renders certain conduct, such as driving a car, dangerous to others.

. . . Although the California decisions that recognize this duty have involved cases in which the defendant stood in a special relationship *both* to the victim and to the person whose conduct created the danger, we do not think that the duty should logically be constricted to such situations. Decisions of other jurisdictions hold that the single relationship of a doctor to his patient is sufficient to support the duty to exercise reasonable care to protect others against dangers emanating from the patient's illness. The courts hold that a doctor is liable to persons infected by his patient if he negligently fails to diagnose a contagious disease, . . . or, having diagnosed the illness, fails to warn members of the patient's family.

Since it involved a dangerous mental patient, the decision in *Merchants Nat. Bank Tust Co. of Fargo* v. *United States* . . . comes closer to the issue. The Veterans Administration arranged for the patient to work on a local farm, but did not inform the farmer of the man's background. The farmer consequently permitted the patient to come and go freely during nonworking hours; the patient borrowed a car, drove to his wife's residence and killed her. Notwithstanding the lack of any "special relationship" between the Veterans Administration and the wife, the court found the Veterans Administration liable for the wrongful death of the wife.

In their summary of the relevant rulings Fleming and Maximov conclude that the "case law should dispel any notion that to impose on the therapists a duty to take precautions for the safety of persons threatened by a patient, where due care so requires, is in any way opposed to contemporary ground rules on the duty relationship. On the contrary, there now seems to be sufficient authority to support the conclusion that by entering into a doctor–patient relationship the therapist becomes sufficiently involved to assume some responsibility for the safety, not only of the patient himself, but also of any third person whom the doctor knows to be threatened by the patient." . . .

Defendants contend, however, that imposition of a duty to exercise reasonable care to protect third persons is unworkable because therapists cannot accurately predict whether or not a patient will resort to violence. In support of this argument amicus representing the American Psychiatric Association and other professional societies cites numerous articles which indicate that therapists, in the present state of the art, are unable reliably to predict violent acts; their forecasts, amicus claims, tend consistently to overpredict violence, and indeed are more often wrong than right. . . .

We recognize the difficulty that a therapist encounters in attempting to forecast whether a patient presents a serious danger of violence. Obviously we do not require that the therapist, in making that determination, render a perfect performance; the therapist need only exercise "that reasonable degree of skill, knowledge, and care ordinarily possessed and exercised by members of [that professional specialty] under similar circumstances." Within the broad range of reasonable practice and treatment in which professional opinion and judgment may differ, the therapist is free to exercise his or her own best judgment without liability; proof, aided by hindsight, that he or she judged wrongly is insufficient to establish negligence.

In the instant case, however, the pleadings do not raise any question as to failure of defendant therapists to predict that Poddar presented a serious danger of violence. On the contrary, the present complaints allege that defendant therapists did in fact predict that Poddar would kill, but were negligent in failing to warn.

. . . Amicus contends, however, that even when a therapist does in fact predict that a patient poses a serious danger of violence to others, the therapist should be absolved of any responsibility for failing to act to protect the potential victim. In our view, however, once a therapist does in fact determine, or under applicable professional standards reasonably should have determined, that a patient poses a serious danger of violence to others, he bears a duty to exercise reasonable care to protect the foreseeable victim of that danger. While the discharge of this duty of due care will necessarily vary with the facts of each case, in each instance the adequacy of the therapist's conduct must be measured against the traditional negligence standard of the rendition of reasonable care under the circumstances.... As explained in Fleming and Maximov, *The Patient or His Victim: The Therapist's Dilemma* (1974): "... the ultimate question of resolving the tension between the conflicting interests of patient and potential victim is one of social polity, not professional expertise.... In sum, the therapist owes a legal duty not only to his patient, but also to his patient's would-be victim and is subject in both respects to scrutiny by judge and jury."...

The risk that unnecessary warnings may be given is a reasonable price to pay for the lives of possible victims that may be saved. We would hesitate to hold that the therapist who is aware that his patient expects to attempt to assassinate the President of the United States would not be obligated to warn the authorities because the therapist cannot predict with accuracy that his patient will commit the crime.

Defendants further argue that free and open communication is essential to psychotherapy; ... that "Unless a patient ... is assured that ... information [revealed by him] can and will be held in utmost confidence, he will be reluctant to make the full disclosure upon which diagnosis and treatment ... depends."... The giving of a warning, defendants contend, constitutes a breach of trust which entails the revelation of confidential communications.

... We recognize the public interest in supporting effective treatment of mental illness and in protecting the rights of patients to privacy, ... and the consequent public importance of safeguarding the confidential character of psychotherapeutic communication. Against this interest, however, we must weigh the public interest in safety from violent assault. ...

We realize that the open and confidential character of psychotherapeutic dialogue encourages patients to express threats of violence, few of which are ever executed. Certainly a therapist should not be encouraged routinely to reveal such threats; such disclosures could seriously disrupt the patient's relationship with his therapist and with the persons threatened. To the contrary, the therapist's obligations to his patient require that he not disclose a confidence unless such disclosure is necessary to avert danger to others, and even then that he do so discreetly, and in a fashion that would preserve the privacy of his patient to the fullest extent compatible with the prevention of the threatened danger.

The revelation of a communication under the above circumstances is not a breach of trust or a violation of professional ethics; as stated in the Principles of Medical Ethics of the American Medical Association (1957), section 9: "A physician may not reveal the confidence entrusted to him in the course of medical attendance ... *unless he is required to do so by law or unless it becomes necessary in order to protect the welfare of the individual or of the community.*" (Emphasis added.) We conclude that the public policy favoring protection of the confidential character of patient–psychotherapist communications must yield to the extent to which disclosure is essential to avert danger to others. The protective privilege ends where the public peril begins....

For the foregoing reasons, we find that plaintiffs' complaints can be amended to state a cause of action against defendants Moore, Powelson, Gold, and Yandell and against the Regents as their employer, for breach of a duty to exercise reasonable care to protect Tatiana.

Justice William P. Clark, Dissenting Opinion

Until today's majority opinion, both legal and medical authorities have agreed that confidentiality is essential to effectively treat the mentally ill, and that imposing a duty on doctors to disclose patient threats to potential victims would greatly impair treatment. Further, recognizing that effective treatment and society's safety are necessarily intertwined, the Legislature has already decided effective and confidential treatment is preferred over imposition of a duty to warn.

The issue whether effective treatment for the mentally ill should be sacrificed to a system of warnings is, in my opinion, properly one for the Legislature, and we are bound by its judgment. Moreover, even in the absence of clear legislative direction, we must reach the same conclusion because imposing the majority's new duty is certain to result in a net increase in violence. ...

Overwhelming policy considerations weigh against imposing a duty on psychotherapists to warn a potential victim against harm. While offering virtually no benefit to society, such a duty will frustrate psychiatric treatment, invade fundamental patient rights and increase violence. ...

Assurance of confidentiality is important for three reasons.

Deterrence from Treatment

First, without substantial assurance of confidentiality, those requiring treatment will be deterred from seeking assistance. It remains an unfortunate fad in our society that people seeking psychiatric guidance tend to become stigmatized. Apprehension of such stigma—apparently increased by the propensity of people considering treatment to see themselves in the worst possible light—creates a well-recognized reluctance to seek aid. This reluctance is alleviated by the psychiatrist's assurance of confidentiality.

Full Disclosure

Second, the guarantee of confidentiality is essential in eliciting the full disclosure necessary for effective treatment. The psychiatric patient approaches treatment with conscious and unconscious inhibitions against revealing his innermost thoughts. "Every person, however well-motivated, has to overcome resistance to therapeutic exploration. These resistances seek support from every possible source and the possibility of disclosure would easily be employed in the service of resistance." . . . Until a patient can trust his psychiatrist not to violate their confidential relationship, "the unconscious psychological control mechanism of repression will prevent the recall of past experiences." . . .

Successful Treatment

Third, even if the patient fully discloses his thoughts, assurance that the confidential relationship will not be breached is necessary to maintain his trust in his psychiatrist—the very means by which treatment is effected. "[T]he essence of much psychotherapy is the contribution of trust in the external world and ultimately in the self, modelled upon the trusting relationship established during therapy." . . . Patients will be helped only if they can form a trusting relationship with the psychiatrist. . . . All authorities appear to agree that if the trust relationship cannot be developed because of collusive communication between the psychiatrist and others, treatment will be frustrated.

Given the importance of confidentiality to the practice of psychiatry, it becomes clear the duty to warn imposed by the majority will cripple the use and effectiveness of psychiatry. Many people, potentially violent—yet susceptible to treatment—will be deterred from seeking it; those seeking it will be inhibited from making revelations necessary to effective treatment; and, forcing the psychiatrist to violate the patient's trust will destroy the interpersonal relationship by which treatment is effected.

Violence and Civil Commitment

By imposing a duty to warn, the majority contributes to the danger to society of violence by the mentally ill and greatly increases the risk of civil commitment—the total deprivation of liberty—of those who should not be confined. The impairment of treatment and risk of improper commitment resulting from the new duty to warn will not be limited to a few patients but will extend to a large number of the mentally ill. Although under existing psychiatric procedures only a relatively few receiving treatment will ever present a risk of violence, the number making threats is huge, and it is the latter group—not just the former—whose treatment will be impaired and whose risk of commitment will be increased.

Both the legal and psychiatric communities recognize that the process of determining potential violence in a patient is far from exact, being fraught with complexity and uncertainty. In fact precision has not even been attained in predicting who of those having already committed violent acts will again become violent, a task recognized to be of much simpler proportions. . . .

This predictive uncertainty means that the number of disclosures will necessarily be large. As noted above, psychiatric patients are encouraged to discuss all thoughts of violence, and they often express such thoughts. However, unlike this court, the psychiatrist does not enjoy the benefit of overwhelming hindsight in seeing which few, if any, of his patients will ultimately become violent. Now, confronted by the majority's new duty, the psychiatrist must instantaneously calculate potential violence from each patient on each visit. The difficulties researchers have encountered in accurately predicting violence will be heightened for the practicing psychiatrist dealing for brief periods in his office with heretofore nonviolent patients. And, given the decision not to warn or commit must always be made at the psychiatrist's civil peril, one can expect most doubts will be resolved in favor of the psychiatrist protecting himself.

Neither alternative open to the psychiatrist seeking to protect himself is in the public interest. The warning itself is an impairment of the psychiatrist's ability to treat, depriving many patients of adequate treatment. It is to be expected that after disclosing their threats, a significant number of patients, who would not become violent if treated according to existing practices, will engage in violent conduct as a result of unsuccessful treatment. In short, the majority's duty to warn will not only impair treatment of many who would never become violent but worse, will result in a net increase in violence.

The second alternative open to the psychiatrist is to commit his patient rather than to warn. Even in the absence of threat of civil liability, the doubts of psychiatrists as to the seriousness of patient threats have led psychiatrists to overcommit to mental institutions. This overcommitment has been authoritatively documented in both legal and psychiatric studies. This practice is so prevalent that it has been estimated that "as many as twenty harmless persons are incarcerated for every one who will commit a violent act." . . .

Given the incentive to commit created by the majority's duty, this already serious situation will be worsened, contrary to Chief Justice Wright's admonition "that liberty is no less precious because forfeited in a civil proceeding than when taken as a consequence of a criminal conviction."

Chapter **2**

Research Ethics and Informed Consent

CASES AND CONTEXTS

Face Transplants: The Dream of Looking Ordinary

Connie Culp's husband shot her in the face with a shotgun. The blast destroyed her nose, teeth, cheeks, one eye, and much of her mouth and upper jaw. Lead pellets and bone splinters lacerated her face, turning it into mangled flesh. Culp lived, but she was horribly disfigured. Even after surgeons performed thirty operations, Culp's face, noseless and puckered with scars, seemed more alien than human. She couldn't eat in the normal fashion and could breathe only through an opening in her trachea. When she went out in public, people turned their heads and called her ugly names. Children ran away.

Connie Culp was shot in 2004 and thought her disfigurement was permanent. On December 10, 2008, however, in a twenty-three-hour operation, Dr. Maria Sieminow and her surgical team at the Cleveland Clinic replaced eighty percent of Culp's face with the face of a deceased donor. This made Culp the first person in the United States, and the fourth person in the world, to receive a face transplant.

By the end of 2009, seven procedures had been performed, and two patients had died. Thus, although the procedure has not been wholly successful, many surgeons believe it is sufficiently promising to justify continuing to offer it as a treatment option to a limited number of appropriate patients—ones like Connie Culp. The hope is that additional research and surgical experience will establish face transplants as a standard treatment for those suffering from significant facial disfigurement due to trauma, birth impairments, or disease.

Surgeons are not yet prepared to endorse face transplants as anything more than an experimental procedure worth pursuing. Even so, this represents a triumph over the bad publicity provoked by the first face transplant. The case raised many of the issues about informed consent and potential risks and benefits that continue to hold for subsequent cases.

Isabelle Dinoire: First Face Transplant

Isabelle Dinoire was a thirty-eight-year-old, divorced, unemployed mother of two living in the town of Valenciennes in northern France. On a Sunday evening in May 2005, Dinoire had an argument with her seventeen-year-old daughter. The daughter, angry, left the house to spend the night with her grandmother. After this point, many facts become hazy and disputed.

In the initial version of events released by one of Dinoire's doctors, Jean-Michel Dubernard, she was upset and wanted to calm herself. To achieve this, she took a couple of pills to help her sleep and went to bed. But this account contradicted an earlier one by Dinoire's daughter, who said her mother tried to commit suicide by taking an overdose of sleeping pills. Dinoire eventually confirmed her daughter's version of what happened, but she said that her reason for trying to kill herself was a "secret." Dubernard, however, continued to insist that his patient had made no effort to commit suicide.

According to Dubernard, after Dinoire took the sleeping drug, she woke up sometime during the night and got out of bed. Walking through the dark house, she stumbled over the large dog she had recently adopted. The dog, startled, then attacked her. But once again, Dinoire's daughter told a different story. According to her, after taking the drug, Dinoire fell to the floor unconscious, and the dog tried to rouse her by clawing at her face.

No matter which version is correct, the result was the same. The dog ripped off Dinoire's lips and tore the flesh off her nose and chin. How she was discovered has not been made public, but she eventually was rushed to the local hospital, bleeding and in great pain.

The dog, justly or not, was later killed by the authorities.

A short time after Dinoire was stabilized medically and her injuries treated, she was examined by Dr. Bernard Devauchelle, Chairman of the Department of Maxillofacial Surgery at Amiens University Hospital. Because of Dinoire's seriously disfiguring wounds but general good health, he decided that she was an excellent candidate for a partial face transplant. It would have to be done without great delay, however, because once scar tissue was fully formed, a transplant would become extremely difficult. Scar tissue lacks blood vessels and so would have to be cut away even to start the transplant. Also, the muscles in her face and jaw might become permanently contracted and incapable of functioning. Eating and speaking in any normal sense would become impossible. Devauchelle listed her as an urgent case with *Agence de la biomédecine*, the French organization responsible for acquiring and distributing transplant organs.

Dinoire's Transplant

Isabelle Dinoire, some seven months later, became the first person to receive a face transplant, albeit a partial one. Yet surgeons and bioethicists in France, Britain, the United States, and elsewhere had been discussing the possibility of and the issues associated with such a transplant for some time. Some transplant programs, including the one at the Cleveland Clinic, were on the verge of finding a suitable candidate for the novel procedure.

France's national ethics committee had ruled that a face transplant should not be performed as an emergency procedure. Under those conditions, the committee decided, the notion of informed consent was an "illusion," even if the patient asked for the transplant and was provided with the relevant information, and even if a donor graft were available. In the absence of experience with face transplants, "The surgeon cannot make any promises regarding the results of his restorative efforts, which are always doubtful. Authentic consent, therefore, will never exist." The committee did approve partial face transplants, assuming the local hospital ethics committee also approved, but warned that such a transplant would be "high-risk experimentation."

In July of 2005, Dr. Dubernard, a noted transplant surgeon and a member of parliament, was asked by Dr. Devauchelle to consult on the case. In August, Dr. Dubernard visited the hospital and examined Isabelle Dinoire. "The moment she removed her mask, which she always wore, I had no more hesitation about doing a transplant," he later said.

Dr. Benoit Lengele, a Belgian plastic and reconstructive surgeon, was also called into the case by Dr. Devauchelle. Dr. Lengele assessed Dinoire's condition and reached the conclusion that at least three or four operations would be needed to reconstruct her face by using bone, cartridge, and skin taken from other parts of her body. The result, he thought, was not likely to be successful either functionally or aesthetically. She was having difficulty eating and talking, because so much of her face was missing, but he was not sure that her problems could be adequately corrected by reconstructive surgery.

Dr. Devauchelle and Dr. Dubernard discussed the possibility of a partial face transplant with Dinoire. They told her that the chance that a transplant would be successful was about thirty-three percent and the chance that it would be rejected was the same. Most important, there was also a thirty-three percent chance that she might die from the surgery, from an infection, or as a result of the immunosuppressive drugs she would have to take to control the tissue rejection.

Dinoire agreed to the transplant at once, even though the doctors reminded her that the procedure was highly experimental and had never been done before. "We got her permission several times," Dubernard later told a reporter, and Dinoire understood the risks she would be taking. He also said that he had secured all the permission required for the transplant from the French national ethics committee and the hospital ethics committee. Dinoire, he said, had asked only that the name of the hospital, as well as her name, be withheld from the public.

On Sunday, November 27, a surgical team headed by Devauchelle operated on Dinoire at Amiens University Hospital. He grafted onto her damaged and disfigured face a large segment of a donor face that included the nose, lips, chin, and the lower cheeks.

The face graft was taken from a suicide victim, a woman declared brain dead in Lille, a city some eighty-five miles north of Amiens. French law permits "presumed consent" in removing organs for transplant, thus making it unnecessary to secure the permission of relatives. Even so, because of the special nature of a facial transplant, the surgeons asked the donor's family for consent before removing the tissue. A team of clinical psychologists provided support to the family on the Saturday before the transplant surgery.

On Saturday night, a surgical team headed by Dr. Devauchelle arrived in Lille to remove the donor face. Meanwhile, in Amiens, Dr. Dubernard and a second surgical team were preparing Isabelle Dinoire for the transplant. This involved cutting away the scar tissue that had already formed in just a few months and identifying the nerves, muscles, and blood vessels that would have to be connected to the donor graft for the transplant to be viable.

Dr. Devauchelle's team finished its work around five in the morning on Sunday, then rushed the face graft to Amiens. It was preserved in a saline solution chilled to thirty-nine degrees Fahrenheit. Once tissue has been removed from its blood supply, cells begin to die. Although keeping a graft cold slows the process, the more quickly its blood supply is re-established, the more likely it is that the transplant will be successful.

Devauchelle's team of eight surgeons began using established microsurgical techniques to attach the graft to the remaining portion of Dinoire's face. The techniques are tedious and demanding, requiring, as Dr. Dubernard later said, sewing together the ends of nerves and muscles no larger than "the fibers hanging from a string bean." If vessels are not connected properly, blood clots may form and the tissue may die, and if muscles are not sewn together correctly, the patient not only will lack facial expressions, but may not be able to speak, drink, or chew.

By nine Sunday morning, four hours after the face graft had been removed from the donor in Lille, its blood supply was reestablished. Surgery could then continue at a slower, more deliberate pace. Eventually, the top layers of muscle, then the layers of the skin, were stitched into place. The surgeons implanted a piece of donor tissue under Dinoire's arm so that it, rather than her face, could be used as a source of biopsies to assess how well her body was accepting the graft of foreign tissue. The operation took a total of fifteen hours of meticulous work, with most of the surgery being performed within the narrow field of an operating microscope. When the operation was over, the nurses applauded.

Dinoire, after she returned to consciousness Sunday evening, wrote "Merci" on the paper she had been given to help her communicate. By Friday morning, her doctors reported, she was eating, drinking, and speaking clearly, although she still lacked sensation and muscle control in the transplanted segment. The scar running around the edges of the segment was thin, and the skin tones of the donor and recipient were an almost perfect match. From the beginning, Dinoire showed signs of accepting her new appearance. "This is my face," she said on Thursday, studying it in a mirror. Because underlying muscles and bone account for much of facial appearance, Dinoire's face looked neither like her donor's nor like her original face.

In addition to treating her with immunosuppressive drugs, Dinoire's doctors injected her with bone marrow taken from the donor. The idea behind the treatment was that the marrow would turn her into a chimera—that is, her body would acquire a mixture of cell types. This, in turn, might lead her immune system to recognize the cells from the face graft as "self," instead of attacking it as a foreign body. If it attacked the graft the drugs might not be able to prevent the face graft from being rejected.

Critical Reactions

On December 1, Dr. Dubernard held a press conference and announced that surgical teams headed by him and Dr. Devauchelle had performed the world's first partial face transplant. The procedure, he reported, had been a success and the patient was recovering well.

Dubernard's announcement was met with an immediate barrage of criticisms and questions from the transplant community. The most common criticism was that Dubernard's group had rushed the transplant. They ought to have attempted standard reconstructive surgery first. Now Isabelle Dinoire would be exposed to all the hazards of a transplant. She would have to take immunosuppressive drugs for the rest of her life, and this would increase her risk of cancer and potentially lethal infections. Also, the face graft might still be rejected at any time, maybe even years down the road. These are risks that might be too great for the treatment of a nonfatal condition. Saving someone's life by giving him a new liver is one thing, but giving someone a new face to improve her appearance . . . can this be worth the risks?

Also, critics charged, Dubernard's group had selected the wrong sort of patient for a transplant. If Dinoire had attempted to kill herself, she might very well lack the psychological strength to cope with the stresses and uncertainties associated with an experimental surgical procedure. Furthermore, people who are emotionally unstable do not do well in keeping to the rigid drug regimen that a transplant patient must follow to prevent rejection. Finally, the first person to receive a face transplant, even a partial one, could be expected to become the subject of intense public interest, and someone like Isabelle Dinoire might lack the psychological strength to cope with the demands of the media and the curiosity of the public.

Critics also charged that even the quality of the informed consent Dinoire gave to become a face transplant patient might be regarded as questionable. Does someone despairing enough to attempt suicide who has also had her face destroyed possess the rational capacity to make a free and informed decision about a new procedure that holds the promise of restoring her appearance? Isn't she more likely to be impulsive and to have unrealistic expectations of the outcome of the surgery?

Transplant professionals directed some of their harshest criticism at the decision by the French surgeons to inject Dinoire with the blood-producing bone-marrow stem cells taken from the deceased donor. This is a treatment that is not standard in organ transplantation, and, although the technique has been used before, the results have been mixed. "They should not be doing two experiments on one patient," said Dr. Maria Siemionow, the surgeon who later operated on Connie Culp. "Ethics aside, it will make it difficult to get clean answers—if [the transplant] works, why does it work, and if it goes wrong, was it the transplant or the stem cells?" This view was also expressed by the French surgeon Dr. Laurent Lantieri, who reviewed Isabelle Dinoire's medical records, although he was not involved with the transplant team.

Dr. Siemionow's group at the Cleveland Clinic was among those who had developed an experimental protocol for doing a full face transplant. Researchers had also framed protocols at Duke University, the University of California–San Francisco, and several other medical centers in the United States and Europe. Criticisms from people at some of these institutions suggested a dissatisfaction with Dubernard's approach to the Dinoire case.

The most common criticisms were that neither he nor Dr. Devauchelle was engaged in face-transplant research and so did not go through the review of the scientific, medical, and ethical issues performed by others. They acted in an impulsive way and, by doing so, acquired immediate celebrity.

Dr. Dubernard had already attracted worldwide attention in 1998 when he performed the first hand transplant. The recipient, Clint Hallum, was a man with a criminal record who fabricated part of his past when he offered himself as a candidate. Hallum failed to adhere to the regimen of immuno-suppressive drugs, and his body eventually rejected the transplant. The hand was amputated in 2001.

Critics of Dubernard speculated that, in proceeding with the face transplant, he might be trying to establish for himself and Devauchelle another high-profile surgical first. Some even wondered whether he had not, as a member of the French parliament, used his political influence to get approval for the face graft from the ethics committee.

Isabelle Dinoire's motives also became clouded by public revelations. She told a French newspaper a week after the transplant that she had been upset by the media coverage. "I need to live through these moments quietly," she said. Yet her attitude toward publicity was soon challenged when the *London Times* revealed that she had signed contracts that would allow her to make tens of thousands of dollars from the sale of photographs of herself and the release of a film.

The French magazine *Paris Match* is reported to have paid about $120,000 for the right to publish photographs of her, and even before the surgery, Dinoire signed a contract with the British director Michael Hughes to make a documentary film of her story. According to the agreement, she will collect all profits from the film, after Hughes has recovered his expenses and the company that distributes his films recouped its costs.

Some have raised the question of whether the possibility of profiting financially from her story was discussed with Isabelle Dinoire before she consented to the transplant. If it was, this would be a prima facie violation of any ethically legitimate informed consent procedure. The possibility of making a substantial amount of money might serve as an inducement for an unemployed single mother to risk her life. Her consent would thus not be freely given.

Establishing the Procedure

Criticisms of the surgeons responsible for the Dinoire transplant did not end face-transplant research. In April 2006, Dr. Guo Shuzhong at China's Xijing Hospital carried out a partial face transplant on Li Guoxing, a thirty-two-year-old farmer from a remote village in China's Yunnan province. While out hunting eighteen months earlier, Li had been attacked by a bear, and about half his face was destroyed. The donor tissue used in the transplant was taken from a twenty-five-year-old man killed in a traffic accident.

Li was the second face-transplant recipient, but the first to die. He survived three episodes of tissue rejection, then decided to treat himself with traditional medicines, rather than immunosuppressive drugs. He died in July 2006, perhaps from liver damage caused by the herbal medicines.

The third face-transplant recipient was another French patient. His name has not been made public, but we know that he was a twenty-nine-year-old man suffering from neurofibromatosis, a genetic disease in which tumors grow on nerve sheaths. His face was covered with numerous bulbous tumors, some the size of ping-pong balls. Tumors around his mouth made it hard for him to eat, and those near his eyes blocked his vision. His face was so disfigured that in public people shied away from him, considering him to be (he reported) a "monster."

In January 2007, his surgeon, Dr. Laurent Lantieri of Henri Mondor Hospital in Paris, replaced most of the patient's face with a graft from a recently deceased man. Lantieri not only changed the patient's appearance, but also used microsurgical techniques to connect facial muscles and nerves, allowing the man to talk, eat, and smile. The patient was delighted by the result, reporting that he could once again move through a crowd without attracting notice.

Dr. Lantieri had criticized the surgeons in the Isabelle Dinoire case for their selection of her as a patient and for injecting her with bone marrow from the face donor. Even so, Lantieri is a strong proponent of face transplants, but only when the surgery is done in accordance with research standards he considers acceptable.

It was Lantieri who performed what is considered to be the first full face transplant. In April 2009, Lantieri operated on a severely burned thirty-year-old man and replaced the upper half of his face: scalp, forehead, ears, nose, and upper and lower eyelids. This was the first time that eyelids were successfully transplanted. The man's hands had also been destroyed in the fire, and in a separate operation by another surgeon, the patient received a double hand transplant.

Surgeons had been working toward full face transplants, and with this operation, Lantieri came close enough to declare the goal achieved. Now that the possibility has been realized, "you transplant according to the patient's needs," whether it is part of the face or the whole face, Lantieri said at a news conference about the case.

Lantieri's patient died on June 8, 2009. His body had not rejected the transplant, but the graft became infected. While undergoing surgery to remove some of the infected tissue, he died of a heart attack. Lantieri praised the young man's courage and reasserted his view that the man "was so badly maimed and disfigured that he could only be treated by transplant surgery."

A Legitimate Option

Despite the death of Lantieri's patient, we may now have reached the point where surgeons should consider face transplants an option for people who are severely disfigured.

Injuries like those suffered by Isabelle Dinoire, Li Guoxing, Connie Culp, and Lantieri's unnamed patient are unusual among civilians, but they occur frequently in military conflicts. Department of Defense (DOD) figures show that more than 16,000 Americans have suffered serious combat injuries in the wars in Iraq and Afghanistan. Improvised explosive devices, rocket-propelled grenades, and rapid-fire assault rifles have produced a wide range of devastating wounds. The DOD figures don't reveal how many of the injured have suffered severe facial trauma, but it is reasonable to assume that, as in past wars, they number in the thousands.

Reconstructive surgery is outstanding at treating most facial trauma. Yet when the damage is severe and extensive, satisfying results aren't possible. Even if problems affecting eating and talking are solved, the patient is left with a face so scarred and distorted as to look hardly human. As Connie Culp's experience indicates, this causes psychological pain to patients and to those who love them. For military casualties, the reward for bravery and sacrifice is often a life of sorrow, disappointment, and depression.

The time may have come for surgeons to offer military personnel with damaged faces the option of a face transplant. Lantieri and others have demonstrated that the procedure can produce excellent results. Although face transplants must still be considered experimental, additional surgical experience may soon move them into the category of a standard treatment.

Face transplants have a serious downside. For the rest of their lives, recipients must take immunosuppressive drugs and live with the possibility of their bodies rejecting the new face. Also, whereas no one dies from a disfigured face, a transplant recipient may (like Lantieri's patient) die from an infection.

Thus, a transplant may not be the option chosen by those with even the most serious facial damage. Some might prefer to live with the face they have, but others may be prepared to take serious risks, if offered the prospect of looking ordinary. For them, a transplant might hold the promise of finding a job, falling in love, and starting a family—possibilities they may have believed their disfigurement closed off forever. What is true of those injured in war is also true for civilians who suffer severe facial trauma or disfigurement from disease.

Donations

Surgical and medical problems are not the only ones that must be solved before face transplants can become a standard therapy. We have mechanisms in place to procure solid organs such as hearts, kidneys, and livers for transplant, but we have no mechanism for procuring faces.

It may be difficult to establish one, given the nature of the graft. People have no direct experience of (say) the liver of a loved one, but the face is of primary importance to them. Thus, even those willing to donate the organs of a family member may be reluctant to donate the face. A face graft doesn't look exactly like the face of the donor, but this may not be enough to overcome a family's hesitation. Because an appropriate face graft must come from someone with the same blood type and skin tone, it may be difficult to find enough donors.

Also, donated kidneys, hearts, and livers can extend the lives of transplant recipients. Face transplants, by contrast, are not lifesaving surgery. It may be difficult to convince a broad public that it is inappropriate to compare a face transplant to a cosmetic procedure like a face-lift. Candidates for face transplants are people who suffer from severe facial deformity, not merely ones who want to enhance their normal appearance.

Yet as face transplants become more common and more successful, it may be that people come to understand the wish of those who are horribly disfigured merely to look ordinary. If that time comes, people may become as willing to donate their faces after they are dead as they are now to donate their hearts.

Jesse Gelsinger: the First Gene-Therapy Death

When Jesse Gelsinger was three months short of his third birthday, he was watching cartoons on TV when he fell asleep. Except it was a sleep from which his parents were unable to rouse him. Panicked, they rushed him to a local hospital.

When Jesse was examined, he responded to stimuli but didn't awaken. The physicians classified him as being in a level-one coma. Laboratory tests showed he had a high level of ammonia in his blood, but it was only after several days and additional blood assays that Jesse's physicians arrived at a diagnosis of ornithine transcarbamylase deficiency—OTC.

OTC is a rare genetic disorder in which the enzyme ornithine transcarbamylase, one of the five involved in the urea cycle, is either missing or in short supply. The enzymes in the cycle break down the ammonia that is a by-product of protein metabolism.

A deficiency of OTC means the body cannot get rid of the ammonia, and it gradually accumulates in the blood. When the ammonia reaches a crucial level, it causes coma, brain damage, and eventually death. The disease results from a mutation on the X chromosome; thus females are carriers of the gene, which they pass on to their sons. The disorder occurs in one of every 40,000 births. Infants with the mutation usually become comatose and die within seventy-two hours of birth. Half die within a month of birth, and half of those who remain die before age five.

Although OTC is a genetic disease, no one else in Jesse's immediate family or ancestry had ever been diagnosed with the disease. His disease was probably the result of a spontaneous mutation. He was a genetic mosaic, which meant his body contained a mixture of normal and mutated cells. For this reason, Jesse had a comparatively mild form of OTC. His body produced enough of the enzyme that he could remain in stable health if he stuck

to a low-protein diet and took his medications. These included substances, like sodium benzoate, that chemically bind to ammonia and make it easier for the body to excrete it.

At age ten, after an episode of consuming too much protein, Jesse once again fell into a coma and was hospitalized. But five days later, he was back home with no apparent neurological damage. During his teens, Jesse's condition was monitored by semiannual visits to a metabolic clinic in his hometown of Tucson, Arizona.

In 1998, Jesse, now seventeen, and his father, Paul Gelsinger, heard from Dr. Randy Heidenreich, a doctor at the clinic, about a clinical trial at the University of Pennsylvania. Researchers at the Institute for Human Gene Therapy, Heidenreich told the Gelsingers, were trying to use gene therapy to supply the gene for OTC. Their success would not be a cure for the disease, but it would be a treatment that might be able to bring babies out of comas and prevent their having brain damage.

The Gelsingers were interested, but Jesse was still a year short of being old enough to participate. In April 1999, during another visit to the clinic, they again talked to Dr. Heidenreich about the trial, and Paul mentioned that the family would be taking a trip to New Jersey in June. They would be able to make a side trip to Philadelphia and talk to the investigators.

Dr. Heidenreich contacted an investigator at the Institute and mentioned the Gelsingers' interest in the research, and Paul received a letter from him in April. Jesse would be interviewed and tested at the university hospital on June 22 to determine whether he met the criteria for becoming a research participant.

A bioethicist at the university, Arthur Caplan, had advised the researchers that it would be morally wrong to use infants born with OTC as participants in the gene-therapy trial. Because they could not be expected to live, Caplan reasoned, their parents would be desperate to find a way to save their child's life. Hence, driven by desperation, their consent would not be free. The appropriate participants would be women who were carriers of the gene or men in stable health with only a mild form of the disease. Jesse would celebrate his eighteenth birthday the day the family flew to the East Coast, and his age would then make him eligible to become a participant.

On June 22, 1999, Jesse and Paul Gelsinger met with Dr. Steven Raper for forty-five minutes to review the consent forms and discuss the procedure for which Jesse might volunteer if he qualified. Dr. Raper, a surgeon, would be the one performing the gene-therapy procedure.

According to Paul Gelsinger's recollections, Raper explained that Jesse would be sedated and two catheters inserted: one in the artery leading to his liver, the second in the vein leaving it. A weakened strain of adenovirus (the virus causing colds), genetically modified to include the OTC gene, would be injected into the hepatic artery. Blood would then be taken from the vein to monitor whether the viral particles were being taken up by the liver cells.

To reduce the risk of a blood clot's breaking loose from the infusion site, Jesse would have to remain in bed for eight hours after the procedure. Most likely, he would soon develop flu-like symptoms lasting for a few days. He might develop hepatitis, an inflammation of the liver. The consent form mentioned that if hepatitis progressed, Jesse might need a liver transplant. The consent form also mentioned that death was a possible outcome.

Paul Gelsinger saw this as such a remote possibility that he was more concerned about the needle biopsy of the liver to be performed a week after the procedure. The risk of death from the biopsy was given as one in 10,000. Paul urged Jesse to read the consent document carefully and to make sure he understood it. Paul thought the odds looked very good.

Dr. Raper explained that Jesse couldn't expect to derive any personal medical benefit from participating in the clinical trial. Even if the genes became incorporated into his cells and produced OTC, the effect would only be transitory. His immune system would attack the viral particles and destroy them within a month to six weeks.

Jesse, at the end of the information session, agreed to undergo tests to determine how well the OTC he produced got rid of ammonia in his blood—a measure of OTC efficiency. Samples of his blood were taken; then he drank a small amount of radioactively tagged ammonia. Later,

samples of his blood and urine were taken to see how much of the ingested ammonia had been eliminated. The results showed his body's efficiency was only six percent of a normal performance.

A month later, the Gelsingers received a letter from Dr. Mark Bratshaw, the pediatrician at the Institute who proposed the clinical trial. Bratshaw confirmed the six percent efficiency figure from additional test results and expressed his wish to have Jesse take part in the study. A week later, Bratshaw called Jesse and talked to him. Jesse had already expressed to his father a wish to participate, but he told Bratshaw to talk to his father.

Bratshaw told Paul about the results of their animal studies. The treatment had worked well in mice, preventing the death of those given a lethal injection of ammonia. Also, the most recent patient treated had shown a fifty percent increase in her ability to excrete ammonia. Paul Gelsinger later recalled saying, "Wow! This really works. So, with Jesse at six percent efficiency, you may be able to show exactly how well this works."

Bratshaw said their real hope was to find a treatment for newborns lacking any OTC efficiency and with little chance of survival. Also, another twenty-five liver disorders could potentially be treated with the same gene-therapy technique. The promise, then, was that hundreds of thousands, if not millions, of lives might be saved. Bratshaw and Paul never talked about the dangers to Jesse of becoming a subject in the clinical trial.

Paul discussed participation with Jesse. They both agreed that it was the right thing to do. Jesse would be helping babies stay alive, and perhaps in the long run, he might even be helping himself.

Approval

The clinical trial was supported by a National Institutes of Health grant awarded to Dr. James Wilson, the head of the Institute, and Mark Bratshaw. Their protocol had been reviewed by the federal Recombinant-DNA Advisory Committee (RAC) and the FDA . The animal studies Bratshaw had mentioned to Paul included twenty studies on mice to show the efficacy of the proposed technique. Wilson and his group had also conducted studies on monkeys and baboons to demonstrate the safety of the procedure.

Three of the treated monkeys had died of severe liver inflammation and a blood-clotting disorder when they had been given a stronger strain of adenovirus at a dose twenty times that proposed in the human trial. Both of the scientists assigned by the RAC to review the proposal thought the trial was too dangerous to include stable, asymptomatic volunteers. But Wilson and Bratshaw, employing Caplan's argument, convinced the panel that using subjects capable of giving consent was morally preferable to using OTC newborns.

The initial protocol called for the modified viruses to be injected into the right lobe of the liver. The thinking was that if the treatment caused damage, the right lobe could be removed and the left lobe spared. But the RAC objected to injecting the viruses into the liver and the investigators agreed to change the protocol. The decision was later reversed by the FDA, on the grounds that wherever the viruses were injected, they would end up in the liver. The RAC was in the process of being reorganized and, in effect, taken out of the approval loop for proposals; it never received notice of the change. The investigators continued to operate under the modified protocol.

Protocol

The study was a Phase I clinical trial. According to its protocol, eighteen patients were to receive an infusion of the genetically modified adenovirus. The aim of the study was to determine "the maximum tolerated dose." The investigators wanted to determine the point at which the transferred gene would be producing OTC in the maximum amount compatible with side effects that could be tolerated.

The eighteen patients were divided into six groups of three. Each successive group was to receive a slightly higher dose than the preceding one. The idea behind this common procedure is to protect the safety of the study participants. By increasing doses slightly, the hope is to spot the potential for serious side effects in time to avoid causing harm to the participants.

Preparation

On Thursday, September 9, Jesse Gelsinger, carrying one suitcase of clothes and another of videos, caught a plane for Philadelphia. He checked into the hospital alone. His father, a self-employed handyman, stayed in Tucson to work. Paul planned to arrive on the 18th to be present for what he considered the most dangerous part of the trial—the liver biopsy.

"You're my hero," Paul told Jesse. He looked him in the eye, and then gave him a big hug.

The level of ammonia in Jesse's blood was tested on Friday and Sunday. Sunday night he called his father, worried. His ammonia level was high, and his doctors had put him on IV medication to lower it. Paul reassured his son, reminding him that the doctors at the Institute knew more about OTC than anybody else in the world.

Tragedy

On the morning of Monday, September 13, Gelsinger became the eighteenth patient treated. He was transported from his room to the hospital's interventional radiology suite, where a catheter was snaked through an artery in his groin to the hepatic artery. A second catheter was placed in the vein exiting the liver.

Dr. Raper then slowly injected thirty milliliters of the genetically altered virus into Jesse's hepatic artery. This was the highest dose given to any participant. Patient 17, however, had received the same-size dose from a different lot of the virus and had done well. The procedure was completed around noon, and Jesse was returned to his room.

That evening Gelsinger, as expected, began to develop flu-like symptoms. He was feeling ill and feverish when he talked to his father and his stepmother, Mickie, that evening. "I love you, Dad," Jesse told his father. They all said what turned out to be their last goodbyes.

During the night, Jesse's fever soared to 104.5 degrees. A nurse called Dr. Raper at home, and when he arrived at the hospital around 6:15 that morning, the whites of Jesse's eyes had a yellowish tinge. This was a sign of jaundice, not something the doctors had encountered with the other trial participants. Laboratory findings revealed that Jesse's bilirubin, the product of red blood cell destruction, was four times the normal level.

Raper called Dr. Bratshaw, who was in Washington, to tell him their patient had taken a serious turn. Bratshaw said he would catch the train and arrive in Philadelphia in two hours. Raper also called Paul Gelsinger to explain the situation.

The jaundice was worrying to Jesse's physicians. Either his liver was not functioning adequately or his blood was not clotting properly and his red blood cells were breaking down faster than his liver could process them. Such a breakdown was life threatening for someone with OTC, because the destroyed cells released protein the body would have to metabolize. Jesse was showing the same problem as the monkeys that had been given the stronger strain of the virus.

Tuesday afternoon Paul received a call from Dr. Bratshaw. Jesse's blood-ammonia level had soared to 250 micromoles per deciliter, with 35 being a normal measure. He had slipped into a coma and was on dialysis to try to clear the ammonia from his blood. Paul said he would catch a plane and be at the hospital the next morning.

By the time Paul arrived at eight o'clock on Wednesday and met Bratshaw and Raper, Jesse had additional problems. Dialysis had brought his ammonia level down to 70 from its peak of 393, but he was definitely having a blood-clotting problem. Also, although placed on a ventilator, he continued to breathe for himself, causing hyperventilation. This increased the pH of his blood, which increased the level of ammonia circulating to his brain. Paul gave his permission for the doctors to give Jesse medications that would paralyze his breathing muscles and allow the machine to take over completely.

By Wednesday afternoon, Jesse's breathing was under control. His blood pH had fallen back to normal, and the clotting disorder was improving. Bratshaw returned to Washington. Paul began to relax, and at 5:30 he went out to dinner with his brother and his wife. But he returned to the hospital to find that Jesse had been moved to a different intensive care ward, and as he watched the monitors, he saw that the oxygen content of Jesse's blood was dropping. A nurse asked him to wait outside.

At 10:30 that evening, a doctor told Paul that Jesse's lungs were failing. Even by putting him on pure oxygen, they were unable to get an adequate amount of oxygen into his blood. The doctors had also talked with a liver transplant team and learned that Jesse was not a good candidate for a transplant.

Raper, very worried, discussed Jesse's problems with Bratshaw and Wilson, and the three of them decided to put Jesse on extracorporeal membrane oxygenation—ECMO. The machine would remove carbon dioxide from Jesse's blood and supply it with the needed oxygen. The procedure was far from standard, however. Only half of the 1000 people placed on ECMO had lived, but Paul was informed that Jesse had only a ten percent chance of surviving without ECMO.

"If we could just buy his lungs a day or two," Raper later told a reporter, "maybe he would go ahead and heal up."

Jesse was not hooked up to the ECMO unit until five o'clock Thursday morning. Bratshaw attempted to return from Washington, but he was trapped in an Amtrak train outside Baltimore. Hurricane Floyd was headed toward the East Coast; Jesse's stepmother arrived from Tucson just before the airport closed.

The ECMO appeared to be working. But Paul was told that Jesse's lungs were so severely damaged that, if he survived, it would take a long time for him to recover.

When Paul finally saw his son at mid-morning, Jesse was still comatose and bloated beyond recognition. Only the tattoo on his right calf and a scar on his elbow assured Paul that the person in the bed was Jesse.

That evening, unable to sleep, Paul walked the half-mile from his hotel to the hospital to check on Jesse. His son was no better, and Paul noticed that the urine-collecting bag attached to Jesse's bed contained blood. He realized that this meant Jesse's kidneys were shutting down. "He was sliding into multiple-organ-system failure," Raper later recalled.

The next morning, Friday, September 17, Raper and Bratshaw met with Paul and Mickie to give them the bad news that Paul had already predicted. Jesse had suffered irreversible brain damage, and the doctors wanted Paul's permission to turn off the ventilator. At Paul's request, he and Mickie were left alone for a few minutes. He then told the doctors he wanted to bring in his family and have a brief service for Jesse.

Paul and Mickie, seven of Paul's fifteen siblings and their spouses, and about ten staff members crowded into Jesse's room. Paul leaned over Jesse, then turned and told the crowd, "Jesse was a hero." The chaplain said a prayer; then Paul gave a signal. Someone flipped one switch to turn off the ventilator, and flipped a second to turn off the ECMO unit.

Dr. Raper watched the heart monitor. When the line went flat, he put his stethoscope against Jesse's chest. At 2:30 P.M. Raper officially pronounced him dead. "Goodbye, Jesse," he said. "We'll figure this out."

Gathering Storm

Dr. James Wilson, the head of the Institute, immediately reported Jesse's death to the FDA. Paul Gelsinger, sad as he was, didn't blame Jesse's physicians for what had happened. Indeed, he supported them in the face of an initial round of criticism. "These guys didn't do anything wrong," he told reporters.

Then journalists began to bring to light information that raised questions about whether Jesse and his father had been adequately informed about the risks of the trial that claimed Jesse's life. Also, it raised questions about a conflict of interest that might have led researchers to minimize the risks. The FDA initiated an investigation, and the University of Pennsylvania conducted an internal inquiry.

Paul Gelsinger decided to attend the December 1999 RAC that discussed his son's death. He learned for the first time at that meeting, according to his account, that gene therapy had never been shown to work in humans. He had been misled, not necessarily deliberately, by the researcher's accounts of success in animals. As Paul listened to criticisms of the clinical trial, his faith in the researchers waned and was replaced by anger and a feeling of betrayal.

Other information fed his anger. When a month earlier he had asked James Wilson, "What is your financial position in this?" Wilson's reply, as Paul recalled, was that he was an unpaid consultant to the biotech company, Genovo, that was partially funding the Institute. Then later Paul learned that both Wilson and the University of Pennsylvania were major stockholders in Genovo and that Wilson had sold his thirty percent share of the company for $13.5 million.

Wilson and the university, as Paul saw it, had good reason to recruit volunteers for the clinical trial and produce positive results. Thus, they might not have been as careful as they should have been, in warning the Gelsingers about the risks of the study. Also, the bioethicist approving the trial was someone who held an appointment in the department headed by Wilson. This, in effect, made Wilson his superior and thus automatically raised a question about the independence of his judgment.

A year and a day after Jesse's death, the Gelsinger family filed a wrongful-death lawsuit against the people conducting the clinical trial and the University of Pennsylvania. The university settled the suit out of court. The terms of the settlement were not disclosed.

FDA Findings

An investigation by the FDA resulted in a report to Wilson and the University of Pennsylvania pointing to two flaws in the way the clinical trial was conducted. First, the investigators failed to follow their protocol and failed to report liver toxicity in four patients treated prior to Gelsinger. Second, the investigators failed to acknowledge the death of two rhesus monkeys injected with a high level of a similar vector.

Wilson's response was that he had sent the FDA the liver-toxicity information prior to the final approval

of the protocol, although his report had been late. Further, the two monkeys that died were part of another study that used a different, stronger virus. In effect, then, Wilson was claiming that he and his colleagues had done nothing wrong and the FDA criticisms were unjustified.

Critics point out, apart from the question of how legitimate the criticisms were, that the FDA itself does not have enough power to oversee clinical trials properly. Most important, it is prohibited by law from distributing some so-called adverse-event reports. Difficulties encountered by patients in the fifty or so gene-therapy trials are often not made public, or even shared with investigators conducting similar trials, because drug-company sponsors regard information about adverse events as proprietary. This, critics say, puts participants in the position of having to take risks that they know nothing about. The law seems to favor protecting the investments of the pharmaceutical industry more than protecting human subjects.

Outcome

What caused the death of Jesse Gelsinger? Even after the autopsy, the answer isn't clear. The most suggestive finding was that Jesse had abnormal cells in his bone marrow. This may have been a preexisting condition, and it may account for why his immune system reacted in such an unpredicted way to the viral injection. He apparently died from an immunological response.

The FDA, after Jesse's death, shut down all gene-therapy operations temporarily for review. The University of Pennsylvania, after its internal review, restricted the role of the Institute for Human Gene Therapy to conducting basic biological research. Unable to carry out clinical trials, the Institute was de facto put out of business. A year or so later, it ceased to exist.

Because of Jesse's death, the Office for the Protection of Human Research Subjects committed itself to a major effort to educate researchers in the requirements for protecting participants in clinical trials and to stress the importance of Institutional Review Boards in seeing to the safety of participants. Even so, adverse-event reporting is still prohibited by law when it can be deemed to constitute proprietary information. Critics continue to see this as incompatible with the idea behind informed consent.

The Cold-War Radiation Experiments

Amelia Jackson was a cook at Pogue's department store in Cincinnati in 1966, when she was diagnosed with colon cancer. In October, she was treated with 100 rads of full-body radiation—the equivalent of 7500 chest X-rays. Until the treatment, Ms. Jackson was strong and still working, but after the treatment, she bled and vomited for days and was never again able to care for herself.

Ms. Jackson was treated as part of a program operated by the University of Cincinnati and supported in part by funds from the Pentagon. She was one of several cancer patients in a research program in which people were subjected to radiation in massive doses to determine its biological effects.

The aim of the study, according to researchers, was to develop more effective cancer treatments. However, the military was interested in determining how much radiation military personnel could be subjected to before becoming disoriented and unable to function effectively.

A Patchwork of Radiation Experiments

The Cincinnati project was only one of a patchwork of human experiments involving radiation that were carried out with funding from a variety of military and civilian agencies of the U.S. government over a period of at least thirty years. The experiments took place at government laboratories and university hospitals and research centers. Some experiments involved exposing patients to high-energy beams of radiation, while others involved injecting them with such dangerous radioactive substances as plutonium.

The experiments started toward the end of World War II. They were prompted by both scientific curiosity and the practical and military need to know more about the damaging effects of radiation on people. The advent of the Cold War between the United States and the Soviet Union and the real possibility that the political conflict would lead to nuclear war gave a sense of urgency to the research. Little was known about the harmful effects of radiation, and researchers believed their experiments not only would contribute to understandings but would provide the basis for more effective medical therapies.

In the late 1940s, Vanderbilt University exposed about eight hundred pregnant women to radiation to determine its effects on fetal development. A follow-up study of the children born to the women showed a higher-than-average rate of cancer.

At the Oak Ridge National Laboratory in Tennessee, patients with leukemia and other forms of cancer were exposed to extremely high levels of radiation from isotopes of cesium and cobalt. Almost two hundred patients, including a six-year-old boy, were subjected to such treatment, until the experiment was ended in 1974 by the Atomic Energy Commission, on the grounds of lack of patient benefit.

From 1963 to 1971, experiments were conducted at Oregon State Prison in which the testicles of sixty-seven inmates were exposed to X-rays to determine the effects of radiation on sperm production. Prisoners signed consent statements that mentioned some of the risks of the radiation. However, the possibility that the radiation might cause cancer was not mentioned. A similar experiment was conducted on sixty-four inmates at Washington State Prison.

At Columbia University and Montefiore Hospital in New York, during the late 1950s, twelve terminally ill cancer patients were injected with concentrations of radioactive calcium and strontium-85 to measure the rate at which the substances are absorbed by various types of tissues.

At a state residential school in Waltham, Massachusetts, from 1946 to 1956, nineteen mentally retarded teenaged boys were fed radioactive iron and calcium in their breakfast oatmeal. The aim of the research was to provide information about nutrition and metabolism. In the consent form mailed to parents of the boys, no mention was made of radiation.

The Experiments Become Public

The radiation experiments became public only in 1993, when reporters for the *Albuquerque Tribune* tracked down five of the eighteen patients who had been subjects in an experiment conducted from 1945 to 1957 in which patients were injected with plutonium. The work was done at the University of Rochester, Oak Ridge Laboratory, the University of Chicago, and the University of California, San Francisco Hospital. Apparently, some of the patients did not receive information about their treatment and were injected with radioactive materials without first giving consent.

Relying on the Freedom of Information Act, Eileen Welsome, a reporter for the newspaper, attempted to get documents from the Department of Energy concerning the radiation research, including ones containing the names of subjects. However, she was able to secure little information, and Tara O'Toole, the Assistant Secretary of Energy for Environment, Safety, and Health at the time, expressed reservations about releasing documents containing the names of research subjects. "Does the public's right to know include releasing names?" O'Toole asked. "It is not clear to me that it is part of the ethical obligation of the Government."

Did Participants Give Their Informed Consent?

Secretary of Energy Hazel R. O'Leary soon committed her department to a full investigation of the radiation experiments. A major focus of the inquiry was on whether patients were fully informed about the risks of the treatments they received and whether they gave meaningful consent to them.

In a number of cases, the government discovered, the experimental subjects were not informed of the risks they faced and did not consent to participate in the research. Patients were sometimes misled about the character of the treatments, and in some cases even the signatures on consent forms were forged. Ms. Jackson's granddaughter claims that although her grandmother was illiterate, she could sign her name, and the signature on the form used by the University of Cincinnati was not hers. The same claim is made by other relatives of subjects in the study.

In one known instance, a researcher found the radiation experiments to be morally suspect and warned his colleagues against pursuing them. C. E. Newton at the Hanford nuclear weapons plant wrote in an internal memorandum about the work done with prisoners at Washington State Prison: "The experiments do not appear to have been in compliance with the criminal codes of the state of Washington, and there is some question as to whether they were conducted in compliance with Federal laws."

Similarly, in a 1950 memorandum, Joseph G. Hamilton, a radiation biologist, warned his supervisors that the experiments "might have a little of the Buchenwald touch." Hamilton warned that the Atomic Energy Commission would be "subject to considerable criticism."

Some observers claim that work carried out twenty or thirty years ago cannot be judged by the same ethical standards as we would use today. Robert Loeb, speaking for Strong Memorial Hospital, where some of the studies were carried out, put the point this way: "In the 1940s, what was typical in research involving human subjects was for physicians to tell the patients that they would be involved in a study and not always give full details. That is not the standard today. Many of these studies would be impossible to conduct today."

By contrast, Dr. David S. Egilman, who has investigated instances of research with human subjects conducted by the military and the Atomic Energy Commission, claims there is adequate evidence to conclude that the researchers and their supporting agencies knew they were conducting immoral experiments. "They called the work, in effect, Nazi-like," he says. "The argument we hear is that these experiments were ethical at the time they were done. It's simply not true."

The initial question about the use of human subjects in radiation experiments conducted under the auspices of what is now the Department of Energy was expanded to include those conducted by several federal agencies. It seems as if at least 1000 people were exposed to varying levels of radiation in a variety of experiments conducted over a number of years at various locations. Some observers believe the actual figures are much higher.

The President's Advisory Committee on Human Radiation Experiments reviewed records from the Energy Department, Defense Department, Central Intelligence Agency, NASA, and federal health agencies in an attempt to locate research projects involving radiation and identify the people who were their experimental subjects. After eighteen months of investigation, the committee reported in 1995 that many of the government-sponsored experiments had been illegal and that their survivors ought to be compensated.

Compensation

In November 1996, the federal government agreed to pay $4.8 million as compensation for injecting twelve people with plutonium or uranium. At the time of the settlement, only one of the twelve was still alive, and the $400,000 award was paid to the families of the other participants. In 1998, the Quaker Oats Company and M.I.T. agreed to pay $1.85 million to the more than one hundred men who, as boys, had been fed the radioactive oatmeal at the Fernald School and other study sites.

A large number of claims from other experiments involving radiation and consent were filed against the federal government, universities, and hospitals. Advocates for those whose rights may have been violated charge the government with failing to make an effort to find the names of the people who were participants in the various radiation experiments. This would be a difficult and time-consuming process, because often names and addresses were not made a part of the experimental records.

The National Archives has placed all the hundreds of thousands of pages of records acquired by the Presidential Commission in files available to the public, and instead of the government notifying people that they may have a legal claim for compensation, individuals must come forward on their own initiative.

New Regulations

In 1997, President Clinton endorsed a stringent set of policies governing all human research receiving federal support. Under the new rules, explicit informed consent is required, the sponsor of the experiment must be identified to the subject, the subject must be told whether the experiment is classified, and permanent records of the experiment and the subjects must be kept. Further, an external review must be conducted before the experiment can proceed. The hope was that the new rules would put an end to secret experiments in which human subjects are subjected to radioactive, chemical, or other dangerous substances without their knowledge or consent.

With respect to the radiation experiments, Representative David Mann of Ohio summed up the views of most citizens: "I believe we have no choice but to conclude that the radiation experiments were simply wrong and that the Government owes a huge apology to the victims, their families, and the nation."

The Willowbrook Hepatitis Experiments

The Willowbrook State School in Staten Island, New York, is an institution devoted to housing and caring for mentally retarded children. In 1956, a research group led by Saul Krugman and Joan P. Giles of the New York University School of Medicine initiated a long-range study of viral hepatitis at Willowbrook. The children confined there were made experimental subjects of the study.

Hepatitis, a disease affecting the liver, is now known to be caused by one of two (possibly more) viruses. Although the viruses are distinct, the results they produce are the same. The liver becomes inflamed and increases in size as the invading viruses replicate themselves. Also, part of the tissue of the liver may be destroyed and the liver's normal functions impaired. Often the flow of bile through the ducts is blocked, and bilirubin (the major pigment in bile) is forced into the blood and urine. This produces the symptom of yellowish or jaundiced skin.

The disease is generally relatively mild, although permanent liver damage can be produced. The symptoms are ordinarily flu-like—mild fever, tiredness, and inability to keep food down. The viruses causing the disease are transmitted orally through contact with the feces and bodily secretions of infected people.

Krugman and Giles were interested in determining the natural history of viral hepatitis—the mode of infection and the course of the disease over time. They also wanted to test the effectiveness of gamma globulin as an agent for inoculating against hepatitis. (Gamma globulin is a protein complex extracted from the blood serum that contains antigen—substances that trigger the production of specific antibodies to counter infectious agents.)

Endemic Hepatitis

Krugman and Giles considered Willowbrook to be a good choice for investigation because viral hepatitis occurred more or less constantly in the institution. In the jargon of medicine, the disease was endemic. That this was so was recognized in 1949, and it continued to be so as the number of children in the school increased to more than 5000 in 1960. Krugman and Giles claimed that "under the chronic circumstances of multiple and repeated exposure . . . most newly admitted children became in-

fected within the first six to twelve months of residence in the institution."

Over a fourteen-year period, Krugman and Giles collected more than 25,000 serum specimens from more than seven hundred patients. Samples were taken before exposure, during the incubation period of the virus, and for periods after the infection. In an effort to get the kind of precise data they considered most useful, Krugman and Giles decided to deliberately infect some of the incoming children with the strain of the hepatitis virus prevalent at Willowbrook.

Justifying Deliberate Infection

They justified their decision in the following way: It was inevitable that susceptible children would become infected in the institution. Hepatitis was especially mild in the three- to ten-year age group at Willowbrook. These studies would be carried out in a special unit with optimum isolation facilities to protect the children from other infectious diseases, such as shigellosis (dysentery caused by a bacillus) and parasitic and respiratory infections, which are prevalent in the institution.

Most important, Krugman and Giles claimed that being an experimental subject was in the best medical interest of the child, for not only would the child receive special care, but infection with the milder form of hepatitis would provide protection against the more virulent and damaging forms. As they say, "It should be emphasized that the artificial induction of hepatitis implies a 'therapeutic' effect because of the immunity which is conferred."

Consent

Krugman and Giles obtained what they considered to be adequate consent from the parents of the children used as subjects. Where they were unable to obtain consent, they did not include the child in the experiment. In the earlier phases of the study, parents were provided with relevant information either by letter or orally, and written consent was secured from them. In the later phases, a group procedure was used:

First, a psychiatric social worker discusses the project with the parents during a preliminary interview.

Those who are interested are invited to attend a group session at the institution to discuss the project in greater detail. These sessions are conducted by the staff responsible for the program, including the physician, supervising nurses, staff attendants, and psychiatric social workers . . . . Parents in groups of six to eight are given a tour of the facilities. The purposes, potential benefits, and potential hazards of the program are discussed with them, and they are encouraged to ask questions. Thus, all parents can hear the response to questions posed by the more articulate members of the group. After leaving this briefing session parents have an opportunity to talk with their private physicians who may call the unit for more information. Approximately two weeks after each visit, the psychiatric social worker contacts the parents for their decision. If the decision is in the affirmative, the consent is signed but parents are informed that signed consent may be withdrawn any time before the beginning of the program. It has been clear that the group method has enabled us to obtain more thorough informed consent. Children who are wards of the state or children without parents have never been included in our studies.

Krugman and Giles point out that their studies were reviewed and approved by the New York State Department of Mental Hygiene, the New York State Department of Mental Health, the Armed Forces Epidemiological Board, and the human-experimentation committees of the New York University School of Medicine and the Willowbrook School. They also stress that, although they were under no obligation to do so, they chose to meet the World Medical Association's Draft Code on Human Experimentation.

Ethical Concerns

The value of the research conducted by Krugman and Giles has been recognized as significant in furthering a scientific understanding of viral hepatitis and methods for treating it. Yet serious moral doubts have been raised about the nature and conduct of the experiments. In particular, many have questioned the use of retarded children as experimental subjects, some claiming children should never be experimental subjects in investigations that are not directly therapeutic. Others have raised questions about the ways in which consent was obtained from the parents of the children, suggesting that parents were implicitly blackmailed into giving their consent

---

CASE PRESENTATION

Echoes of Willowbrook or Tuskegee? Experimenting with Children

In April 1998, the National Bioethics Advisory Committee was asked to investigate three experiments conducted from 1993 to 1996 at the New York State Psychiatric Institute.

The subjects of the experiment were almost one hundred boys ranging in age from six to eleven. All were from New York City, and many were black or Hispanic. The boys were chosen as subjects because their older brothers had been legally charged with some form of delinquency.

Researchers identified the potential subjects by combing through court records and by interviewing the mothers of the boys charged with crimes. The ones chosen for the experiment were considered by the researchers to be boys who had experienced "adverse rearing practices." The mothers of the boys selected were asked to take their children to the Psychiatric Institute to take part in the experiment. Mothers bringing in their boys were given a $125 cash payment.

The research subjects were given a small intravenously administered dose of the drug fenfluramine, and their blood was then assayed for a change in the level of neurotransmitters. The aim of the experiment was to test the hypothesis that violent behavior can be predicted by the use of neurochemical markers. The boys were given only a single dose of the drug.

In two of the three studies conducted at the Psychiatric Institute, the sixty-six boys who served as subjects were between seven and eleven and had been diagnosed as having attention deficit hyperactivity disorder. They were taken off their medication for a time before the fenfluramine was administered.

Fenfluramine has now been withdrawn from medical practice by the Federal Drug Administration. In combination with another drug ("fen–phen"), it was used to treat obesity until it was discovered that in some people it caused damage to the heart valves. Experts on the use of fenfluramine consider it unlikely that the boys in the experiments suffered any harm from the drug. They were given only a single small dose, whereas those with heart damage used the drug in larger doses over a period of months.

Even so, critics of the experiments charge that the boys were exposed to a substantial risk in experiments in which they had no chance of receiving any benefit. The experiments were for the sake of science, not for their own sake. Further, the drug is not free of such side effects as nausea, headache, dizziness, anxiety, and irritability. The children, then, suffered to some extent without gaining any advantage.

While the critics have not mentioned the role played by the boys' mothers, we might ask whether they can be said to have acted in the best interest of their children. Some of the women may have been induced to ignore their child's interest by the $125 payment. Thus, the payment itself raises the question of whether the consent of the mothers to their children's participation was legitimate. If their income was low, the prospect of receiving money may have tainted the quality of their consent.

"What value does the President's apology for Tuskegee have when there are no safeguards to prevent such abuses now?" asked Vera Sharay, director of Citizens for Responsible Care in Psychiatry and Research. "These racist and morally offensive studies put minority children at the risk of harm in order to prove that they are generally predisposed to violence in the future," she charged. "It demonstrates that psychiatric research is out of control."

A spokesperson for Mount Sinai Hospital, which participated in the studies, refused to reveal how many of the subjects were black or Hispanic. He commented only that the subjects chosen reflected "the ethnically diverse population of the catchment area."

Dr. John Oldham, director of the New York Psychiatric Institute, said during an interview that such studies are crucial to acquiring an understanding of the biological basis of behavior. "Is there a correlation between certain biological markers and conduct disorders or antisocial behaviors?" he asked. "This study was an effort to look at this with a relatively simple method using fenfluramine."

CASE PRESENTATION

The Use of Morally Tainted Sources: The Pernkopf Anatomy

In November 1996, Howard A. Israel and William E. Seidelman wrote a letter to *JAMA*, the *Journal of the American Medical Association*, asking that the University of Vienna attempt to determine the source of the cadavers used as subjects of the illustrations in the multivolume book known as the *Pernkopf Anatomy*. Rumors surrounding the book's author and artists had long suggested that some of the cadavers employed in the dissections might have been victims of the Nazis.

Eduard Pernkopf, the book's author, was a member of the Nazi party, and, although never charged with war crimes, he spent three years in an Allied prison camp. He returned afterward to his academic position at the University of Vienna and worked on his atlas of anatomy until he died in 1955. The four main artists illustrating the anatomy were also Nazi party members, and one of them sometimes incorporated into his signature a swastika and the lightning bolts of the SS. These have been airbrushed out in contemporary printings of the book.

Pernkopf began his work in 1933, well before the beginning of the war, but he died in 1955; the book was completed by others and published in 1960. The American edition has dropped Pernkopf's text, but it uses the original illustrations, which some anatomists consider to be masterpieces of medical paintings. The atlas is admired for its accuracy and is widely used by anatomists and others in medical schools.

After investigating the charge that cadavers from concentration camps or the bodies of Nazi opponents from the district prison were used as subjects, the anatomist David P. Williams concluded that either was possible but couldn't be proved one way or the other. Because of this doubt about the source of the cadavers, uncertainty about the moral legitimacy of using the atlas continues to be debated.

Anatomist E. W. April expressed the opinion of one faction. The atlas is "a phenomenal book," he told reporter Nicholas Wade, "very complete and thorough and authoritative, and you can't detract from that regardless of the fact that [Pernkopf] might not have been a good person or belonged to the wrong party."

The opposite view is expressed by Howard Israel, the coauthor of the letter to *JAMA.* "I have looked at a lot of anatomy textbooks, and these [volumes] are terrific in terms of the quality of pictures," he told Wade. "But that doesn't mean it's right to use them."

What if the source of the cadavers was known? What if they turned out to be the bodies of victims of the Holocaust? Would it be wrong to use an anatomy text based on the dissection of the victims? This is one aspect of the general question of whether it is morally acceptable to use scientific data or any other sort of information that has been obtained in an immoral way. In the view of some, we have a moral duty to avoid tainted data, because to use it is in an indirect way of benefit from the wrongdoing that produced it. Others, however, believe that using the data is a way of rescuing something worthwhile from something that was wrong. As such, it is a way of honoring those who suffered a terrible injustice by making sure their sacrifice is not wasted.

CASE PRESENTATION
Stopping the Detrozole Trial: A Case of "Ethical Overkill"?

Tamoxifen is one of the new drugs helping to transform breast cancer from an acute, fatal disease into one that is chronic and treatable. Tamoxifen blocks the uptake of estrogen, a hormone some tumors need to grow, and it is remarkably effective in treating post-menopausal women. Tamoxifen stops producing any benefit after five years, however. Thus, whether women continue to take the drug or not, they all have the same two to four percent chance of having a recurrence of their disease.

The need for a drug to reduce or even eliminate this chance was obvious as soon as researchers realized the limits of tamoxifen's effectiveness. The pharmaceutical manufacturer Novartis decided that its drug letrozole (marketed as Femera) was a good candidate for following tamoxifen. Letrozole was already approved by the FDA for cancer treatment, but it had never been studied as a treatment for breast cancer specifically.

Novartis initiated a clinical trial of letrozole in 2001, and researchers enrolled more than 5000 women at medical centers in the United States, Canada, and Europe. The investigator's plan was to recruit women treated with tamoxifen whose breast cancer was in remission, then randomly assign them (with their consent) to one of two groups. One group would be treated with letrozole, the other with a placebo. The use of a placebo was justified, because, after tamoxifen stopped being effective, no drug was known that would reduce the risk of a recurrence of the disease. Physicians would examine the women regularly, keep records on their medical condition, and then, at the end of five years, assess the effectiveness of letrozole.

But in November 2003, less than halfway into the study, Novartis called a halt to the clinical trial. The study's Data and Safety Monitoring Committee had reviewed the accumulating treatment data and discovered that letrozole was so much more effective than the placebo in reducing the recurrence of breast cancer that, the investigators decided, it would not be ethical to continue the study. Statistics showed that women taking letrozole were only half as likely to develop breast cancer again as women taking the placebo.

More precisely, 2.4 years after receiving the last tamoxifen treatment, 132 women taking the placebo either had a recurrence of their disease or developed cancer in their other breast. By contrast, this happened to only seventy-five women taking letrozole. This amounted to almost half the number of cases—forty-three percent—expected on the basis of previous data. Letrozole clearly worked.

The investigators viewed taking letrozole as offering women with breast cancer such a large advantage that it would be unfair to deny it to women taking a placebo. This was fair in the beginning, because the situation was one of clinical equipoise—so far as anyone knew, the placebo was just as good a treatment as the letrozole—but now the data had shifted the balance.

The investigators also thought it would be wrong to keep quiet about what they had learned about letrozole and allow the study to continue for another 2.5 years. Because letrozole already had FDA approval, women with breast cancer who had completed their course of tamoxifen could then take letrozole and improve their chances of avoiding a recurrence of their cancer. Some ten thousand women would immediately have a chance to benefit from the drug.

The decision by Novartis and the investigators to stop the trial of letrozole halfway through met with sharp criticism. An editorial in the *New York Times* asked whether scientists weren't engaging in "ethical overkill" in stopping the trial to bring immediate benefit to eligible women. A patient advocacy group, the National Breast Cancer Coalition, condemned ending the study prematurely. Both the editorial and the advocacy group pointed to the questions left unanswered by the uncompleted trial—whether letrozole (in addition to preventing the recurrence of breast cancer) prolonged lives, how likely and how severe were the cardiovascular problems and the osteoporosis already known to be associated with it, and how long letrozole remains effective.

"There seems little doubt that a trial must be terminated if it is harming the participants," the *Times* editorial said. "But it is much less clear that trials should be halted to spread the presumed benefits before the full data are at hand."

So far as the critics are concerned, some may wonder whether there is a relevant moral difference between withholding a treatment that evidence suggests reduces the likelihood of the recurrence of a potentially fatal

disease and administering a treatment likely to cause harm. Breast cancer does not always cause the death of patients with the disease, so it is true that reducing the chance of its recurrence is not equivalent to preventing death. Even so, preventing a potentially fatal disease may be a compelling reason for not waiting to see whether a drug that cuts in half the recurrence of breast cancer also reduces deaths.

The case can be made that the data accumulating from patients treated with letrozole compared with patients treated with a placebo reached the point that the situation could no longer be described as one of therapeutic equipoise. Letrozole, it became clear, was better at preventing a recurrence of breast cancer than a placebo. At that point, the investigators could no longer justify treating half the participants with a placebo. While it would be useful to know whether letrozole extends lives and to learn the frequency and seriousness of its side effects, this is not knowledge that can be purchased at the expense of the study's participants. Thus, Novartis and the investigators were right to stop the clinical trial when they did. Indeed, had they continued, they might legitimately be charged with exploiting the women in the placebo group, as well as with depriving other women with breast cancer access to an apparently effective drug.

CASE PRESENTATION
Baby Fae

On October 14, 1984, a baby was born in a community hospital in southern California with a malformation known as hypoplastic left-heart syndrome. In such a condition, the mitral valve or aorta on the left side of the heart is underdeveloped, and essentially only the right side of the heart functions properly. Some 300 to 2000 infants a year are born with this defect, and most die from it within a few weeks.

The infant, who became known to the public as Baby Fae, was taken to the Loma Linda University Hospital Center. There, on October 26, a surgical team headed by Dr. Leonard Bailey performed a heart transplant; Baby Fae became the first human infant to receive a baboon heart. She died twenty days later.

Baby Fae was not the first human to receive a so-called xenograft, or cross-species transplant. In early

1964, a sixty-eight-year-old deaf man, Boyd Rush, was transplanted with a chimpanzee heart at the University of Mississippi Medical Center. The heart failed after only an hour, and the patient died. Before Baby Fae, three other cross-species transplants had also ended in a quick death.

Moral Questions

In the case of Baby Fae, questions about the moral correctness and scientific legitimacy of the transplant were raised immediately. Hospital officials revealed that no effort had been made to find a human donor before implanting the baboon heart, and this led some critics to wonder if research interests were not being given priority over the welfare of the patient. Others questioned whether the parents were adequately informed about alternative corrective surgery, the Norwood procedure, available from surgeons in Boston and Philadelphia.

Other observers wondered whether the nature of the surgery and its limited value had been properly explained to the parents. Also, some critics raised objections to sacrificing a healthy young animal as part of an experiment not likely to bring any lasting benefit to Baby Fae.

Scientific critics charged that not enough is known about crossing the species barrier to warrant the use of transplant organs at this time. The previous record of failures, with no major advances in understanding, did not make the prospect of another such transplant reasonable. Furthermore, critics said, chimpanzees and gorillas are genetically more similar to humans than baboons, so the choice of a baboon heart was not a wise one. The only advantage of baboons is that they are easier to breed in captivity. Also, other critics claimed Dr. Bailey was merely engaged in "wishful thinking" in believing that Baby Fae's immune system would not produce a severe rejection response because of its immaturity.

Postmortem

An autopsy on Baby Fae showed that her death was caused by the incompatibility of her blood with that of the baboon heart. Baby Fae's blood was type O, the baboon's type AB. This resulted in the formation of blood clots and the destruction of kidney function. The heart showed mild signs of rejection.

In an address before a medical conference after Baby Fae's death, Dr. Bailey commented on some of the criticisms. He is reported to have said that it was "an oversight on our part not to search for a human donor from the start." Dr. Bailey also told the conference that he and his team believed that the difference in blood types between Baby Fae and the baboon would be less important than other factors and that the immunosuppressive drugs used to prevent rejection would also solve the problem of blood incompatibility. "We came to regret those assumptions," Dr. Bailey said. The failure to match blood types was "a tactical error that came back to haunt us."

On other occasions, Dr. Bailey reiterated his view that, because infant donors are extremely scarce, animal-to-human transplants offer a realistic hope for the future. Before the Baby Fae operation, Dr. Bailey had transplanted organs in more than 150 animals. None of his results were in published papers, however, and he performed all his work on local grants. He indicated that he would use the information obtained from Baby Fae to conduct additional animal experiments before attempting another such transplant.

NIH Report

In March of 1985, the National Institutes of Health released a report of a committee that made a site visit to Loma Linda to review the Baby Fae matter. The committee found that the informed-consent process was generally satisfactory, in that "the parents were given an appropriate and thorough explanation of the alternatives available, the risks and benefits of the procedure and the experimental nature of the transplant." Moreover, consent was obtained in an "atmosphere which allowed the parents an opportunity to carefully consider, without coercion or undue influence, whether to give permission for the transplant."

The committee also pointed out certain flaws in the consent document. First, it "did not include the possibility of searching for a human heart or performing a human heart transplant." Second, the expected benefits of the procedure "appeared to be overstated," because the consent document "stated that 'long-term survival' is an expected possibility with no further explanation." Finally, the document did not explain "whether compensation and medical treatment were available if injury occurred."

The committee did not question the legitimacy of the cross-species transplant. Moreover, it made no mention of the Norwood procedure, except to say that it had been explained to the mother at the community hospital at the birth of the infant. (The consent document described the procedure as a generally unsuccessful "temporizing operation.")

Although the committee was generally critical of Loma Linda's Institutional Review Board in "evaluating the entire informed-consent process," it reached the conclusion that "the parents of Baby Fae understood the alternatives available as well as the risks and reasonably expected benefits of the transplant."

Officials at Loma Linda University Medical Center promised that, before performing another such transplant, they would first seek a human infant heart donor.

BRIEFING SESSION

In 1947, an international tribunal meeting in Nuremberg convicted fifteen German physicians of "war crimes and crimes against humanity." The physicians were charged with taking part in "medical experiments without the subjects' consent." But the language of the charge fails to indicate the cruel and barbaric nature of the experiments. Here are just some of them:

- At the Ravensbrueck concentration camp, experiments were conducted to test the therapeutic powers of the drug sulfanilamide. Cuts were deliberately made on the bodies of people; then the wounds were infected with bacteria. The infection was worsened by forcing wood shavings and ground glass into the cuts. Then sulfanilamide and other drugs were tested for their effectiveness in combating the infection.

- At the Dachau concentration camp, healthy inmates were injected with extracts from the mucous glands of mosquitos to produce malaria. Various drugs were then used to determine their relative effectiveness.

- At Buchenwald, numerous healthy people were deliberately infected with the spotted-fever virus merely for the purpose of keeping the virus alive. Over ninety percent of those infected died as a result.

- Also at Buchenwald, various kinds of poisons were secretly administered to a number of inmates to test their efficacy. Either the inmates died or they were killed at once so that autopsies could be performed. Some experimental subjects were shot with poisoned bullets.

- At Dachau, to help the German Air Force, investigations were made into the limits of human endurance and existence at high altitudes. People

were placed in sealed chambers, then subjected to very high and very low atmospheric pressures. As the indictment puts it, "Many victims died as a result of these experiments and others suffered grave injury, torture, and ill-treatment."

Seven of the physicians convicted were hanged, and the other eight received long prison terms. From the trial there emerged the Nuremberg Code, a statement of the principles that should be followed in conducting medical research with human subjects.

Despite the moral horrors that were revealed at Nuremberg, few people doubt the need for medical research involving human subjects. The extent to which contemporary medicine has become effective in the treatment of disease and illness is due almost entirely to the fact that it has become scientific medicine. This means that contemporary medicine must conduct inquiries in which data are gathered to test hypotheses and general theories related to disease processes and their treatment. Investigations involving nonhuman organisms are essential, but the ultimate tests of the effectiveness of medical treatments and their side effects must involve human beings as research subjects. Human physiology and psychology are sufficiently different to make animal studies alone inadequate.

The German physicians tried at Nuremberg were charged with conducting experiments without the consent of their subjects. The notion that consent must be given before a person becomes a research subject is still considered the basic requirement that must be met for an experiment to be morally legitimate. Moreover, it is not merely consent—saying yes—but informed consent that is demanded. The basic idea is simply that a person decides to participate in research after he or she has been provided with background information relevant to making the decision.

This same notion of informed consent is also considered a requirement that must be satisfied before a person can legitimately be subjected to medical treatment. Thus, people are asked to agree to submit themselves to such ordinary medical procedures as blood transfusion or to more extraordinary ones such as surgical operations or radiation therapy.

The underlying idea of informed consent in both research and treatment is that people have a right to control what is done to their bodies. The notion of informed consent is thus a recognition of an individual's autonomy—of the right to make decisions governing one's own life. This right is recognized both in practice and in the laws of our society. (Quite often, malpractice suits turn on the issue of whether a patient's informed consent was valid.)

In the abstract, informed consent seems a clear and straightforward notion. After all, we all have an intuitive grasp of what it is to make a decision after we have been supplied with information. Yet, in practice, informed consent has proved to be a slippery and troublesome concept. We will identify later some of the moral and practical difficulties that make the application of the concept difficult and controversial.

Our focus will be on informed consent in the context of research involving human subjects. But most of the issues that arise here also arise in connection with giving and securing informed consent for the application of medical therapies. (They also arise in special forms in abortion and euthanasia.) In effect, then, we will be considering the entire topic.

Before discussing the details of informed consent, it's useful to have an idea of what takes place in a typical clinical trial. Clinical trials account for the great majority of all medical research involving human subjects.

CLINICAL TRIAL PHASES

Testing a new drug, surgical procedure, or other therapy takes place in the sequence of phases that follows. Animal testing, when appropriate, is done before human studies begin, although additional testing may be done in parallel with human studies.

Phase I: Investigators test the therapy in a small number of people (10–80) to evaluate its safety, identify its side effects, and (if a drug) determine the range of a safe dose. Testing the effectiveness of the therapy is not the aim of the trial.

Phase II: Investigators test the treatment in a larger group of people (100–300) to determine whether the therapy is effective and to further test its safety. Both effectiveness and safety are usually measured statistically.

Phase III: Investigators test the therapy in a significantly larger number of people (1000–3000) to confirm its effectiveness, monitor its side effects, and compare it with accepted therapies. Investigators also collect data that may be relevant to improving the therapy or increasing its safety.

Phase IV: Investigators collect data about the therapy's effects after the therapy has become established as a standard treatment. The aim is to refine the use of the therapy and improve its safety.

Clinical Trials

The United States spends almost $100 billion per year on medical research, and a large proportion of the money goes to fund clinical trials. A clinical trial is a form of research in which the effectiveness and side effects of a treatment are tested by administering it to human subjects. The treatment may be a drug, surgical procedure, special diet, medical device, or even a form of behavior, such as getting out of bed or listening to music. The most common clinical trials are ones in which the effectiveness of a new drug is tested, so let's sketch just what this involves.

Traditions of medical research and regulations of the U.S. Food and Drug Administration more or less guarantee that the development of new drugs follows a set procedure. The procedure consists of two major parts: preclinical and clinical testing. When investigators think that a particular chemical compound might be useful in treating a particular disorder, they conduct animal experiments to determine how toxic it is. They use these tests to estimate the drug's therapeutic index (the ratio of a dose producing toxic effects to a dose producing desired effects). The effects of the substance on particular organs and tissues, as well as on the whole animal, are also studied. In addition, the investigators make an effort to determine the drug's potential side effects and hazards. (Does it produce liver or kidney damage? Is it carcinogenic? Does it cause heart arrhythmias?) If a drug shows promise in animal testing and its side effects are acceptable, it is then tested in humans in randomized clinical trials.

Clinical testing of the substance occurs in three phases. In Phase I, healthy human volunteers are used to determine whether the drug can be tolerated and whether its side effects are acceptable. If it causes serious "adverse events" (e.g., severe headaches, rashes, anemia, or a suppressed immune response), it may be too dangerous to give to people. The aim of a Phase I trial is to answer questions about safety and effectiveness, not to determine whether the drug is effective.

In a Phase II trial, the drug is administered to a limited number of patients who might be expected to benefit from it. If the drug produces desirable results, and causes no serious side effects, then Phase III studies are initiated.

In Phase III, the drug is administered to a larger number of patients by (typically) a larger number of clinical investigators. Such multi-center trials usually take place at teaching hospitals or in large public institutions. Often, they are sponsored by the drug's manufacturer. Successful results achieved in this phase ordinarily lead to the licensing of the drug for general use. If this happens, a Phase IV study may be conducted to gather more data about the drug and determine whether it is more effective—or perhaps more dangerous—for certain types of patients.

In the clinical part of testing, careful procedures are followed to attempt to exclude bias in the results. Investigators want their tests to be successful and patients want to get well, and either or both of these factors may influence test results. Investigators may perceive a patient as "improved" because they want or expect him to be. What is more, medications themselves may produce a "placebo effect." That is, when patients are given inactive substances (placebos), they nevertheless may show improvement. Their hopes and expectations may affect how their bodies respond and how they feel. (In a pain-relief study, patients responded better to a placebo they were told cost $2.50 than to one said to cost ten cents.)

To rule out these kinds of influences, a common procedure followed in drug testing is the "double-blind" (or "doubles masked") test design. In the classic version of this design, a certain number of patients are given the drug being tested and the remainder of the test group is given placebos. Patients are assigned to the treatment group or the placebo group in a random fashion (e.g., by the flip of a coin). Neither the investigators nor the patients are allowed to know who is receiving the drug and who is not—both are kept "blind." (A variant of the double-blind trial is a trial with "three arms": part of the test group gets placebos all of the time, part gets them only some of the time, and part gets genuine medication all of the time.)

Placebos may be no more than sugar pills. Yet, frequently, substances are prepared to produce side effects like those of the drug being tested. If, for example, the drug causes drowsiness, a placebo will be used that produces drowsiness. In this way, investigators will not be able to learn, on the basis of irrelevant observations, which patients are being given placebos.

In recent decades, clinical trials involving placebos are most often designed so that a patient is never given only a placebo to treat a serious medical problem. Rather, patients in one group are given a placebo *plus* a drug established as effective, while those in another group are given the established drug *plus* an experimental drug. The established drug represents the "standard of care," and the aim of the trial is to determine whether the new drug is more effective than the old. In this design, no patient is denied the standard of care—that is, the best available treatment.

In 2008, the FDA dropped the requirement that clinical trials compare a new drug with one recognized as the most effective one currently available. This allows pharmaceutical companies to conduct trials in which a new drug is tested against a placebo. Critics have charged that, by dropping the old requirement, the FDA is failing to provide the most effective protection for patients who volunteer to participate in studies.

The double-blind test design is employed in many kinds of clinical investigations, not just in drug testing. Thus, the testing of new vaccines and even surgeries often follows the same form. A major variation is the "single-blind" design, in which those who must evaluate the results of some treatment are kept ignorant of which patients have received it.

Randomized clinical trials are typically referred to as constituting the "gold standard" of medical research. Thus, a treatment or drug that has not gone through the process of such a trial is often regarded with suspicion or considered unproven. Some critics consider this view too extreme and point to cases in which experience over a long time has shown a treatment to be effective.

Clinical trials may also fail to establish a treatment as effective for a whole population if those who participated as subjects failed to represent the population. Thus, the subjects in a clinical trial for prostate cancer were predominately men in their fifties; a treatment shown to be effective might not be effective for men in their sixties. Similarly, if 90% of the participants were white, the results may not apply to Asians or African-Americans. Clinical trials—even ones that are well designed—don't always produce trustworthy results, unless they include very large and diverse groups of participants.

The "Informed" Part of Informed Consent

Consent, at first sight, is no more than agreement. A person consents when he or she says "yes" when asked to become a research subject. But legitimate or valid consent cannot be merely saying yes. If people are to be treated as autonomous agents, they must have the opportunity to decide whether they wish to become participants in research.

Deciding, whatever else it may be, is a process in which we reason about an issue at hand. We consider such matters as the risks of our participation, its possible advantages to ourselves and others, the risks and advantages of other alternatives that are offered to us, and our own values. In short, valid consent requires that we deliberate before we decide.

But genuine deliberation requires both information and understanding. These two requirements are the source of difficulties and controversies. After all, medical research and treatment are highly technical enterprises. They are based on complicated scientific theories that are expressed in a special vocabulary and involve unfamiliar concepts.

For this reason, some physicians and investigators have argued that it is virtually useless to provide patients with relevant scientific information about research and treatment. Patients without the proper scientific background, they argue, simply don't know what to make of the information. Not only do patients find it puzzling, but they find it frightening. Thus, some have suggested, informed consent is at worst a pointless charade and at best a polite fiction. The patient's interest is best served by allowing a physician to make the decision.

This obviously paternalistic point of view (see Chapter 1) implies, in effect, that all patients are incompetent to decide their best interest and that physicians must assume the responsibility of acting for them.

An obvious objection to this view is its assumption that, because patients lack a medical background, they cannot be given information in a form they can understand that is at least adequate to allow them to decide how they are to be treated. Thus, proponents of this view confuse difficulty of communication with impossibility of communication. While it is true that it is often hard to explain technical medical matters to a layperson, this hardly makes it legitimate to conclude that people should turn over their right to determine what is done to them to physicians. Rather, it imposes on physicians and researchers the obligation to find a way to explain medical matters to their patients.

The information provided to patients must be usable. That is, patients must understand enough about the proposed research and treatment to deliberate and reach a decision. From the standpoint of the researcher the problem here is to determine when the patient has an adequate understanding to make informed consent valid. Patients, being people, do not like to appear stupid and say they don't understand an explanation. Also, they may believe they understand an explanation when, as a matter of fact, they don't.

Until recently, little effort was made to deal with the problem of determining when a patient understands the information provided and is competent to assess it. In the last few years, researchers have investigated situations in which individuals have been asked to consent to become research subjects. Drawing upon these data, some writers have attempted to formulate criteria for assessing competency for giving informed consent. The problem is not one that even now admits of an ideal solution, but, with additional empirical investigation and philosophical analysis, the situation may improve even more.

The "Consent" Part of Informed Consent

We have talked so far as though the issue of gaining the legitimate agreement of someone to be a research subject or patient involved only providing information to an ordinary person in ordinary circumstances and then allowing the person to decide. But the matter is more complicated than this, because often either the person or the circumstances possess special features. These features can call into question the very possibility of valid consent.

It's generally agreed that, in order to be valid, consent must be voluntary. The person must of his or her "own free will" agree to become a research subject. This means that the person must be capable of acting voluntarily. That is, the person must be competent.

This is an obvious and sensible requirement accepted by all. But the difficulty lies in specifying just what it means to be competent. One answer is that a person is competent if he or she is capable of acting rationally. Because we have some idea of what it is to act rationally, this is a movement in the direction of an answer.

The problem with it, however, is that people sometimes decide to act for the sake of moral (or religious) principles in ways that may not seem reasonable. For example, someone may volunteer to be a subject in a potentially hazardous experiment because she believes the experiment holds out the promise of helping countless others. In terms of self-interest alone, such an action would not be reasonable.

Vulnerable Populations

Even in the best of circumstances, it is not always easy to determine who is competent to consent and who is not. Yet researchers and ethicists must also face the issue of how children, the mentally retarded, prisoners, and those suffering from psychiatric illnesses are to be considered with respect to consent. Should no one in any of these vulnerable populations be considered capable of giving consent? If so, then is it ever legitimate to secure the consent from some third party—from a parent or guardian—in some cases?

One possibility is simply to rule out all research that involves such people as subjects.

FDA REGULATIONS

1906   **Pure Food and Drug Act:** Makes it illegal to sell adulterated or mislabeled medicines.

1938   **Food, Drug, and Cosmetics Act (FDCA):** Requires the FDA to test drugs for safety. The FDCA was prompted by deaths and illnesses caused by a pharmaceutical company's distribution of an elixir of acetaminophen that used diethylene glycol, an ingredient in antifreeze, as the flavoring syrup.

1962   **Kefauver–Harris Amendment to the FDCA:** Requires pharmaceutical companies to present data to the FDA demonstrating the effectiveness of a drug and gives the FDA the power to regulate clinical trials.

The amendment was prompted by the 1960 refusal of Frances Kelsey, an FDA physician–pharmacologist, to approve the drug Thalidomide on the basis of the safety data submitted by the manufacturer. Thalidomide had been approved in forty-two European countries as an antinausea agent and sedative and prescribed widely to pregnant women to treat morning sickness. The drug turned out to produce severe arm and leg deformities, gum anomalies, and undeveloped ear canals in children born to women who had taken the drug. The United States was spared the epidemic.

1987   **FDA "compassionate use" and "expanded access" program:** Allows doctors to provide drugs that have completed Phase II clinical trials to patients who are too debilitated to participate in clinical trials or too far away from a center conducting a trial.

Prompted by AIDS activists who argued that people with AIDS not in clinical trials should not be denied access to potentially useful drugs. At the time, no effective treatment for AIDS was available.

But this has the undesirable consequence of severely hampering efforts to gain the knowledge that might be of use either to the people themselves or to others with similar medical problems. Later we will consider some of the special problems that arise with children and other vulnerable groups as research subjects.

The circumstances in which research is done can also call into question the voluntariness of consent. This is particularly so with prisons, nursing homes, and mental hospitals. These are all what the sociologist Erving Goffman called "total institutions," for within then, all aspects of a person's life are connected with the social structure. People have a definite place and particular social roles in the structure. Moreover, there are social forces at work that both pressure and encourage an inmate to do what is expected of him or her.

Later in this chapter, we will discuss some of the special problems that arise in research with prisoners. Here we need only point out that gaining voluntary consent from inmates in institutions may not be possible, even in principle. If it is possible, it's necessary to specify the kinds of safeguards that must be followed to free them from the pressures resulting from the very fact that they are inmates. Those who suffer from psychiatric illnesses may be considered just as capable intellectually of giving consent, but here too safeguards to protect them from the pressures of the institution need to be specified.

In recent years, researchers have expanded the testing of new drugs and drug regimens into developing countries. The citizens of these countries are typically less well educated and less scientifically sophisticated than their counterparts in industrialized nations. They may also be more likely to trust that what they are asked to do by some medical authority will be in their best interest. Hence, securing informed consent from them that is valid presents particular difficulties.

It's important to keep in mind that ordinary patients in hospitals may also be subject to pressures that call into question the voluntariness of the consent that they give. Patients are psychologically predisposed to act in ways that please physicians. Not only do physicians possess a social role that makes them figures of authority, but an ill person feels very dependent on those who may possess the power to make her well. Thus, she will be inclined to go along with any suggestion or recommendation made by a physician.

The ordinary patient, like the inmate in an institution, needs protection from the social and psychological pressures that are exerted by circumstances. Otherwise, the voluntariness of consent will be compromised, and the patient cannot act as a free and autonomous agent.

Medical Research and Medical Therapy

Medical therapy aims at relieving the suffering of people and restoring them to health. It attempts to cure diseases, correct disorders, and bring about normal bodily functioning. Its focus is on the individual patient, and his or her welfare is its primary concern.

Medical research, by contrast, is a scientific enterprise. Its aim is to acquire a better understanding of the biochemical and physiological processes involved in human functioning. It is concerned with the effectiveness of therapies in ending disease processes and restoring functioning. But this concern is not for the patient as an individual. Rather it's directed toward establishing theories. The hope, of course, is that this theoretical understanding can be used as a basis for treating individuals. But helping a particular patient get well is not a goal of medical research.

The related but distinct aims of medical research and medical therapy are a source of conflict in human experimentation. It's not unusual for a physician to be acting both as a researcher and as a therapist. This means that although she must be concerned with the welfare of her patient, her aims must also include

acquiring data that are important to her research project. It is possible, then, that she may quite unconsciously encourage her patients to volunteer to be research subjects, provide them with inadequate information on which to base their decisions, or minimize the risks they are likely to be subject to.

The patient, for his part, may be reluctant to question his physician to acquire more information or to help him understand his role and risks in research. Also, as mentioned previously, the patient may feel pressured into volunteering for research, just because he wants to do what his physician expects of him.

Medical research is a large-scale operation in this country and affects a great many people. It has been estimated that 400,000–800,000 people a year are patients in research programs investigating the effectiveness of drugs and other therapies. Since 1980, the number of clinical studies has increased more than thirty percent, from about 3500 to 5000. Informed consent is more than an abstract moral issue.

The aims of therapy and the aims of research may also cause moral difficulties for the physician that go beyond the question of consent. This is particularly so in certain kinds of research. Let's look at some of the ethical issues more specifically.

Investigators and Financial Conflict

Paul Gelsinger's eighteen-year-old son Jesse died in a clinical trial of gene therapy. Although devastated by his loss, Paul was initially prepared to support the work of James Wilson, the project's principal investigator at the University of Pennsylvania. Then he learned that Wilson and the university were major stockholders in Genovo, the biotech company sponsoring the research, and that Wilson had sold his thirty percent share of the company for $13.5 million. Gelsinger not only stopped defending Wilson; he sued him and the university. (See the Classic Case Presentation for more details.)

Private industry now supports academic research to the tune of about $1.5 *billion* a year. One study showed that 2.8 percent of researchers in the biomedical sciences received at least some funding from private sponsors. Such sponsors are mainly pharmaceutical, medical-device, and biotech companies that expect to profit from patents based on the research.

It is not unusual, as was the case with James Wilson, for an investigator to have a financial stake in the research. The stake may be slight, or when the investigator is a major shareholder in the company sponsoring the research, it may be significant. In 2006, forty-one universities reported to the National Institutes of Health that 165 researchers had a potential financial conflict of interest with the NIH-funded research.

These figures probably represent only a small fraction of the cases in which conflicts of interest are present.

Other studies have shown that one-fifth to one-third of all doctors providing patient care in clinical trials have financial ties to drug or device makers. Some were paid to be speakers (at fees ranging from $250 to $20,000 a year), while thirty-two percent of them held positions on the company's advisory committee or board of directors.

An investigator who stands to earn a considerable sum of money from the success of the clinical trial he is conducting has a clear conflict of interest. He may (even quite unconsciously) minimize the risks of participating when seeking the consent of a volunteer. Or he may be inclined to delay reporting adverse events associated with the trial to a regulatory agency or institutional review board (IRB), to avoid having the agency or IRB halt the study. He may also be prone to overestimating the value of the treatment or device being tested.

Federal agencies and the IRBs of most institutions now require investigators to reveal whether they have a financial stake in the outcome of the research. Yet having such a stake does not automatically disqualify an investigator from conducting the research, and

IRBs work to accommodate the interest of the investigator.

A 2009 study by the Department of Health and Human Services found that ninety percent of universities relied completely on researchers themselves to decide whether the money they earned as consultants constituted a potential conflict of interest with respect to their work on projects sponsored by federal funds. Also, almost half of the universities didn't require researchers to disclose the amount of money they were paid. Yet in the absence of such information, it is hard to determine the extent of an investigator's personal stake in the outcome of the research.

Institutions at which research is funded privately, rather than by federal grants, may not require an investigator to inform potential participants that the investigator has a financial interest in the research. Further, even when investigators are required to reveal a potential conflict of interest, if they fail to do so, the consequences may consist only of a notice of violation or a scolding letter. Universities do not see it as in their interest to press researchers to avoid conflicts of interest. Even if a university is not in line to make money from particular research projects, if it puts too many restrictions on its leading investigators, the investigators may take jobs elsewhere or leave the university to start their own companies.

Because more and more investigators are acquiring a financial stake in the results of their research, we need to develop national regulations for avoiding financial conflicts of interest and effective mechanisms for enforcing the regulations. It may not be a good idea to forbid researchers to profit financially from the success of their research, but it does raise questions we must address.

Placebos and Research

As we saw earlier in the description of a typical drug experiment, placebos are often considered essential to determine the true effectiveness of the drug being tested. In practice, this means that, during all or some of the time they are being "treated," patients who are also subjects in a research program will not be receiving genuine medication. They are not, then, receiving the best available treatment for their specific condition.

This is one of the risks that a patient needs to know about before consenting to become a research subject. After all, most people become patients in order to be cured, if possible, of their ailments, not to further science or anything of the kind. The physician-as-therapist will continue to provide medical care to a patient, for under double-blind conditions the physician does not know who is being given placebos and who is not. But the physician-as-researcher will know that a certain number of people will be receiving medication that cannot be expected to help their condition. Thus, the aims of the physician who is also a researcher come into conflict.

This conflict is particularly severe in cases in which it is reasonable to believe (on the basis of animal experimentation, in vitro research, and so on) that an effective disease preventative exists, yet, to satisfy scientific rigor, tests of its effectiveness involve the giving of placebos.

This was the case with the development of a polio vaccine by Thomas Weller, John F. Enders, and Frederick C. Robbins in 1960. The initial phase of the clinical testing involved injecting 30,000 children with a substance known to be useless in the prevention of polio—a placebo injection. It was realized, statistically, that some of those children would get the disease and die from it.

Since Weller, Enders, and Robbins believed they had an effective vaccine, they can hardly be regarded as acting in the best interest of these children. As physicians they were not acting to protect the interest and well-being of the children. They did, of course, succeed in proving the safety and effectiveness of the polio vaccine. The moral question is whether they were justified in failing to provide 30,000

children with a vaccine they believed to be effective, even though it had not been tested on a wide scale with humans. That is, did they correctly resolve the conflict between their roles as researchers and their roles as physicians?

Placebos also present physician-researchers with another conflict. As we noticed in the earlier discussion, placebos are not always just "sugar pills." They often contain active ingredients that produce in patients effects that resemble those caused by the medication being tested—nervousness, vomiting, loss of appetite, and so on. This means that a patient receiving a placebo is sometimes not only failing to receive any medication for his illness, but also receiving a medication that may do him some harm. Thus, the physician committed to care for the patient and to relieve his suffering is at odds with the researcher who may be harming the patient. Do the aims of scientific research and its potential benefits to others justify treating patients in this fashion? Here is another moral question that the physician must face in particular and we must face in general.

We should not leave the topic of the use of placebos without the reminder of what was mentioned earlier—that it is possible to make use of an experimental design in research that does not require giving placebos to a control group. An investigator can compare the results of two treatment forms: a standard treatment whose effectiveness is known and a new treatment with a possible but not proven effectiveness. This is not as scientifically satisfactory as the other approach, because the researcher must do without a control group that has received no genuine treatment. But it does provide a way out of the dilemma of both providing medical care and conducting research.

This way of proceeding has associated with it another moral issue. If a clinical trial of a drug is scheduled to last for a long period of time (perhaps years) but accumulating-statistical results indicate that the drug is more effective in the treatment or prevention of a disease than the established one it is being compared with, should the trial be stopped so that all the patients in the study can gain the benefits of the test drug? Or does the informed consent of the participants warrant continuing the trial until the therapeutic value of the test drug is fully established?

The view generally accepted now is that if the evidence strongly indicates that a treatment being tested is more effective than the standard one, researchers have an obligation to discontinue the trial and offer the new treatment to those who were not receiving it.

Therapeutic and Nontherapeutic Research

We have mentioned the conflict that faces the physician who is also an investigator. But the patient who has to decide whether to consent to become a research subject is faced with a similar conflict.

Some research holds out the possibility of a direct and immediate advantage to those patients who agree to become subjects. For example, a new drug may, on the basis of limited trials, promise to be more effective in treating an illness than drugs in standard use.

Or a new surgical procedure may turn out to give better results than one that would ordinarily be used. By agreeing to participate in research involving such a drug or procedure, a patient may have a chance of gaining something more beneficial than he or she would gain otherwise.

Yet the majority of medical research projects do not offer any direct therapeutic advantages to patients who consent to be subjects. The research may eventually benefit many patients, but seldom does it bring more than usual therapeutic benefits to research participants. Ordinarily, the most that participants can expect to gain are the advantages of having the attention of physicians who are experts on their illness and receiving close observation and supervision from researchers.

Some patients don't get even this much advantage. Pharmaceutical companies may pay physicians in private practice to conduct a study of a drug they manufacture in order to get the physician to prescribe the drug more often. Typically, in such research projects the study is not well designed, the number of participants is too small to be statistically meaningful, and the results are never published. The physician gets paid and the company gets its drug prescribed more often, but the patient is not likely to benefit. Indeed, the patient may not even get the drug that is best for her.

All these are matters an investigator ought to present to the patient as information that is relevant to the decision the patient must make. The patient must then decide whether he or she is willing to become a participant, even if there are risks involved and no special therapeutic advantages to be gained. It is in making this decision that one's moral beliefs can play a role. Some people volunteer to become research subjects without hope of reward because they believe that their action may eventually be of help to others. (See the Jesse Gelsinger Case Study on page 123.)

* * *

In the sections that follow, we will examine some problems of clinical research when special groups are its focus.

Offshore Research

In recent years, researchers have expanded the testing of new drugs and drug regimens into other countries. A 2009 study by Seth Glickman and Charles Cairns showed that, during the decade 1995–2005, almost half of Phase III clinical trials sponsored by drug companies were carried out somewhere other than the United States. The countries favored were often Eastern Europe and Russia, but studies were also conducted in Malaysia and India.

Several reasons lie behind the increase in offshore drug testing. First, in the United States it is difficult to get subjects to volunteer for clinical trials. Only half the trials sponsored by the National Cancer Institute enrolled the number of participants needed to produce statistically significant results. Second, the United States has stringent requirements to protect human subjects, and these requirements slow the testing process. The result is that drugs both take longer to test and are more expensive to test in the United States than in many other countries.

The cost of a clinical trial conducted in a major medical center in India is $1,500–$2000. By contrast, a trial conducted in the United States at a second-tier institution costs $15,000–$20,000. Testing a drug in a clinical trial is a major part of the expense of drug development. Given that the cost for developing a drug in the United States averages $800–$900 million, the incentive for drug companies to turn to overseas test sites is understandable.

However, significant ethical questions arise about offshore testing. In poorer countries, even a small amount of money can serve as an inducement for people to ignore their best interest and become a participant. The citizens of such countries are also likely to have a low level of education and scientific sophistication. They may not understand what the clinical trial of a drug requires of them and what the risks are. They may put their trust in the researcher, even though the researcher has a conflict of interest.

The countries where companies decide to conduct drug tests are not likely to have strong regulations to protect test subjects. Hence, the primary question that arises with respect to every offshore clinical trial is whether the conditions for legitimate informed consent have been satisfied. Furthermore, participants in trials may not be monitored as carefully as they are in the United States. Even very serious adverse events (e.g., kidney damage) affecting some participants may not be caught and the trial ended before others are harmed. If serious adverse events are detected, they might be ignored so that the trial can continue as planned. Participants are thus put at greater risk than they would be in a United States trial.

Such considerations are relevant to the decision that must be made by federal agencies and professional organizations in the United States about accepting the results of clinical trial conducted elsewhere. If the research was carried out in an impoverished country that lacks strong and enforced regulations to protect human subjects, should United States scientific and medical institutions accept the results without raising ethical questions about how they were obtained? If the trial doesn't satisfy regulations comparable to those of the United States, should the results be rejected as morally tainted?

This might mean that a potentially lifesaving drug shown to be effective in a trial wouldn't be available to patients who need it. A new trial would have to be conducted. Not only would that add to the cost of developing the drug, but it might be months or even years before patients could be treated with it. Many patients could die while the second trial is being conducted.

Accepting the results of an offshore drug trial without questioning whether the autonomy and safety of participants were protected also has a cost associated with it. Patients in the United States could benefit immediately from a drug proved effective in the trial, but the benefit might come as a result of exploiting the poor and ignorant in some other country. In such a case, the cost of the benefit would be a moral one.

Research Involving Children

One of the most controversial areas of all medical research has been that involving children as subjects. The Willowbrook project discussed in a Case Presentation earlier in the chapter is just one among many investigations that have drawn severe criticism and, quite often, court action.

Why Study Children at All? The obvious question is, why should children ever be made research subjects? Children clearly lack the physical, psychological, and intellectual maturity of adults. It does not seem that they are as capable as adults of giving informed consent, because they can hardly be expected to grasp the nature of research and the possible risks to themselves.

Furthermore, because children have not yet developed their capacities, it seems wrong to subject them to risks that might alter the course of their lives for the worse. They are in a position or relative dependency, relying upon adults to provide the conditions for their existence and development. It seems almost a betrayal of trust to allow children to be subjected to treatment that is of potential harm to them.

Such considerations help explain why we typically regard research involving children with deep suspicion. It is easy to imagine children being exploited and their lives blighted by callous researchers. Some writers have been sufficiently concerned by the possibility of dangers and abuses that they have advocated an end to all research with children as subjects.

But there is another side to the coin. Biologically, children are not just small adults. Their bodies are developing, growing systems. Not only are there anatomical differences; there are also differences in metabolism and biochemistry. For example, some drugs are absorbed and metabolized more quickly in children than in adults, whereas other drugs continue to be active for a longer time. Often, some drugs produce different effects when administered to children.

Also, precisely because the bodies of children are still developing, their nutritional needs are different. Findings based on adult subjects cannot simply be extrapolated to children, any more than results based on animal studies can be extrapolated to human beings.

Further, children are prone to certain kinds of diseases (measles or mumps, for example) that either are less common in adults or occur in different forms. It is important to know the kinds of therapies that are most successful in the treatment of children afflicted with them.

Children also have problems that are not seen in adults, because with such problems they do not survive unless they are treated effectively. Various heart anomalies, for example, must be corrected to keep children alive. Thus, the development of new surgical techniques must necessarily involve children.

Finally, even familiar surgical procedures cannot be employed in a straightforward way with children. Their developing organ systems are sufficiently different that special pediatric techniques must often be devised.

For many medical purposes, children must be thought of almost as if they were wholly different organisms. Their special biological features set them apart and mark them as subjects requiring special study. To gain the kind of knowledge and understanding required for effective medical treatment of children, it is often impossible to limit research solely to adults.

Excluding Children. Failing to conduct research on children raises its own set of ethical issues. If children are excluded from investigations, then the development of pediatric medicine will be severely hindered. In general, this would mean that children would receive medical therapies that are less effective than might be possible. Also, since it is known that children differ significantly from adults in drug reactions, it seems wrong to subject children to the risks of drugs and drug dosages that have been tested only on adults.

Research involving children can also be necessary to avoid causing long-term harm to numerous people. The use of pure oxygen in the environments of prematurely born babies in the early 1940s resulted in hundreds of cases of blindness and impaired vision. It was not until a controlled study was done that retinal damage was traced to the effects of the oxygen. Had the research not been allowed, the chances are very good that the practice would have continued and thousands more infants would have been blinded.

Ethical Issues. Yet, even if we agree that not all research involving children should be forbidden, we still have to face up to the issues that such research generates. Without attempting to be complete, we can mention the following three issues as among the more prominent:

Who Is a Child? Who is to be considered a child? For infants and children in elementary school, this question is not a difficult one. But what about people in their teens? Then the line becomes hard to draw. Indeed, perhaps it is not possible to draw a line at all without being arbitrary.

The concern behind the question is with the acquisition of autonomy—of self-direction and responsibility. It is obvious on the basis of ordinary experience that people develop at different rates, and some people at sixteen are more capable of taking charge of their own lives than others are at twenty. Some teenagers are more capable of understanding the nature and hazards of a research project than are many people who are much older.

This suggests that many people who are legally children may be quite capable of giving their informed consent. Of course, many others probably are not, so that decisions about capability would have to rest on an assessment of the individual. Where medical procedures that have a purely therapeutic aim are concerned, an individual who is capable of deciding whether it is in his or her best interest should probably be the one to decide. The issue may be somewhat different when the aim is not therapy. In such cases, a better policy might be to set a lower limit on the age at which consent can be given, and those below that limit should not be permitted to consent to participate in research. The problem is, of course, what should that limit be?

Parental Consent. Can anyone else consent on behalf of a child? Parents or guardians have a duty to act for the sake of the welfare of a child under their care. In effect, they have a duty to substitute their judgment for that of the child. We generally agree to this because most often we consider the judgment of an adult more mature and informed than a child's. And because the responsibility for care rests with the adult, we customarily recognize that the adult has a right to decide. It is almost as though the adult's autonomy is being shared with the

child—almost as though the child were an extension of the adult.

Society and its courts have recognized limits on the power of adults to decide for children. When it seems that the adult is acting in an irresponsible or unreasonable manner, society steps in to act as a protector of the child's right to be cared for. Thus, courts have ordered that lifesaving procedures or blood transfusions be performed on children even when their parents or guardians have decided against it. The criterion used in such judgments is "the best interest of the child."

What sort of limits should govern a parent's or guardian's decision to allow a child to become a research subject? Is it reasonable to believe that if a parent would allow herself to be the subject of research, then it is also right for her to consent to her child's becoming a subject? Or should something more be required before consent for a child's participation can be considered legitimate?

Therapeutic Benefits. Should children be allowed to be subjects of research that does not offer them a chance of direct therapeutic benefits? Perhaps the "something more" that parents or guardians ought to require before consenting on behalf of a child is the genuine possibility that the research will bring the child direct benefits. This would be in accordance with a parent's duty to seek the welfare of the child. It is also a way of recognizing that the parent's autonomy is not identical with that of the child: one may have the right to take a risk oneself without having the right to impose the risk on someone else.

This seems like a reasonable limitation, and it has been advocated by some writers. Yet there are difficulties with the position. Some research that is virtually free from risk (coordination tests, for example) might be stopped because of its lack of a "direct therapeutic value."

More important, however, much research promising immense long-term benefits would have to be halted. Research frequently involves the withholding of accepted therapies without any guarantee that what is used in their place will be as effective. Sometimes the withholding of accepted treatment is beneficial. Thus, as it turned out, in the research on the incidence of blindness in premature infants in the 1940s, premature infants who were not kept in a pure oxygen environment were better off than those who received ordinary treatment.

But no one could know this in advance, and such research as this is, at best, ambiguous as to the promise of direct therapy. Sheer ignorance imposes restrictions. Yet if the experiment had not been done, the standard treatment would have continued with its ordinary course of (statistically) disastrous results. Here, at least, there was the possibility of better results from the experimental treatment.

But in research that involves the substitution of placebos for medications or vaccines that are acknowledged to be effective, it is known in advance that some children will not receive medical care considered to be the best. A child who is a subject in such research is then put in a situation in which he or she is subjected to a definite hazard. The limitation on consent that we are considering would rule out such research. But the consequence of doing this would be to restrict the development of new and potentially more effective medications and treatment techniques. That is, future generations of children would be deprived of at least some possible medical advances.

These, then, are some of the issues that we have to face in arriving at a view of the role of children in research. Perhaps the greatest threat to children, however, has to do with social organization. Children, like prisoners, are often grouped together in institutions (schools, orphanages, detention centers, and so on) and are attractive targets for clinical investigators because they inhabit a limited and relatively controlled environment, can be made to follow orders, and do not ask too many questions that have to be answered. It is a misimpression to see researchers in such situations as "victimizing" children, but at the same time, careful controls are needed to see that research involving children is legitimate and carried out in a morally satisfactory way.

Guidelines. In response to some of these difficulties, the Department of Health and Human Services has issued guidelines designed specifically to protect children as research subjects. First, for children to become participants, permission must be obtained from parents or guardian and children must give their "assent." Second, an Institutional Review Board is assigned the responsibility of considering the "ages, maturity, and psychological states" of the children and determining whether they are capable of assenting. (A failure to object cannot be construed as assent.)

Third, children who are wards of the state or of an institution can become participants only if the research relates to their status as wards or takes place in circumstances in which the majority of subjects are not wards. Each child must also be supplied with an "advocate" to represent her or his interest.

Research Involving Prisoners

Prisoners are in some respects social outcasts. They have been found guilty of breaking the laws of society and, as a consequence, are removed from it. Stigmatized and isolated, prisoners in the relatively recent past were sometimes thought of as less than human. It seemed only reasonable that such depraved and corrupt creatures should be used as the subjects of experiments that might bring benefits to the members of the society that they wronged. Indeed, it seemed not only reasonable, but fitting.

Accordingly, in the early part of the twentieth century, tropical medicine expert Richard P. Strong obtained permission from the governor of the Philippines to inoculate a number of condemned criminals with plague bacillus. The prisoners were not asked for their consent, but they were rewarded by being provided with cigarettes and cigars.

Episodes of this sort were relatively common during the late nineteenth and early twentieth centuries. But as theories about the nature of crime and criminals changed, it became standard practice to use only volunteers and to secure the consent of the prisoners themselves.

In the 1940s, for example, the University of Chicago infected more than four hundred prisoners with malaria in an attempt to discover new drugs to treat and prevent the disease. A committee set up by the governor of Illinois recommended that potential volunteers be informed of the risks, be permitted to refuse without fear of such reprisals as withdrawal of privileges, and be protected from unnecessary suffering. The committee suggested also that volunteering to be a subject in a medical experiment is a form of good conduct that should be taken into account in deciding whether a prisoner should be paroled or have his sentence reduced.

But the committee also called attention to a problem of great moral significance. They pointed out that, if a prisoner's motive for volunteering is the wish to contribute to human welfare, then a reduction in his sentence would be a reward. But if his motive is to obtain a reduction in sentence, then the possibility of obtaining one is really a form of duress. In this case, the prisoner cannot be regarded as making a free decision. The issue of duress, or "undue influence," as it is called in law, is central to the question of deciding whether and under what conditions valid informed consent can be obtained for research involving prisoners. Some ethicists have argued that, to avoid undue influence, prisoners should never be promised any substantial advantages for volunteering to be research subjects. If they volunteer, they should do so for primarily moral or humane reasons.

Others have claimed that becoming research subjects offers prisoners personal advantages that they should not be denied. For example, participation in a research project frees them from the boredom of prison life, gives them an opportunity to increase their feelings of self-worth, and allows them to exercise their autonomy as moral agents. It has been argued, in fact, that prisoners have a right to participate in research if the opportunity is offered to them and they wish to do so. To forbid the use of prisoners as research subjects is thus to deny to them, without adequate grounds, a right that all human beings possess. As a denial of their basic autonomy—of their right to take risks and control their own bodies—not allowing them to be subjects might constitute a form of cruel and unusual punishment.

By contrast, it can also be argued that prisoners do not deserve to be allowed to exercise such autonomy. Because they have been sentenced for crimes, they should be deprived of the right to volunteer to be research subjects: that right belongs to free citizens. Being deprived of the right to act autonomously is part of their punishment. This is basically the position taken by the House of Delegates of the American Medical Association. The delegates passed a resolution in 1952 expressing disapproval of the use as research subjects of people convicted of "murder, rape, arson, kidnapping, treason, and other heinous crimes."

A more worrisome consideration is the question of whether prisoners can be sufficiently free of undue influence or duress to make their consent legitimate. As we mentioned earlier, prisons are total institutions and the institutional framework itself puts pressures on people to do what is desired or expected of them. There need not be, then, either promises of rewards (such as reduced sentences) or overt threats (such as withdrawal of ordinary privileges) for coercion to be present. That people may volunteer to relieve boredom is itself an indication that they may be acting under duress. That "good conduct" is a factor in deciding whether to grant parole may function as another source of pressure.

The problem presented by prisoners is fundamentally the same as that presented by inmates in other institutions, such as nursing homes and mental hospitals. In these cases, once it has been determined that potential subjects are mentally competent to give consent, then it must also be decided whether the institutional arrangements allow the consent to be "free and voluntary."

To protect prisoners from exploitation, the FDA instituted stringent regulations governing research conducted in prisons. The regulations constituted such barriers that most academic investigators and pharmaceutical companies essentially stopped using prisoners as research subjects. In 2006, the National Institute of Medicine issued a report that aimed to protect prisoners as research subjects, while also making it easier for prisoners to participate in research that might benefit them. Critics of the report charged that the prison environment alone makes it impossible for inmates to act autonomously and provide informed consent. (See "Social Context: Prisoners as Test Subjects?" at the end of this Briefing Session.)

Research Involving the Poor

In the eighteenth century, Princess Caroline of England requested the use of six "charity children" as subjects in the smallpox vaccination experiments she was directing. Then, and well into the twentieth century, charity cases, like prisoners, were regarded by some medical researchers as prime research subjects.

A horrible example of medical research involving the poor is the Tuskegee Syphilis Study that was conducted under the auspices of the U.S. Department of Public Health (USPH). From 1932 to 1970, a number of black males suffering from the later stages of syphilis were examined at regular intervals to determine the course their disease was taking. The men in the study were poor and uneducated and believed that they were receiving proper medical care from the state and local public health clinics.

As a matter of fact, they were given either no treatment or inadequate treatment, and at least forty of them died as a result of factors connected with their disease. Their consent was never obtained, and the nature of the study, its risks, and the alternatives open to them were never explained.

It was known when the study began that those with untreated syphilis have a higher death rate than those whose condition is treated, and although the study was started before the advent of penicillin (which is highly effective against syphilis), other drugs were available but were not used in ways to produce the best results. When penicillin became generally available, it still was not used.

The Tuskegee Study clearly violated the Nuremberg Code, but it was not stopped even after the War Crimes trials. It was reviewed in 1969 by a USPH ad hoc committee, and it was decided that the study should be phased out in 1970. The reasons for ending the experiment were not moral ones. Rather, it was believed nothing much of scientific value was to be gained by continuing the work. In 1973, a United States Public Health Department Ad Hoc Advisory Panel, which had been established as a result of public and congressional pressure to review the Tuskegee Study, presented its final report. It condemned the study both on moral grounds and because of its lack of worth and rigor. (See the Case Presentation "Bad Blood, Bad Faith" in Chapter 4 for more details.)

No one today argues that disadvantaged people ought to be made subjects of research simply because of their social or economic status. The "back wards" in hospitals whose poor patients once served as a source of research subjects have mostly disappeared as a result of such programs as Medicare and Medicaid. Each person is now entitled to his or her own physician and is not under the general care of the state or of a private charity.

Yet many research projects continue to be based in large public or municipal hospitals. And such hospitals have a higher percentage of disadvantaged people as patients than do private institutions. For this reason, such people are still more likely to become research subjects than are the educated and wealthy. If society continues to accept this state of affairs, special precautions must be taken to see to it that those who volunteer to become research subjects are genuinely informed and free in their decisions.

Research Involving the Terminally Ill

People who have been diagnosed with a terminal illness characteristically experience overwhelming feelings of despair. Within a few days or weeks, some are able to acknowledge and accept the situation, but others are driven to desperation by the imminent prospect of their death.

When they learn that conventional therapies offer little hope of prolonging their lives, they vow to fight their disease by other means. They look for hope in a situation that seems hopeless, and with the encouragement of family and friends, they seek new therapies.

Some turn to quack medicine or suspect remedies, but others seek out clinical trials of new drugs for their diseases. They seek acceptance into trials from the hospitals and medical centers where they are being conducted.

Critics of the policy of accepting terminally ill patients into clinical trials base their objections on the vulnerability of patients. Most often, critics charge, such patients are not sufficiently aware of what they are getting into, nor are they aware of how little personal payoff they may reasonably expect to receive from an experimental therapy.

To be enrolled in a drug trial, patients must satisfy the study's research protocol. They must meet diagnostic criteria for having a particular disease, or their disease must be at a certain stage in its natural history. Or perhaps the patients must not have received certain treatments, such as radiation, or must not have been taking a particular drug for several weeks. Perhaps the patients must not have signs of liver damage or kidney disease. Some of the criteria may require that patients be tested. The testing may involve only drawing blood for analysis,

but it may also require submitting to painful and potentially harmful surgical procedures to biopsy tissue.

A patient who qualifies for admission to a study may still have a difficult time ahead. If the study is at an institution that is hundreds, even thousands, of miles away, the patient must either move nearer or travel to the institution regularly. In either case, much expense and inconvenience may be involved.

Critics also charge that patients may have unreasonable expectations about the effectiveness of experimental therapies. Patients may believe, for example, that a drug has at least some record of success, but in fact the therapeutic benefits of the drug may be uncertain at best. Indeed, in the initial stage of drug testing with human subjects, Phase I trials, the aim is not to determine the therapeutic effectiveness of the drug, but to determine such matters as its toxicity, rate of metabolism, or most effective mode of administration.

The chance that a drug under investigation will actually prolong the life of a patient in the final stages of a terminal illness is small. One study reviewed the results of forty-two preliminary reports on drugs used to treat colon cancer and thirty-three on drugs used to treat non-small-cell lung cancer, but only one drug was found to have therapeutic effects.

Furthermore, critics charge, patients may not realize the extent to which an experimental drug may turn out to cause unpleasant, painful, or harmful side effects. Patients may suffer nausea, vomiting, chills, fevers, neurological damage, or lowered immunological functioning.

Such effects may not even be known to the investigators, so they cannot inform patients about them at the time consent is sought. The last weeks or months of terminally ill patients may thus be spent more painfully than if they had simply waited for death, and in fact, patients may even shorten their lives by becoming subjects in a study.

As a sort of final disappointment, critics point out, the study that a dying patient was counting on to give her a last chance at lengthening her life might drop her as a subject. The aim of a clinical trial of a new drug, for example, is to discover such medically important characteristics of the drug as its side effects, what constitutes an effective dosage, and whether the drug has therapeutic benefits. Patients in the study are sources of data, and if a patient who is receiving no therapeutic benefit from a drug turns out to be of no value to the study, she may be dropped from it. Dying patients may be hit particularly hard by such a rejection.

In the view of critics, the desperation of terminally ill patients makes them too vulnerable to be able to give meaningful consent to participate in experimental trials. Even if they are fairly informed that a drug trial will offer them only a remote possibility of prolonging their lives, they are under such pressure from their illness that, in a sense, they are not free to consent. Patients and their families may be so frightened and emotionally distraught that they hear only what they want to hear about an experimental therapy. They may be unable to grasp the fact that the therapy probably will not benefit them and may even harm them.

Opponents of enrolling terminally ill patients in clinical investigations charge that the patients are often treated as though they are only a research resource, a pool from which subjects can be selected for whatever testing needs to be done. That people are dying does not mean that it is justifiable to exploit them, and the only way to avoid this is to exclude them as eligible candidates for research subjects.

While no one advocates the exploitation of terminally ill people, most observers believe it is morally legitimate to include them in clinical trials. The patients themselves may have something to gain. The very act of trying a new drug might make some patients feel better, even if it is only a placebo effect. Also, patients and their families can feel that they are genuinely doing everything possible to improve the patient's health. Moreover, the drug might be of some therapeutic benefit to the patient, even

if the chance of its prolonging the patient's life is remote.

Furthermore, defenders of the policy hold, allowing dying patients to participate in research is to recognize their status as autonomous persons, while to exclude them as candidates for research subjects is to deny them that status.

Finally, defenders claim, in connection with their status as moral agents, dying patients deserve to be given a chance to do something for others. In fact, when dying patients are recruited or seek to enroll in a study, instead of stressing the possible therapeutic benefit they might secure, the experimenter should emphasize the contribution that patients' participation might make to helping others in the future.

To put this last point in perspective, consider the responses of twenty-seven cancer patients enrolled in a Phase I clinical trial who were interviewed by Mark Siegler and his colleagues at the University of Chicago. Eighty-five percent of the patients said they had agreed to participate because they hoped for therapeutic benefits, eleven percent enrolled at the suggestion of their physicians, and four percent did so at the urging of their families. No one reported enrolling out of a desire to help others.

Research Involving Fetuses

In 1975, legal charges were brought against several physicians in Boston. They had injected antibiotics into living fetuses that were scheduled to be aborted. The aim of the research was to determine by autopsy, after the death of the fetuses, how much of the drug got into the fetal tissues.

Such information is considered to be of prime importance because it increases our knowledge of how to provide medical treatment for a fetus still developing in its mother's womb. It also helps to determine ways in which drugs taken by a pregnant woman may affect a fetus and so points the way toward improved prenatal care.

Other kinds of research involving the fetus also promise to provide important knowledge. Effective vaccines for preventing viral diseases, techniques for treating children with defective immune-system reactions, and hormonal measurements that indicate the status of the developing fetus are just some of the potential advances that are partially dependent on fetal research.

But a number of moral questions arise in connection with such research. Even assuming that a pregnant woman consents to allow the fetus she is carrying to be injected with drugs prior to abortion, is such research ethical? Does the fact that the fetus is going to be aborted alter the moral situation in any way? For example, prior to abortion, should the fetus be treated with the same respect and concern for its well-being as a fetus that is not scheduled for abortion?

After the fetus is aborted, if it is viable—if it can live separated from the mother—then we seem to be under an obligation to protect its life. But what if a prenatal experiment threatens its viability? The expectation in abortion is that the fetus will not be viable, but this is not in fact always the case. Does this mean that it is wrong to do anything before abortion to threaten the life of the fetus or reduce its chance for life, even though we do not expect it to live?

These are difficult questions to answer without first settling the question of whether the fetus is to be considered a person. (See the discussion of this issue in the Briefing Session in Chapter 9.) If the fetus is a person, then it is entitled to the same moral considerations that we extend to other persons. If we decide to take its life, if abortion is considered to be at least sometimes legitimate, then we must be prepared to offer justification. Similarly, if we are to perform experiments on a fetus, even one expected to die, then we must also be prepared to offer justification. Whether the importance of the research is adequate justification is a matter that currently remains to be settled.

If the fetus is not a person, then the question of fetal experimentation becomes less important

morally. Because, however, the fetus may be regarded as a potential person, we may still believe it is necessary to treat it with consideration and respect. The burden of justification may be somewhat less weighty, but it may still be there.

Let us assume that the fetus is aborted and is apparently not viable. Typically, before such a fetus dies, its heart beats and its lungs function. Is it morally permissible to conduct research on the fetus before its death? The knowledge that can be gained, particularly of lung functions, can be used to help save the lives of premature infants, and the fetus is virtually certain of dying, whether or not it is made a subject of research.

After the death of a fetus that is either deliberately or spontaneously aborted, are there any moral restraints on what is done with the remains? It is possible to culture fetal tissues and use them for research purposes.

These tissues might, in fact, be commercially grown and distributed by biological supply companies in the way that a variety of animal tissues are now dealt with. Exactly when a fetus can be considered to be dead so that its tissues and organs are available for experimentation, even assuming that one approves of their use in this manner, is itself an unsettled question.

Scientists have long been concerned about federal guidelines and state laws regulating fetal research. Most investigators feel that they are forced to operate under such rigid restrictions that research is slowed and, in some instances, even prohibited. Everyone agrees, however, that fetal research involves important moral and social issues. (See Chapter 9 for more detail.)

Fetal research has to be considered a part of human research. Not only are some fetuses born alive even when deliberately aborted, but all possess certain human characteristics and potentialities. But who should give approval to what is done with the fetus? Who should be responsible for consent?

To some it seems peculiar to say that a woman who has decided to have an abortion is also the one who should consent to research involving the aborted fetus. It can be argued that in deciding to have an abortion she has renounced all interest and responsibility with respect to the fetus. Yet, if the fetus does live, we would consider her, at least in part, legally and morally responsible for seeing to its continued well-being.

But if the woman (or the parents) is the one who must give consent for fetal experimentation, are there limits to what she can consent to on behalf of the fetus?

With this question, we are back where we began. It is obvious that fetal research raises both moral and social issues. We need to decide, then, what is right as a matter of personal conduct and what is right as a matter of social policy. At the moment, issues in each of these areas remain highly controversial.

Research Involving Animals

The seventeenth-century philosopher René Descartes doubted whether animals experience pain. They may act as if they are in pain, but perhaps they are only complicated pieces of clockwork designed to act that way. Humans feel pain, but then, unlike animals, humans have a "soul" that gives them the capacity to reason, be self-conscious, and experience emotions. The *bodies* of humans are pieces of machinery, but the *mental states* that occur within the bodies are not.

If the view of animals represented by Descartes and others in the mechanistic tradition he initiated is correct, we need to have no moral concern about the use of animals in research. Animals of whatever species have the status of any other piece of delicate and often expensive lab equipment. They may be used in any way for any purpose.

Here are some of the ways in which animals are being or have been used in biomedical research:

- A standard test for determining the toxicity of drugs or chemicals is the "lethal dose-50" (LD-50) test. The LD-50 is the amount of a substance that, when administered to a group of experimental animals, will kill fifty percent of them.

- The Draize test, once widely used in the cosmetics industry, involves dripping a chemical substance into the lidless eyes of rabbits to determine its potential to cause eye damage.

- The effects of cigarette smoking were investigated by a series of experiments using beagles with tubes inserted into holes cut into their tracheas so that, when breathing, they were forced to inhale cigarette smoke. The dogs were then "sacrificed" and autopsied to look for significant changes in cells and tissues.

- Surgical procedures are both developed and acquired by using animals as experimental subjects. Surgical residents spend much time in "dog labs" learning to perform standard surgical procedures on live dogs. Limbs may be deliberately broken and organs damaged or destroyed to test the usefulness of surgical repair techniques.

- A traditional medical-school demonstration consisted in exsanguinating (bleeding to death) a dog to illustrate the circulation of the blood. High school and college biology courses sometimes require that students destroy the brains of frogs with long needles (pithing) and then dissect the frogs to learn about physiological processes.

- Chimpanzees and other primates have served as experimental subjects for the study of the induction and treatment of infectious diseases. Perfectly healthy chimps and monkeys have been inoculated with viruses resembling the AIDS virus; then the course of the resulting diseases is studied.

A list of the ways in which animals are used would include virtually all basic biomedical research. The discovery of an "animal model" of a disease typically signals a significant advancement in research. It means that the disease can be studied in ways it cannot be in humans. The assumption is that animals can be subjected to experimental conditions and treatments that humans cannot be subjected to without violating basic moral principles.

Is the assumption that we have no moral obligation toward animals warranted? Certainly the crude "animal machine" view of Descartes has been rejected, and no one is prepared to argue that no nonhuman animal can experience pain.

Exactly which animals have the capacity for suffering is a matter of dispute. Mammals undoubtedly do, and vertebrates in general seem to experience pain, but what about insects, worms, lobsters, and clams? Is the identification of endorphins, naturally occurring substances associated with pain relief in humans, adequate grounds for saying that an organism that produces endorphins must experience pain?

Once it is acknowledged that at least some animals can suffer, most philosophers agree that we have some moral responsibility with respect to them. At the least, some (like W. D. Ross) say that, since we have a prima facie duty not to cause unnecessary suffering, we should not inflict needless pain on animals.

This does not necessarily mean that biomedical research should discontinue the use of animals. Strictly construed, it means only that the animals should be treated in a humane way. For example, surgical techniques should be practiced only on dogs that have been anesthetized. Understood in this way, the principle raises no objection to humanely conducted animal research, even if its purpose is relatively trivial.

Philosophers like Kant and most of those in the natural law tradition would deny that we have any duties to animals at all. The only proper objects of duty are rational agents; unless we are prepared to argue that animals are rational, we have to refuse them the status of moral persons. We might treat animals humanely because we are magnanimous, but they are not in a position to lay claims against us. Animals have no rights.

Some contemporary philosophers (Tom Regan, in particular) have argued that, although animals are not rational agents, they have preferences. This gives them an autonomy that makes them "moral patients." Like humans, animals possess the right to respectful treatment, and this entails that they not be treated only as a means to some other end. They are ends in themselves, and this intrinsic worth makes it wrong to use them as subjects in research, even when alternatives to animal research are not available.

Contrary to Regan, a number of philosophers have taken a utilitarian approach to the issue of animal experimentation. Some (like Peter Singer) have argued that, although animals cannot be said to have rights, they have interests. If we recognize that the interests of humans are deserving of consideration, then so, too, are the interests of nonhuman animals. Hence, we can recognize that animals have inherent worth without assigning them rights, but this does not mean that we must treat them exactly as we treat humans.

Most people, whether utilitarians or not, argue that at least some forms of animal experimentation can be justified by the benefits produced. After all, they point out, the understanding of biological processes we have acquired since the time of Aristotle has been heavily dependent on animal experimentation. This understanding has given us insights into the causes and processes of diseases, and, most important, it has put us in a position to invent and test new therapies and modes of prevention.

Without animal experimentation, the identification of the role played by insulin, the development of the polio vaccine, and the perfection of hundreds of major surgical techniques surely would not have been possible. The list could be extended to include virtually every accomplishment of medicine and surgery. Countless millions of human lives have been saved by using the knowledge and understanding gained from animal studies.

Animals, too, have benefited from the theoretical and practical knowledge of research. An understanding of nutritional needs has led to healthier domestic animals, and an understanding of environmental needs has produced a movement to protect and preserve many kinds of wild animals. At the conceptual and scientific levels, veterinary medicine is not really distinct from human medicine. The same sorts of surgical procedures, medicines, and vaccines that benefit the human population also benefit many other species.

However, even from a broadly utilitarian perspective, accepting the general principle that the results justify the practice does not mean that every experiment with animals is warranted. Some experiments might be trivial, unnecessary, or poorly designed. Others might hold no promise of yielding the kind or amount of knowledge sufficient to justify causing the animal subjects to suffer pain and death.

Furthermore, the utilitarian approach supports (as does a rights view like Regan's) looking for an alternative to animal experimentation. If good results can be obtained, for example, by conducting experiments with cell cultures (in vitro), rather than with whole organisms (in vivo), then in vitro experiments are to be preferred. However, if alternatives to animal testing are not available and if the benefits secured promise to outweigh the cost, animal testing may be morally legitimate.

The utilitarian justification faces what some writers see as a major difficulty. It is one posed by the fact that animals like chimpanzees and even dogs and pigs can be shown to possess mental abilities superior to those of humans suffering from severe brain damage and retardation. If experiments on mammals are justifiable by appealing to the benefits, then why aren't experiments on humans with serious mental impairments equally justified? Indeed, shouldn't we experiment on a human in a chronic vegetative state, rather than on a healthy and alert dog?

The use made of animals in biomedical research is a significant issue, but it is no more than one aspect of the general philosophical question about the status of animals. Do animals have rights? If so, what grounds can be offered for them? Do animals have a right to coexist with humans? Do animals have a right to be free? Is it wrong to eat animals or use products made from their remains? These questions and many others like them are now being given the most careful scrutiny they have received since the nineteenth century. How they are answered will do much to shape the character both of medical research and of our society.

Women and Medical Research

Critics have charged that medical research has traditionally failed to include women as experimental subjects, even when women might also stand to benefit from the results. Most strikingly, a study showing the effectiveness of small doses of aspirin in reducing the risk of heart attack included 2201 subjects—all male. The relevance of the study to women is in doubt, but the need to include women in such studies is clear from the fact that, although more men than women die of heart disease, after women reach menopause the difference in mortality rates between genders becomes much smaller.

Until recently, studies of the therapeutic effectiveness of drugs characteristically included only males. Although the effects of many drugs are the same for women as for men, this is not always true. Hormonal differences may alter drug reactions, so conclusions based on the reactions of men may be misleading when applied to women.

In the view of critics, the traditionally male-dominated research establishment has been responsible for perpetuating an unacceptable state of affairs. To change the situation so that both women and men are included in studies adds to their costs. By introducing gender as a variable, a study must include more subjects in order to get the degree of statistical reliability that could be achieved with fewer subjects of the same gender. However, such studies have the additional value of yielding results known to be applicable to women.

That this issue is a matter of social fairness is obvious, but its connection with informed consent is less direct. As we mentioned in connection with prisoners, not allowing someone to consent may be viewed as treating that person as having less worth than someone who is allowed to consent. From this perspective, then, women have traditionally been denied the opportunity to be full persons in the moral sense. They have not been able to exercise their autonomy in ways permitted to men. Of course, they have also not been permitted to gain benefits that might be associated with the research projects from which they have been excluded. (For more details on women and medical research, see Chapter 4, "Race, Gender, and Medicine.")

Summary

There are other areas of medical experimentation that present special forms of moral problems. We have not discussed, for example, research involving military personnel or college and university students. Moreover, we mentioned only a few of the special difficulties presented by the mentally retarded, psychiatric patients, and old people confined to institutions.

We have, however, raised such a multiplicity of questions about consent and human research that it is perhaps worthwhile to attempt to restate some of the basic issues in a general form.

Basic Issues Three issues are particularly noteworthy:

1. Who is competent to consent? (Are children? Are mental patients? If a person is not competent, who—if anyone—should have the power to consent for him or her?) Given that animals have no power to consent, is research involving them legitimate?

2. When is consent voluntary? (Is any institutionalized person in a position to offer free consent? How can even hospitalized patients be made free of pressures to consent?)

3. When are information and understanding adequate for genuine decision making? (Can complicated medical information ever be adequately explained to laypeople? Should we attempt to devise tests for understanding?)

Standards Although we have concentrated on the matter of consent in research, there are other morally relevant matters connected with research that we have not discussed. These often relate to research standards. Among them are the following:

1. Is the research of sufficient scientific and medical worth to justify the human risk involved? Research that involves trivial aims or that is unnecessary (when, for example, it merely serves to confirm what is already well established) cannot be used to justify causing any threat to human well-being.

2. Can the knowledge sought be obtained without human clinical research? Can it be obtained without animal experimentation?

3. Have animal (and other) studies been done to minimize as far as is possible the risk to human subjects? A great deal can be learned about the effects of drugs, for example, by using "animal models," and the knowledge gained can be used to minimize the hazards in human trials. (Ethical issues involving animals in research may also be called into question.)

4. Does the design of the research meet accepted scientific standards? Sloppy research that is scientifically worthless means that people have been subjected to

risks for no legitimate purpose and that animals have been harmed or sacrificed needlessly.

5. Do the investigators have the proper medical or scientific background to conduct the research effectively?

6. Is the research designed to minimize the risks and suffering of the participants? As we noted earlier, it is sometimes possible to test new drugs without using placebos. Thus, people in need of medication are not forced to be without treatment for their condition.

7. Have the aims and the design of the research and the qualifications of the investigators been reviewed by a group or committee that is competent to judge them? Such "peer review" is intended to ensure that only research that is worthwhile and that meets accepted scientific standards is conducted. And although such review groups can fail to do their job properly, as they apparently did in the Tuskegee Syphilis Study, they are still necessary instruments of control.

Most writers on experimentation would agree that these are among the questions that must be answered satisfactorily before research involving human subjects is morally acceptable. Obviously, however, a patient who is asked to give his or her consent is in no position to judge whether the research project meets the standards implied by these questions. For this reason, it is important that there be social policies and practices governing research. Everyone should be confident that a research project is, in general, a legitimate one before having to decide whether to volunteer to become a participant.

Special problems are involved in seeing to it that these questions are properly answered. It is enough for our purposes, however, merely to notice that the character of the research and the manner in which it is to be performed are factors that are relevant to determining the moral legitimacy of experimentation involving human subjects.

Ethical Theories: Medical Research and Informed Consent

We have raised too many issues in too many areas of experimentation to discuss how each of several ethical theories might apply to them all. We must limit ourselves to considering a few suggestions about the general issues of human experimentation and informed consent.

Utilitarianism

Utilitarianism's principle of utility tells us, in effect, to choose those actions which will produce the greatest amount of benefit. Utilitarianism must approve human research in general, since there are cases in which the sacrifices of a few bring great benefits to many. We might, for example, design our social policies to make it worthwhile for people to volunteer for experiments with the view that, if people are paid to take risks and are compensated for their suffering or for any damage done to them during the course of a research project, then the society as a whole might benefit.

The principle of utility also tells us to design experiments to minimize suffering and the chance of harm. Further, it forbids us to do research of an unnecessary or trivial kind—research that is not worth its cost in either human or economic resources.

As to the matter of informed consent, utilitarianism does not seem to require it. If more social good is to be gained by making people research subjects without securing their agreement, then this is morally legitimate. It is not, of course, necessarily the best procedure to follow. A system of rewards to induce volunteers might be more likely to lead to an increase in general happiness. Furthermore, the principle of utility suggests that the best research subjects would be "less valuable" members of the society, such as the mentally retarded, the habitual criminal, or the dying. This, again, is not a necessary consequence of utilitarianism, although it is a possible one. If the recognition of rights and dignity would produce a better society in general, then a utilitarian would also say that they must be taken into account in experimentation with human beings.

For utilitarianism, that individual is competent to give consent who can balance benefits and risks and decide what course of action is best for him or her. Thus, if informed consent is taken to be a requirement supported by the principle of utility, those who are mentally ill or retarded or senile have to be excluded from the class of potential experimental subjects. Furthermore, investigators must provide enough relevant information to allow competent people to make a meaningful decision about what is likely to serve their own interests the most.

Kant

For Kant, an individual capable of giving consent is one who is rational and autonomous. Kant's principles would thus also rule out as research subjects people who are not able to understand experimental procedures, aims, risks, and benefits. People may volunteer for clinical trials if they expect them to be of therapeutic benefit to themselves, or they may act out of duty and volunteer, thus discharging their imperfect obligation to advance knowledge or to improve human life.

Yet, for Kant, there are limits to the risks that one should take. We have a duty to preserve our lives, so no one should agree to become a subject in an experiment in which the likelihood of death is great. In addition, no one should subject himself to research in which there is considerable risk that his capacity for rational thought and autonomy will be destroyed. Indeed, Kant's principles appear to require us to regard as morally illegitimate those experiments which seriously threaten the lives or rationality of their subjects. Not only should we not subject ourselves to them, but we should not subject others to them.

Kant's principles also rule out as potential research participants those who are not in a position to act voluntarily, that is, those who cannot exercise their autonomy. This makes it important to determine, from a Kantian point of view, whether children and institutionalized people (including prisoners) can be regarded as free agents capable of moral choice. Also, as in the case of abortion, the status of the fetus must be determined. If the fetus is not a person, then fetal experimentation presents no particular moral problems. But if the fetus is a person, then we must accord it a moral status and act for its sake and not for the sake of knowledge or for others.

Kant's view of people as autonomous rational beings requires that informed consent be obtained for both medical treatment and research. We cannot be forced to accept treatment for "our own good," nor can we be turned into research subjects for "the good of others." We must always be treated as ends and never as means only. To be treated in this way requires that others never deliberately deceive us, no matter how good their intentions. In short, we have a right to be told what we are getting into so that we can decide whether we want to go through with it or not.

Ross

Ross's theory imposes on researchers prima facie duties to patients that are similar to Kant's requirements. The nature of people as autonomous moral agents requires that their informed consent be obtained. Researchers ought not to deceive their subjects, and protocols should be designed in ways in which suffering and the risk of injury or death are minimized.

These are all prima facie duties, of course, and it is possible to imagine situations in which other duties might take precedence over them.

In general, however, Ross, like Kant, tells us that human research cannot be based on what is useful; it must be based on what is right. Ross's principles, like Kant's, do not tell us, however, how we are to deal with such special problems as research involving children or prisoners.

Natural Law

The principle of double effect and the principle of totality, which are based on the natural law theory of morality, have specific applications to experimentation. (See Part V, "Foundations of Bioethics.") Because we hold our bodies in trust, we are responsible for assessing the degree of risk to which we might be put if we agree to become research subjects. Thus, others have an obligation to supply us with the information that we need in order to make our decision. If we decide to give our consent, it must be given freely and not be the consequence of deception or coercion.

If available evidence shows that a sick person may gain benefits from participating in a research project, then the research is justified. But if the evidence shows that the benefits may be slight or if the chance of serious injury or death is relatively great, then the research is not justified.

In general, the likelihood of a person's benefiting from becoming a participant must exceed the danger of the person's suffering greater losses. The four requirements that govern the application of the principle of double effect determine what is and what is not an allowable experiment. (See Part V, "Foundations of Bioethics," for a discussion of these requirements.)

People can volunteer for experiments from which they expect no direct benefits. The good they seek in doing so is not their own good but the good of others. But there are limits to what they can subject themselves to. A dying patient, for example, cannot be made the subject of a useless or trivial experiment. The probable value of the knowledge to be gained must balance the risk and suffering the patient is subjected to, and there must be no likelihood that the experiment will seriously injure or kill the patient.

These same restrictions also apply to experiments involving healthy people. The principle of totality forbids a healthy person to submit to an experiment that involves the probability of serious injury, impaired health, mutilation, or death.

The status of the fetus is clear in the Roman Catholic version of the natural law theory: the fetus is a person. As such, the fetus is entitled to the same dignity and respect we accord to other persons. Experiments that involve doing it injury or lessening its chances of life are morally prohibited. But not all fetal research is ruled out. That which may be of therapeutic benefit or which does not directly threaten the fetus's well-being is allowable. Furthermore, research involving fetal tissue or remains is permissible, if it is done for a serious and valuable purpose.

Rawls

From Rawls's point of view, the difficulty with utilitarianism with respect to human experimentation is that the principle of utility would permit the exploitation of some groups (the dying, prisoners, the retarded) for the sake of others. By contrast, Rawls's principles of justice would forbid all research that involves violating a liberty to which a person is entitled by virtue of being a member of society.

As a result, all experiments that make use of coercion or deception are ruled out. And since a person has a right to decide what risks she is willing to subject herself to, voluntary informed consent is required of all subjects. Society might, as in utilitarianism, decide to reward those who volunteer to become research subjects. As long as this is a possibility open to all, it is not objectionable.

It would never be right, according to Rawls, to take advantage of those in the society who are least well off to benefit those who are better off. Inequalities must be arranged so that they bring benefits (ideally) to everyone or, at least, to those who are most disadvantaged. Research involving direct therapeutic benefits is clearly acceptable (assuming informed consent), but research that takes advantage of the sick, the poor, the retarded, or the institutionalized and does not benefit them is unacceptable. The status of the fetus—whether or not it is a person in the moral senses—is an issue that has to be resolved before we know how to apply Rawls's principles to fetal research.

We have been able to provide only the briefest sketch of some of the ways in which our moral theories might apply to the issues in human experimentation. The remarks are not meant to be anything more than suggestive.

A satisfactory moral theory of human experimentation requires working out the application of principles to problems in detail, as well as resolving such issues as the status of children and fetuses and the capability of institutionalized people to act freely.

In the Case Presentations and Social Contexts presented earlier in the chapter, the issues we have discussed can be recognized as pressing problems requiring decisions about particular situations and general policies.

Part II

Controls

Chapter **3**

Genetic Control

CASES AND CONTEXTS

Genae Girard and Gene Patents

Genae Girard was only thirty-six years old in 2006, when she was diagnosed with breast cancer. She had been working hard building a veterinary supply business in Austin, Texas, and as with so many others, the cancer caught her off guard. She felt she still had many more things to accomplish in her life, but the breast cancer threatened to destroy all her plans.

Following the advice of her doctor, Girard agreed to a genetic test, and the results showed that she was positive for the BRCA2 gene mutation. That she had the gene made it likely that she would develop cancer in the other breast as well. She needed to have a mastectomy to treat her cancer, and to reduce the chances of developing cancer in the other breast, her doctor recommended that she have a double mastectomy.

The bad news got worse for Girard. She learned that BRCA2 also put her at risk for ovarian cancer. By some estimates, women who carry one of the known BRCA mutations have as high as a sixty percent chance of a developing ovarian cancer by age 65. To improve her chances of remaining alive, she would need to have her ovaries surgically removed.

Girard was unmarried and had no children, and without ovaries, she would never be able to have children of her own. This caused her to wonder, What if the test were wrong? What if she didn't have the BRCA2 mutation? Then maybe she wouldn't have to have the double mastectomy, and she wouldn't have to lose her ovaries. After all, she recalled later, "There is human error, and labs make mistakes." She was being asked to make a decision about her future on the basis of a single laboratory test.

Girard told her doctor that she wanted to have another test, one performed by another lab. That was when she learned—to her surprise—that there was no other test available, because Myriad Genetics owned the patent on the BRCA1 and BRCA2 genes. This gave Myriad the sole right to test for the presence of the mutations. Thus, Girard learned, Myriad was not merely the only game in town, it was the only game legally allowed.

Patenting Life?

When most people learn that it is possible to secure a patent on a gene, they are disbelieving. Common sense seems to suggest that genes have the same status as things in the world like oak trees, granite boulders, and sheet lightning. How could anyone patent such things?

No one can. The patent laws of the United States explicitly rule out patents on natural objects, processes, or laws of nature. Nor is it possible to patent naturally occurring organisms such as the oak tree, grizzly bear, army ant, or *E. coli* bacterium. With the development of molecular biology in the 1960s and recombinant-DNA technology in the 1970s, however, the line between "naturally occurring" organisms and altered or "manufactured" organisms began to blur.

Consider what was done with the bacterium *Pseudomonas* by Ananda Chakrabarty. *Pseudomonas,* which is found in soil the world over, was known to metabolize hydrocarbons, and for decades it was referred to as an "oil-eating" bacterium. The bacterium does its metabolic work very slowly, however, and Chakrabarty, a microbiologist employed by General Electric, conceived the idea of developing a strain of *Pseudomonas* that would be what he called a "superbug."

The new strain would be highly effective in breaking down hydrocarbons, and this would make it valuable in cleaning up oil spills rapidly and cheaply. A superbug would also be valuable financially, if it were possible to secure a patent on it. It could then be licensed, and the patent owners could demand a fee every time the bacterium was employed.

Chakrabarty began experimenting with four strains of *Pseudomonas,* and he soon realized that the bacterial enzymes that break down hydrocarbons aren't produced by genes in the nucleus. Rather, the relevant genes were in the extranuclear DNA in a cell's plasmids. The bacterial strains naturally exchange plasmids, and after much experimental work, Chakrabarty discovered that, following a plasmid transfer, he could use ultraviolet light to induce a host plasmid to incorporate DNA from other plasmids into its genetic material. Thus, after six years' work, he succeeded in creating a new strain of *Pseudomonas.*

Chakrabharty gave the new strain the descriptive name "multiplasmid hydrocarbon-degrading pseudomonas." Tests showed that the new strain would degrade oil ten to one hundred times faster than any of the four naturally occurring strains that he had worked with.

Patent Applied For

Chakrabarty (along with General Electric) applied for a patent on the superbug he had developed. The application was rejected on the ground that the law does not permit living things to be patented. Chakrabarty filed an appeal with the Board of Patent Appeal, but the board allowed the original decision to stand.

Chakrabarty then took the issue to the U.S. Court of Patent Appeals. This time his luck changed, and the appeals court ruled that Chakrabarty had produced a novel microorganism, one that does not appear in nature.

Moreover, the court held, "The fact that microorganisms are alive is without legal significance" with respect to the patent law.

This time it was the Patent Office that appealed. Sidney A Diamond, the Commissioner of Patents, took the case to the U.S. Supreme Court. On June 16, 1980, the Court, in a five to four ruling, upheld the decision of the Court of Patent Appeals.

Patent law states, "Whoever invents or discovers any new and useful process, machine, manufacture, or composition of matter, or any new and useful improvement thereof, may obtain a patent therefore. . . ." The majority of the Supreme Court decided that Chakrabarty's "microorganism constitutes a 'manufacture' or 'composition of matter' within the meaning of the law." This was the legal precedent for the thousands of biotech patents that would follow, but the courts had already upheld patents on products found in the human body.

Human Products

The first U.S. patent for a naturally occurring product was granted to Jokichi Takamine, a Japanese chemist who spent most of his professional life in New York. In 1906, Takamine and his sponsor, the drug company Parke-Davis, applied for a patent on "a blood pressure raising" substance that he had isolated from secretions of the "supradrenal glands" and purified. Parke-Davis gave the substance the trade name Adrenaline.[2] (It was later found to be a combination of epinephrine and norepinephrine.)

The patent was challenged in court by a rival drug company, on the ground that the substance was "a part of nature and not something invented or manufactured." Judge Learned Hand ruled in 1911 that Adrenaline could be patented, and his decision established the legal precedent that patents could be issued on isolated and purified versions of substances found in the human body. Such versions of the substances, Hand reasoned, wouldn't be available without the procedures chemists performed to produce them.

Human insulin, as soon as it was available in a purified form, was patented in 1923. A variety of other biological products, including vaccines, medical tests, and medical treatments, were patented in the decades that followed. Such patents became so common that it was striking news in 1955 (and remains so today) when Jonas Salk, the developer of the first effective polio vaccine, announced that he wouldn't seek a patent on it, because to do so would be as wrong as "to patent the sun."

Human Genes

The steady stream of patents for human and other biological materials became a flood with the increasing success of recombinant-DNA techniques. In 1977, three years before the Chakrabarty decision, the University of California applied for a patent on the genes for the production of human insulin and human grown hormone by genetically modified bacteria. The patents were granted in 1982 and 1987, and in 1985 the Cetus Corporation was granted a patent for the protein interleukin-2, an immune system activator used in the treatment of some cancers.

Patents were also issued for specific antibodies, various human hormones and growth factors, and blood factors used in the treatment of hemophilia, as well as for a variety of genetically engineered viruses. Many of the specialized viruses are vaccines, while others are used to transport genes into cells in gene-therapy experiments. Animals that have been genetically modified to allow the study of human diseases (animal models) have also been patented. (Transgenic organisms that include genes from other species, including humans, are themselves a source of controversy.)

The Human Genome Project decoded major amounts of the human genetic material, and as large numbers of human genes were identified, they were quickly patented. (See "Social Context: The Human Genome Project," in this chapter.) The patents include DNA sequences that encode instructions for making particular proteins or for regulating the way a gene is expressed, but they also encompass variants of normal genes associated with diseases. The BRCA1 and BRCA2 mutations patented by Myriad Genetics fall into this category. So does the HHF gene, a mutation leading to hemochromatosis (a disease in which so much iron accumulates in the blood as to cause organ damage), and the genetic variants that produce hypocholesterolimia (a lipid disorder in which excess cholesterol increases the risk of heart disease and stroke). Patents have also been issued for RNA sequences, such as those which function as switches to turn genes off or on.

The genes mapped and sequenced by the Human Genome Project now number from twenty to twenty-five thousand. Some experts estimate that about twenty percent of these genes, three to five thousand, have been patented. In addition, as many as fifty thousand patents involving genetic material—RNA sequences, transgenic animals, and modified bacteria—may have been issued.

Myriad Flexes Its Patents

The United States is not the only country that allows genes, genetically altered organisms, and products based on genetic material to be patented. Because these patents include tests designed to detect the presence of a gene or a mutation, tests themselves have sparked a great amount of concern and anger.

Holders of gene patents have not, in general, made it expensive for a scientist to get a license to work on a gene or to develop diagnostic tests for it. The most glaring exception has been Myriad Genetics. In 2001, the company sent letters to biological and medical researchers in industrialized countries, informing them that Myriad owned the rights to BRCA1 and BRCA2 and that all testing for the presence of these genes had to be done in a laboratory operated or licensed by Myriad.

Canada refused to recognize the terms of Myriad's patents, and in Europe the patents were challenged in court. The patent claims on BRCA1 were reduced, and a BRCA2 patent was granted to the British Cancer Research Campaign, a research organization that has pledged to offer unrestricted access to scientists.

Myriad, as Genae Girard discovered, has a monopoly on testing for the breast-cancer genes in the United States Critics claim that the $3,000 Myriad charges for a test could be reduced if Myriad allowed them to perform the tests. (The cost of the test in Canada is about $1,000.) Other labs might also be able to perform the tests more quickly, but so long as Myriad asserts its patent rights, hospitals and clinical laboratories don't want to risk a lawsuit. Before Myriad sent its warning letter, some physician-researchers had been testing breast-cancer patients for the mutations, but they stopped.

The cost of the tests can have a personal impact on patients. Genae Girard wanted a second test by another lab before she agreed to have a double mastectomy and her ovaries removed. Lisbeth Ceriani, according to reporter John Schwartz, had a double mastectomy for breast cancer, then wanted to be tested for BRCA1 and BRCA2 to see if she was at risk for ovarian cancer and needed to have her ovaries removed. Myriad refused to accept her insurance, and Ceriani was unable to come up with the cash. Ceriani hesitated to have surgery she might not need, but as the mother of an eight-year-old daughter, she also wanted to know if her child might have inherited gene mutations predisposing her to breast cancer and ovarian cancer.

Con and Pro

Critics of gene patenting point to its negative impact on patients, but they also worry about the consequence it may have on biomedical research. If no one is able to conduct research on the BRCA1 and BRCA2 genes without paying Myriad or at least getting the company's permission, this alone has a chilling effect. Researchers who attempt to understand the still unknown ways in which genetic variants operate to produce disease, but who do not gain Myriad's approval, risk lawsuits for patent infringement.

Indeed, researchers can't even compare a normal stretch of DNA with one containing mutated genes without Myriad's permission. Rather than court legal entanglements, research institutions, universities, and scientists work in areas where patents are not a problem. In the view of a representative of the American Civil Liberties Union, Myriad's patent claims constitute restrictions on the free exchange of ideas and thus violate the First Amendment.

Defenders of gene patents reject these criticisms and argue that, without patent protection, research wouldn't flourish the way it has for the last several decades. Researchers, institutions, and venture capitalists would not invest the talent, time, and money that are necessary to advance genetic research without the promise of a significant financial payoff.

The very purpose of a patent system, they point out, is to encourage innovation and effort by rewarding those who succeed in acquiring potentially useful knowledge. For example, the processes and materials involved in the production of microchips couldn't be patented, the computer industry probably wouldn't have made such great strides forward in such a short time. If we want to see biotech industries flourish in a similar way, we need to recognize the importance of the patent system in providing the promise of incentives. Refusing to recognize the legitimacy of gene patents could have the effect of slowing the development of "personalized medicine," medical practice in which treatments are tailored to fit the genetic profile of individual patients.

Genae Girard's Day in Court

Genae Girard, with the backing of the American Civil Liberties Union and the Association for Molecular Pathology, filed a lawsuit against Myriad Genetics challenging several of its BRCA1 and BRCA2 patent claims. The case was heard by Judge Robert Sweet of the United States District Court of New York, and Judge Sweet issued his ruling on March 29, 2010.

Judge Sweet rejected seven of Myriad's patent claims involving the BRCA1 and BRCA2 genes. Myriad, he decided, had no legitimate patent claim on the DNA sequences related to the two genes or to the methods of analyzing or comparing the sequences to detect the presence or absence of the mutated genes. The Patent Office, he said, should not have granted the patents, because the genes are a "law of nature" and do not therefore qualify, according to the law, as something for which patents can be granted.

Judge Sweet did not deny the importance of the research performed by Myriad leading to the identification of the genes. Even so, the importance of the discoveries does not mean that Myriad can patent them. As Sweet wrote in the decision

> The identification of the BRCAI and BRCA2 gene sequences is unquestionably a valuable scientific achievement for which Myriad deserves recognition, but this not the same as concluding that it is something for which they are entitled to a patent.

Although the suit against Myriad had challenged the patents on the ground that they, in effect, restricted the free exchange of ideas and thus violated the First Amendment, Judge Sweet declined to rule on the issue. In his view, the case could be settled within the area of patent law alone.

The ACLU attorney, Chris Hansen, underscored the nature of the ruling: "The human genome, like the structure of blood, air or water, was discovered, not created. There is an endless amount of information on genes that begs for further discovery, and gene patents put up unacceptable barriers to the free exchange of ideas."

Genae Girard declared that the court decision was "a big turning point for all women in the country that may have breast cancer that runs in their family."

Promote or Impede

Myriad Genetics issued no public statement, but knowledgeable observers expect their attorneys to file an appeal. The legal battle over gene patents may take years to resolve, but if higher courts uphold Judge Sweet's ruling, thousands of patents granted to biotech companies may be either invalidated or considerably restricted.

Whether such an outcome would promote or impede the advancement of our understanding of genetics and the development of personalized medicine is a debate that will continue.

CASE PRESENTATION

Huntington's Disease: Deadly Disease, Personal Dilemmas

Huntington's disease (HD) is a particularly cruel and frightening genetic disorder. It has no effective treatment and is invariably fatal. Furthermore, each child of an affected parent has a fifty percent chance of developing the disease.

The disease typically makes its appearance between the ages of thirty-five and forty-five in men and women who have shown no previous symptoms. The signs of its onset may be quite subtle—a certain clumsiness in performing small tasks, a slight slurring of speech, a few facial twitches. But the disease is progressive. Over time, the small signs develop into massive physical and mental changes. Walking becomes jerky and unsteady, the face contorts into wild grimaces, the hands repeatedly clench and relax, and the whole body writhes with involuntary muscle spasms. The victim eventually loses the power of speech, becomes disoriented, and gives way to irrational emotional outbursts. Before mental deterioration becomes too advanced, HD victims often kill themselves out of sheer hopelessness and despair. Death may occur naturally from fifteen to twenty years after the beginning of the symptoms. Usually, it results from massive infection and malnutrition—as the disease progresses, the victim loses the ability to swallow normally.

In the United States, at any given time, some 30,000 people are diagnosed as having the disease, and as many as 150,000 more may have the gene responsible for it. The incidence of the disease is only one in 10,000, but for the child of someone with the disease, the chances of having it are one in two.

Gene Identified

The gene causing the disease was identified in 1993 after ten years of intensive research carried out in six laboratories in the United States, England, and Wales. Following the leads provided by genetic markers for the disease, the gene was finally located near the tip of chromosome 4. When researchers sequenced the nucleotides making up the gene, they discovered that the mutation was a trinucleotide repeat. In healthy individuals, the nucleotides CAG are repeated eleven to thirty-four times, whereas in individuals with HD, the repetitions typically range from thirty-seven to eighty-six. Some evidence suggests that higher numbers of repetitions are associated with earlier onset.

When the HD gene was identified, it was expected that this would have almost immediate consequences for the development of an effective treatment. This has not turned out to be the case, because the mechanism of the gene's action is not yet understood. Furthermore, the gene was expected to be found functioning only in the brain, but in fact radioactive tagging has shown that the gene operates in virtually every tissue of the body, including the colon, liver, pancreas, and testes. The protein the gene codes for is believed to be toxic to neuronal development, but the protein itself has not yet been isolated. (In 1998, it was discovered that the disease involves the formation of a protein plaque in brain cells that destroys them, but this hasn't yet led to a therapy.)

Before the HD gene was identified or a marker for it discovered, the disease was known to be transmitted from generation to generation in the sort of hereditary pattern indicating that it is caused by a single gene. However, because the disease makes its appearance relatively late in life, an unsuspecting victim may already have passed on the gene to a child before showing any sign of the disease. In the absence of a genetic test to detect the gene, the individual could not know whether he or she was a carrier.

In 1983, a major step toward the development of such a test was announced by James F. Gusella and his group at Massachusetts General Hospital. The team did not locate the gene itself, but discovered a "genetic marker" indicating its presence. They began by studying the DNA taken from members of a large American family with a history of Huntington's disease, then employed recombinant-DNA techniques to attempt to locate DNA segments that might be associated with the HD gene.

The techniques involved using proteins known as restriction enzymes. A particular enzyme, when mixed with a single strand of DNA, cuts the strand at specific locations known as recognition sites. After the DNA strand has been cut up by restriction enzymes, short sections of radioactive, single-stranded DNA are added to serve as probes. The probes bind to particular segments of the DNA. Because the probes are radioactive, the segments to which they are attached can be identified on photographic film. The various fragments of DNA produced by the restriction enzymes and identified by probes form a pattern that is typical of individuals. Thus, if the pattern of someone who does not have the disease is compared with the pattern of a family member who does, the fragments that include the faulty gene can be identified, even when the gene itself is unknown. The pattern serves as a marker for the presence of the gene.

Gusella's group faced the problem of finding a marker consistently inherited by those with Huntington's disease but not by those free of the disease. This meant identifying perhaps as many as eight hundred markers and determining whether one could serve as the marker for the HD gene. Incredibly, the team identified a good candidate on its twelfth try. It was a marker found in all members of the family they were studying. Those with the disease had the same form of the marker, while those free of the disease had some other form.

Gusella and other researchers were supported in their work by the Hereditary Disease Foundation. The organization was founded by Milton Wexler after his wife was diagnosed with Huntington's. Wexler hoped a treatment for the disease could be found that might benefit his daughters, Nancy and Alice, who stood a fifty percent chance of developing the disease. Nancy Wexler soon became an active participant in research activities aimed at discovering a genetic marker.

In collaboration with the Hereditary Disease Foundation, plans were made to test Gusella's candidate marker in a large population. It was known that a large family with a high incidence of HD lived along the shores of Lake Maracaibo in Venezuela. Nancy Wexler led a team to this remote location to collect a family history and to obtain blood and skin samples for analysis. The lake-dwelling family included some 100 people with the disease and 1100 children with the risk of developing it. Analysis of the samples showed that those with the disease also carried the same form of the marker as their American counterparts. Gusella estimated that the odds were one hundred million to one that the marker was linked to the HD gene. Subsequent work by Susan Naylor indicated that the marker was on chromosome 4. When the gene itself was identified in 1993, this turned out to be correct.

Genetic Test Available

Once the location of the gene for Huntington's disease was known, a genetic test for its presence was quickly developed. The availability of the test, however, raises a number of serious ethical and social issues. The basic question people with a family history that puts them at risk for the disease must ask is whether they should have the test.

A study conducted in Wales revealed that more than half of those whose parents or relatives were victims of Huntington's disease would not want to have a test that would tell them whether they had the HD gene, even if such a test were available. Considering that the disease cannot be effectively treated and is invariably fatal, this is not a surprise finding.

Nancy Wexler confided to a reporter that she and her sister had assumed that once a test for determining whether they were carrying the HD gene was available, they would take it. However, when they met with their father to work out the details for a test based on a genetic marker, he suddenly said, "What are we doing here? Are we sure we want to do this?" The sisters, Nancy recalled, "had a visceral understanding that either one of us could get bad news and that it would certainly destroy my father."

But do those who are at risk have obligations to others? Because a test is available, is it fair to a potential marriage partner to marry without finding out whether one is a carrier of the HD gene and informing the potential partner of the result? Perhaps he or she may be willing to take the chance that the offspring of an HD parent will not have the disease. Even so, because of the tremendous burden the disease places on the other spouse, the possibility of being tested for the presence of the gene deserves serious consideration.

The decision about whether to have children can also be affected by the knowledge that one partner is a carrier of the HD gene so that there is a fifty percent chance that any child will also develop the disease. Should a potential carrier of the gene impose on the other partner the risk of having a child who will inherit the gene? Should such a risk be imposed on a potential child? The genetic test can determine whether an individual carries the gene. If he or she does, then the couple has knowledge of the relevant facts that will put them in a position to make a decision about having a child.

Prenatal Testing and Embryo Screening

The test now in use can also be employed in conjunction with amniocentesis to determine whether a developing fetus carries the HD gene. This fact raises problems for potential parents. A child born with the HD gene will inevitably develop the disease but may not do so for three, four, or even five or more decades. Does this mean that an abortion is not justified in the event of a positive test? But if the potential parents aren't prepared to seek an abortion, why should they have wanted the test? Finally, is the fact that the fetus can be expected to develop into an adult who will eventually succumb to the disease reason enough to make an abortion morally obligatory?

A disadvantage of the direct testing of the fetus for the presence of the HD gene is that if the fetus is found to have the gene, then the parent with a family history of the disease will know that she or he also has the gene. To avoid this consequence, a "nondisclosing" prenatal test may be possible. The test employs a gene-probe method to determine how a segment of fetal chromosome 4 compares with segments from grandparents. If the segment resembles that of a healthy grandparent, the child is not likely to have the HD gene. If it matches that of a grandparent with the disease, the chances are one in two that the child possesses the gene.

This is the same as the risk for a mother or father with one parent who developed the disease. Hence, the potential parent has learned nothing new about his or her own chance of having the gene, and it is this that makes the test nondisclosing. However, if the potential parents do not plan to abort the fetus should they learn that it has a fifty-fifty chance of possessing the HD gene, they have no reason to perform the nondisclosing test.

An alternative to abortion for potential parents who worry about one of them passing on the HD gene to a child is to make use of the techniques of assisted reproduction. Once embryos have been produced by artificial insemination from the parents' donated ova and sperm, the embryos can be tested for the HD gene. Only embryos without the gene can then be transferred to the woman's uterus for development.

Personal Risks

The advent of a standard, inexpensive test for the HD gene raises various other personal and social issues. For example, insurance companies may refuse to provide life insurance to those from families with Huntington's disease, unless they prove that they are not carriers of the gene. (The Genetic Information Nondiscrimination Act—GINA—does not forbid insurers from using genetic information in underwriting life insurance.) Adoption agencies have requested that infants offered for adopting be tested to assure adopting families that the children are not at risk for HD. (Whether such would violate GINA screening has not been tested.) As Nancy Wexler put the point, "In our culture, people assume that knowledge is always good. . . . But our experience with Huntington's has shown that some things may be better left unknown."

Informing someone that he or she carries the gene also has problems associated with it. Such news can be devastating, both to the person and to the person's family. The most recent evidence indicates that the suicide rate among those with HD is ten times the rate of the general population. In a recent survey of 175 medical centers in which a total of 4,527 people tested positive for the HD gene, 5 killed themselves, 21 attempted suicide, and 18 were hospitalized for psychiatric reasons. Thus, the mere act of conveying the information that someone will later develop the signs of a fatal disease can itself constitute a threat to life. Nancy Wexler has refused to disclose publicly whether she has been tested for the HD gene. "I don't want to influence anyone's decision," she says.

Envoi

In the best of worlds, an effective means of preventing the onset of Huntington's disease or treating it effectively would be available. Then the moral, social, and personal issues associated with a genetic test for it would disappear without having to be resolved. Regrettably, that world still lies in the future.

SOCIAL CONTEXT
Testing for Disease Predispositions: Is It Better Not to Know?

The discovery of hundreds of disease-predisposing genes has been accompanied by the development of new genetic tests. Given the increasing sophistication of biotechnology, tests that were complex and expensive have become simple and cheap. By using cells from a cheek swab or a blood sample in an automated process involving biochip arrays of genetic probes, it should be possible to screen simultaneously for the presence of literally hundreds of genes. (For more details, see "Social Context: What Are My Chances? Direct to Consumer Genetic Testing," in this chapter.)

Genetic Disease: Blurred Concept

Researchers are well on the way to identifying an entire catalogue of genes and diseases associated with them, but the concept of a genetic disease is not as clear-cut as it may seem. Rarely is it the case that if a person carries a certain gene, she will invariably develop a certain disease. Although single-gene disorders such as sickle-cell disease, cystic fibrosis, and Huntington's disease have been at the focus of much research, they account for only about two percent of genetic disorders. Most diseases result from a multiplicity of conditions, including the particular form of a gene (many genes have scores, and even hundreds, of mutated versions), the presence or absence of other genes, and the presence or absence of specific environmental factors. Being predisposed to develop a disease raises a number of questions

about the value and dangers of genetic testing.

Individual Choice

The ambivalence most people feel about genetic testing is shown by the results of a recent survey. When five hundred people were asked if they would like to take a genetic test that would tell them what diseases they would suffer from later in life, fifty percent said they would want to take it and forty-nine percent said they wouldn't. We all seem torn between seeing the value of knowing and the comfort of not knowing.

Information about a genetic predisposition to a particular disease can be beneficial to people. It can alert them to the need to seek medical surveillance so that they can receive appropriate therapy for the disease, should it develop, at the earliest time. Further, it can make them aware of the need to avoid environmental factors that may trigger the disease. For example, those with the gene for xeroderma pigmentosum are extremely sensitive to ultraviolet radiation, and exposure to it is likely to lead to a form of skin cancer (melanoma) that is usually incurable. However, if those with the gene avoid prolonged exposure to sunlight, they have a good chance of avoiding developing melanoma.

By contrast, in the case of some single-gene diseases like Huntington's, knowing that one is a carrier of the gene opens up no ways of altering the outcome of the disease. No way of preventing the disease is known, and early

A Sample of DNA Tests Currently Available	
Disease	**Description**
Huntington's disease	Progressive neurological disorder, onset in 40s or 50s
Polycystic kidney disease	Multiple kidney cysts leading to loss of kidney function
Cystic fibrosis	Mucus clogs lungs and pancreas; death in 30s is common
Sickle-cell disease	Hemoglobin defect; anemia, strokes, and heart damage
Alpha-1-antitrypsin deficiency	Can cause hepatitis, cirrhosis, and emphysema
Familial adenomatous polyposis	Colon polyps by age 35, often leading to cancer
Muscular dystrophy	Progressive muscle deterioration
Hemophilia	Blood fails to clot properly
Tay–Sachs disease	Lipid metabolism disorder causing death in first one to four years of life
Retinoblastoma	Cancerous tumor of the eye; most common in childhood
Phenylketonuria	Enzyme deficiency producing mental retardation
Retinitis pigmentosa	Progressive retinal degeneration leading to blindness
Familial breast cancer	five to ten percent of breast cancers
Familial hypercholesterolemia	High levels of cholesterol leading to early heart disease
Spinocerebellar ataxia	Neurological disorder producing lack of muscle control

intervention makes no difference in the course of the illness. Although some might want to know whether they are carriers of the gene in order to make informed decisions about such personal matters as marriage, childbearing, and lifestyle, others might prefer to live their lives without knowing. (See "Case Presentation: Huntington's Disease," in this chapter.)

Equally difficult issues are associated with testing for the genes known to be associated with familial breast cancer. The mutated gene BRCA1, located on chromosome 17, was identified in 1994 as responsible for the susceptibility to breast cancer and ovarian cancer in a group of families with multiple incidence of the diseases.

A "frame-shift mutation" involving an extra nucleotide apparently causes the translation of codons to start in the wrong place, producing a nonsense protein. A second gene, BRCA2, located on chromosome 13, that also causes susceptibility to breast cancer was discovered in 1995. More than two hundred mutations have been identified on the BRCA genes, but one study suggests that it is a mutation in BRCA1 which is most likely to cause cancer in younger women.

Women who carry one of the mutated genes are estimated to have an eighty-five percent chance of developing breast cancer and a sixty percent chance of developing ovarian cancer by age 65. Whether these figures can be generalized to any carrier of the gene is in dispute, because they are based on samples from families with a history of breast cancer. Some suggest that a more realistic figure for breast cancer for a woman with the BRCA mutation is fifty-six percent.

The two mutated genes may explain the majority of hereditary breast cancers. (BRCA1 appears responsible for about 50% and BRCA2 for 30–40 %.) Yet to the surprise of researchers, no evidence suggests that the BRCA1 or BRCA2 gene plays a role in the 90% to 95% of "sporadic" breast cancers—ones not known to be due to inherited susceptibility. (The possibility that mutations in other genes are responsible is under investigation.)

But susceptibility to breast cancer means only that a woman is more likely than average to develop the disease. The extent to which she might control the outcome by altering such factors as diet, alcohol consumption, and exercise isn't known.

The evidence shows that a woman's chances of developing cancer can be significantly reduced by a prophylactic double mastectomy. Even so, cancer can still occur in the remaining tissue. Also, ovarian cancer remains as likely as before, so to lower those odds, a woman at risk must also have her ovaries removed. Should a woman with a strong family history of breast and ovarian cancer be tested for BRCA1 and BRCA2?

The generally accepted view is that this is a question that should be answered by the woman herself. Some women want to know, because they want to have the surgery that may extend their lives. Other women, particularly those who may be looking to find a partner or to have children, may be unwilling to have the surgery. Thus, from this point of view, they may see no practical value in finding out.

Another group of women might value discovering something important about themselves. Even if they don't plan to have surgery, what they learn from the test might influence the way they live their lives. If they test negative for the genes, knowing that they are no more likely than other women to develop breast or ovarian cancer would allow them to go about their lives without the worry that speculation and uncertainty might produce. If they test positive, they are in a position to reconsider the surgery option and have been alerted to the need to make sure that they get regular mammograms and, perhaps, a blood test for ovarian cancer.

Should We Tell the Children?

Researchers attempting to identify a gene predisposing women to breast cancer conducted their work among families with a high incidence of the disease. During the course of their work, they learned which females in the family had to be carriers of the BRCA1 gene and so had an eighty-five percent chance of developing the disease. The question they faced was, Should they inform the women that they or their children were at such risk?

Some researchers decided that they would not volunteer any information and would provide it only to women eighteen or older who asked for it. They refused to divulge any information about children, even when pressed to do so by their parents, because being predisposed to breast cancer is not a condition for which there is a treatment. Also, the researchers reasoned, if a child knew she was predisposed to breast cancer, she might be inclined to think of herself as sick and her breasts as likely to kill her.

Some critics of testing have argued that children should not be included in screening tests, except when there is some direct benefit for them. The acquisition of knowledge is not in itself a justification for testing children, the critics hold, nor is the usefulness of the knowledge in the treatment of others. Genetic tests and the results they yield have the potential to damage or destroy a child's self-esteem, causing emotional harm or altering the way the family views the child. In some instances, upon learning that a child is likely to develop a disease, some families distanced themselves from the child, even to the point of placing the child in a foster home. When the child herself receives no benefit, the threat of such outcomes makes the test unjustifiable.

At least one survey shows, however, that parents often believe that children should be aware of their risks for developing a particular disease. Some sixty-one percent of parents visiting prenatal testing clinics said that they should be permitted to have their children tested for Alzheimer's, and forty-seven percent said that parents should inform the children of the results.

However, another survey of families with members already diagnosed with genetic diseases shows a different result. Survey participants seemed to feel strongly that parents should have their children tested for a disease only when it is a treatable or preventable one. When the disease is neither, as is the case with Alzheimer's, the screening should not be done.

The issue may be complicated in some cases by the discovery that a disease, which is mild or even asymptomatic in a parent may be much worse in an offspring. This was found to be the case with myotonic muscular dystrophy, the most common form of the disease. A segment of DNA on chromosome 19 appears to repeat itself with increasing frequency over generations. Hence, someone who does not have any clinical sign of the disease may pass on the gene to a child, who will develop a devastating form of the disease. It could be argued that if a parent knows that a child is at high risk for developing a life-threatening disease, the parent has a duty to inform the child, although perhaps only after the child has reached a certain level of maturity.

Whether children should be given genetic tests for diseases for which there is no immediate treatment is likely to remain controversial. The views of parents, genetic counselors, and physicians may conflict where certain diseases are concerned. Who should make the decision? How much should the child be told? These are questions likely to become more pressing as the number of tests for disease-associated genes increases.

Protection against Discrimination

Until recently, the main worry associated with our newly acquired abilities to test adults for genes associated with diseases was that the information could be used by employers and insurers to the disadvantage of those who decided to be tested. Thus, genetic testing was seen as opening the way for new forms of discrimination—discrimination based on genetic predisposition.

Indeed, the discrimination became real. Some employers refused to hire people whose genetic profile suggested that they might develop diseases such as breast cancer, ovarian cancer, Huntington's disease, or hypercholesterolemia (and the heart and vascular diseases accompanying it) that might lead to many absences from work or to expensive treatments that would raise a company's health insurance

costs. Similarly, insurance companies often turned down for coverage people likely to file claims for costly treatments and medicines. Insurers were also moving in the direction of regarding a genetic predisposition to develop a disease as a "prexisisting condition," something not covered by most health insurance policies.

The Genetic Information Nondiscrimination Act (GINA) was framed to prevent discrimination of the sort just described. The act took effect in November 2009 and is supposed to make it possible for people to keep genetic information about themselves private without suffering a penalty. Employers and insurers can no longer require, for example, that people be tested for specific genetic predispositions, nor can they make use of such information if they find it in someone's medical record. (See "Social Context: GINA," in this chapter.) GINA extends to children as well, so that parents will not be expected to pay higher premiums for a child who tests positive for a genetic disorder.

Not enough time has passed to determine how effective GINA will be in protecting the genetic privacy of individuals. Before a realistic assessment can be made, the regulations and penalties specified in the legislation will need to be tested in court. Most observers agree, however, that GINA is a significant step in the direction of safeguarding personal genetic information.

"Genetic Undesirables"

A part from issues connected with employment and insurance, genetic testing opens up the possibility of identifying a class of people that may become regarded as socially undesirable.

As genetic sophistication and genetic information spread, people can be expected to develop a better understanding of what it means to be genetically predisposed to develop a disease such as ovarian cancer or to be carrying the gene for retinitis pigmentosa or sickle-cell disease. In a society that prizes health, being predisposed to a genetic disease may become a stigma. Genetic carriers of disease-causing genes might be shunned as marriage partners or find it difficult to make their way into positions of social power and influence. Regarded as genetic pariahs, they might come to be outcasts in their own society, stigmatized by their biological inheritance.

The more we learn about our genes and the more individuals learn about their personal genome, people's genetic profile might come to be considered as important as their appearance, income, or personality.

Envoi

The difficulties discussed here are only some of those raised by the new possibilities of testing for the genetic predisposition to diseases. The promise of being able to prevent the occurrence of some disease in many individuals is genuine, but we have yet to make an adequate effort to resolve the social and moral issues that fulfilling the promise presents. Until we deal with them satisfactorily, a powerful technology may remain underutilized. Genetic information may become a case of dangerous knowledge that we shy away from using because of its destructive potential.

SOCIAL CONTEXT
Predictive Genetic Testing: To Test or Not to Test?

The success of genetic testing in predicting that a baby may be born with one of a variety of possible diseases or conditions is considered by many a triumph of contemporary biomedical science. No longer must we acknowledge genetic fate and accept what happens with resignation. Rather, in many cases we have the power to avoid the outcome of having a child with a serious or even fatal disease. Genetic testing is thus a way of dodging a bullet that can destroy hopes and shatter lives.

Don't Test

Not everyone takes such a positive view of predictive genetic testing, however. The optimistic view celebrates the fact that genetic testing can allow parents a certain amount of control over what their child will be like. But critics worry about the use of this power and about its consequences for people born with certain genetic traits or disorders.

First, the critics ask, what condition is sufficiently serious to justify a decision to have an abortion (or, alternatively, avoid implanting an embryo with a certain gene)? Those who accept the legitimacy of abortion for serious reasons may agree that the prospect of having a child with a disease like Tay–Sachs that is untreatable and fatal in early childhood would warrant an abortion.

By contrast, people with the Huntington's gene don't develop the disease until middle age, and the lives of those with cystic fibrosis can be extended into their thirties or even forties. Should these lives be prevented by abortion or embryo selection? Moreover, what about hereditary conditions like some forms of deafness and blindness? Should we even consider these as diseases, much less view them as conditions that justify aborting a fetus carrying the genes responsible for them?

Second, some critics maintain that genetic testing with the aim of aborting fetuses considered in some way "abnormal" is a form of discrimination against people with disabilities. It is, they say, an implicit endorsement of the notion that someone who has Down syndrome or is born blind, deaf, or a dwarf is not the equal of (not as good as) someone who is "normal." Thus, genetic testing can be seen as a socially approved eugenics program that devalues the worth of people with disabilities.

Third, critics worry that diminishing the number of people with conditions such as cystic fibrosis, Down syndrome, muscular dystrophy, and hereditary deafness will have a negative impact on those now living with those conditions. For one, a reduction in the number of affected people will mean that those with the condition will have a smaller community. Thus, they risk becoming even more socially isolated than they are now.

Also, a smaller number of affected people means that the group might lose much of its political influence. Public programs established to move disabled people into the mainstream of school and life will either have their funding cut or become so small that their aims can no longer be achieved. For example, school districts can have a program in special athletics if only three people qualify to participate. Thus, individuals for whom such programs were designed will no longer be able to benefit.

Finally, critics say, a drastic reduction in the number of people born with genetic diseases or conditions would mean that researchers will no longer be motivated to develop new drugs or treatments for the diseases or disabilities people now live with. If cystic fibrosis can be eliminated by early genetic screening and the number of people with the disease falls below some crucial level, researchers aren't likely to devote their careers to improving the lot of a handful of people, because the rewards and support aren't there. Rather, cystic fibrosis will become another "orphan" disease—a disease affecting so few people that it can't command the resources and talent needed to find a better way to treat it. Such an investment is more likely to be made in finding better ways of treating breast cancer or heart disease.

Test

The preceding criticisms do not meet with much sympathy from those who believe that prenatal genetic testing, when combined with abortion and screening embryos before implantation, offers a way to reduce the amount of misery in the world by preventing the birth of children who may suffer from one of a large number of devastating and incurable diseases or may lack some beneficial natural capacity such as sight or hearing.

Advocates of prenatal genetic testing answer the critics' first point by arguing that potential parents are the ones who should decide whether they want to accept the burden of caring for a child with a debilitating disease. Someone with cystic fibrosis may live thirty or even forty years, but this is not likely to happen unless the parents make keeping their child alive their central priority and devote the majority of their time and effort to that task. Typically, such devotion shortchanges other children in the family and requires parents to become martyrs. Some people may want to make this decision, but others may not.

Also, defenders of testing say, some believe it is not morally responsible to have a child with a disease or condition that can significantly shorten his life or seriously affect his prospects in life. Yes, someone with Huntington's disease may live more than forty years, but the final years will be spent in a condition of physical and mental decline. The person will suffer greatly and become a burden to himself or others. Similarly, if we recognize a gene in an embryo that, if implanted in a women's uterus, will lead to the birth of a blind child, why should the woman not ask that an embryo lacking that gene be implanted? Such a limiting condition as blindness will make the child's lot in life harder in general and eliminate many possibilities of both pleasure and accomplishment. A blind child also imposes burdens on the parents, the family, and society. In these cases and in similar ones, defenders of testing say, we can see ourselves as having an obligation to both prevent suffering and protect an individual's range of possibilities.

Defenders of genetic testing are equally unconvinced by the second criticism. In their view, the idea that making a reproductive decision on the grounds that a genetic test predicting a disorder is equivalent to devaluing individuals with the disorder involves two errors. First, the critics assume that an embryo or a fetus has the same moral status as a person. Some people believe this, but it is not an idea accepted by everyone and so cannot be used as a general objection to genetic testing. Second, the critics confuse people with their condition. That we don't want a child to be born blind (for example) does not mean we don't value blind people. We value them because they are *people*, though, not because they are blind. People who are blind lack a capacity (sight) that is of value in coping with the world and in appreciating the things in it. The world would be better, in this respect, if those who are blind could see. Yet to say it would be a better world if there were no blind people is not to devalue the people or wish them out of existence. Rather, it is to wish for everyone to possess the capacity of sight.

Most defenders of prenatal genetic testing reject the idea that deciding not to implant an embryo that will lead to the birth of a child with a serious disease or disability is eugenics. Such a practice can be regarded as negative eugenics in a narrow, technical sense, but it isn't what we usually think of as eugenic. It is not, that is, part of a social policy intended to improve the human race. Typically, the use of prenatal genetic testing is only the attempt by potential parents to have a child as free of diseases and problems as possible. Although people who seek genetic testing in connection with reproduction are often described as attempting to have a "perfect baby," the great majority say they want only a healthy baby.

Defenders of genetic testing reject the third and fourth criticisms as little more than expressions of self-interest. The critics tend to be people with diseases (or family members of such people) that would be decreased in frequency if genetic testing became widely used in making reproductive decisions. Thus, the Cystic Fibrosis Foundation, the main organization of people with the disease and their families, does not promote prenatal testing for the CF gene. By contrast, the American College of Obstetrics and Gynecology recommends it to pregnant women.

The critics, it appears, want to maintain the number of similarly affected people so that they or their family members can receive benefits gained by their political activism. These benefits may be directly personal (medical expenses, educational mainstreaming, etc.) or they may be ones such as improved treatments that benefit everyone with their condition. But, defenders say, this is an approach that is both unimaginative and of doubtful moral legitimacy.

So far as getting benefits is concerned, wouldn't it be better for the critics to advocate for reforms in education and health care that would provide all people in the society with the support they need? Similarly, instead of wanting to increase the number of people born with (say) cystic fibrosis so that the disease would continue to attract research money and talent, wouldn't it be better to advocate a change in the way that medical research takes place? Finding a way to encourage research on "orphan" diseases seems a more reasonable way to approach the problem than trying to make sure that a large number of people are born with cystic fibrosis.

As to moral legitimacy, can we believe that people are doing the right thing in promoting and welcoming the birth of more children with serious diseases to benefit themselves or members of their family? Surely, advocates for people with disabilities should not want to encourage the birth of *more* people with disabilities.

Research Results

Instead of giving answers either favoring or objecting to reproductive genetic testing in a wholesale fashion, people often make more nuanced, case-by-case decisions. A study of the choices of 53,000 women that was published in *Obstetrics and Gynecology* in 2002 (the most recent study of its kind) showed that when prenatally diagnosed conditions would have no impact on the quality of a child's life, the termination rate was only about one percent. However, when the conditions would have a serious negative impact, the rate rose to fifty percent.

When a diagnosis indicated a disability likely to affect cognitive functioning, the women in the study were much more likely to choose to terminate their pregnancy. If a condition was predicted that would require surgery or special medical treatment, the abortion rate was sixteen percent. This rate doubled, though, when the condition was likely to cause some form of mental dysfunction, such as cognitive impairment.

The disposition favoring cognitive abilities found in the 2002 study also seems to hold when decisions are made about Down syndrome. The condition invariably involves, among other traits, mental retardation. While the statistics are not wholly reliable, physicians in reproductive medicine estimate that when prenatal tests show that a fetus will develop Down syndrome, about eighty percent of the women decide to terminate their pregnancy.

The issues connected with prenatal genetic testing, embryo testing, and abortion are complex and vexed. People who advocate one view sometimes find themselves behaving at odds with it when their own circumstances force them to make a decision. When an issue becomes personal, abstract ideological commitments are frequently discarded.

SOCIAL CONTEXT
GINA: Genetic Information Nondiscrimination Act

Judith Berman Carlisle was forty-eight years old and in the process of setting up a therapy practice when she realized that she had a reason to be worried about her health.

The year before, her sister had been diagnosed with ovarian cancer and her aunt had died of the disease. Earlier, her grandmother and another aunt had died of breast cancer. Carlisle knew that she could be tested for the BRCA1 or BRCA2 gene mutations and learn whether she was predisposed to develop breast or ovarian cancer.

She decided against the test, however. She was planning on becoming self-employed, and if she tested positive for either of the genes, she might not be able to get health insurance. Instead, she told reporter Amy Harmon, she decided to tell her doctor about her family history and request surgery to remove her ovaries.

Carlisle suspected that the surgery wouldn't raise a red flag the way genetic information would. She saw an important difference between saying "I have a strong family history predisposing me to breast cancer" and saying "I only have a thirteen percent chance of not getting breast cancer during the time you are insuring me."

Carlisle had the surgery to remove her ovaries; then, after she got health insurance and couldn't be turned down because of a "pre-existing condition," she had herself tested for BRCA1 and BRCA2. The test results were negative. She hadn't needed to have her ovaries removed after all, but she hadn't dared to be tested to find that out.

Insurance Driven

Stories like Judith Carlisle's are common in the American health care system. They will most likely remain common until 2014, which is when health care reforms take effect that forbid insurers to reject applicants for having a preexisting medical condition. Since the beginning of genetic testing, Americans have been extremely cautious about agreeing to tests that can become part of their medical records and perhaps lead to health insurance coverage being denied or even canceled.

The insurance industry has frequently denied that health insurers engage in genetic discrimination. A study conducted by Georgetown University, however, supports the generally accepted view that they do. Researchers, as part of their experiment, provided insurance underwriters with health and genetic information about hypothetical applicants and asked the underwriters to decide which people they would insure. In seven of ninety-two decisions, when genetic tests indicated that an applicant had an increased risk of disease, the underwriters said they would deny coverage, exclude coverage for certain disorders, or charge higher premiums.

In a few notorious instances, employers have attempted to control their insurance costs by denying coverage to employees on the grounds that their genetic makeup constitutes a preexisting condition. Health insurance policies typically do not pay medical costs for conditions that existed before the policy went into effect.

The Burlington Northern Railroad company took this path when it required each employee making an insurance claim for treatment of carpal tunnel syndrome to have blood drawn by a company doctor. The railway then, without telling the employees, had the blood tested to see if a genetic factor predisposing them to carpal tunnel syndrome could be found.

If such a factor were found, the company could then say it was a preexisting condition. The claim would be that carpal tunnel syndrome was, in effect, already present in the employee's genes. Thus, the company wouldn't have to pay the employee's medical costs. The railway was sued by the Equal Employment

Opportunities Commission, and the case was settled out of court in 2002.

Protecting Themselves

To avoid putting themselves in a position that would allow their employer or insurer to use genetic information to their disadvantage, Americans have either avoided finding out such information or tried to acquire it in such a way that it does not become part of their medical record. Consider the following illustrations:

- People who have a parent or sibling with Huntington's disease have a fifty percent chance of also having the gene that causes the disease. HD typically appears between the ages of 35 and 44. It is a progressive neurological disorder that cannot be effectively treated and is invariably fatal. (See "Case Presentation: Huntington's Disease," in this chapter.)

  Some who are at risk for the disease may not wish to know whether they are carrying the gene, but others may want to know so that they can better plan their lives. Comparative data suggest, however, that the decision whether to find out about one's HD genetic status has more to do with fears about keeping health insurance than an individual's wishes. In the United States only five percent of those at risk for HD choose to be tested for the HD gene. In Canada, twenty percent of those at risk decide to have the test.

  Although it is possible that the fourfold difference can be ascribed to cultural differences, the most likely explanation is that the Canadian health care system does not deny treatment on the basis of a preexisting condition. The U.S. figures may change after health care reforms eliminate having a preexisting condition as a reason to deny health insurance coverage.

- The head of the breast cancer research program at Weil–Cornell Medical Center in New York estimated in 2008 that twenty percent of the patients who chose to be tested for BRCA1 and BRCA2 paid for the tests in cash. This meant that they would not have to file a claim with their insurer and thus tip off the insurer that they might be predisposed to develop breast and ovarian cancer.

- Thousands of people who worry about whether they have genes known to predispose them to specific diseases don't consult a physician. Rather, they pay private companies such as DNA Direct and deCODE Genetics for genetic testing. The companies promise confidentiality, and thus the test results do not become a part of their clients' medical record. If someone asked his doctor for the tests, the results would become part of his medical chart and available to his insurance company.

Hindering Medicine

Physicians need reliable information about their patients to make accurate diagnoses and prescribe the most effective treatments. When, for whatever reason, a patient withholds relevant information, the physician is hindered in carrying out the tasks essential to taking care of her patient. The case of Katherine Anderson shows how things can go badly wrong for a patient when information is withheld.

Katherine Anderson's parents were told by their doctor that Katherine might have inherited from her father the gene for Factor V Leiden, a disorder in which life threatening blood clots may form. If Katherine tested positive for the gene, the doctor warned, she might find it difficult to get insurance. The Andersons decided not to have her tested.

When Katherine turned sixteen and began having irregular periods, her gynecologist prescribed a birth-control drug to regulate them. She didn't mention to him that she might be positive for the Factor V Leiden gene. The result was life threatening.

The blood in a vein extending from Katherine's abdomen to her knee formed a single long clot. The drug her doctor had prescribed was a hormone, and, in combination with her genetic

predisposition, it raised the chance of Katherine's developing blood clots to thirty times the average risk. If Katherine's gynecologist had known that she was prone to developing blood clots, he wouldn't have put her life in jeopardy by prescribing the drug.

Katherine eventually recovered, but her case illustrates what can happen when patients fail to provide their physicians with information relevant to making diagnostic or treatment decisions. If patients are worried that employers or insurers may use genetic information as grounds for firing them or denying them insurance, it makes sense for patients to want to keep that information private. A society with policies that encourage such secrecy, however, is not one in which medicine of the highest order can be practiced.

GINA

The Genetic Information Nondiscrimination Act took effect on November 21, 2009. GINA was designed to address problems like those in the cases discussed in this section and to make it possible for people to keep genetic information about themselves private without suffering a penalty.

The major provisions of GINA and its accompanying regulations are better summarized than described. GINA:

- Prohibits employers from requiring any genetic test as a condition of hiring, firing, promotion, setting compensation, or determining other terms, conditions, or privileges of employment.

- Prohibits employers from requesting or purchasing genetic information about an employee or any member of an employee's family.

- Prohibits insurers from requiring or requesting that an individual take any genetic test.

- Prohibits insurers from using genetic information to determine an individual's eligibility for health insurance or to set the amount of an individual's premium for either individual or group health care coverage.

- Prohibits both employers and health insurers from disclosing genetic information about an individual.

The "genetic information" that employers and insurers are prohibited from acquiring, using, or revealing encompasses more than the results of genetic tests. It includes, for example, family histories of breast cancer, heart disease, or Huntington's disease. It also includes information about prescribed medications that would allow someone to draw the inference that someone may have a particular genetic disorder.

Accidental Knowledge

GINA acknowledges the possibility that employers may acquire genetic information in an inadvertent or accidental way. For example, an employee who requests a leave of absence under the Family Medical Leave Act may tell an employer that she needs the time to help her mother through breast-cancer surgery. Similarly, an employer may hear gossip that an employee's father died from a heart attack at age 48 or read an obituary which says that an employee's oldest child died at age 20 from cystic fibrosis. Such information about family history might lead an employer to draw conclusions about the genetic risks of the employees.

Even though such information may be acquired accidentally, as distinct from intentionally, GINA forbids employers and insurers from making decisions based on it. What is likely to have to be decided in court in particular cases is whether any genetic information an employer accidentally acquired about an individual played a role in the employer's decision to fire him. Like discrimination on the basis of age, gender, or race, genetic discrimination may be easy to suspect but difficult to prove.

GINA allows employers' group health plans to ask employees to provide their family histories for the purpose of assigning employees to "wellness" programs designed to reduce employees' risk factors for disorders like heart attacks, high blood pressure, or diabetes. This information must be volunteered by each employee, and the health plan cannot use it as a condition for granting, denying, or limiting insurance coverage.

GINA also does not allow any penalty or reward to be connected to an employee's providing a family history. The no-reward provision seems incompatible with the way many large companies have structured their wellness programs. To encourage participation, some employers award bonuses or extra vacation days to employees who participate regularly or achieve goals like losing weight or lowering blood pressure. No administrative or court decision has yet determined whether such programs violate the provisions of GINA.

What GINA Permits

The framers of GINA were concerned not to place so many restrictions on genetic information to prevent its abuse that it would make its legitimate uses difficult. It is important to notice what GINA does not prohibit:

- A health care professional treating a patient is free to ask the patient or the patient's family members to take a genetic test.

- Health plans and insurers that operate wellness programs are free to notify and discuss with employees the availability and potential usefulness of genetic tests.

- Insurers are free to evaluate an applicant for health insurance on the grounds of the applicant's current health status.

- Genetic data can be collected for the purposes of monitoring toxic conditions in the workplace, auditing employer-sponsored wellness programs, and administering federal and state family leave laws. Data about individuals, however, may not be disclosed to the employer.

- GINA does not cover life, disability, or long-term-care insurance.

Redundant?

Before GINA was passed into law, critics argued that the legislation wasn't necessary, because the Americans with Disabilities Act makes it illegal to use the results of a genetic test to turn down someone for a job or to justify denying someone a promotion. This interpretation of the ADA has yet to be tested in a court, however.

The ADA also does not explicitly bar insurers from regarding a positive test for a disease-associated gene (like one for familial breast cancer) as a preexisting condition and denying health insurance to an applicant on those grounds. GINA eliminates ambiguities and gray areas: neither employers nor health insurers can require individuals to provide them with genetic information, nor can they use such information to make decisions about individuals.

The health care legislation passed in 2010 contains provisions that will not permit health insurers to refuse to insure individuals or to terminate their insurance on the basis of preexisting conditions. These conditions may include being genetically predisposed to the development of diseases like breast and colon cancer and cystic fibrosis. The legislation may eventually make GINA seem unnecessary. However, some of its provisions will not take effect until 2014 or later, and no one is sure how the overall plan will work in practice.

GINA may become redundant, but for the moment it makes clear in a useful way what can and cannot be done with genetic information. Besides, when something as important as individual rights is at stake, it is better that the laws protecting them be redundant than ambiguous or nonexistent.

Retrospect and Prospect

Consider again the cases of Judith Carlisle and Katherine Andersons—people who put themselves at risk so that an insurance company wouldn't be able to deny them health insurance coverage on the basis of their genetic inheritance.

GINA has changed that. No longer need people fear that a genetic test will stand in the way of their getting or keeping their health insurance, getting or keeping a job, or winning a promotion. No longer must people get genetic tests in secret and worry that the result will find its way into their medical records.

All people carry genes that predispose them to diseases and disorders. This means that GINA is a shield against discrimination of a kind that could be exercised against literally anyone.

SOCIAL CONTEXT

What Are My Chances? Direct-to-Consumer Genetic Testing

As soon as Kathy Klowsky (we will call her) turned thirty, she decided it was time to take charge of her health. She planned to improve her diet, lose weight, and get more exercise. But was there something else, she wondered, that she ought to be doing?

Her mom was extremely overweight—fat, really—and her dad had died of colon cancer when he was only fifty-eight. So should she be worried that maybe she inherited genes for obesity and colon cancer? If she were sure she had, she would work particularly hard to stick to her diet. She would also talk to a doctor and see if she should start getting colonoscopies earlier than most people.

So when Kathy read a magazine article about genetic tests you could get without going to a doctor, she was immediately interested. You could read about the services on-line, and all you had to do was wipe the inside of your cheek with a swab and then mail it to the company. Depending on how much you paid, they would tell you how likely you were to develop a number of common diseases. They would also tell you such things as whether you were a "supertaster" and could detect bitter flavors at low concentrations or whether your ear wax was the dry or wet kind. She cared nothing about any of those things, but she did want to know how much at risk she was for obesity and colon cancer.

Genetic-Testing Companies

About thirty genetic-testing companies are in the business of analyzing a client's DNA for a fee. Some companies check for the presence of a few specific genes, such as ones associated with baldness or sickle-cell disease, and others determine paternity or trace genetic ancestry. The major companies, however, sample an individual's entire genome and provide various amounts of information, depending on the level of service requested (and paid for) and the company's policy. The largest genetic-testing companies offering services to consumers are deCODE Genetics, 23andMe, DNA Direct, and Navigenics.

SNPs

The tests performed by all companies involve analyzing hundreds of thousands of segments of DNA known as *single-nucleotide polymorphisms,* or SNPs (pronounced "snips"). SNPs are variations in nucleotides (the adenine, cytosine, guanine, or tyrosine on a DNA strand) that occur at the same location in a genome. In one person's genome, for example, cytosine might occur where most genomes have guanine. Or, possibly, at that location, the nucleotide may be missing or an additional nucleotide may be present.

These substitutions, deletions, and insertions may be harmless human variants that reflect population-related or racial differences. SNPs themselves aren't genes, but they can occur within genes. (They can also occur in nongene segments of DNA.) Thus, they may be found in gene mutations (a variant form of a gene), or they may alter the way a gene is expressed. (The gene fails to make an enzyme, for example.) Some of those expressions may be harmless, but others may prove disastrous.

SNPs function as genetic markers. Whether or not they are responsible for a disease or trait, SNPs have been shown to be associated with diseases like breast cancer, asthma, bipolar disorder, macular degeneration, cluster headaches, Crohn's disease, amyotrophic lateral sclerosis (ALS, Lou Gehrig's disease), diabetes, and colon cancer. SNPs have also been associated with traits like height, eye and hair color, obesity, lactose intolerance, and muscle performance. Also, some SNPs may predict how individuals will respond to chemotherapy drugs, antibiotics, or antidepressants.

SNPs and Risks

If an individual's entire genome were sequenced, the variants in the nucleotides would show up. But such sequencing is still too expensive to be performed as a matter of course. (The aim is to bring the cost down from $5,000 to about $1,000.) An alternative to sequencing is made possible by biochips programmed to detect nucleotide differences at locations along a DNA strand known to vary. The biochip provides, in effect, a catalogue of the variants displayed by an individual's DNA. The SNPs in the catalogue are then compared with those in a database that associates particular SNPs with particular diseases. (The same holds for traits.)

This technique establishes the individual's relative risk of developing particular diseases. Some SNPs may correlate strongly with (say) obesity, but other SNPs may correlate weakly. Thus, someone whose genome includes several weakly correlated SNPs may have an increased risk of obesity, compared with someone whose genome lacks all or most of those SNPs.

Associating SNPs with diseases is not a genetic test in the usual sense that the SNPs indicate the presence of a particular gene. This can happen, though, when a SNP identifies a mutated gene known to be responsible for a disease. Some companies will not test clients for a SNP known to be associated with a high degree of probability of certain diseases. DeCODE, for example, refuses to test for the mutation

ApoE4. This mutation is associated with high cholesterol, and it could be useful for a client to know that he carries the gene. However, as many as ninety-five percent of those who test positive for the gene develop Alzheimer's.

Kathy would be able to find out from XY Genetics and most other companies that her genetic profile indicates that she has a number of genetic "risk factors" which predispose her to heart disease. When the separate risks associated with each SNP are added up, it may be that she has a sixty-five percent chance of developing arteriosclerosis and cardiac problems. She is not doomed by the findings, and she may have learned something that will guide her in changing her behavior in order to avoid having a heart attack.

Inconsistent Results

Suppose Kathy is a cautious person and sends in a cheek swab to PDQGenetics to be tested for a predisposition to developing heart disease. She may be surprised to get back results that are very different from the results she received from XYGenetics.

Inconsistent results are possible because genetic testing companies may use different biochips to sort through personal genomes, so different SNPs are searched for and identified. Perhaps one company will look for more SNPs connected with obesity than another, and the client may learn from the first company that she has more "risk factors" than that showed up on the second analysis.

Also, companies may use different databases to look for an association between SNPs and common diseases. This makes it possible, given a difference in the size of the databases, for a client to appear to be more at risk for a particular disease as a result of one analysis than another.

Finally, even given the same data, different companies may provide different estimates of disease risks because they don't use the same method to calculate risk. XYGenetics may figure a client's risk of colon cancer over a lifetime, while PDQGenetics calculates the risk for the decade between the ages of 40 and 50. The result

of these differences is that a client may be given test results that are so disparate as to be unhelpful, confusing, or misleading.

Clinical laboratories used by hospitals and physicians must be approved by the Centers for Medicare and Medicaid Services. This federal agency certifies that labs have met the standards required by the federal Clinical Laboratory Improvement Amendment, which includes quality-control procedures, proficiency testing by outside experts, and educational qualifications for laboratory personnel. The way the law is written, genetic-testing companies are exempt from these regulations.

In April 2008, a federal advisory committee recommended that new federal rules be introduced to regulate the genetic-testing industry. The California Department of Health sent letters to thirteen companies warning them to stop doing business in California until they could prove that they were compliant with state laws. (California law allows only physicians to order laboratory tests, and the labs must have federal certification.) New York State sent letters to thirty-one companies informing them that a state license was required to solicit DNA samples from state residents.

Partly in response to the threat of being put out of business by federal and state regulation, several major genetic-testing companies (including deCODE, 23andMe, and Navigenics) made a commitment to develop their own industry-wide standards. They pledged to work with the nonprofit educational organization Personalized Medicine Coalition to develop shared guidelines.

Medical Advice?

Companies that offer genetic testing directly to consumers typically deny that they are providing medical advice. They are, in their view, providing people with information about themselves that they want to know.

Critics claim that, whether or not what the genetic information companies provide should be considered medical advice, it can pose risks to clients. Although some companies provide genetic counseling as part of the testing package,

Personal Genomics at Berkeley

The University of California, Berkeley, announced in 2010 that it will mail a DNA-collecting kit, consisting of a cotton swab and a plastic tube, to incoming freshmen of the class of 2014.

Returning the DNA sample is voluntary, but those returned will be tested for three genetic markers associated with the ability to metabolize alcohol, lactose, and folates. The three genes were selected because the students who test positive for them could use the information to live healthier lives by consuming less alcohol, avoiding dairy products, and eating more leafy, green vegetables. The privacy of students will be protected by sending each student two labels with a bar code. A student will keep one and send in the other on the sample tube. The test results will be posted by code number on a website, and the student may get access to the results by using the code number. The university will not make a record that associates names with code numbers.

Jasper Rine, the geneticist heading the project, sees it as an opportunity for students to learn about personalized medicine and their own genetic traits. "The history of genetics is the history of finding bad things," he is quoted as saying. "But in the future, nutritional genetics is probably going to be the sweet spot."

Once the freshmen are on campus, they will have the opportunity to hear a lecture by Rine on the three genetic markers for which they were tested. They will also be able to explore the benefits and risks of personal genomics by attending lectures and panel discussions by biologists, bioethicists, philosophers, and statisticians.

Critics worry that because genetic information can be harmful, it ought to be provided only by physicians and in a setting in which counseling is offered. Defenders consider such a view paternalistic and argue that people should be able to learn about their own genes. For some people, learning how much they weigh can be harmful, but we don't think that only doctors should weigh people.

not all do. Hence, some clients may not know what to make of the information they are given. They may believe, for example, that they are at a much greater risk for colon cancer or mental illness than they are. The test results may thus provoke needless anxiety. Indeed, a client might become depressed or suicidal if informed that she tested positive for BRCA1.

The results may also keep people from getting the medical attention they need. Companies (unlike deCODE) which inform clients that they are at risk for Alzheimer's or carry a mutation that puts them at risk for breast and ovarian cancer are not equipped to carry out the appropriate medical follow-up. The clients, even those receiving genetic counseling from a company, may think they have done all that needs to be done. This may lead them to avoid going to a doctor and getting a genetic test from a certified clinical laboratory to confirm that they are predisposed to developing the disease indicated by SNP testing. Thus, the clients may fail to become patients and gain the benefit of medical advice and treatment.

Failing Business?

The three major genetic-testing companies that began in the late 1990s—deCODE Genetics, 23andMe, and Navigenics—have recently become struggling enterprises that have had to redefine themselves to remain in business.

The most successful company, 23andMe, has had only 3500 clients, and the other two have had fewer. Navigenics cut its staff, replaced its CEO twice, and expanded its marketing to include services to physicians and corporate wellness programs. deCODE Genetics, which includes research and drug development divisions, went through bankruptcy and was acquired by new owners. The newly organized company markets genetic tests directly to doctors. Although it still has a consumer division, in 2010 the company raised its prices to around $2000 to avoid hurting the tests sold to physicians. This is about twice the costs of personal genome scans sold by 23andMe.

Over-the Counter Sales

On May 9, 2010, Pathway Genomics of San Diego announced that it planned to offer a testing kit that would be sold nationwide for $20–$30 at 7500 Walgreens drugstores. The kit is to be sold in a box labeled "Discover Your DNA," but it will contain nothing more than a saliva-collecting tube and a mailer to send the tube to a Pathway laboratory. The customer must then go to the company website, set up an account, and decide which of the tests offered by Pathway he wants to order. The tests range in costs from $79 to $249 for the full panel. The consumer's information will be protected by a privacy code.

Pathway also operates an on-line testing service, but by making kits available in stores, it thinks it can boost its business. Like the other companies, it will use biochips and DNA probes to test for the presence of genes or markers that are associated with about two dozen particular diseases. The company will also (for a price) test for the likelihood of a bad reaction to certain drugs and estimate the likelihood that the gene for a particular disease (e.g. cystic fibrosis) will be passed on to an offspring. The tests offered are thus open to the same objections: that such tests are unreliable and, because of the lack of understanding of the connection between genes and diseases in most cases, they promise more information than they can deliver.

Only two days after Pathway's announcement, Walgreens issued a statement saying that it would delay selling the test kits. Although similar kits have been sold on-line for years, the Pathway announcement reawakened the interest of the FDA. It is concerned, once again, with the question of whether the tests offered are medical tests. If they are, they must meet FDA requirements and be licensed and regulated. But if the tests are a way for people to acquire information about themselves, the FDA has no authority over them.

Pathway is not likely to have been more successful in attracting customers than the other on-line companies, which may be why it moved to over-the-counter sales. Perhaps the testing companies in general have misjudged the interest people have in their risks for developing common diseases or learning a little about their genetically determined traits. Those who are genetically sophisticated may see the limited value of the tests, while those who are not fail to see the point of them. Whether the kits are bought on-line or in a drugstore, the tests may be viewed by many as little more than an expensive form of entertainment.

GINA

The genetic-testing companies may have had their business undermined by a major piece of legislation. Before the Genetic Information Nondiscrimination Act (GINA) took effect in November 2009, people hesitated to have any genetic test, because it would become part of their medical record. They might lose their job, or their insurer might refuse to cover their medical expenses on the ground that their problem was a preexisting condition. (See "Social Context: GINA," in this chapter.) Hence, anyone wanting to know if she was at risk for a genetic disease would try to get the information from a source that would guarantee privacy.

Genetic-testing companies offered the best possibility of acquiring the information and escaping the social consequences. Most likely, although no one knows for sure, much of the business of 23andMe and the other major and minor testing services came from people worried about the confidentiality of their results. With the passage of GINA, keeping such results private is no longer so important. GINA makes it illegal to discriminate on the basis of genetic data, and this ban extends to employment, promotion, and insurance coverage.

Depending on the way GINA changes the legal environment, people who want to acquire information about their genetic predisposition to diseases may be confident enough to seek it from their doctors. We may not need to worry about regulating the genetic-testing companies, because they will either disappear or transform themselves into organizations that meet the standards of clinical laboratories.

Gene Therapy: Slowly Delivering on the Promise

On September 14, 1990, at the National Institutes of Health in Bethesda, Maryland, a four-year-old girl became the first patient to be treated by gene therapy under an approved protocol. The child, whose parents initially asked that her identity not be made public, lacked the gene for producing adenosine deaminase (ADA), an enzyme required to keep immune cells alive and functioning.

Her life expectancy was low, because, without ADA, she would almost certainly develop cancers and opportunistic infections that cannot be effectively controlled by conventional treatments. The aim of the therapy was to provide her with cells that would boost her immune system by increasing the production of essential antibodies. During the months that followed, she received four injections of altered cells.

The treatment, under the direction of W. French Anderson, R. Michael Blaese, and Kenneth Culver, involved taking blood from the patient, isolating the T-cells, and then growing a massive number of them. These cells were infected with a weakened retrovirus into which a copy of the human gene for ADA had been spliced. The cells were then injected into the patient in a blood transfusion.

The Therapy

The idea behind the therapy was for the ADA gene to migrate to the cellular DNA, switch on, and begin producing ADA. If the cells produced enough of the enzyme, the child's immune system would not be destroyed. Because most T-cells live for only weeks or months, the process had to be repeated at regular intervals.

The girl's parents, from a Cleveland suburb, later revealed their daughter's identity. She is Ashanthi Desilva, and more than a decade later she is alive and doing well. Soon after her treatment, on January 30, 1991, nine-year-old Cynthia Cutshall became the second person to receive gene therapy.

Laboratory tests showed that both children's immune systems were functioning effectively. But the need to replace short-lived T-cells means that Ashanthi and Cynthia had to continue to receive regular injections of altered cells. However, Anderson and his collaborators had always hoped to find a way around this need, and the break came when an NIH group developed a procedure for isolating stem cells from the bone marrow. If enough stem cells could be obtained and genetically altered, then, when injected back into the patient, the cells might produce enough T-cells for an adequately functioning immune system.

In May 1993, Cynthia's stem cells were harvested, exposed to the retrovirus containing the normal ADA gene, and reinjected. She tolerated the procedure with no apparent ill effects, and later that year essentially the same procedure was repeated with Ashanthi. The immune systems of both children continued to function within the normal range.

This may seem to be an unequivocal success for gene therapy, but the value of the experiment in establishing this is difficult to assess. Both subjects continued to be treated with a standard drug regimen, so was it gene therapy or the drugs that saved the lives of the children? Although gene therapy can't be said to have produced a cure for ADA, advocates believe that eventually it will.

Definitive Evidence, Potential Risks

More definitive evidence for the effectiveness of gene therapy comes from results of clinical trials conducted at Paris' Necker Hospital in 2000 by Alain Fischer. Fischer's group treated eleven patients (ten infants and a teenager) with severe combined immunodeficiency disease (SCID), a disorder caused by a defect on the X chromosome. Nine of those treated by using a retrovirus to insert new genes were cured. This is an astounding outcome, considering that most children born with the defect die from the disease by the end of their first year. Bone marrow transplants, the standard treatment, are successful only about seventy-five of the time.

Then, in 2002, a three-year-old boy in the study developed leukemia-like symptoms. The clinical trial was immediately halted. Regulatory agencies in the United States were already particularly inclined to caution because of the death of eighteen-year-old Jesse Gelsinger in 1999 (see the case presentation in Chapter 2), so the adverse event in France once more raised the question of whether gene-therapy trials were so unsafe as to be discontinued. After a period of suspension to permit a safety review, the FDA once again allowed the trials to go forward.

Parkinson's Disease

Parkinson's disease, which affects more than 500,000 people in the United States, is a progressive disorder in which cells in the part of the brain called the substantia nigra die off, resulting in a lack of the neurotransmitter dopamine. This condition leads to symptoms such as hand tremors, impaired balance, and "freezing" in place. As more cells die, the symptoms become progressively worse, and the disease may have a fatal outcome.

In August 2007, the results of a Phase 1 clinical trial conducted by Michael Kaplitt using gene therapy to increase the amount of gamma-aminobutyric acid (GABA) in the brain were published in the *Lancet*. GABA is one of the major inhibitory neurotransmitters in the central nervous system, and in Parkinson's patients it is in short supply. By using a retrovirus to introduce billions of copies of the gene that encodes GABA into brain cells, Kaplitt's group was able to increase the amount of the neurotransmitter present in the brains of the trial's subjects. This resulted in bringing under control the sort of unchecked movements characteristic of the disease.

The trial involved twelve patients, and all of them continued to take their prescribed medications. They also continued to have some of the symptoms of the disease. Even so, over the year the patients were monitored, they showed general improvement in symptoms, such as less difficulty walking, less rigidity, and fewer hand tremors. The researchers claimed a twenty-four percent improvement in patients who were off their medications and a twenty-seven percent improvement in those who were on their medications. Most important for gene therapy, none of the patients showed any side effects from the treatment.

Inherited Retinal Degeneration

Photoreceptors in the retina convert light energy into electrical impulses that travel along the optic nerve to the brain. Retinol, a form of vitamin A that plays key role in the process of converting light into a nerve impulse, is active in the pigmented epithelium—the layer of cells under the photoreceptors. Retinol is kept available by an enzyme (the protein RPE65) that recycles it as it is used by cells,

and when retinol is missing, the photoreceptors can't do their job. The result is a disruption of the visual cycle, and the functional outcome is blindness.

Leber's congenital amaurosis (LCA) is a genetic disorder in which mutations in the gene RPE56 result in a shortage or the complete absence of the enzyme required to recycle retinol. Children born with the mutated gene are not born with normal sight, and what sight they have continues to deteriorate. Over time, photoreceptors deteriorate, and the outcome is significant, if not total, blindness.

In May 2007, a team at Moorfields Eye Hospital in London used a virus to transfer healthy copies of the RPE56 gene into the cells of the pigmented epithelium of seventeen-year-old Robert Johnson. Johnson, diagnosed with LCA, had been steadily losing his sight, but within months of the gene therapy, his vision improved measurably. The same procedure was carried out on eleven other LCA patients, and they, too, showed improvement.

Researchers concluded that younger subjects were most likely to show the greatest amount of improvement. The reason for this is that the gene therapy works only when the photoreceptor cells are intact, and as people with LCA grow older, those cells began to lose their function.

In 2009, an American study reported results similar to the British study. Researchers used viruses to introduce normal copies of REP65 into areas of the pigmented epithelium in which photoreceptor cells seemed most intact. Within two weeks, the five children and seven adults treated began to show significant improvement in their vision. Children improved the most, but the oldest participant, a forty-four-year-old woman who was once housebound, became able to walk outside to meet her children coming home from school.

AIDS Treatment

In 2009, the results of a Phase 2 clinical trial using gene therapy to treat AIDS were characterized by some researchers as a major advance in treating AIDS. A patient's blood stem cells were cultured with OZ1, a genetically altered mouse virus, to get the gene for the so-called hairpin ribozyme incorporated into the DNA of the blood stem cells. The ribozyme chemically slices up RNA, and because HIV depends on RNA for replication, blood cells with altered DNA prevent the virus from reproducing. The idea was for the genetically altered stem cells to populate the bone marrow of the patient and then begin producing blood cells containing the ribosome. When enough altered blood cells are present in an HIV-positive person, the viral load is lowered.

The trial involved seventy-four patients; thirty-eight were transfused with genetically altered blood stem cells, and thirty-six were transfused with an inactive placebo solution. All patients had HIV infections, which were being kept under control by highly active antiretroviral therapy (HAART).

During the one-hundred-week period of the trial, patients receiving altered stem cells had a higher number of CD4 T-cells, which indicated that HIV wasn't killing them off at the same rate as before. During nontreatment intervals, treated patients had higher CD4 counts and a lower HIV load than those patients in the placebo group. Also, when HAART was stopped, those in the treatment group were able to wait longer before starting the drugs again than those in the placebo group.

Enormous Promise

Gene therapy holds enormous promise for those who suffer from a variety of genetic disorders. Experimental clinical protocols for the treatment of a wide range of relatively common diseases such as cystic fibrosis, hemophilia, phenylketonuria, sickle-cell disease, hypercholesterolemia, AIDS, cardiovascular disease, cancer, lupus erythematous, and blood-clotting disorders are either underway or in the planning stage. Following are a few examples.

Sickle-cell disease Sickle-cell disease, affecting about one in four hundred African Americans, is produced by a gene that affects the folding of the two chains making up the hemoglobin molecule. In a proposed treatment, molecular fragments called chimeraplasts will be induced to enter the stem cells in the bone marrow that produce red blood cells.

If a stem cell incorporates the chimeraplast into the nucleus, the cell's own repair system should eliminate the gene for the defective hemoglobin chain and substitute that provided by the chimeraplast. If enough stem cells are altered and function properly, the amount of red blood cells produced should eliminate the heart damage and strokes that can cause early death in those who develop the disease.

Malignant melanoma In one proposed cancer treatment, researchers will make trillions of copies of the gene for the antigen HLA-B7 and then inject them directly into the tumors of those with melanoma. The DNA is expected to enter the cells of the tumor, insert itself in the nuclear DNA, and trigger the production of HLA-B7. The antigen will then extrude from the cell, causing the cell to be attacked by killer T-cells. Two patients were successfully treated by this approach in 2006, demonstrating that gene therapy can be used as a cancer treatment.

Leukemia A genetic abnormality known as the Philadelphia chromosome triggers cancerous changes in stem cells in the bone marrow. The resulting disease is chronic myelogenous leukemia, which affects about 4600 people a year and is responsible for about 1000 deaths a year. The best standard treatment is to inject patients with stem cells from a bone marrow donor. Sometimes, however, a compatible donor can't be located; also, the therapy has a lower level of success in people over fifty-five.

A gene-based therapy is being developed to alter the patient's own stem cells by adding an antisense sequence to the cellular DNA. The sequence is designed to block the formation of the protein leading to cancerous growth, thereby making the cancer cells behave like normal cells. The sequence will also have attached to it a gene making the altered cells more resistant to the chemotherapeutic drug methotrexate. Thus, when a patient receives chemotherapy, the cancerous cells will be killed while the altered ones will survive and reproduce. The altered stem cells should then produce normal red blood cells. The main difficulty, at present, is to get the stem cells to incorporate the new genes.

Hypercholesterolemia Familial hypercholesterolemia is a disease in which an excess production of cholesterol often leads to heart attacks and early death. The gene therapy developed to treat it involves removing part of a patient's liver, culturing the cells that have been collected, and inserting into them a gene that produces the low-density lipoprotein receptor. The receptor plays an important role in removing cholesterol from the blood. The treated cells are then injected into the patient's liver, where they attach themselves to the liver's capillaries and start producing the protein of the receptor.

A clinical trial carried out by James Wilson in 2003–2005 demonstrated that gene therapy could successfully treat the disease. Questions about the safety of the modified virus used in the trial have kept the therapy from being approved.

Collateral blood vessel growth Every year, thirty to forty thousand people in the United States develop almost complete blockage in the arteries of their legs. Shut off from a blood supply, the tissues in the leg develop ulcers that don't heal, and, and, eventually, when gangrene sets in, the leg must be amputated to save the life of the person. Twenty percent of the patients die in the hospital, and forty percent die within the next year. No drugs are available to increase the blood flow to the legs.

A new treatment under development uses the gene for vascular endothelial growth factor, or vegF, a protein that stimulates the growth of collateral blood vessels. When billions of vegF genes are injected into leg muscle, about five percent of them are incorporated into muscle cells, causing them to start producing the vdgF protein. Because the vessel cells beyond the blockage are deprived of blood, their membranes become altered so as to be more receptive to the vegG molecule. When it attaches to the surface of the cells, the cells begin to produce tiny new blood vessels that grow around the blockage.

While only a few people have been treated with vegF gene therapy, it has shown itself to be effective. Trials are also underway to test the effectiveness of the therapy in heart disease. If vegF can establish collateral circulation in the heart, the need for coronary artery bypass surgery may be reduced or even eliminated. Those too frail or sick to undergo a bypass or even angioplasty might eventually be helped by the new technique.

Cystic fibrosis In April 1993, a twenty-three-year-old man became the first patient to receive human gene therapy for the treatment of cystic fibrosis. An altered form of the adenovirus was used to transport the gene for cystic fibrosis transmembrane conductance regulator into his lungs. The regulator controls the flow of chloride through body cells. Cystic fibrosis patients lack the regulator gene, and as a result, they suffer severe salt imbalances that cause abnormal mucous excretions in the lungs and pancreas.

The therapy was evaluated in 1996. Although the evidence did not demonstrate that it was effective, most investigators think that it ultimately will be. Part of the difficulty is to find a way of getting the gene into the cells of the lungs. If the problems can be solved, gene therapy will offer the 30,000 Americans who suffer from cystic fibrosis a cure for the disease.

Germ-Line Therapy

The gene therapy currently under developments in humans is somatic-cell therapy, wherein modifications take place in the body cells of patients, not in the sex cells. This means that even if the therapy can eliminate the disease produced in an individual who has inherited a defective gene, the therapy will do nothing to alter the probability that a child of that person will inherit the same defective gene. To change this circumstance, germ-line cells would have to be altered. That is, the defective gene in an ovum or sperm cell would have to be replaced.

If this were possible, then certain genetic diseases could be eliminated from families. Germ-line therapy would make it unnecessary to perform somatic-cell therapy for each generation of affected individuals. As appealing as this prospect may be, at present germ-line therapy has many more technical difficulties associated with it than does somatic-cell therapy. No uniformly encouraging results have so far been produced in animal research, and even most forms of somatic-cell therapy in humans remain a distant prospect.

The value of germ-line therapy is also open to question. If the aim is to eliminate heritable diseases from a family, the most direct and effective way to achieve this is to screen embryos and avoid implanting those which carry the flawed gene. This process is currently available at fertility clinics and doesn't involve the risks and uncertainties of tinkering with the DNA of germ cells.

Germ-line therapy, unlike somatic-cell therapy, possesses a potential that has made it the focus of most ethical criticisms. Germ-line therapy holds out the prospect of genetically engineering sex cells to produce offspring with virtually any set of characteristics desired. This possibility has led many critics to warn that "genetic surgery" may be leading us into a sort of "Brave New World" in which we practice eugenics and manufacture our children to order. (See the briefing session in this chapter for a fuller discussion.) However, any dangers posed by germ-line therapy are far from immediate.

Envoi

Somatic-cell therapy continues to be experimental, but some of its forms are likely to become standard therapies within the next decade. Other forms will for some time remain experimental and, as such, will raise the same sorts of moral questions that are typical of any experimental procedure—questions of informed consent, benefit, and risk. As long as viruses and retroviruses must be used to deliver new genes into cells, the risk of serious harm, and even death, will be present. (See "Case Presentation:

Jesse Gelsinger: First Gene-Therapy Death," in Chapter 2.) This circumstance has slowed the development of gene therapy more than anyone imagined it would.

Germ-line therapy is not likely ever to be developed as a way to engineer the human future.

SOCIAL CONTEXT

The Human Genome Project: Genes, Diseases, and the Personal Genome

Scientists considered sequencing the human genome so important that they referred to it as the Holy Grail of biology. The Grail, in medieval Christian legend, is the lost cup used by Christ at the Last Supper. Because the Grail delivers salvation to whoever possesses it, finding the Grail was the aim in many tales of valorous quests.

Deciphering the human genome never offered the promise of eternal life, but it offered the benefits of genetic knowledge, including the possibility of understanding genetic diseases and bringing them under control. This has turned out to be harder than those who set out on the quest believed, yet sequencing the genome has brought the goal within sight.

Genome Success

On June 26, 2000, Francis Collins, Director of the National Genome Research Institute, and J. Craig Venter, president of Celera Genetics, announced that, thanks to the joint work of the two groups, the human genome had been sequenced.

This means that the estimated 3.2 billion base pairs making up human DNA have been identified and sequenced; that is, the precise order of the base pairs has been established. Human DNA is now thought to contain about 30,000 genes. Earlier estimates had put this figure around 100,000, so the lower number came as a considerable surprise. Using the comparison by writer Nicholas Wade, if the complete DNA sequence were published in the *New York Times*, it would cover 75,490 pages.

This complete set of genes contained in the forty-six chromosomes is known as the *genome*. Metaphorically, it is the total set of encoded instructions for assembling a human being that is stored in the nucleus of each cell. About seventy-five percent of the genome is thought to be (as geneticists say) junk, consisting of repetitive DNA sequences accumulated during evolution and contributing nothing to human development or functioning. Yet biologists are also quick to say that we don't yet know enough to declare the junk DNA absolutely useless. It may contain sequences that in the future we will realize are crucially important.

Background

In 1985, biologist Robert Sinsheimer began promoting the idea that the entire human genome should be mapped and its genes sequenced. Because the genome was recognized as involving some 3 billion base pairs, the genome project would be on a scale unprecedented in the biological sciences. It would compare with the efforts of physicists to develop the atomic bomb during World War II and with the manned space project in the 1960s.

The size of the genome project made many scientists skeptical about supporting it. Some believed it would drain money away from smaller projects of immediate value in favor of one with only distant and uncertain promise. Also, some feared the genome project would turn out to be too much like the space project, emphasizing the solution to engineering problems more than the advancement of basic science.

Attitudes changed in 1988, when the National Research Council endorsed the genome project and outlined a gradual approach of coordinated research that would protect the interest of the basic sciences. When James Watson (who, along with Francis Crick, worked out the structure of DNA in 1953) agreed to be director of the project, most critics dropped their opposition and many became enthusiastic participants. Watson headed the project with great success until he resigned in 1993, when the position was taken over by Francis S. Collins.

Mapping and sequencing the human genome was expected to take fifteen to twenty years and cost between $3 and $5 billion. In 1989, Congress approved $31 million to initiate the program, but the project eventually came to cost about $200 million per year, and most biological and medical scientists view the money as well and wisely spent. The project was divided among nine different centers at both national laboratories and universities, and hundreds of scientists participated in the research and contributed to the final product.

The project was expected to be completed by 2005, but in response to a challenge by a commercial enterprise to the federal project and eventual cooperation between the two, the project was completed five years ahead of schedule.

Biologist J. Craig Venter, head of Celera Corporation, claimed he would begin sequencing in 1999 and finish in 2001. Venter's group took an approach different from the federal project. Celera sequenced millions of DNA fragments, then used a computer program to piece them together on the basis of their overlaps. Unlike the HEP approach, Celera did not break DNA into fragments and then create a map of each piece's location.

The payoff of the genome project is considered by most biological and medical researchers to be of inestimable worth. The information has already provided us with a better understanding of the patterns and processes of human evolution and clarified our degree of genetic relatedness to other organisms.

The detailed genetic information acquired by sequencing the human genome continues to give us a much-improved understanding of the relationships between certain genes and particular diseases. This information is a crucial step along the path to understanding genetic diseases and devising treatments that will eliminate or control them.

Early Successes

In 1997, a team led by David Schlessinger of the Washington University Medical School completed a high-resolution map of the X chromosome. The 160 million base pairs of the chromosome were mapped, with markers around every 75,000 pairs. Because a number of sex-linked diseases, such as hemophilia, result from a defective gene on the X chromosome, the map made it easier to locate the genes responsible for them. (Females have two copies of the X chromosome. Males have only one; so if it carries a defective gene, they lack a backup gene to prevent the consequences.)

With astonishing rapidity, using human-genome data, researchers identified the genes responsible for a large number of human diseases. A sampling from a list of several thousand gives some idea of the success of researchers in locating actual genes or gene markers for diseases.

Colon cancer. For the familial form of colon cancer, a marker was found on the upper end of chromosome 2 for a "repair" gene that corrects minor errors in cellular DNA. In its mutant form, the gene seems to function by triggering hundreds of thousands of mutations in other genes. One in two hundred people has the gene; sixty-five percent of the carriers are liable to develop cancer. The familial form accounts for about fifteen percent of all colon tumors. (A blood test is expected to be available soon.)

Amyotrophic lateral sclerosis. The familial form of ALS (Lou Gehrig's disease) results from a mutation of a gene on chromosome 21 that encodes the enzyme superoxide dismutase, which plays a role in eliminating free radicals. It is believed that if these radicals aren't controlled, they may damage motor neurons, which will then lead to muscle degeneration. The familial form of the disease accounts for only about ten percent of cases, but those with a family history of the disease can now be screened for the defective gene.

Type II (adult-onset) diabetes. A still unidentified gene on chromosome 7 encodes glucokinase, an enzyme that stimulates the pancreas to produce insulin. At least twenty-three mutated forms of the gene may cause the disease by encoding for a faulty enzyme that apparently fails to trigger insulin production. A screening test for the mutated genes is available.

Alzheimer's disease. The gene ApoE on chromosome 19 encodes a protein that transports cholesterol. People who have both alleles for the form of the protein known as E4 have eight times the risk of developing Alzheimer's; those with one allele have two to three times the risk. The gene could account for as many as half of those with the disease, although the causal role of E4 in producing it is not yet known.

X-linked SCID. Severe combined immunodeficiency diseases (SCID) is caused by a defective gene passed from mothers to sons on the X chromosome. The normal gene encodes part of the receptor of interleukin-2, which serves in the cytokine messenger system that keeps the T-cells of the immune system functioning. Newborns with the mutated gene have few or no T-cells, and even a mild infection is life threatening. The disease occurs in only one in every 100,000 births. (The cells used in the study were from "David," who died in Houston after he was removed from the sterile environment where he had spent almost twelve years of his life and was given a bone marrow transplant. Because of the publicity surrounding him, SCID is known popularly as "the Bubble Boy disease.")

This list can be multiplied to include spinocerebellar ataxia (a degenerative disease linked to a gene on chromosome 6), Huntington's disease (see "Case Presentation: Huntington's Disease" in this chapter), Lorenzo's disease (adrenoleukodystrophy, or ALD, which involves the degeneration of the myelin sheath around nerves), Canavan disease (a rare and fatal brain disorder affecting mostly Ashkenazi Jews and similar to ALD), achondroplastic dwarfism (the gene, FGR3, causes about one-third of the cases of dwarfism), and cystic fibrosis (in which mucus accumulates in the lungs and pancreas; the gene, discovered on chromosome 7, is known to exist in hundreds of mutant forms).

HapMap

The map of the genome is a powerful tool for understanding the role of genes that in the past could only be guessed at or located only by determined research and good luck. Unlike cystic fibrosis or sickle-cell disease, however, most diseases are not the result of a single gene mutation. Breast cancer is caused by a mutated gene, but it also occurs in so-called sporadic ways.

In 2002, an international project was launched to supplement the human genome by assembling a haplotype map—a HapMap. A haplotype is stretch of alleles of different genes that lie closely together on the same chromosome and tend to be inherited together. The idea behind the HapMap was to chart nucleotide differences in haplotypes. These differences could then be linked with particular diseases by comparing the genomes of those with the disease with those who don't have the disease.

Such studies don't compare entire genomes. Rather, they rely on analyzing hundreds of thousands of segments of DNA known as *single-nucleotide polymorphisms*, or SNPs (pronounced "snips"). SNPs are variations in nucleotides (the adenine, cytosine, guanine, or tyrosine on a DNA strand) that occur at the same location in a genome. In one person's genome, for example, cytosine might occur where most genomes have guanine. Alternatively, at that location, the nucleotide may be missing or an additional nucleotide may be present.

These substitutions, deletions, and insertions may be harmless human variants that reflect population-related or racial differences. SNPs themselves aren't genes, but they can occur within genes. Thus, they may be found in a gene mutation (a variant form of a gene), or they may alter the way a gene is expressed. The gene fails to make an enzyme, for example, and the result can be a disease such as Tay–Sachs.

The analysis of SNPs is made possible by biochips programmed to detect nucleotide differences at locations along a DNA. The biochip provides, in effect, a catalogue of the variants displayed by an individual's DNA. The SNPs in the catalogue are then compared with those in a database that associates particular SNPs with particular diseases. The location of the gene containing the SNP variant can then be mapped onto the genome. We should, in principle, be able to eventually have a complete catalogue of all genetic diseases and the genes and mutations responsible for them.

Many researchers have recently concluded that the main assumption behind the HapMap was wrong. It appears not to be true that, as Nicholas Wade put the point, "Mutations causing common diseases are common." Although some 2000 SNPs are found at sites on the human genome that are linked to diseases, the SNPs often occur in nongene segments of DNA—that is, in the so-called junk DNA of the genome. This suggests that the association between a SNP and a disease may often be no more than a statistical artifact. (The SNP may be a genetic marker for a disease, even though it is not causally responsible for it.)

The HapMap approach has turned out to be not completely wrong, but more limited in value than researchers first believed.

Personal Genomes

Researchers now believe that (to quote Nicholas Wade again) "Common diseases are caused by rare mutations." This suggests that the best way to find the gene responsible for a

disease is to compare the genome of someone with the disease with the genome of someone who doesn't have it. This approach, unlike the HapMap approach, requires looking at *whole* genomes (about three billion nucleotides each), not just using SNPs as a sample. The genomes must be sequenced—the whole string of nucleotides must be listed in the order in which they occur. Thus, if the entire genome of someone with a disease is compared with that of someone lacking the disease, variants in the nucleotides will show up.

A paradigmatic example of this approach is Richard A. Gibbs's analysis of the genome of James R. Lupski. Gibbs and Lupski are colleagues at Baylor College of Medicine, and Lupski, a medical geneticist, has an inherited neurological disorder called Charcot–Marie–Tooth (CMT) disease.* The disease involves myelin (the insulating sheath around nerves) and leads to a progressive loss of control of the feet, legs, hands, and arms. A single normal copy of the gene involved is enough to prevent a full-blown version of the disease, although those who inherit one normal and one mutated copy may experience mild symptoms. Mutations in any of thirty-nine (known) genes can cause CMT.

Gibbs had already sequenced the genomes of ten healthy people before he asked Lupski to serve as a test case. When Lupski's genome was compared with those of the healthy people, Gibbs found that Lupski had mutations in both copies (alleles) of the gene SH3TC2. Nor did each allele have the same mutation. The one Lupski had inherited from his father was different from the one he inherited from his mother. His mother had one normal gene and one mutated, and his father had one normal and one with a different mutation.

Lupski was one of eight children, and the way the two mutations were distributed from the parents determined whether they were free

---

* The disease is named for its discoverers: Jean-Martin Charcot, Pierre Marie, and Howard Henry Tooth. It has nothing to do with one's teeth.

of CMT, mildly affected, or like Lupski, had a full-blown version of the disease. Two children inherited normal copies of the genes—one from each parent. Two others inherited the mother's mutation and the father's normal copy. Four, including Lupski, inherited each parent's mutated copy and thus developed CMT.

The cost of sequencing Lupski's genome was $50,000. Because of its cost, sequencing the genomes of individuals is primarily a research tool. In 2009, only seven genomes had been sequenced, but by 2010, geneticists Leroy Hood and David Galas planned to try to sequence one hundred genomes a year over the course of several years. They intended to look at multi-generational families, identify disease-causing genes, and trace the way they are inherited. They also planned to search for new mutations in the family lines.

Such research will be impossible unless the costs of sequencing come down. The aim is to bring the cost down from $50,000 to $5,000, then to about $1,000. The way this will be achieved, researchers think, is by getting the automated machines that use microarrays of DNA (biochips) and computer programs to work faster and require fewer people. The pay-off, researchers hope, will be an increasingly more detailed understanding of how genes cause particular diseases. Just as important, being able to sequence someone's genome might allow the development of what is usually known as "personalized medicine."

Not by Genes Alone: Proteins

Being able to locate a gene is a crucial step toward understanding the complex roles of genes, but a knowledge of where genes appear in the human (or individual) genome is incomplete in a crucial way. Such knowledge must be accompanied by an understanding of what proteins the genes encode and what role those proteins play.

Genes do most of their work by producing proteins. The proteins interact with other proteins to regulate human development, cell division, physiological functioning, immunological responses, tissue repair, and so on. An enzyme or hormone that is missing or deficient, for example, is responsible for diseases like Tay–Sachs and diabetes. Indeed, perhaps all diseases can be viewed as involving genetically based responses.

We have identified genes that predispose people to heart disease and breast cancer, and many researchers think it is reasonable to believe that there are scores (if not hundreds) of predisposing genes for many other diseases, ranging from schizophrenia to glaucoma.

We can expect researchers in the future to unravel more connections between proteins and diseases. We can then hope to see new approaches to diagnosing and treating diseases that have often been mysterious and lacking an effective therapy. Instead of a broad diagnostic category like "breast cancer," for example, the disease may be subdivided into many more specific categories, and each may have its own prognosis and its own therapy. Indeed, pharmaceutical companies may be able to design drugs that are specific for individuals and their particular genetic makeup. By tailoring an individual treatment to an individual version of a disease, not only could such designer drugs be more effective, but they could lack some of the worst side effects of drugs aimed at a general population of patients. Thus, if Sonia Henty is treated for breast cancer, she will receive drugs designed to treat her genetically characterized disease, and if the drugs hit their target more specifically, she may not suffer the literally sickening effects of wide-spectrum chemotherapy.

Personalized Medicine

Medicine is already personalized to an extent. Patients allergic to penicillin, for example, are prescribed some other antibiotic. Imagine, though, a form of medicine that is based on an understanding of how your genes are connected with the specific form of a disease that you have and how your particular genetic makeup might determine the treatment you receive. The understanding we have of genes and proteins has already allowed us to move in this direction.

Perhaps the best example of what personalized medicine might look like is the use of trastuzumab (brand name Herceptin®) to treat some types of breast cancer. The gene Her2/neu codes for the protein human epidermal growth factor 2, part of the system that regulates cell growth. All breast tissue contains some Her2, but fifteen to twenty percent of women with breast cancer have a mutation that increases Her2 to a hundred times the usual amount. Tumors identified as Her2 positive tend to be aggressive and to respond poorly to the standard hormone treatment.

Herceptin binds to Her2 receptors on the surface of cells. It kills cancer cells and ends the abnormal cell growth that an overabundance of Her2 produces. Herceptin, taken over a period of years, also keeps the cancer from returning. For some women with breast cancer, the drug can seem almost miraculous in its effects.

Still, Herceptin works only in some fifty percent of women who are Her2 positive. Why that is so is not now known. That the treatment can be so effective suggests that comparing personal genomes of patients would allow researchers to find genetic differences that would account for why some patients respond to the treatment but others don't.

Personalized medicine of the future is likely to feature more targeted therapies. Rather than simply subject every cancer patient to a round of standard chemotherapy, the chemotherapy will be tailored to the genetic predispositions of the patient. A knowledge of those predispositions will come from examining the patient's genome and comparing it with genomes stored in a massive database.

Envoi

When we understand the interplay among genes, proteins, developmental processes, and environmental factors, we will be well on the way to grasping the causes of diseases. Understanding these causes will put us on the road to finding effective measures to prevent them, treat them, or even cure them. Those measures are likely to be designed for the individual on the basis of an analysis of her genome.

That is the new promise of the secular Holy Grail.

SOCIAL CONTEXT
Stem Cells: The End of the Battle?

Research groups headed by John Gearhart of Johns Hopkins University and James Thomson of the University of Wisconsin, Madison, announced in November 1998 that they had succeeded in isolating and culturing human embryonic stem cells.

Embryonic Stem Cells vs. Adult Stem Cells

Embryonic stem cells are undifferentiated cells produced after a fertilized egg has divided several times and developed into a blastocyst. The blastocyst, a hollow ball of cells, contains a little lump called the inner-cell mass consisting of fifteen to twenty embryonic stem cells.

As development proceeds, embryonic stem cells differentiate and become specialized. They turn into so-called *adult* stem cells. These cells go on to produce the approximately 120 different cell types that form tissues and organs such as the blood, brain, bone, and liver. Adult stem cells have been found in the bone marrow and the brain, and some biologists believe that specific adult stem cells are associated with every organ.

Before embryonic stem cells begin to differentiate, they have the potential to become any of the specialized cells. Afterward, their fate is determined, and they do not go back to their previous state. When heart cells divide, for example, they produce only heart cells. Success in cloning mammals demonstrated, however, that the genetic material in a body cell can be made to return to its "default" position, in which each cell retains the genetic information needed to develop into a complete individual—including all the cell types. (As will be discussed later, returning a cell to its "default" position may offer a method for producing embryonic stem cells that does not involve an embryo.)

Original Sources of Stem Cells

Thomson retrieved embryonic stem cells from surplus embryos produced for fertility treatments. (He obtained consent from the egg and sperm donors.) Gearhart used a different method. A group of cells known as *embryonic germ cells* forms the sperm and ova that transmit genetic information to the next generation, and these cells are protected from the process that turns stem cells into specialized components of tissues and organs.

Gearhart retrieved embryonic germ cells from aborted fetuses and cultured them to produce stem cells. Stem cells obtained in this way are apparently no different from the ones obtained directly from blastocysts.

Treatment Dreams

The identification of embryonic stem cells and the ability to culture them are important steps in opening up an amazing new range of possibilities for treating many chronic, debilitating, and life-threatening diseases.

Cultures of embryonic stem cells appear to be what biologists call *immortal* cell lines. That is, the cells can replicate for an indefinite number of generations without dying or accumulating genetic errors. This capacity reduces the need to acquire new stem cells with great frequency. Cell lines can be established to supply the needs of researchers and physicians. If scientists learn how to control the system of chemical messengers and receptors that regulate the development of "blank" embryonic stem cells into specialized brain, heart, liver,

or pancreas cells, it may be possible to repair those organs by injections of stem cells.

This approach may make it possible, for example, to treat Parkinson's disease by injecting stem cells into the substantia nigra in the brain to boost the production of the neurotransmitter dopamine. (The lack of dopamine produces the symptoms of the disease.) Or diabetes might be brought under control by inducing the pancreas to incorporate insulin-producing islet cells developed from stem cells. Or we might be able to produce a potentially limitless amount of red blood cells, sterile and free of viruses, for use in transfusions.

Because embryonic stem cells have the capacity to become cells of any type, it looks as if they could be used to produce whatever sort of cells are needed to treat a particular disease. Damaged spinal nerves that keep people from walking or even moving their bodies might be repaired, and faulty retinas that cause blindness might be replaced with functional ones.

An even more dramatic prospect is that embryonic stem cells might be used to grow body tissues and even whole organs for transplantation. People could be provided with bone or skin grafts, liver segments, lung lobes, or even new kidneys or hearts. The problems caused by the intractable shortage of transplant organs would simply disappear. (See Chapter 8.)

The study of embryonic stem cells may make it possible to understand more about how genes are turned on and off during the process of development. This, in turn, may lead to our ability to control gene expression and eliminate diseases such as cystic fibrosis and muscular dystrophy. We might even be able to treat certain forms of cancer if we can understand how to control the growth of cells.

The problem of the rejection of tissue and organ transplants is now dealt with by using powerful immunosuppressive drugs. Three different strategies are made possible by stem cells:

1. **Stem-Cell Banks.** Good antigen (a collection of proteins on the cell surface) matching, which reduces the severity of

the immune response, might be achieved by maintaining a bank of stem cells. With a wide range of (say) embryonic stem-cell lines to choose from, transplant physicians could select the cells most compatible with the individual.

2. **Suppression of Markers.** A second solution is to find a way to suppress or disguise markers on the surfaces of stem cells so that they don't provoke the immune response. But researchers concerned with preventing the rejection of transplant organs have been trying to accomplish this for a long time and have been thus for unsuccessful.

3. **Cloning (Somatic-Cell Nuclear Transfer).** The third and most elegant solution is to make use of embryonic stem cells acquired from an embryo created by the techniques of cloning. This involves removing the nucleus from a donor egg, then replacing it with the DNA taken from a somatic (body) cell of an individual. The egg will contain only the DNA of the donor. Thus, when the egg develops into an embryo and the stem cells are removed, they will be genetically identical with those of the individual contributing the DNA. The process, technically known as somatic-cell nuclear transfer, is often called *therapeutic cloning*, in contrast to *reproductive cloning*.

Opponents of cloning often reject the use of "therapeutic," because of its positive associations and on the ground that therapeutic benefit has yet to be demonstrated. By contrast, advocates of cloning often prefer to avoid the word "cloning," because of its often negative associations, in favor of "cellular nuclear transfer," or CNT. (For more details on cloning, see "Social Context: Cloning," in Chapter 4.)

Regenerative Medicine

Stem cells have the potential to serve as the foundation for treatments that will allow us to repair or replace most, if not all, of our ailing organs. They hold the promise of a secular miracle. They could provide a way to still the tremors of Parkinson's disease, knit together a severed spinal cord, supply the cells needed to produce the enzyme required to metabolize sugar, replace the cells in a malfunctioning retina, and heal a damaged heart. Stem cells could become treatments for diseases such as Alzheimer's and Huntington's, for which there are no effective therapies. The list goes on and on.

Research using animals has already led to promising results. In 2008, scientists at Novocell announced that they had succeeded in converting mouse embryonic stem cells into insulin-producing cells. When the cells were transplanted into mice that had been made diabetic, the new cells kept their blood sugar within acceptable limits.

Stem cells may offer us the chance to redeem the lives of countless numbers of people from disease and injury. In this respect, they may usher in a new era of medicine. Regenerative medicine, a collection of therapies that produce new tissues and perhaps whole organs, holds out the promise of cures in dozens of cases where no effective treatments now exist.

First Stem-Cell Clinical Trial

In 2001, Hans Keirstead used human embryonic stem cells to produce oligodendrocyte progenitor cells. He injected these cells into rats with partial spinal cord injuries. The cells matured into glial cells, which produce myelin, the material forming the insulating sheath around nerves. The myelin allows impulses to travel from the brain to the motor nerves that operate the muscles.

The injections restored nerve transmission to a limited degree. Rats with injuries older than ten months had a lot of scarring, and the cells failed to help them. Rats with more recent injuries that had rendered them unable to move their rear legs, tails, or trunk muscles recovered substantial movement and function within two months after treatment.

This success prompted the Geron Corporation, which had funded Keirstead's study, to fund additional research, with the aim of testing oligodendrocyte cells in a clinical trial. A treatment reducing the crippling effects of spinal-cord injuries would be of significant medical importance, but it would also be a valuable product. Eventually, partly at the insistence of the FDA, Geron carried out twenty-three studies and spent $45 million to develop the therapy.

(Some observers claim that the Bush administration, not wanting to see embryonic stem-cell therapies develop, pressured the FDA to stall Geron's application for a clinical trial by asking for additional studies. The application was approved only when the Obama administration took office. Geron, however, does not confirm this view.)

Geron secured FDA approval for a Phase 1 clinical trial in January 2009. The trial will eventually enroll eight to ten people with spinal-cord injuries that are recent and severe enough to render them paralyzed from the waist down. The participants must all be volunteers and have no realistic hope of recovering from their injuries. The cells will be injected at the site of the injury during the seven to fourteen days after the injury occurs. The hope is that the growth factors produced by the injected cells will trigger nerve regeneration. The trial will be carried out at as many as seven medical centers, and patients will be closely monitored. During the first year, they will receive regular MRIs, and then they will be followed with regular examinations over a period of fifteen years.

The safety of the trial is of great concern to those who think that embryonic stem cells have the potential to transform medicine. The death of one of the participants could halt the development of all stem-cell–based therapies. Because stem cells have not been extensively studied, the possibility that they might harm a human subject is real.

The cells may cause a lethal form of cancer, for example, or they may provoke a fatal immune response. ("We don't want another Jessie Gelsinger here," the CEO of Geron said, explaining that the company was as certain as it could be that the clinical trial would be safe; see "Case Presentation: Jesse Gelsinger," in Chapter 2.) Because the effects of the therapy on humans are completely unknown, some suggest that the participants should be people with a fatal neurological disease, such as amyotrophic lateral sclerosis, rather than someone with a spinal-cord injury, who may be able to look forward to many decades of life.

The trial employing embryonic stem cells is only Phase 1, so its aim is just to test the safety and side effects of the treatment. Even if the treatment appears safe and effective, it will need to go through Phase 2 and Phase 3 testing. Thus, decades may pass before the treatment becomes available to people with spinal-cord injuries.

Treatments with Adult Stem Cells

The therapeutic promises of embryonic stem cells are, to an extent, paralleled by the promises of adult stem cells. How adult stem cells can be used in treatments is currently being investigated vigorously.

Evidence from animal studies suggests, for example, that heart muscle damaged by a heart attack can be treated effectively by an injection of adult stem cells. These cells produce normal heart cells, forming new tissue to replaced damaged tissue. Amazingly, the stem cells employed come from the bone marrow, where they ordinarily produce blood cells. No adult stem cells have been found in the heart. Apparently, the bone-marrow cells respond to the biochemical environment of the heart, and it reprograms them to produce heart cells.

In January 1999, Swedish scientists identified neural stem cells. These are brain cells that have differentiated to become cavity-lining cells, yet when they divide, their progeny can differentiate into either glial (structural) cells or neurons. When the brain is injured, the cavity-lining cells begin reproducing and the neural stem cells produce glial cells that form scars. If a way could be found to induce the neural stem cells to produce more neurons at the site of the injury, more brain function might be preserved.

Most researchers are not satisfied with the prospect of restricting research to adult stem cells. They point out that we don't yet know enough about embryonic stem cells to determine whether their therapeutic potential could be equaled by using adult stem cells. Only research with embryonic and adult stem cells will answer this question.

Ethical Issues over Acquiring Embryos

The retrieval of embryonic stem cells from human embryos or fetuses raises ethical problems for those who oppose abortion or believe that a fetus or embryo has a special moral status. From this perspective, a fertilized egg (an embryo) has the potential to develop into a human being, and (in a strong version) that entitles it to be treated as a person in the moral sense. Because it is wrong to kill an innocent person, it is thus wrong to destroy a human embryo. (See the discussion in Chapter 5.)

Taking embryonic stem cells from an aborted fetus is also seen as morally wrong by the same critics. Because abortion is viewed as a wrongful act, it is considered morally wrong to benefit from it. Also, as with the use of fetal tissue generally, by giving stem cells an instrumental value (using them to treat a disease, for example), we are tacitly encouraging abortion and endorsing its practice. In addition, by treating the fetus as a product or commodity that we use to suit our needs, we are disrespecting it, given the special status bestowed on the fetus by its potential to develop into a human being.

Some also object to using human eggs to produce embryos. Acquiring eggs has the potential for exploiting women, but more important, the use of eggs to produce embryos for the purpose of research turns the eggs into commodities with an instrumental value. The purpose of the research (acquiring knowledge or

developing new treatments) may be laudable, but even so, the eggs are being put to a use that is incompatible with their natural purpose, which is to play a role in reproduction.

Those who do not assign a special status to a fetus or embryo typically do not oppose the use of embryonic stem cells. Rather, their concerns resemble ones associated with cloning and genetic manipulation in general. They oppose reproductive cloning, for example, because they think it cheapens human life. To consider another example, suppose genes could be added to embryonic stem cells to produce individuals with some special trait that could be inherited. In that case, the whole human species might be altered by altering stem cells.

Some critics maintain that to choose such a course of action would be dangerous, because of its unforeseeable biological and social consequences. Others hold that it would be wrong because tampering with the human genome would violate our notion of what it is to be human.

Three Problematic Sources for Embryonic Stem Cells

Most stem-cell opponents object to the ways embryonic stem cells are acquired, rather than to the ways the cells are used. Hence, if it were possible to acquire stem cells without violating moral prohibitions, some critics might drop their opposition. Following are four alternative sources that most critics have found unobjectionable. A fifth source, discussed in the next sections, is sufficiently morally unproblematic to win over the great majority of critics and is still under debate.

1. **Miscarriages.** Those who consider the destruction of an embryo to obtain stem cells immoral, may (but not necessarily) consider it legitimate to obtain stem cells from spontaneously aborted fetuses. If no one did anything to cause the miscarriage, the stem cells cannot be seen as acquired as the result of a morally wrong action.

Practically speaking, however, this way of getting stem cells is difficult, uncertain, and expensive. Also, because a fetus is spontaneously aborted, the stem cells may be abnormal in some way.

2. **Parthenogenesis.** Some who oppose acquiring stem cells from embryos or aborted fetuses would find stem cells produced by a process of parthenogenesis morally acceptable. That is, if an unfertilized human egg could be induced by biochemical means to divide and produce stem cells, the stem cells recovered could be legitimately used. Because the unfertilized egg would lack the genetic information needed for development, even if implanted into a uterus, it would not be a human embryo and thus would have no special moral status.

3. **Blastomeres.** Some might find it acceptable to use stem cells if they could be obtained from fertilized eggs that are not destroyed in the process. In a technique developed in 2006 at Advanced Cell Technology, researchers removed embryonic stem cells from an embryo after only two days of development without destroying it. After two days, a fertilized egg divides into eight cells, or blastomeres. Researchers removed one of the blastomeres and took the stem cells from it. This blastomere was destroyed, but the other seven blastomeres retained the capacity to develop into a normal child if the embryo were implanted into a uterus. There is no reason to believe that a single blastomere, even if implanted, would develop into a child.

The technique is based on a standard procedure of preimplantation genetic testing. One blastomere is removed so that its DNA can be tested for a particular genetic disorder, and if the embryo is found free of the gene connected with the disorder, the embryo (i.e., the other seven blastomeres) is implanted into the uterus of the woman seeking the test. The technique

has been used thousands of times during the last two decades, and it has not been associated with abnormal births.

For some people, employing this technique would remove a moral roadblock to the use of stem cells. For most Roman Catholics and social conservatives, however, the technique only compounds the serious moral wrongs of in vitro fertilization and preimplantation genetic screening. In vitro fertilization is wrong, in their view, because it separates procreation from love, may require masturbation to acquire sperm, and turns embryos into a product.

Preimplantation genetic screening, they believe, is also wrong. It involves choosing which embryos to implant and thus allows humans to exercise control over procreation that rightfully belongs only to nature or God. Also, because embryos that are not implanted are discarded, the process involves the destruction of innocent human life. Hence, no matter how reasonable it may seem to some to sidestep the issue of destroying embryos by using a nondestructive method for obtaining stem cells, so many object to other aspects of the method that, if it were perfected, its use would not put an end to the ethical and political debate over stem cells.

These three alternative ways of obtaining embryonic stem cells, which have excited controversy for years, have been superseded by a method that promises to provide embryonic stem cells without provoking serious moral objections.

Cell Conversion: Induced Pluripotent Stem Cells

In 2007, Shinya Yamanaka and Kazutoshi Takahashi of Kyoto University published a paper in which they reported how, after numerous trials, they identified four genes essential to restoring a somatic cell to a pluripotent state. In a process known as cell conversion, they used a retrovirus to insert the four genes into the DNA of mouse skin cells, and the incorporated genes reprogrammed the skin cells into embryonic stem cells. The genes, in effect, restored the cells to their "default" state. (Two groups of American scientists repeated the experiment and confirmed the result.)

The Japanese researchers were not the only ones who succeeded in resetting adult cells to a pluripotent condition. James A. Thompson, one of the researchers who first isolated human embryonic stem cells, working with colleagues at the University of Wisconsin, also identified four genes, two of them different from those identified by Yamanaka and Takahashi, that would reset an adult cell to its default state. Thompson and his colleagues used cells from human foreskins and got the same results as Yamanaka.

Induced pluripotent stem cells, like embryonic stem cells, apparently have the capacity to develop into any of the 120 kinds of cells that form tissues and organs. No one knows, however, whether the induced stem cells will always behave in the body the same way as embryonic stem cells do. Additional studies with converted mouse cells have shown that when they are injected into embryos, they form different types of tissue and developmental layers in ways that are indistinguishable from the actions of embryonic stem cells. It is reasonable to believe that converted human cells would behave in the same way.

Potential Problems

Some difficulties may have to be overcome before many of the promises associated with pluripotent stem cells can be realized. One of the genes used by Yamanaka in his original work, for example, is known to cause cancerous tumors. Yamanaka later showed that he could achieve cell conversion without the gene, but the possibility that pluripotent cells will produce cancer is one of the reasons that using them to treat human diseases remains a problem.

A second major problem is the use of a retrovirus to insert the genes needed for conversion into a cell. Retroviruses themselves are known to induce mutations that can lead to cancer.

Conversion Possibilities

The possibilities of using the cell conversion techniques pioneered by Yamanaka and Thompson are currently being explored at the level of basic science. In August 2008, for example, Harvard researchers reported using transcription factors to convert exocrine cells from a mouse pancreas into insulin-producing beta cells. Transcription factors are proteins that control which genes in a cell are expressed and thus what the cell does. Each type of cell is believed to have a particular set of transcription factors that determine its characteristics, and the identification and use of those factors may make it possible to develop cells of specific types without starting from pluripotent cells.

The mice in the Harvard experiment had been rendered diabetic, but when they were injected with the converted cells, their diabetes was brought under control for as long as the cells lasted. Although the converted cells produced insulin, they did not organize themselves into the characteristic clumps of cells (the islets) in the pancreas. For this reason, the researchers identified the converted cells only as "cells that closely resemble beta cells."

Cells produced by converting the cell of an individual would be genetically compatible with the rest of that person's cells. Thus, they could be used to repair tissues and organs without the risk of provoking a response from the immune system. Until now, the only way scientists could imagine doing this was to acquire stem cells from an embryo created by transferring the nucleus of a somatic cell from the intended recipient into a donor egg. (See the earlier discussion of cloning, or somatic-cell nuclear transfer.)

One of the most exciting prospects is that cells acquired by conversion from someone with a disease like Alzheimer's or Parkinson's would allow researchers to study the ways in which the cells depart from the path of normal development and lead to the disease.

Acceptance by Critics?

The immediate appeal of being able to acquire human embryonic stem cells by converting somatic cells is the possibility that researchers will no longer need to create or destroy human embryos. Thus, the arguments over the moral legitimacy of stem-cell research and treatments based on stem cells should significantly abate, if not wholly disappear.

Obtaining stem cells by conversion, some believe, means that we don't need to worry about the moral status of a blastomere, debate issues connected with using human eggs, or argue about cloning for therapeutic purposes. The status of somatic cells has not been a matter of controversy, so converting them into embryonic stem cells is not likely to generate significant ethical issues. "You should have a solution here that will address the moral objections that have been percolating for years," said Tadeusz Pacholczyk of the National Catholic Bioethics Center.

Yet some observers are not so sure that the debate can be resolved so easily. They point out, first, that if researchers can produce pluripotent cells, then, most likely, with a bit more work, they should be able to convert somatic cells into totipotent cells, ones that have all the capacities of a fertilized egg. Thus, the moral status of such a cell would be the same as that of an embryo. Second, those who think that an embryo has the same status as a person in the moral sense because of its capacity to develop into a person who is born may apply this same line of reasoning to somatic cells. If such cells can be converted and given the capacity to become totipotent, then every cell in the body must be considered the moral equivalent of an embryo—which means that it has the moral status of a person.

From this point of view, the stem-cell debate is not resolved by our new capacity to convert body cells into pluripotent cells. Rather, the debate becomes even more complicated: we must now address the issue raised by the developmental capacities of somatic cells converted into pluripotent cells and, perhaps, into totipotent cells. The dust of serious controversy will not settle until these new issues are resolved. Meanwhile, the old issues will continue to be debated, because scientists still need to answer the question whether stem cells produced by converting somatic cells are exactly the same as the pluripotent cells extracted from an embryo.

The new discoveries may complicate the debate for many. Even so, they still point in the direction of a resolution. Faced with the reality of converted pluripotent cells, those who hold that an embryo is a person may be compelled to rethink their view. They may decide that what they took to be the condition for being a person (having the developmental capacity to become a child) is not as nonarbitrary as they assumed. They may have to look for other criteria, and it is possible that those criteria will exclude embryos from the category of persons in the moral sense.

Laws and Regulations

Only when embryonic stem cells no longer need to be studied will the controversy about them come to an end. Until then, the research must be conducted in an environment of laws and regulations that politics and political pressure make subject to change.

No Federal Funds

The 1995 Dickey–Wicker Amendment prohibits the use of federal funds to create human embryos for research purposes or to support research in which a human embryo is destroyed. (The amendment, which has the status of law, has been attached to appropriation bills that fund the National Institutes of Health.) The research by Thomson and Gearhart leading to the recovery and culturing of stem cells was supported, not by federal grants, but by the Geron Corporation, a small biotechnology company.

When Gearhart and Thomson announced their success, the question of the moral legitimacy of obtaining and using embryonic stem cells quickly became the topic of a national debate.

The National Conference of Catholic Bishops and other social conservative groups and politicians opposed spending federal money on stem-cell research. The opposition included many traditional opponents of abortion. They argued that human embryos have the status of persons, so retrieving their stem cells, and thus killing them, would be morally wrong.

In contrast, many disease-advocacy groups, seeing the possibility of cures by means of stem cells, proposed making stem-cell research eligible for federal funding. Without such funding, they argued, the chances that effective treatments would be found for many diseases would be significantly reduced. Private funding would be inadequate. Also, the United States would fall behind in medical innovation as other countries moved into the research gap that a lack of federal support would produce. Those pressing for going ahead with research included many politicians who ordinarily aligned themselves with social conservatives.

Many people, politicians included, found it hard to object to removing stem cells from embryos created at reproductive clinics and then not used. Ordinarily, such embryos are discarded. If so, then why not retrieve the stem cells and use them to develop treatments for diseases?

Social conservatives—Roman Catholics in particular—did not find this argument persuasive. So far as they were concerned, it was morally wrong to create and destroy embryos for the purpose of assisted reproduction. Hence, destroying them to acquire stem cells would also be wrong. (Even if the stem cells are used to treat disease, it would be wrong: The morally poisoned tree, they argued, bears only poisoned fruit.)

Bush Rules

President George Bush faced this politically vexed situation in 2001, and in August of that year he announced a policy to guide future federal funding of research involving human embryonic stem cells. His decision was to allow research on the (alleged) 64 human embryonic stem-cell lines already established, but not permit federal funds to be used to acquire new stem cells through the destruction of embryos.

The new policy met with a mixed response. It was denounced by the National Conference of Catholic Bishops as "morally unacceptable," while many researchers and patient advocates viewed the policy as placing an unwarranted restriction on research. Scientists were particularly concerned about limiting research to already established cell lines. No one could say in advance, they pointed out, exactly how many genetically different kinds of stem cells would be adequate for treating diseases.

Yet many observers also welcomed the decision as being less restrictive than they had feared. Perhaps the most unfortunate effect of the policy, in the view of patient advocates and researchers, was that it foreclosed the possibility of therapeutic cloning (somatic-cell nuclear transfer). Because the destruction of embryos was not allowed, the earlier mentioned process of acquiring embryonic stem cells genetically identical with one's own cells could not be employed.

Advocates of cloning for therapeutic purposes stressed—and still stress—that they are not advocating reproductive cloning—that is, producing an embryo that will be transferred to a woman's uterus and allowed to develop into a child. Critics of cloning, however, generally oppose its use for any purpose.

Also, the federally approved cell lines have proved to be fewer in number than President Bush initially suggested. Some are apparently contaminated with nonhuman cells, and others are the property of private companies and thus not available to all researchers.

Private and State Funding

In March 2002, the NIH broadened the path for researchers a bit by issuing an interpretation of the federal restrictions on using stem cells. The interpretation holds that scientists can study new stem-cell lines and even create them, so long as the work is not supported by federal money.

This loosening of the Bush restrictions was welcomed by researchers, but they claimed that they were still hampered by the federal policy. Private money for basic research is a scarce commodity, and most progress is made when large amounts of federal grant money is available. Grants drive research, and their absence slows it down.

The restrictions also required a duplication of facilities, equipment, and laboratory supplies. Because federal money cannot be used to create embryos for the purpose of research or for the study of embryonic stem cell lines other than those approved by federal policy, stem-cell research that departs from the guidelines must be carried out without the use of any federal money. Thus, laboratories in universities, and medical schools, and government facilities, nearly all of which are supported to some extent by federal grants, cannot legally engage in research that violates federal guidelines. Some institutes, such as the one at Harvard University, have been established and funded exclusively with private resources. Other universities, like the University of California at San Francisco, used rented space off campus.

Federal regulations do not forbid states from funding stem-cell research. Even though several states attempted to initiate stem-cell research programs, most attempts to substitute state funding for federal funding met with stiff opposition that consigned the proposed programs to legislative limbo.

California remains the exception. In 2004, fifty-nine percent of voters approved Proposition 71, establishing the California Institute for Regenerative Medicine. The Institute, once in operation, is supposed to distribute $3 billion to researchers to develop stem-cell technologies. Quite apart from helping people, however, the Institute is supposed to become such a powerhouse of stem-cell research that it will attract leading scientists and biotech companies to the state and produce a significant amount of money in the form of patent revenues.

For several years after Proposition 71 was approved, the Institute was tied up in court fighting lawsuits filed by those opposed to cloning. These legal entanglements meant that the state was prohibited from pursuing its plan to sell bonds to raise the money needed to fund the Institute. Finally, in May of 2008, California awarded $270 million in grants to build a dozen stem-cell research centers in the state. The universities and institutes receiving the grants pledged to try to raise an additional $560 million of private money.

Obama Rules

In March 2009, President Barack Obama issued an executive order instructing NIH to draft guidelines lifting some of the Bush rules governing stem-cell research. The most important change in the regulations was to make thirteen new human embryonic stem-cell lines eligible for research receiving federal funding. The lines were established by researchers working in privately funded laboratories, and ninety-six more lines are currently under review. (An estimated seven hundred lines have been established with private money.)

The newly approved lines are ones in which stem cells were obtained from embryos created at fertility clinics and then not needed. It remains illegal to use federal money to carry out research on stem cells obtained from human embryos created solely for research purposes. Cloning for therapeutic purposes, the process of somatic-cell nuclear transfer, also remains illegal.

Under the new rules, donors of surplus embryos must be informed that the embryos will be destroyed and that there are other ways of disposing them. Donors must provide written consent, retain the right to change their minds, and receive no payment. For cell lines established before the new regulations, an NIH review panel will decide whether they were produced in an ethically acceptable way and thus are eligible for research supported by federal funding. Critics object to applying standards retroactively that may result in excluding some potentially valuable cell line.

Many researchers and advocates for developing regenerative medicine were disappointed at the comparatively limited changes Obama made in federal policy. During his 2008 campaign, Obama explicitly endorsed the "therapeutic cloning of stem cells." Unless pluripotent stem cells produced by cell conversion turn out to be both equivalent to embryonic stem cells and safe to use in humans, some of the main promises of regenerative medicine can't be achieved without therapeutic cloning.

Critics of stem-cell research were quick to condemn the Obama changes. Because the new rules permit the destruction of discarded embryos, some saw them as a major step toward permitting embryos to be created so they can be "killed" to serve the needs of research.

Envoi

Embryonic stem-cell research is likely to remain a flashpoint of controversy for the immediate future. The production of pluripotent embryonic stem cells by the conversion of somatic cells promises eventually to drain away controversy about the use of such cells, but until research establishes that cells produced by conversion are exactly the same as those acquired from embryos, the conflict will continue. Ironically, the research needed to prove equivalence will require the destruction of embryos, and those who consider the destruction of embryos the moral equivalent of murder will argue for its end.

Furthermore, those who assign the embryo the status of a person will need to face the issues raised by cell conversion. If every cell has the potential to become the equivalent of a pluripotent or totipotent cell, does this mean that every cell in the body must be regarded as the moral equivalent of a person? Most likely, no one wants to endorse such a view. On what grounds, then, can an embryo continue to be assigned a status that is denied to converted somatic cells?

Controversies over stem cells will continue to rage. Even so, for the first time since human embryonic stem cells were identified and isolated in 1998, an end to the stem-cell wars can be imagined.

BRIEFING SESSION

The two great triumphs of nineteenth-century biology were Darwin's formulation of the theory of organic evolution and Mendel's statement of the laws of transmission genetics. One of the twentieth century's outstanding accomplishments was the development of an understanding of the molecular structures and processes involved in genetic inheritance. All three great achievements give rise to moral and social issues of considerable complexity. The theories are abstract, but the problems they generate are concrete and immediate.

Major problems are associated with our increased knowledge of inheritance and genetic change. One class of problems concerns the use we make of the knowledge we possess in dealing with individuals. We know a great deal about the ways genetic diseases are transmitted and the sorts of errors that can occur in human development. We have the means to make reliable predictions about the chances of the occurrence of a disease in a particular case, and we have the medical technology to detect some disorders before birth.

To what extent should we employ this knowledge? One possibility is that we might use it to detect, treat, or prevent genetic disorders. Thus, we might require that everyone submit to screening and counseling before having children. We might require that children be tested either prenatally or immediately after birth. We might recommend or require selective abortions. For some couples, we might require or recommend in vitro fertilization, then the selection of embryos free of a disease-producing gene for implantation. Using some combination of these methods, we might be able to bring many genetic diseases under control (although we could never eliminate them) in the way we have brought contagious diseases under control.

Requiring screening and testing suggests another possibility, one that involves taking a broader view of human genetics. Eliminating genetic disease might simply become part of a much more ambitious plan for deliberately improving the entire species. Shall we attempt to control human evolution by formulating policies and practices designed to alter the genetic composition of the human population? Shall we make use of "gene surgery" and recombinant-DNA technology to shape physical and mental attributes of our species? That is, shall we practice some form of eugenics?

Another class of problems has to do with the wider social and environmental consequences of genetic research and technology. Research in molecular genetics concerned with recombinant DNA has already revealed to us how the machinery of cells can be beneficially altered. We are able to make bacteria synthesize such important biological products as human insulin, and we are able to alter bacteria to serve as vaccines against diseases. In effect, recombinant-DNA technology produces life-forms that have never existed before. Should biotech industries be allowed to patent such forms in the way that new inventions are patented? Or do even altered organisms belong to us all?

Also, what are we to say about the deliberate release of genetically modified organisms into the environment? Is the threat that such organisms pose greater than the benefits they are likely to produce? We have already witnessed the great damage that can be done by pesticides and chemical pollution. Is there any way we can avoid damage that might be caused by genetically engineered organisms?

In the next three sections, we shall focus attention on the issues raised by the actual and potential use of genetic information. Our topics are these: genetic intervention (screening, counseling, and prenatal diagnosis), eugenics, and genetic research (therapy, technology, and biohazards).

Genetic Intervention: Screening, Counseling, and Diagnosis

Our genes play a major role in making us what we are. Biological programs of genetic information work amazingly well to produce normal, healthy individuals. But sometimes things go wrong, and when they do, the results can be tragic.

Almost 5000 human diseases have been identified as involving genetic factors. Some of the diseases are quite rare, whereas others are relatively common. Some are invariably fatal, whereas others are comparatively minor. Some respond well to treatment, whereas others do not.

The use of genetic information in predicting and diagnosing diseases has significantly increased during the last few decades. New scientific information, new medical techniques, and new social programs have all contributed to this increase.

Three approaches in particular have been adopted by the medical community as means of acquiring and employing genetic information related to diseases: genetic screening, genetic counseling, and prenatal genetic diagnosis. Each approach has been the source of significant ethical and social issues, but before examining the approaches and the problems associated with them, we need to consider the idea of a genetic disease.

Genetic Disease

The concept of a "genetic" disease is far from being clear. Roughly speaking, a genetic disease is a disease in which genes or the ways in which they are expressed are causally responsible for particular biochemical, cellular, or physiological defects. Rather than rely upon such a general definition, it's more useful for understanding genetic diagnosis to consider some of the ways genes play a role in producing diseases.

Gene Defects. The program of information coded into DNA (the genetic material) may in some way be abnormal because of the occurrence of a mutation at some time or other. (That is, a particular gene may have been lost or damaged, or a new gene added.) Consequently, when the DNA code is "read" and its instructions are followed, the child that develops will have impairments.

For example, a number of diseases, like phenylketonuria (PKU), are the result of inborn errors of metabolism. (For an explanation of PKU, see "Genetic Screening" later in the Briefing Session.) The diseases are produced by the lack of a particular enzyme necessary for ordinary metabolic functioning. The genetic coding required for the production of the enzyme is simply not present—the gene for the enzyme is missing.

A missing or defective gene may be due to a new mutation, but more often the condition has been inherited. It has been transmitted to the offspring through the genetic material contributed by the parents. Because defective genes can be passed on in this way, the diseases they produce are themselves described as heritable. (Thus, PKU is a genetically transmissible disease.) The diseases follow regular patterns through generations, and tracing out those patterns has been one of the great accomplishments of modern biology and medicine.

Developmental Defects. The biological development of a human being from a fertilized egg to a newborn child is an immensely complicated process. It involves an interplay between both genetic and environmental factors, and the possibility of errors occurring is quite real.

Mistakes that result as part of the developmental process are ordinarily called "congenital." Such defects are not in the original coding (genes) but result either from genetic damage or from the reading of the code. When either happens, the manufacture and assembly of materials required for normal fetal development are affected.

Radiation, drugs, chemicals, and nutritional deficiencies can all cause changes in an otherwise normal process. Also, biological disease agents, such as certain viruses, may intervene in development. They may alter the machinery of the cells, interfere with the formation of tissues, and defeat the carefully programmed processes that lead to a normal child.

Finally, factors internal to fetal development may also alter the process and lead to defects. The most common form of Down syndrome, for example, is caused by a failure of chromosomes to separate normally. The outcome is a child who has failed to develop properly and displays physical anomalies and some degree of mental retardation.

Defects occurring during the developmental process are not themselves the results of inheritance. Consequently, they cannot be passed on to the next generation.

Genetic Carriers. Some diseases are produced only when an individual inherits two copies of a gene (two alleles) for the disease from the parents. Parents who possess only one copy of the gene generally show none of the disease's symptoms. However, sometimes a parent may have symptoms of the same kind that are associated with the disease, although much less severe.

In the metabolic disease PKU, for example, individuals who have inherited only one allele (i.e., who are heterozygous, rather than homozygous) may show a greater-than-normal level of phenylalanine in their blood. Such people are somewhat deficient in the enzyme required to metabolize this substance, but the level of the substance may not be high enough to cause them any damage. Even so, they are carriers of a gene that, when passed on with another copy of the same gene from the other parent, can cause the disease PKU in their offspring. (As we will see later, this is also true for carriers of the sickle-cell trait.) The individual who receives both alleles for PKU obviously has the disease, but what about the parents? The point at which a condition becomes a disease is often uncertain.

Genetic Predisposition. It's been suggested that every disease involves a genetic component in some way or other. Even when people are exposed to the same new virus, their bodies react differently: some may destroy the virus, while others may become infected. Genetic variations may play a role in these differences. For example, although AIDS researchers noted in the 1980s that some who had been HIV positive for years hadn't developed AIDS, it wasn't until a mutation in the gene called CCR5 was identified that a potential explanation was found. The mutation is present in ten to fifteen percent of whites and appears to be absent in blacks and Asians.

In some cases, genes play a larger role in producing disease than in others. We have good evidence that hypertension, heart disease, various forms of cancer, and differential responses to environmental agents (such as sunlight, molds, and chemical pollutants) run in families, and the genetic makeup of particular individuals may predispose them to specific diseases.

For example, women who carry the BRCA1 gene are more likely to develop breast cancer at an early age than others in the population. Of course, not every woman who carries the gene develops breast cancer. What distinguishes the two groups? Their diet? Possessing other genes? No one knows, and what's true for familial breast cancer is also known to hold for dozens of other diseases.

Even granted the role of genes in producing diseases, it is important to keep in mind that predispositions are not themselves diseases. At best, they can be regarded only as causal conditions that, in conjunction with other conditions (likely to be unknown), can produce disease.

The action of genes in disease processes is even more complicated than described here. Nevertheless, our general categories are adequate to allow us to talk about the use made of information in genetic diagnosis.

Genetic Screening

In 1962, Dr. Robert Guthrie of the State University of New York developed an automated procedure for testing the blood of newborn children for the disease PKU. Although a diagnostic test for PKU had been available since 1934, it was time consuming and labor intensive. The Guthrie test made it practical to diagnose a large number of infants at a relatively low price.

PKU is a serious metabolic disorder. Infants affected are deficient in the enzyme phenylalanine hydroxylase. Because the enzyme is necessary to convert the amino acid phenylalanine into tyrosine as part of the normal metabolic process, a deficiency of the enzyme leads to a high concentration of phenylalanine in the infant's blood. The almost invariable result is severe mental retardation.

If the high level of phenylalanine in an infant's blood is detected very early, the infant can be put on a diet low in that amino acid. Keeping children on the diet until they are around the age of six significantly reduces the severity of the retardation that is otherwise inescapable.

The availability of the Guthrie test and the prospects of saving newborn children from irreparable damage encouraged state legislatures to pass mandatory screening laws. Massachusetts passed the first such law in 1963, and by 1967 similar legislation had been adopted by forty-one states.

The term *genetic screening* is sometimes used to refer to any activity having to do with locating or advising people with genetically connected diseases. We will restrict the term's application here and use it to refer only to public health programs that survey or test target populations with the aim of detecting individuals at risk of disease for genetic reasons.

The Massachusetts PKU law pointed the way to the development of public screening programs. PKU was the first disease tested for, but before long others were added to the list. A number of public health programs now screen particular populations for such conditions as sickle-cell anemia, sickle-cell trait, metabolic disorders, hypothyroidism, and chromosome anomalies. All fifty states now require screening for at least twenty-one of a standard panel of twenty-nine diseases. Some ninety-six percent of the four million babies born in the United States each year are routinely tested. Technological developments make it possible to use a single drop of blood to test for some forty disease conditions in a single analysis. New York state introduced a plan in 2002 to test newborns for all forty.

Although genetic screening is relatively new as a social program, the concept is historically connected with public health measures for the detection and prevention of communicable diseases like tuberculosis and syphilis. (HIV has been added to the list by states and the federal Centers for Disease Control.) If an individual with such a disease is identified, he can receive treatment, but most important, he can be prevented from spreading the disease to other members of the population.

Similarly, it is possible to think of diseases with a genetic basis as resembling contagious diseases. Individuals are affected, and they can pass on the disease. With genetic diseases the potential spread is not horizontal through the population, however, but vertical through the generations.

In terms of this model, public health measures similar to the ones that continue to be effective in the control of contagious diseases

might be used to help bring genetic diseases under control. When screening locates an individual with a genetic disorder, steps can be taken to ensure that she receives appropriate therapy. Furthermore, when carriers of genes that produce diseases are identified, they can be warned about their chances of having children who are genetically impaired. Thus, a limited amount of control over the spread of genetic disease can be exercised, and the suffering of at least some individuals can be reduced or eliminated. Public health experts estimate that about 3000 babies a year are identified as having diseases in which early intervention can save their lives or prevent serious disabilities.

The justification of laws mandating screening programs can be sought in the power and responsibility of government to see to the welfare of its citizens. Here again, the public health measures employed to control contagion might be looked to as a model. This is complicated because state laws vary. Some allow religious exemption, some don't. The general rule is that vaccination is required to go to school, except for medical exemptions. Except in special circumstances, we do not permit the parents of a child to decide on their own whether the child should be vaccinated against measles. We believe that society, operating through its government, has a duty to protect the child. Similarly, some argue that society owes it to the child with PKU to see to it that the condition is discovered as quickly as possible so that treatment can be instituted.

Critics of screening programs haven't been convinced that the contagious-disease model is appropriate in dealing with genetic diseases. Because the way in which genetic diseases are spread is so different, only a very small part of the population can be said to suffer any risk at all. By contrast, an epidemic of smallpox may threaten millions of people. Furthermore, some genetic screening programs don't have follow-up or counseling services attached to them, so often nothing is done that benefits the participants. By being told they are the carriers of a genetic disease, people may be more harmed than helped by the programs.

In general, whether the benefits of screening programs are sufficient to outweigh the liabilities remains a serious question. In particular, are screening programs so worthwhile that they justify the denial of individual choice entailed by required participation? What if

parents don't want to know whether their child has the genes responsible for a particular disease? Is it legitimate for a state, in the interest of protecting the child, to require parents to find this out, whether or not they want to know?

These issues and others related to them are easier to appreciate when they are considered in the context of particular kinds of screening programs. We'll discuss briefly two programs that have been both important and controversial.

Screening Newborns

PKU Metabolic disorder causing seizures and retardation; 1 in 25,000 newborns.

MCAD Enzyme needed to convert fat to energy is missing; causes seizures, respiratory failure, cardiac arrest, and death; 1 in 15,000 newborns.

Congenital hypothyroidism Deficiency of thyroid hormone retards growth and brain development; 1 in 5000 newborns.

Congenital adrenal hyperplasia Defects in the synthesis of the adrenal hormones; can alter sexual development and in severe cases of metabolic disturbance results in death; 1 in 25,000 newborns.

Biotinidase deficiency Results in failure to synthesize biotin (a B vitamin), causing seizures, uncontrolled movements, deafness, and mental retardation; 1 in 75,000 births.

Maple-syrup urine disease (branched-chain ketoaciduria) Inborn metabolic error causing mental retardation and death; 1 in 180,000 births.

Galactosemia Missing enzyme needed to convert galactose sugar into glucose, causing mental retardation, blindness, and death; 1 in 34,000 births.

Homocystinuria Missing enzyme needed to convert galactose sugar into glucose, causing mental retardation, blindness, bone abnormalities, and stroke; 1 in 34,000 births.

Sickle-cell disease Disorder of the red blood cells, causing damage to vital organs resulting in heart attack and stroke, pain, ulceration, and infection; 1 in 400 births among blacks (including African Americans), 1 in 1100 among Hispanics born in the eastern United States.

Source: March of Dimes Foundation to Prevent Birth Defects, 2010

PKU Screening. Screening for PKU was not only the first mass testing program to be mandated by state laws; it's generally agreed that it has also been the most successful program.

PKU is a relatively rare disease. It accounts for only about 0.8% of mentally retarded people who are institutionalized, and among the infants screened during a year in a state like Massachusetts, only three or four cases of PKU may be discovered. (The incidence is 5.4 per 100,000 infants.) Given this relatively low incidence of the disease, critics have argued that the abrogation of the freedom of choice required by a mandatory program doesn't make the results worthwhile.

This is particularly true, they suggest, because of the difficulties with the testing procedure itself. The level of phenylalanine in the blood may fluctuate so that not all infants with a higher-than-normal level at the time of the test actually have PKU. If they are put on the restricted diet, then they may suffer consequences from the diet that are harmful to their health. Thus, in attempting to protect the health of some infants, a mandatory program may unintentionally injure the health of other infants.

Tests more refined than the Guthrie one are possible. However, their use increases the cost of the screening program considerably, even if they are employed only when the Guthrie test is positive for PKU. From the statistical standpoint of public health, then, the financial cost of preventing a few cases of PKU may be much greater than allowing the cases to remain undetected and untreated.

Furthermore, there are additional hidden social costs. Female infants successfully treated for PKU may grow into adults and have children of their own. Their children run a very high risk of being born with brain damage. The reason for this is not genetic but developmental. The uterine environment of PKU mothers is one high in phenylalanine, and in high concentrations it causes damage to the infant. Thus, one generation may be saved from mental retardation by screening, only to cause mental retardation in the next.

Sickle Cell. Sickle-cell disease is a group of genetic disorders involving the hemoglobin in red blood cells. Because of faulty hemoglobin, the cells assume a characteristic sickle shape and do not transport oxygen as well as normal red cells. They are also fragile and break apart more frequently. The result is anemia and, often, the blocking of blood vessels by fragments of ruptured cells. The pain can be excruciating, and infections in tissues that have broken down because of oxygen deprivation can be life threatening. Stroke and heart disease often cause death in the early thirties.

The disease occurs only in those who have inherited both alleles for the disease from their parents. (That is, the gene for the disease is recessive, and those who are homozygous for the gene are the ones who develop the disease.) Those with only one allele for the disease (that is, those who are heterozygous) are said to have sickle-cell trait. Sickle-cell disease may develop in infancy, or it may manifest itself later in life in painful and debilitating symptoms. Those with sickle-cell trait rarely show any of the more serious clinical symptoms.

In the United States, the disease is most common among African Americans, but it is also found among those of Mediterranean, Caribbean, and Central and South American ancestry. The trait is carried by about seven to nine percent of African Americans (about three million people), and the disease occurs in about 0.3 percent of the population. Many people with the disease are not severely affected and can live relatively normal lives. However, the disease may also be fatal, and at present there is no cure for it. It can be diagnosed prenatally, however.

In 1970, a relatively inexpensive and accurate test for sickle-cell hemoglobin was developed, making it possible to identify the carriers of sickle-cell trait. This technological development, combined with political pressures generated by rising consciousness among African Americans, led to the passage of various state laws mandating sickle-cell screening. During 1971 and 1972, twelve states enacted sickle-cell legislation.

The results were socially disastrous. Some laws required African Americans who applied for a marriage license to undergo screening. Because the only way to reduce the incidence of the disease was for two carriers to avoid having children (now embryos may be screened before implantation), many African Americans charged that the mandatory screening laws were a manifestation of a plan for genocide.

Medical reports that carriers of sickle-cell trait sometimes suffer from the pain and disability of sickling crises served as a new basis of discrimination. Some employers and insurance companies began to require tests of African American employees, and as a result some job possibilities were closed off to people with sickle-cell trait.

In 1972, Congress passed the National Sickle-Cell Anemia Control Act. In order to qualify for federal grants under the act, states were required to make sickle-cell screening voluntary, provide genetic counseling, and take steps to protect the confidentiality of participants. The most significant impact of the act was to force states to modify their laws to bring them into conformity with the act's requirements. In response, thirty-four states with sickle-cell screening laws now require universal screening.

The National Genetic Diseases Act, passed in 1976 and funded annually since then, provides testing and counseling for the diagnosis and treatment of a number of genetic diseases. The act further strengthens the commitment to voluntary participation and to guarantees of confidentiality.

The lesson learned from the public controversy over the first sickle-cell screening programs is that genetic information can be used in ways that are harmful to the interests of individuals. Furthermore, the information can be used as a basis for systematic discrimination.

In April 1993, an expert panel assembled by the Agency for Health Care and Policy (a part of the Public Health Service) recommended that all newborns, regardless of race, be screened for sickle cell. In making its recommendations, the panel stressed that sickle cell is not uniquely a disease of African Americans or blacks and that the general belief that it is can result in failing to see to it that people of non-African origin receive appropriate treatment.

Furthermore, the panel claimed, targeted screening of high-risk groups is not adequate to identify all infants with sickle-cell disease because it is not always possible to know an individual's racial heritage. Targeted screening, according to one study, may miss as many as twenty percent of cases.

What the panel did not point out was that one advantage of universal screening is that it permits individuals needing treatment to be identified without stigmatizing them just by requiring screening. However, whether having the disease or the trait becomes a social stigma is not a matter that can be resolved by an expert panel. It's something that must be dealt with by law, social policy, and public education.

Genetic Counseling

Much is known about the ways in which a number of genetic diseases are inherited. Those like PKU, sickle cell, and Tay–Sachs follow the laws of Mendelian genetics. Accordingly, given the appropriate information, it is often possible to determine how likely it is that a particular couple will have a child with a certain disease.

Suppose, for example, an African American couple is concerned about the possibility of having a child with sickle-cell disease. Then they will be tested to discover whether either or both of them are carriers of sickle-cell trait.

Sickle-cell disease occurs only when two recessive alleles are present—one inherited from the mother, one from the father. If only one of the parents is a carrier of the trait (is heterozygous), no child will have the disease. If both parents are carriers of the trait, the chances are one out of four that their child will have the disease. (This is determined simply by considering which combinations of the two genes belonging to each parent will produce a combination that is a homozygous recessive. The combination of Ss and Ss will produce ss in only twenty-five percent of the possible cases.)

Such information can be used to explain to potential parents the risks they might run in having children. But, as the case of sickle-cell disease illustrates, it is often very difficult for individuals to know what to do with such information.

Is a twenty-five percent risk of having a child with sickle-cell disease sufficiently high that a couple ought to decide to have no children at all? If the couple is opposed to abortion, the question becomes especially crucial. Answering it is made more difficult by the fact that sickle-cell disease varies greatly in severity. A child with the disease may be virtually normal, or doomed to a short life filled with suffering. No one can say in advance of its birth which possibility is more likely.

If a couple isn't opposed to abortion, is a twenty-five percent risk high enough to warrant a prenatal test? Or perhaps they should avoid the question of abortion by relying on artificial insemination so the embryos could be screened before one is implanted. This would be expensive and probably not be covered by insurance.

It is generally agreed that the question of whether or not to have a child when a serious risk is involved is a decision that must be made by the couple. The counselor may provide information about the risk, and—just as important—the counselor may provide information about medical therapies that are available for a child born with a hereditary disease.

In diseases in which prenatal diagnosis is possible, the option of abortion may be open to potential parents. Here, too, the object of counseling is to see to it that the couple is educated in ways relevant to their needs.

Prenatal Genetic Diagnosis

A variety of new technological developments now make it possible to secure a great amount of information about the developing fetus while it is still in the uterus. Ultrasound, radiography, and fiber optics allow examination of soft-tissue and skeletal development. Anatomical abnormalities can be detected early enough to permit an abortion to be safely performed if that is the decision of the woman carrying the fetus.

Amniocentesis and CVS. Yet the most common methods of prenatal diagnosis are amniocentesis and chorionic villus sampling (CVS), which involve direct cell studies. In amniocentesis, the amnion (the membrane surrounding the fetus) is punctured with a needle and some of the amniotic fluid is removed for study. The procedure cannot be usefully and safely performed until fourteen to sixteen weeks into the pregnancy. Until that time, there is an inadequate amount of fluid. The risk to the woman and to the fetus from the procedure is relatively small, usually less than one percent. (The risk that the procedure will result in a miscarriage is about one in 200.) A recent study shows that if amniocentesis is performed eleven to twelve weeks after conception, there is an increase in foot deformity from 0.1 to 1.3% in the child.

Chorionic villus sampling involves retrieving hairlike villi cells from the developing placenta. The advantage of the test is that it can be employed six to ten weeks after conception. Although the procedure is as safe as amniocentesis, a 1994 study by the Centers for Disease Control found that infants whose mothers had undergone CVS from 1988 to 1992 had a 0.03% risk of missing or undeveloped fingers or toes. The normal risk is 0.05%. A later study questioned this finding and found reason to believe that the risk of fetal damage is greater than normal.

Amniocentesis came into wide use only in the early 1960s. At first, it was restricted mostly to testing fetuses in cases in which there was a risk of Rh incompatibility. When the mother lacks a group of blood proteins called the Rh (or Rhesus) factor, and the fetus has it, the immune system of the mother may produce antibodies against the fetus. The result for the fetus may be anemia, brain damage, and even death.

It was soon realized that additional information about the fetus could be gained from further analysis of the amniotic fluid and the fetal cells in it. The fluid can be chemically assayed, and the cells can be grown in cultures for study. An examination of the DNA can show whether there are any known abnormalities that are likely to cause serious physical or mental defects. Some metabolic disorders (such as Tay–Sachs disease) can be detected by chemical analysis of the amniotic fluid. However, some of the more common ones, such as PKU and Huntington's or muscular dystrophy, require an analysis of the genetic material. Because only males have a Y chromosome, it's impossible to examine fetal cells without also discovering the gender of the fetus.

Amniocentesis and CVS do have some hazards attached to them. Accordingly, prenatal genetic diagnosis is not at all regarded as a routine procedure to be performed in every pregnancy. There must be some indication that the fetus is at risk from a genetic or developmental disorder. One indication is the age of the mother, Down syndrome is much more likely to occur in fetuses conceived in women over the age of thirty-five. Because the syndrome is produced by a chromosome abnormality, an examination of the chromosomes in the cells of the fetus can reveal the defect.

A relatively new test for Down syndrome employs a blood sample taken from the pregnant woman. The sample is examined for the presence of three fetal proteins. At about sixteen to eighteen weeks of gestation, fetuses with the syndrome are known to produce abnormally small quantities of estriol and alpha fetoprotein and abnormally large amounts of chorionic gonadotropin. The levels of the proteins, plus such factors as the woman's age, can be used to determine the statistical probability of a child with the syndrome.

Genetic screening can also provide an indication of a need to perform amniocentesis. For example, Tay–Sachs disease is a metabolic disorder that occurs ten times as often among Jews originating in central and eastern Europe (the Ashkenazi) as in the general population. (The disease is invariably fatal and follows a sad course. An apparently normal child progressively develops blindness and brain damage, then dies at an early age.) Carriers of the Tay–Sachs gene can be identified by a blood test, and couples who are both carriers of the trait run a twenty-five percent risk of having a child with the disease. In such a case, there would be a good reason to perform amniocentesis.

When Is a Test Justified? Our ability to test for the presence of certain genes can give rise to cases some people find particularly troubling. Suppose, for example, a woman with a family history of breast and ovarian cancer wants to know whether the fetus she is carrying has the BRCA1 gene. If the gene is present, she wants to have an abortion, then get pregnant again.

Chances are good that no clinic or testing center would agree to test the fetus for the BRCA1 gene. After all, its presence only increases the probability that a woman will develop breast and ovarian cancer. Unlike, say, the gene for Huntington's disease, the BRCA1 gene doesn't inevitably produce the disease. Hence, a testing center is likely to reject the woman's request, on the grounds that it's unwilling to support anyone's attempt to get a "perfect baby."

Yet the woman, not the center, is the one who has responsibility for her child. Hence, if she wants to have a child that, so far as can be determined by the tests available, is free from the threat of disease, shouldn't she be allowed to seek that aim? What's wrong about trying to have a baby lacking the gene predisposing her to two forms of cancer?

Another controversy has developed as pregnant women younger than thirty-five with no particular risk factors in their background have increasingly sought prenatal screening. The women argue that even though their risk of having a child with a detectable genetic abnormality is small, the financial and emotional consequences of raising an impaired child are so serious that they should be allowed to take advantage of the technology available to minimize even the slight risk.

Opponents of this view point out that the risk of a miscarriage from a diagnostic procedure is around one in 200 while the risk of a woman below the age of forty having an impaired child is about one in 192. Hence, the chance of losing a normal child to miscarriage is almost as great as the chance of having an impaired child. Further, amniocentesis costs from $1000 to $2500 to perform, and the money spent on such unnecessary screening procedures contributes to the general rise in health care costs.

Such replies aren't convincing to those advocating wider access to prenatal testing. Some see the issue as one of the right of a woman to make choices affecting her body and her life. For some, the distress caused by a miscarriage is much less than that they would experience by having to raise an impaired child, but in any case, women should be the ones to decide what risks and burdens they are willing to bear. Such decisions should not be made unilaterally by physicians, hospitals, and health-policy planners.

Advocates of access to prenatal testing argue that, as far as increasing the cost of health care is concerned, when the costs of raising an impaired child are considered, the money spent on testing is insignificant. It costs about $100,000 to support a Down syndrome child during just the first year of life, and expenditures in the millions may be required to meet the needs of a severely impaired person over a lifetime. In addition, the potential emotional burden of the parents and other family members must be taken into account, even though they can't be assigned a dollar cost.

Some women want the added feeling of control prenatal screening can provide. The test can give them information that will put them in a position to make a decision about abortion, depending on the test results, or will provide them the peace of mind which comes from knowing that their pregnancy is proceeding with only a small likelihood that the developing child will suffer a serious impairment. The general attitude is that the technology to secure relevant information exists and it should be available to anyone who wants to make use of it. It certainly shouldn't be under the complete control of physicians.

Selective Abortion. In most cases in which prenatal diagnosis indicates that the fetus suffers from a genetic disorder or developmental defect, the only means of avoiding the birth of an impaired child is abortion. Because those who go through the tests required to determine the condition of the fetus are concerned with having a child, abortion performed under such circumstances is called *selective*. That is, the woman decides to have an abortion to avoid producing a child with birth impairments, not just to avoid having a child.

Those who oppose abortion in principle (see Chapter 9) also oppose selective abortion. In the view of some, the fact that a child will be born impaired is in no way a justification for terminating the life of the fetus.

Those prepared to endorse abortion at all typically approve of selective abortion as an acceptable way of avoiding suffering. In their view, it's better that the potential person—the

fetus—not become an actual person, full of pain, disease, and disability.

The painful decision between having an abortion or giving birth to an impaired child may be avoided by employing ova, sperm, or embryo screening. This means, however, using the techniques developed in assisted reproduction (see Chapter 6), and the costs in time, frustration, and money can be considerable.

In the last few years, another way to avoid abortion has opened up as the techniques of fetal surgery have been employed to correct at least some abnormal physical conditions. Repairs to the heart, the insertion of shunts to drain off excess brain fluids, and the placement of tubes to inflate collapsed lungs are some of the intrauterine surgical procedures now being performed. Some surgeons believe it may be possible to expose the fetus within the uterus, perform surgery, then close up the amnion again. This would allow more extensive surgery for a greater variety of conditions.

The present hope is that as new surgical techniques for the treatment of fetuses are perfected and extended, the need to rely on abortion to avoid the birth of impaired children will decline significantly. Of course, surgery cannot, even in principle, provide a remedy for a large number of hereditary disorders. For example, it can do nothing for a child with Tay–Sachs, sickle cell, cystic fibrosis, muscular dystrophy, or PKU.

Helplessness in this regard is balanced by the hope that in future years pharmaceutical and biochemical therapies will be available to employ in cases involving missing enzymes; or perhaps gene therapy will make it possible to insert the proper gene for manufacturing a needed biochemical into the DNA of the cells of a fetus.

Embryo Selection. Potential parents who learn that they are carriers of genes responsible for lethal or life-threatening diseases may decide to use the techniques of assisted reproduction to avoid having a child affected with the disease.

Their embryos, produced by in vitro fertilization, can be genetically screened, then only those free of the disease-causing genes transferred to the woman's uterus. (See Chapter 6 for a fuller discussion.)

Embryo screening allows couples to avoid the risk their genetic heritage poses for their offspring. Those carrying the Tay–Sachs gene or the gene responsible for cystic fibrosis, for example, can be sure they don't have children with these diseases. It also makes selective abortion unnecessary. (However, some consider destroying embryos, for whatever reason, the moral equivalent of abortion.)

The painful present reality is that, for most children born with genetic diseases or defects, little can be done. Embryo selection and selective abortion are the primary means of avoiding the birth of a child known to be genetically impaired, and only abortion offers the possibility of avoiding the birth of a child discovered to be developmentally impaired.

Ethical Difficulties with Genetic Intervention

Genetic screening, counseling prenatal diagnosis, and embryo selection present bright possibilities for those who believe in the importance of exercising control through rational planning and decision making. They see the prospect of avoiding the birth of children with crippling impairments as one of the triumphs of contemporary medicine.

Furthermore, the additional prospect of wholly eliminating some genetic diseases by counseling and reproductive control holds the promise of an even better future. For example, if people who are carriers of diseases caused by a dominant gene (such as Huntington's) produced no children with the disease, the disease would soon disappear entirely. The gene causing the disease would simply not be passed on to the next generation.

A vision of a world without the misery caused by genetic defects is a motivating factor among those who are strong advocates of programs of genetic intervention. (See the section titled "Eugenics" later in this Briefing Session.) The vision must have its appeal to all who are moved by compassion in the face of suffering. Yet whether or not one shares this vision and is prepared to use it as a basis for social action, serious ethical questions about genetic intervention must be faced.

We've already mentioned some of the issues in connection with particular programs and procedures. We can now add some more general questions to that list. The moral and social issues connected with genetic intervention are woven into a complicated fabric of personal and social considerations, and we can merely sketch the main outline of the pattern.

Is there a right to have children who are likely to be impaired? Suppose a woman is informed, after an alphafetoprotein (AFP) test and amniocentesis, that the child she's carrying will be born with a neural tube defect. Does she have the right to refuse an abortion and have the child anyway?

Those opposed to all abortion on the grounds of natural law would favor the woman's having the child. By contrast, a utilitarian might argue that the decision would be wrong. The amount of suffering the potential child might be expected to undergo outweighs any parental loss. For different reasons, a Kantian might endorse this same point of view. Even if we assume the fetus is a person, a Kantian might argue that we are obliged to prevent its suffering.

Suppose we decide that a woman does have a right to have a child who is almost certain to be impaired. If so, then is society obligated to bear the expense of caring for the child? On the natural law view, the answer is almost certainly yes.

The child, impaired or not, is a person and, as such, is entitled to the support and protection of society. If we agree that the impaired child is a person, he or she is also a disadvantaged person. Thus, an argument based on Rawls' principles of justice would support the view that the child is entitled to social support.

Is society justified in requiring that people submit to genetic screening, counseling, or prenatal diagnosis? Children born with genetic diseases and defects require the expenditure of large amounts of public funds. Mandatory diagnosis need not be coupled with mandatory abortion or abstention from bearing children. (A related question is whether society ought to make available genetic testing to all who wish it, regardless of their ability to pay.)

On utilitarian grounds, it might be argued that society has a legitimate interest in seeing to it that, no matter what people ultimately decide, they should at least have the information about the likelihood that they will produce an impaired child.

If this view is adopted, then a number of specific medically related questions become relevant. For example, who should be screened? It's impractical and unnecessary to screen everyone. For example, why should we screen schoolchildren or prisoners, those who are sterile, or those past the age of childbearing?

This is closely connected with a second question: What should people be screened for? Should everyone be screened for Tay–Sachs disease, even thought it is the Ashkenazi Jewish population that is most at risk? Should everyone be screened for the cystic-fibrosis gene, even though the disease occurs primarily among whites?

Those who accept the contagious-disease model of genetic screening frequently defend it on the utilitarian grounds that screening promotes the general social welfare. However, one might argue that screening can also be justified on deontological grounds. It could be claimed that we owe it to developing fetuses, regarded as persons, to see to it they receive the opportunity for the most effective treatment. For example, it might be said that we have an obligation to provide a PKU child with the immediate therapy required to save him or her from severe mental retardation. The restriction of the autonomy of individuals by requiring screening might be regarded as justified by this obligation. If screening is voluntary, the welfare of the child is made to depend on ignorance and accidental opportunity.

Do physicians have an obligation to inform their patients who are prospective parents about the kinds of genetic tests that are available? A study of one population of women screened for Tay–Sachs disease showed that none had sought testing on the recommendation of her physician.

If the autonomy of the individual is to be preserved, then it seems clear that it is the duty of a physician to inform patients about genetic testing. A physician who disapproves of abortion might be reluctant to inform patients about tests that might encourage them to seek an abortion or embryo screening. Nevertheless, to the extent that abortion is a moral decision, it is a decision properly made by the individual, not by someone acting paternalistically in her behalf.

The duty of a physician to inform patients about the possibility of genetic tests seems quite straightforward. Yet the issue becomes more complicated in light of the next question about truth telling.

Do patients have a right to be informed of all of the results of a genetic test? Ethical theories based on respect for the autonomy of the individual (such as Kant's and Ross') suggest that patients are entitled to know what has been learned from the tests.

But what if the test reveals that the fetus carries the gene for a minor genetically transmissible disease or for increased susceptibility to a serious disease? Should the physician risk the patient's deciding to have an abortion merely because she is committed to the ideal of a "perfect" baby? Or , is such a decision even one for the physician to make?

Furthermore, what about the matter of sex determination? Screening tests can also reveal the gender of the fetus. Are prospective parents entitled to know this information? When an abortion is elective, it is possible for the woman to decide to avoid giving birth to a child of a particular gender. (The same possibility is presented by embryo selection.)

It might be argued on both utilitarian and deontological grounds that the sex of the fetus is information that isn't relevant to the health of the fetus. Accordingly, the physician is under no obligation to reveal the gender. Indeed, the physician may be under an obligation not to reveal the gender to avoid the possibility of its destruction for a trivial reason. But, again, is this really a decision for the physician?

Should public funds be used to pay for genetic tests when an individual is unable to pay? This is a question that holders of various ethical theories may not be prepared to answer in a simple yes-or-no fashion. Those who oppose abortion on natural law grounds might advocate providing funds only for genetic testing and counseling. That is, they might favor providing prospective parents with information they might use to decide whether to refrain from having children. Yet opponents of abortion might be against spending public money on tests that might encourage the use of abortion to prevent the birth of an impaired child.

The views of Rawls and of utilitarianism might support the use of public funds for genetic testing as part of a more general program of providing for health-care needs. Whether genetic testing programs are funded and what the level of funding might be would then depend on judgments about their expected value in comparison with other health-care programs.

A present ethical and social difficulty is caused by the fact that federal funds may be employed to pay for genetic screening and testing, yet federal money cannot legally be used to pay for abortions. Consequently, it's possible for a woman to discover she is carrying a fetus with a serious genetic disease, wish to have an abortion, yet lack the means to pay for it.

Issues about the confidentiality of test results, informed consent, the use of genetic testing to gather epidemiological information, and a variety of other matters might be mentioned here in connection with genetic intervention. Those that have been discussed are sufficient to indicate that the difficulties presented by genetic intervention are at least as numerous as the benefits it promises.

Eugenics

Like other organisms, we are the products of millions of years of evolutionary development. This process has taken place through the operation of natural selection on randomly produced genetic mutations. Individual organisms are successful in an evolutionary sense when they contribute a number of genes to the gene pool of their species proportionately greater than the number contributed by others.

Most often, this means that the evolutionarily successful individuals are those with the largest number of offspring. These are the individuals favored by natural selection. That is, they possess the genes for certain properties that are favored by existing environmental factors. (This favoring of properties is natural selection.) The genes of "favored" individuals will thus occur with greater frequency than the genes of others in the next generation. If the same environmental factors continue to operate, these genes will spread through the entire population.

Thanks to Darwin and the biologists who have come after him, we now have a sound understanding of the evolutionary process and the mechanisms by which it operates. This understanding puts us in a position to intervene in evolution. We no longer have to consider ourselves subject to the blind working of natural selection, and if we wish, we can modify the course of human evolution. As the evolutionary biologist Theodosius Dobzhansky expressed the point: "Evolution need no longer be a destiny imposed from without; it may conceivably be controlled by man, in accordance with his wisdom and values."

Those who advocate eugenics accept exactly this point of view. They favor social policies and practices that, over time, offer the possibility of increasing the number of genes in the human population responsible for producing or improving intelligence, beauty, musical ability, and other traits we value.

The aim of increasing the number of favorable genes in the human population is called *positive eugenics.* By contrast, *negative eugenics* aims at decreasing the number of undesirable or harmful genes. Those who advocate negative eugenics are most interested in eliminating or reducing from the population genes responsible for various kinds of genetic diseases.

Both positive and negative eugenics require instituting some sort of control over human reproduction. Several kinds of policies and procedures have been advocated, and we will discuss a few of the possibilities.

Negative and Positive Eugenics

The discussion of genetic screening, counseling, prenatal genetic diagnosis, and embryo selection makes it unnecessary to repeat here information about the powers we possess for predicting and diagnosing genetic diseases. It is enough to recall that, given information about the genetic makeup and background of potential parents, a large number of genetic diseases can be predicted with a certain degree of probability as likely to occur in a child of such parents. Or the presence of the genes can be determined by genetic analysis of the chromosomes. This is true of such diseases as PKU, sickle-cell disease, hemophilia, Huntington's disease, Tay–Sachs, and muscular dystrophy.

When genetic information isn't adequate for a reliable prediction or direct determination, information about the developing fetus can often be obtained by employing one of several procedures of prenatal diagnosis. Even when information is adequate for a reliable prediction, whether the fetus has a certain disease can be determined by prenatal testing. Thus, in addition to the genetic disorders named previously, prenatal tests can be performed for such developmental defects as neural tube anomalies and Down syndrome. Also, other tests can be performed on ova, sperm, or embryos.

A proponent of negative eugenics might advocate that a screening process for all or some currently detectable genetic diseases or dispositions (or developmental impairments) be required by law. When the probability of the occurrence of a disease is high (whatever figure that might be taken to be), the potential parents might be encouraged to have no children. Indeed, the law might require that such a couple either abstain from having children or rely on embryo selection. The law also might prescribe a penalty for going against the decision of the screening board.

If those carrying the genes for some genetic diseases could be prevented from having children, over time the incidence of the diseases would decrease. In cases when the disease is the result of a dominant gene (as it is in Huntington's disease), the disease would eventually disappear. (It could appear again with new mutations, however.)

When the disease is of the sort that can be detected only after a child is conceived and if the results of a prenatal diagnosis show that the developing fetus has a heritable disease, an abortion might be encouraged. Or a couple identified as at risk might be encouraged to seek artificial insemination and embryo testing and transfer.

Short of a law requiring abortion, a variety of social policies might be adopted to make abortion or embryo selection an attractive option. (For example, the cost of an abortion might be paid for by government funds, or women choosing abortion might be financially rewarded. Or the costs of embryo selection might be paid for under a federal program.) The aborting of a fetus found to have a transmissible genetic disease would not only prevent the birth of an impaired infant, but would also eliminate a potential carrier of the genes responsible for the disease.

Similarly, the sterilization of people identified as having genes responsible for certain kinds of physical or mental impairments would prevent them from passing on these defective genes. In this way, the number of such genes in the population would be proportionately reduced.

Currently, no state or federal laws make it a crime for couples who are genetically a bad risk to have children. Yet a tendency toward more genetic regulation may be developing. Screening newborns for certain genetic diseases that respond well to early treatment is an established practice. Also, genetic testing programs are frequently offered in communities to encourage people to seek information about particular diseases.

At present, genetic testing (for adults) and counseling are voluntary. They aim at providing information and then leave reproductive decisions up to the individuals concerned. Most often, they are directed toward the immediate goal of decreasing the number of children suffering from birth defects and genetic diseases. Yet genetic testing and counseling might also be viewed as a part of negative eugenics. To the extent that they discourage the birth of children carrying deleterious genes, they also discourage the spread of those genes in the human population.

Obviously, genetic testing and genetic counseling programs might also be used to promote positive eugenics. Individuals possessing genes for traits society values might be encouraged to have large numbers of children. In this way, genes for those traits would increase in relative frequency in the population.

No programs of positive eugenics currently operate in the United States. It is easy to imagine, however, how a variety of social and economic incentives (such as government bonuses) might be introduced as part of a plan to promote the spread of certain genes by rewarding favored groups of people for having children.

Use of Desirable Germ Cells

Developments in reproductive technology have opened up possibilities once considered so remote as to be the stuff of science fiction.

Artificial insemination by the use of frozen sperm is already commonplace. So, too, is the use of donor eggs and embryos. While some of the embryos may be donated by couples who don't need or want them, some are produced in infertility clinics by combining sperm from commercial sperm banks with donor ova. The developing embryos can be divided into several genetically identical embryos, and before long it may be possible to clone a human being from a single body cell.

Those wishing to have a child now have the option of selecting donor eggs or sperm from individuals with traits considered desirable. Alternatively, they may select a frozen embryo on the basis of descriptions of the gamete contributors. They may also turn to physicians who may offer them embryos they've created from sperm and eggs obtained from people who have what they judge to be outstanding traits.

We have available to us right now the means to practice both negative and positive eugenics at the level of both the individual and the society. If we wished, we could encourage groups of individuals to avoid having their own biological children and, instead, make use of the "superior" sperm, ova, and embryos currently offered at sperm banks and infertility centers. In this way, we could increase the number of genes for desirable traits in the population. (See Chapter 6.)

Ethical Difficulties with Eugenics

Critics have been quick to point out that the proposals mentioned suffer from serious drawbacks. First, negative eugenics isn't likely to make much of a change in the species as a whole. Most hereditary diseases are genetically recessive and so occur only when both parents possess the same defective gene. Even though a particular couple might be counseled (or required) not to have children, the gene will still be widespread in the population among people we would consider wholly normal. For a similar reason, sterilization and even embryo selection would have few long-range effects.

Also, the uncomfortable fact is that geneticists have estimated that, on the average, everyone carries recessive genes for five genetic defects or diseases. Genetic counseling and the use of the techniques of assisted reproduction may help individuals, but negative eugenics doesn't promise much for the population as a whole.

Positive eugenics can promise little more. It's difficult to imagine that we would all agree on what traits we'd like to see increased in the human species. But even if we could, it's not clear that we'd be able to increase them in any simple way.

For one thing, we have little understanding of the genetic basis of traits such as "intelligence," "honesty," "musical ability," "beauty" and so on. It's clear, however, that there isn't just a single gene for them, and the chances are that they are the result of a complicated interplay between genetic endowment and social and environmental factors. Consequently, the task of increasing their frequency is quite different from that of say, increasing the frequency of shorthorn cattle. Furthermore, desirable traits may be accompanied by less desirable ones, and we may not be able to increase the first without also increasing the second.

Quite apart from biological objections, eugenics also raises questions of a moral kind. Have we indeed become the "business manager of evolution," as Julian Huxley once claimed? If so, do we have a responsibility to future generations to improve the human race? Would this responsibility justify requiring genetic screening and testing? Would it justify establishing a program of positive eugenics? Affirmative answers to these questions may generate conflicts with notions of individual dignity and self-determination.

Of the ethical theories we have discussed, it seems likely that only utilitarianism might be construed as favoring a program of positive eugenics. The possibility of increasing the frequency of desirable traits in the human species might, in terms of the principle of utility,

justify placing restrictions on reproduction. Yet the goal of an improved society or human race might be regarded as too distant and uncertain to warrant the imposition of restrictions that would increase current human unhappiness.

As far as negative eugenics is concerned, the principle of utility could be appealed to in order to justify social policies that would discourage or prohibit parents who are carriers of the genes for serious diseases from having children. The aim here need not be the remote one of improving the human population but the more immediate one of preventing the increase in sorrow and pain that would be caused by an impaired child.

Natural law doctrines of Roman Catholicism forbid abortion, sterilization, and embryo selection. Thus, these means of practicing negative eugenics are ruled out. Also, the natural law view that reproduction is a natural function of sexual intercourse seems, at least prima facie, to rule out negative eugenics as a deliberate policy altogether. It could be argued, however, that voluntary abstinence from sexual intercourse or some other acceptable form of birth control would be a legitimate means of practicing negative eugenics.

Ross' prima facie duty of causing no harm might be invoked to justify negative eugenics. If there is good reason to believe a child is going to suffer from a genetic disease, we may have a duty to prevent the child from being born. Similarly, Rawls' theory might permit a policy that would require the practice of some form of negative eugenics for the benefit of its immediate effects of preventing suffering and sparing all the cost of supporting those with genetic diseases.

It is difficult to determine what sort of answer to the question of negative eugenics might be offered in terms of Kant's ethical principles. Laws regulating conception or forced abortion or sterilization might be considered to violate the dignity and autonomy of individuals. Yet moral agents as rational decision makers require information on which to base their decisions.

Thus, programs of genetic screening and counseling might be considered to be legitimate.

Genetic Research, Therapy, and Technology

By replacing natural selection with artificial selection that is directly under our control, we can, over time, alter the genetic composition of populations of organisms. This has been done for thousands of years by animal and plant breeders, and our improved understanding of genetics allows us to do it today with more effectiveness and certainty of results. Yet such alterations take a long time. Molecular genetics holds out the possibility of immediate changes. Bacteria continue to be the major organisms of research, but genetic technology is already being applied to plants and animals. The same technology is now on the verge of being applied to humans.

Recombinant DNA

The information required for genetic inheritance is coded in the two intertwined strands of DNA (deoxyribonucleic acid) found in plant and animal cells—the double helix. The strands are made up of four kinds of chemical units called nucleotides, and the genetic message is determined by the particular sequence of nucleotides. Three nucleotides in sequence form a triplet codon. Each codon directs the synthesis of a particular amino acid and determines the place it will occupy in making up a protein molecule. Since virtually all properties of organisms (enzymes, organs, eye color, and so on) depend on proteins, the processes directed by DNA are fundamental.

Alterations in the nucleotide sequence in DNA occur naturally as mutations—random changes introduced as "copying errors" when DNA replicates (reproduces) itself. These alterations result in changes in the properties of organisms, because the properties are under the control of DNA. Much research in current molecular genetics is directed toward bringing about desired changes by deliberately manipulating the nucleotide sequences in DNA. The major steps toward this goal have involved the development of techniques for recombining DNA from different sources.

The recombinant process begins by taking proteins known as restriction enzymes from bacteria and mixing them with DNA that has been removed from cells. These enzymes cut open the DNA strands at particular nucleotide locations. DNA nucleotide sequences from another source can then be added, and certain of these will attach to the cut ends. Thus, DNA from distinct sources can be recombined to form a single molecule.

This recombinant DNA can then be made to enter a host cell. The organism most widely employed is the one-celled bacterium *E. coli* that inhabits the human intestine by the billions. In addition to the DNA in its nucleus, *E. coli* has small circular strands of DNA known as *plasmids*. The plasmid DNA can be recombined with DNA from an outside source and returned to the cell. When the plasmid replicates, it will make copies of both the original nucleotides and the added segments. Thus, a strain of bacteria can be produced that will make limitless numbers of copies of the foreign DNA.

The obvious question is, What benefits might recombinant-DNA technology produce? From the standpoint of theory, it might lead to a better understanding of the molecular processes involved in such diseases as cancer, diabetes, and hemophilia. Or it might provide more effective treatment for metabolic diseases like PKU and Tay–Sachs.

From the practical standpoint, recombinant-DNA technology has already led to the development of new breeds of plants able to utilize nitrogen from the air and requiring little or no fertilizer. Specially engineered bacteria might be used to clean up the environment by breaking down currently nonbiodegradable compounds like DDT. Other bacteria might convert petroleum into other useful chemical compounds, including plastics.

The most immediate benefit of recombinant-DNA technology is the use of bacteria modified into chemical factories that produce biological materials of medical importance. A glance at a few of the many recent research developments gives an appreciation of the powerful potential of genetic technology:

- Hypopituitary dwarfism is a condition caused by a deficiency in growth hormone. The hormone itself consists of molecules too large and structurally complex to synthesize in the laboratory, but as early as 1979 researchers employed recombinant-DNA technology to induce bacteria to produce the hormone. It's now available in quantities large enough to be used as a therapy.

- Modified bacteria now produce human insulin in quantities large enough to meet the need of diabetics, some of whom are allergic to swine or bovine insulin.

- Genetically engineered bacteria have been used to produce a vaccine against hepatitis B and against a strain of genital herpes. The clotting factor employed in the treatment of hemophilia has been similarly produced.

- Genetically engineered flu vaccines grown in moth cells may replace some of those currently grown in fertilized chicken eggs, reducing production time from six to nine months to two to three.

- In 1985, the Cetus Corporation was awarded the first patent for an altered form of the protein interleukin-2. Il-2 activates the immune system and is used in the treatment of some cancers. It occurs naturally but in very small amounts; thus, it wasn't possible to use it therapeutically until it was produced in quantity by genetically altered bacteria.

- Researchers have inserted human genes into plants and induced the plants to produce large quantities of medically significant proteins. Antibodies, serum albumin, enkephalins, hormones, and growth factors are among those currently produced.

- Substances occurring in the human body in minute amounts that can be important as drugs when widely available are now being produced in large quantities by genetic engineering. For example, tissue plasminogen activator (TPA), which is produced in blood vessels, dissolves blood clots and is a useful drug in the treatment of heart attacks. Also, blood factor-VIII, a clotting agent, may improve the lives and health of hemophiliacs by reducing their chances of viral infection from donated blood.

- In 1997, researchers genetically engineered mice to serve as an animal model for sickle-cell disease by inserting into the mice human genes for the defective hemoglobin that causes the disease. Having animal models may speed up the testing of new drugs and suggest approaches for an effective treatment.

- Researchers have inserted into mouse embryos human DNA equivalent to an entire chromosome and discovered that the DNA is passed on to the next mouse generation. Such research promises to lead to an understanding of the ways in which genes work normally and in disease processes. Further, animals containing segments of human DNA might be induced to produce medically useful products. (See the Case Presentation "Hello, Dolly," in Chapter 6.)

Gene Therapy

The rapid advancement in genetic knowledge during the last few years has led to the use of recombinant-DNA techniques in experimental medical therapies. Therapy in which a missing or nonfunctioning gene is inserted into a patient's cells is already being employed. So is the use of altered cells to induce the formation of new blood vessels to treat unhealing leg ulcers and, perhaps soon, coronary artery blockages. (See the Case Presentation "Gene Therapy," in this chapter, for more details.)

The ability to alter the basic machinery of life to correct its malfunctioning is surely the most powerful form of therapy imaginable. The immediate prospects for gene therapy involve the relatively modest, but very dramatic, task of splicing into the DNA of body cells a gene that controls the production of a specific substance. Diseases such as PKU that are caused by the absence of an enzyme might then be corrected by inducing the patient's cells to manufacture that enzyme. Some genetic diseases involve dozens or even hundreds of genes, and often the mechanism by which the genes produce the disease is not understood. Consequently, it is likely to be a long while before most genetic diseases can be treated by gene therapy. Even so, the effective treatment of single-gene disorders is a most promising possibility.

Few special moral or social issues are raised by the use of gene therapy as long as the cells modified are somatic (body) cells. The issues change significantly with the prospect of modifying human germ-line (sex) cells. Somatic-cell changes cannot be inherited, but germ-line cell changes can be. This possibility holds out the benign prospect of eliminating forever a number of genetic diseases. However, we need not wait for germ-line therapy to accomplish this. Embryo testing and selection before implantation, a technology already in common use, would be a simpler way to achieve the same goal.

While germ-line therapy may have no medical use, it points toward a frightening prospect. It offers us a way of "engineering" human beings by tinkering with the sex cells to produce people who meet our predetermined specification. Because we will discuss this possibility later in the chapter, it's relevant to note here only that the technology required to alter human sex cells doesn't exist at present.

Biohazards

The issues connected with gene therapy, testing, and screening may be overshadowed in significance by questions concerning dangers inherent in the development of genetic technology and the release of its products into the environment.

The question of whether recombinant-DNA research ought to be halted is no longer a serious social issue. However, this hasn't always been so. In 1974, a group of scientists active in such research issued a report recommending that scientists be asked to suspend work voluntarily on recombinant experiments involving tumor viruses, increased drug resistance in harmful bacteria, and increased toxicity in bacteria. The discussion that ensued resulted in the formulation of guidelines by the National Institutes of Health to regulate research.

The major concern initially was that recombinant techniques might be employed to produce essentially new organisms that would threaten human health. Suppose that the nucleotide sequence for manufacturing a lethal toxin were combined with the DNA of *E. coli*. Then this usually harmless inhabitant of the intestine might be transformed into a deadly organism that would threaten the existence of the entire human population. (In recent years we've seen how deadly naturally occurring mutant forms of *E. coli* can be when they appear in the food supply.)

Or to take another scenario, perhaps a nucleotide sequence that transforms normal cells into cancerous ones might trigger an epidemic of cancer. Without a thorough knowledge of the molecular mechanisms involved, little could be done to halt the outbreak. Indeed it isn't even clear what would happen if one of the engineered insulin-producing strains of bacteria escaped from the lab and spread through the human population.

These and similar dangers prompted some critics to call for an end to all genetic-engineering research. However, almost two decades of recombinant-DNA research have passed without the occurrence of any biological catastrophes. Most observers regard this as sufficient proof of the essential safety of the research. Yet, in the view of others, the fact that no catastrophes have yet occurred must not be allowed to give us a false sense of security. Almost no one advocates that the research be abandoned, but several molecular geneticists have argued that the very fact that we still do not know enough to estimate the risks involved with a high degree of certainty is a good reason for continuing to control it severely.

Quite apart from the possible hazards associated with genetic engineering, many people continue to be uneasy about the direction of research. A number of biotechnological possibilities are on the horizon, some of which might have far-reaching consequences. As we discussed earlier, gene surgery offers more possibilities than just medical therapy. If undesirable DNA segments can be sliced out of the genetic code and replaced with others, this would permit the "engineering" of human beings to an extent and degree of precision never before imagined.

The eugenic dream of producing people to match an ideal model would be a reality. What would happen then to such traditional and moral values as autonomy, diversity, and the inherent worth of the individual?

The same techniques employed to manufacture the ideal person might also be used to design others to fit special needs. It's not difficult to imagine using genetic surgery to engineer a subhuman race to serve as a slave class for the society. The scenarios of cautionary science fiction might be acted out in our own future.

Further, the technique of asexual reproduction known as cloning might be employed to produce individuals who are exact genetic copies of someone whose DNA has been engineered to suit our needs or ideals. While human cloning is not yet a practical reality, a giant step toward it was taken in 1997 when Ian Wilmut and his colleagues at the Roslin Institute in Scotland cloned a sheep. (See Case Presentation: "Hello, Dolly," in Chapter 6.)

We might use reproductive technology in combination with genetic engineering to have several children who are copies of ourselves. If the embryos were stored, some of these might be born years apart.

Consider one last possibility. Virtually new organisms might be produced by splicing together DNA from two or more sources. Thus, the world might be faced with creatures of an unknown and unpredictable nature that are not the product of the natural processes of evolution.

It's little wonder that molecular biologists have become concerned about the nature and direction of their research. As Robert Sinsheimer says, "Biologists have become, without wanting it, custodians of great and terrible power." Such power in the hands of a tyrannical government could be used with irresistible effectiveness to control its subjects. Societies might create a race of semihuman slaves or armies of genetically engineered soldiers. The possibilities are both fantastic and unlimited.

Ethical Difficulties with Genetic Research, Therapy, and Technology

The risks involved in gene therapy are not unique ones. In most respects, they exactly parallel those involved in any new medical treatment. Accordingly, it seems reasonable to believe that the same standards of safety and the same consideration for the welfare of the patient that are relevant to the use of other forms of therapy should be regarded as relevant to gene therapy.

The principles of Kant and Ross suggest that the autonomy of the individual must be respected and preserved. The individual ought not to be viewed as an experimental case for testing a procedure that may later prove helpful. If the person is adequately informed and competent to consent, and if no alternative therapy is likely to be effective, it would be morally legitimate for the patient to be given the opportunity to benefit from the therapy. However, if the hazards are great or completely unknown, it's doubtful whether the patient would be justified in risking his or her life.

By contrast, on utilitarian principles, if the outcome of gene therapy can be reasonably expected to produce more benefit than harm, its use might be considered justifiable. If we assume that a person is likely to die anyway, that in itself might be enough to warrant the use of the therapy. In addition, since each case treated is likely to contribute to increased understanding and to benefit others, this tends to support the use of gene therapy, even in cases in which it is of doubtful help to the individual. (See the Case Presentation "Gene Therapy," in this chapter, for a fuller discussion.)

Genetic research and its associated technology present issues much greater in scope than those raised by gene therapy. They are issues that require us to decide what sort of society we want to live in.

Very few responsible people currently believe we should call a halt to research in molecular genetics and forgo the increase in power and understanding that it has already brought. However, the possibilities of genetic engineering include ones that are frightening and threatening, ones that could wholly alter our society and destroy some of our most cherished values. These are the possibilities that require us to make decisions about whether or to what extent we want to see them realized.

The natural law view of ethics would not, in general, support any policy of restricting scientific inquiry in the area of molecular genetics. For, on this view, there is a natural inclination (and hence a natural duty) to seek knowledge. Yet certain types of experiments and gene engineering would be ruled out. Those which aim at altering human beings or creating new species from mixed DNA are most likely to be considered to violate the natural order. On the Roman Catholic view, such a violation of nature would run counter to God's plan and purpose and so be immoral.

The principle of utility might be invoked to justify limiting, directing, or even ending research in molecular genetics. If research or its results are likely to bring about more harm than benefit, regulation would be called for. Yet if the promise of relieving misery or increasing well-being is great, then some risk that we might also acquire dangerous knowledge in the process might be acceptable.

On the utilitarian view, knowledge may be recognized as a good, but it's only one good among others. Possessing the knowledge to alter human beings in accordance with a eugenic ideal or to create new species means we have to make a decision about whether doing so would result in an overall benefit. That judgment will then be reflected in our social policies and practices.

Such an analysis also seems to be consistent with Rawls' principles. For Rawls, there is no absolute right to seek knowledge, nor is there any obligation to employ knowledge that is available. Restrictions might well be imposed on scientific research and on the technological possibilities it presents if the good of society seems to demand it.

Chapter **4**

Reproductive Control

CASES AND CONTEXTS

The Octomom and the McCaughey Septuplets: The Perils of Multiple Pregnancies

Multiple births were once greeted with amazement and the mothers of multiples applauded as having achieved something difficult and admirable. The role of reproductive medicine in causing multiple births, however, has altered the public's attitude toward them, and multiple births are now more likely to evoke criticism than admiration.

The two most extreme recent cases are Nadya Suleman, who gave birth to eight babies in 2009, and Bobbi McCaughey, who gave birth to seven in 1997. In both cases, the birth announcements were met with interest and approval, but as people began to understand more about what such extreme multiple births involved, much of the approval turned into criticism. This transformation took place faster in the Suleman case. This is likely due in part to differences in the women's personal circumstances, but it may also be that the public has now grown more sophisticated about assisted reproduction and come to understand more about its costs and perils.

The Octomom

When Nadya Suleman gave birth to eight babies at Kaiser-Permanente Hospital in Bellflower, California, in January 2009, she attracted the world's attention and received an outpouring of warmth and good wishes.

People thought of the thirty-three-year-old Suleman as an infertile, single woman who wanted a child so badly that she had been forced to turn to a fertility specialist for help. She was, people imagined, as surprised by the results as they were: instead of having one baby, she had ended up with eight.

This portrait of Suleman was almost entirely a projection of the public's romantic imagination. Perhaps it is part of the reason that, when facts began to emerge that presented a less flattering image of Suleman, much of the public turned against her with an indignation so severe, it amounted to spite. Nearly everything the public assumed to be true of her tuned out to be false.

What shocked people most was that Suleman already had six children—all born with the help of fertility specialist Tien C. Chieu. She was married at the time these children were born, but her husband, Marcus Gutierrez, wasn't their father. She apparently used sperm donated by her friend David Solomon to conceive all fourteen children. She collected the sperm herself and took it to Dr. Chieu's clinic. Chieu used it to fertilize eggs that he removed from Suleman. The resulting embryos were frozen.

Suleman had six pregnancies using the embryos, and in each instance six embryos were transferred to her uterus. Her first five pregnancies, which were presided over by Chieu, resulted in the birth of a single child in four cases and fraternal twins in one. "She wanted to have many, many babies," Chieu told reporter Stephanie Saul.

Suleman's mother, Angela, a retired teacher, begged Dr. Chieu not to help her daughter get pregnant again. Although Chieu agreed, Suleman was not satisfied with only six children, so she sought help from Dr. Michael M. Kamrava of the West Coast IVF Clinic in Beverly Hills. Suleman wanted to use up the remainder of her frozen embryos, so she asked Kamrava to transfer all six at the same time.

Kamrava agreed to this, even though it violated the guidelines of the American Society for Assisted Reproduction. Not only did all six embryos develop in Suleman's uterus, two of them split into twins. Thus, she gave birth to eight babies.

State Support

The public was also shocked to learn that Suleman, who had divorced her husband in 2008, was unemployed and lived with her parents. Her only income was money she received from public welfare programs. She was thus unable to pay even a small fraction of the $1.3 million hospital costs that resulted from delivering her eight fragile, low-birth-weight babies and providing them with the intensive care they required. What's more, Suleman had no way to support her fourteen children. For the foreseeable future, she and her children would be dependent on state and federal assistance programs for food, shelter, clothing, and medical care.

The services of fertility specialists are rarely covered by insurance and are not covered by Medicaid, and each round of treatment costs at least $12,000–15,000. So where did Suleman get the money to pay Chieu and Kamrava? Apparently, she used her worker's compensation benefits. She had been employed as a psychiatric technician at Metropolitan State Hospital, and in 1999 she filed a claim alleging that she had suffered a back injury in performing her duties. She took her case to the Workers Compensation Appeals Board in 2001 and eventually received about $167,000.

Hostile Public

Public attention turned hostile as these facts emerged. Some people suggested that Suleman was deliberately exploiting the welfare system, having children to guarantee that she would never have to work again. Others thought she might be suffering from some unusual psychiatric disorder, such as a compulsion to have children. She acquired an agent, gave a long interview to NBC-TV, and seemed to be angling for a media deal. The tabloid media reflected the new public attitude toward Suleman by dubbing her "the Octomom."

Suleman deflected all criticisms. She loved children, she said, and she wanted a large family because she had been lonely growing up. Also, she planned to go back to work and support her children as soon as she was able.

Nothing Suleman said seemed to convince her critics, for what sort of job could Suleman, with her limited education, get that would pay enough to support fourteen children? Everyone who paid taxes would be paying for her foolish whim, a whim abetted by medical professionals who should have known better and refused to help her take such irrevocable steps. Instead, they accepted her money and violated professional guidelines.

A few people came to Suleman's defense. She didn't deserve to be vilified, they argued, because she didn't do anything wrong. Having a lot of children was neither illegal nor immoral. A number of people pointed out that the McCaughey family had escaped public condemnation when they had decided to go through with a pregnancy that would leave them with seven children. Like Suleman, the McCaugheys also couldn't pay their medical bills, nor could they afford to house, care for, feed, and educate their children.

McCaughey Septuplets

Shortly before noon on November 19, 1997, in Des Moines, Iowa, twenty-nine-year-old Bobbi McCaughey gave birth to seven babies by cesarean section.

McCaughey had set what was then a world record for the number of live babies born in a single pregnancy. The family was immediately bathed in the glare of worldwide media attention, and for a while they became emblems of the American family: hardworking, religious, and committed to the welfare of their children. Bobbi McCaughey was admired for her courage and fortitude for coping so well with a difficult thirty-one-week pregnancy.

To help prevent a miscarriage, she had been confined to bed in the nineteenth week, and for the last two months she had been hospitalized. Although all the babies had a lower than normal birth weight, ranging from 2.5 to 3.4 pounds, with the help of the more than forty obstetricians, neonatologists, pediatricians, and other specialists who attended the birth, the babies all survived. Some suffered difficulties, but eventually even they were pulled to safety by aggressive medical management.

Fertility Drugs

Because the McCaugheys had experienced difficulty conceiving their first child, Mikayla, they sought help from an infertility clinic when they were ready to have another. Bobbi McCaughey was treated with Pergonal to increase her chances of becoming pregnant, which she soon did.

Pergonal is one of several fertility drugs associated with multiple pregnancies. The drugs increase the likelihood of pregnancy by causing more than one egg to be released per menstrual cycle, and this also increases the likelihood that more than one egg will be fertilized.

Early in Mrs. McCaughey's pregnancy, her physician informed the couple that she was carrying seven fetuses and recommended that some of them be terminated. The elimination procedure, called *selective reduction*, involves deliberately destroying and removing fetuses and is performed to increase the chances that the remaining fetuses will develop into healthy babies. The McCaugheys rejected the recommendation on the ground that their religious beliefs made abortion unacceptable. "God gave us those babies," Mrs. McCaughey told a reporter. "He wants us to raise them."

Dangers

A multiple pregnancy increases the risk of a miscarriage. Mark Evans, a fertility expert at Wayne State Hospital, estimates that a woman pregnant with quadruplets has a twenty-five percent chance of a miscarriage in the first trimester; a woman pregnant with quintuplets has a fifty percent chance. Cases of pregnancies with a larger number of fetuses are too few to permit significant generalizations.

The risk of losing all fetuses to a miscarriage was sadly illustrated by the case of Mary Atwood in England. Pregnant with eight fetuses, she arranged to sell her story to a tabloid, with the amount she would be paid dependent on the number of surviving babies. All eight were lost in a miscarriage.

Even when a miscarriage doesn't occur, multiple pregnancies rarely reach the end of a full forty-week term. Triplets are born after an average of 33.5 weeks and quadruplets after thirty-one weeks. The result is that babies born as multiples often suffer from one or more of the many problems of prematurity: retinal damage causing blindness, bleeding into the brain producing permanent brain damage, retardation, learning disabilities, impaired motor skills, chronic lung problems, or cerebral palsy.

Irresponsible?

The McCaugheys, like Nadya Suleman, were luckier than Mary Atwood, but fertility specialists who permit multiple pregnancies to continue have many critics. Some believe Bobbi McCaughey's specialists should have stopped the fertility drugs sooner and perhaps prevented the release of so many eggs. Others think the specialists should have required the McCaugheys to agree to a selective reduction of multiple fetuses before starting Mrs. McCaughey's treatment. Also, when it became apparent how many fetuses were present, they should have pressed the McCaugheys harder to eliminate some of them.

Critics also see the McCaugheys as having acted irresponsibly. If they weren't prepared to accept selective reduction, they shouldn't have sought help from an infertility clinic. Also, because they were lucky enough to have a good outcome, their example may suggest that multiple pregnancies are now safe and reliable, and thus others may be encouraged to believe they can safely have multiple babies.

Costs

The cost of medical care for Mrs. McCaughey and her children is estimated to be around $1.5 million. This was the money the McCaugheys couldn't afford to pay, so it had to be picked up in some way by the health care system and the society. With so much medical need unmet, society cannot afford to indulge the wishes of others like Nadya Suleman and the McCaugheys.

Responsible Specialists

Responsible infertility specialists discourage multiple pregnancies. Their aim is to assist a woman in having one or at most two healthy babies. A multiple pregnancy carried to term is viewed not so much as a mark of success as a sign of failure. In 2009, in an effort to reduce the number of multiple pregnancies, the American Society for Reproductive Medicine and the Society for Assisted Reproduction offered revised guidelines regarding the number of embryos that should be transferred into the uterus. For women younger than 35 and likely to become pregnant, the recommended number is no more than two. For women 35–37 and less likely to become pregnant, the number is two to three; for women between 38 and 40 and even less likely to become pregnant, the number is no more than four. For women older than 40 the recommend number is five for fewer.

Infertility clinics are almost completely self-regulated, however, and the guidelines are not binding. Thus, the penalty for the failure to prevent multiple births is borne by the woman, her babies, the family, and the society, but not by the clinic treating her. This situation has led many critics to demand that the fertility industry, an industry worth a billion dollars a year, be brought under the law and reasonable regulations enforced.

Figures published in 2010 showed that the number of multiple births has leveled off. Even so, they still occur with sufficient frequency that infertility clinics are likely to remain under pressure either to reduce the number or become subject to government regulation. Births are almost always occasions for joy, but almost invariably multiple births are occasions for trouble and tragedy.

Shopping the Sperm Supermarket

Jane Nuffield (as we will call her) is a thirty-four-year-old product-liability attorney who has risen to the rank of partner in her law firm. She owns a large house in a gated community in a Chicago suburb and spends a month every year in Paris. She earns a mid-six-figure income and regularly receives bonuses.

Jane works hard, but she is generally happy with her life. Although she had hoped to be married by her age, nothing ever quite worked out with the men she dated. They had expected her either to act deferential and dependent, which she wasn't about to do, or to support them in comfort and leisure, which she wasn't about to do either. Now she was in no particular hurry to get married, but she did want to have a baby.

She wanted it enough that she decided to become a single mother. She had always gotten what she wanted out of life by her own efforts, and she saw no reason why having a baby should be any different. Her first step, before she even consulted a fertility expert, was to go online and do a Google search, then explore the offerings of the various sperm banks that turned up.

A New Breed

Jane was one of the many women taking a new road. Traditionally, single mothers in our society haven't been treated with respect. More likely than not, they have been young adults with little education, no money, and few job skills. Thus, as a group, they have been regarded as presenting a social problem, and the most effective way of addressing the problem, reformers have claimed, is to introduce policies and educational programs to reduce the number of single mothers.

The new breed of single mothers that is emerging runs completely counter to this social stereotype. Like Jane, they are women from their late twenties to mid-thirties who occupy the upper tiers of income, education, and occupations. They are lawyers, psychologists, physicians, and executives. They aren't women who find themselves accidentally pregnant and then decide to have the child and cope with the ensuing problems of poverty and unemployment. Rather, like Jane, they decide they want to become mothers and then set out in a deliberate fashion to achieve that aim.

Mothers by Choice

Women wanting to become pregnant have traditionally planned on getting married first. Yet many professional women now don't see marriage as a necessary or even particularly desirable step to take. Those who are like Jane and well along in their careers might once have settled for marrying Mr. Okay if they had failed to find Mr. Right. Now, however, they are unwilling to make such a compromise.

The increase in the number of physicians specializing in reproductive medicine and easy access to the technology of assisted reproduction, particularly sperm banking, makes it possible for single women to exercise more control over their own procreation than has ever before been possible. If they are in good health and have the financial resources required, they can guarantee themselves a good chance at having a child without directly involving a man.

Employing easily available fertility services is a new way for women to take control of their own reproduction without becoming involved in any personal complications. A single woman wanting to become pregnant without getting married might once have approached a male friend with the idea of making him (with or

without his consent) the father of her child. Now she doesn't need to ask any man for a favor or engage in either deception or bargaining. If she can afford to, she can seek out medical methods for becoming pregnant.

This approach has the advantage of allowing her to avoid the emotional entanglements of having a child with a man she knows. Also, she can avoid the possibility that the man might either discover that the child is also his or change his mind about remaining silent and letting her have custody of the child. In either case, he may decide that he wants joint or even complete custody.

In addition, some lesbian couples are now deciding that one of them should become pregnant so that they can have a child and form a family. They need not spend time attempting to locate a sympathetic and obliging man willing both to become a father and to relinquish all claims on the child. Like Jane or any other single woman, the would-be lesbian mother with the financial resources need only locate a sperm bank that will accept her as a candidate for insemination.

Numbers?

No one knows exactly how many "choice moms" (as some call themselves) there are or whether they represent a trend that is increasing. Some evidence suggests that the number is going up. For example, reporter Amy Harmon learned that the local chapters of Single Mothers by Choice, a support group, doubled from twelve to twenty-five over a three-year period and that about 3000 of its 4000 members had used donor sperm. Some evidence also comes from census figures. The latest census found that more than 150,000 women with college degrees are single mothers who have never been married and are heads of their households. This is triple the number from the 2000 census. It is unlikely that even half these women used a sperm donor to become pregnant, but the large increase suggests that the number of choice moms is also on the increase.

Browsing the Catalogue

Some women deciding to become choice moms are enthusiastic about the possibilities that commercial sperm banks offer. Rather than selecting a mate, they get to select from a range of genetic material, often guided by the sort of background genetic information that is not available when a woman chooses a mate. (How many women ask potential mates to submit to a genetic analysis?)

Most commercial sperm banks have websites that allow potential mothers to browse through a catalogue of sperm donors and choose the one they prefer. The sperm banks typically provide detailed information about a donor, including age, race, medical history, family history, appearance, interests, educational attainments, and occupation. Some, with the permission of donors, include photographs, either baby pictures or recent ones. Other services offered, such as listening to a recording of a donor's voice, generally cost more.

Some sperm banks also offer ways for donors to reveal aspects of their personality. Thus, donors may write a personal essay or a letter about themselves that can be read by a prospective purchaser–recipient. Later, the letter can be given to a child conceived by the use of the donor's sperm. Donors are sometimes even asked to indicate their willingness to meet their biological child in the future if the child requests it.

Rather than browsing, women using the websites of some sperm banks can use a search function to see if the bank has available sperm from donors possessing particular characteristics. The traits sought range from race and blood type to level of education, eye and hair color, height, build, and physical appearance.

Some choice moms worry about having a child who will develop a severe mental illness like schizophrenia. Thus, they make a point of selecting donors who are past the age of the early to mid-twenties, when such illnesses usually appear. Other choice moms see selecting sperm as a chance of having a child who has physical characteristics (auburn hair, gray-green eyes, a tall stature) that they admire. By contrast, some women try to choose characteristics more like their own, so that their child will be more likely to resemble them, rather than an anonymous donor.

Other choice moms look for evidence of outstanding intelligence. They choose sperm acquired from men with advanced academic degrees who are in occupations requiring a high level of intellectual achievement. But for almost all choice moms, the very fact that they are free to make a choice is regarded as empowering. Although they may regret not having met a man to marry and father their child, they are pleased that this doesn't mean that they must give up their idea of motherhood.

A woman can learn only a limited amount from the description of a sperm donor, and if she knew the person, she might not have chosen his sperm. This was illustrated in 2007 when fifty-year-old Jeffrey Harrison responded to a newspaper ad placed by two teenagers. The young women had discovered that their mothers had both bought the sperm of Donor 150, and they asked him to get in touch with them.

Harrison, who sold his sperm frequently to California Cryobank in the late 1980s, had been described to potential clients as someone with blue eyes who was six feet tall and interested in philosophy, music, and drama. They were also told that Donor 150 was one of the sperm bank's most requested donors. Some two decades after his stint as a donor, Harrison was living in an RV with four dogs near Venice Beach in Los Angeles and scraping out a living by doing odd jobs and taking care of people's dogs. After meeting him, one of his biological daughters described him as "a free spirit."

Why Now?

Assisted reproduction has found a niche in our society. Its accomplishments are well publicized, and its techniques have become more sophisticated. Also, the stigma once attached to it as a producer of "test-tube babies" has mostly dissipated, and it has become a recognized medical specialty. Thus, single women wanting to have a child are likely to be aware of the possibility of using a sperm donor and to feel no shame about doing so. Becoming a single mother with the help of assisted reproduction no longer brings with it the taint of social disapproval.

Not only are women now free to control their own procreation, but the experiences of other women may prompt them to do so. A widely read book published in 2002 by economist Sylvia Hewlett found that about a third of professional women in their forties had no children. Hewlett later suggested to reporter Amy

Harmon that women in their fifties had more regrets about not having a child than they did about not having a partner. Thus, choice moms may be reacting to the experiences of women a generation older: those who set aside the traditional wife-and-mother role to pursue opportunities offered to them by a more open society.

The choice moms may be determined to have professional success while also preserving the option of motherhood, even if this means that they must exercise this option by making use of commercial sperm donors and the techniques of assisted reproduction. In an ironic social twist, women are now more able to create their own brave new world than men are.

SOCIAL CONTEXT

The Price of Eggs—Egg Donors: Rewards, Risks, and Exploitation

Amanda Criswell (as we will call her) was a twenty-six-year-old nursing student when she saw the ad in her college paper:

Earn Up to $10,000!

Help infertile couples have a family by becoming an egg donor. If you are between the ages of 20 and 30 and in good health, you may be a candidate. Height and weight are important.

Amanda had borrowed all the money she could from the student loan program, and her part-time job as a receptionist at a restaurant didn't pay enough to let her stay in school. Dropping out and getting a full-time job meant giving up her dream.

Amanda called the number in the ad. She became an egg donor, and somewhat to her surprise, she discovered that being a donor was personally satisfying as well as financially rewarding. She liked the idea that she could help people have a family. The second time she donated eggs was easier than the first, because she knew what to expect. The experience wasn't

pleasant, but she found it satisfying. It also let her stay in school and complete her degree.

Advertising

An ad in the Columbia University student newspaper several years ago offered students $35,000 for becoming an egg donor, and similar offers have appeared in publications at Harvard, Princeton, and other Ivy League institutions. Ads in college newspapers throughout the country typically offer fees of up to $10,000–15,000 to recruit young women students to donate eggs, and some of the same ads appear on Craigslist and Facebook. In large cities, it is not unusual to see billboards with the headline "EGG DONORS NEEDED," followed by a telephone number and a promise of confidentiality.

Such advertisements have become so common that most people screen them out as just more litter in the media landscape. Even so, their frequency is an indicator that human donor ova are more in demand than ever before. The Centers for Disease Control reported that in

2006 (the most recent figures) donor eggs were used in the birth of some 10,000 children in the United States alone. This is almost double the number just a year earlier, and it is reasonable to believe that the number of children born from donor eggs has continued to increase since 2006.

In addition to donor eggs needed by fertility clinics, centers specializing in privately funded stem-cell research need eggs so that researchers can produce the embryos required to acquire embryonic stem cells. No agency keeps a count of how many eggs have been acquired from donors, but the number appears to be very low. The 2005 guidelines of the National Academy of Sciences discourages paying donors, and the California Institute for Regenerative Medicine pays only for a donor's travel expenses and lost wages. New York's Empire State Stem Cell Board, by contrast, adopted a policy in 2009 allowing researchers to pay up to $10,000 to an ovum donor. Fertility clinics, rather than research labs, are by far the main recruiters of egg donors.

Donor Risks

The significant increase in the use of "donated" eggs raises ethical and social issues about the process by which eggs are acquired and about the risks their acquisition poses to the donors. All are young women, many are college students, and most are motivated to contribute their eggs for the money they are promised. In the past, egg donors were sisters, relatives, or close friends, and money was not involved.

Age, relative inexperience, and the need for money may make potential ova donors vulnerable to exploitation: they may not be adequately informed about foreseeable risks or warned about the possibility of unknown risks. Also, young women, particularly those under financial pressure, may discount the seriousness of the risks they will be taking or not appreciate the serious nature of the commitment they are making. In addition to running the risk of serious injury or even death, a potential donor must accept the prospect of having a biological child born to another woman, a child she most likely will never meet.

Sperm donors (see Briefing Session) usually receive only about $50 to $200, but the process of making the donation is virtually risk free. By contrast, women who become egg donors must invest a couple of weeks of their time, experience pain and discomfort, and put their health and very lives at risk. They must agree to be injected with a series of hormones to stimulate their ovaries, and the hormones are likely to produce such symptoms as nausea, bloating, weight gain, moodiness, and fatigue. Such side effects are temporary, but the hormones may also cause ovarian hyperstimulation syndrome, a condition that can result in blood clots, kidney failure, and even death.

Donors must also submit to frequent blood tests and ultrasound scans to determine when the ova are ready to be harvested. They must then be anesthetized and the eggs retrieved from their follicles. This may be done by a small surgical incision or (most often) by aspiration through a hollow needle inserted through the vagina into the follicles.

The risks of the process include a bad (potentially fatal) reaction to the anesthesia, the possibility of damaging an organ, and the possibility of uncontrollable bleeding.

The entire donation process takes about two weeks. The chance that an egg donor may be injured by the procedures used in causing ovulation and in retrieving the eggs may be relatively small, but it is real. The risks of donation have not been scientifically studied, but five deaths have been reported in Britain.

Some critics express concern about the long-term cancer risk the ovary-stimulating hormones pose to the donor. This risk has not been studied, but a 2009 Danish study followed 54,362 women who had been given fertility drugs to help them become pregnant. The study found that after fifteen years the women were no more at risk for developing ovarian cancer than other women experiencing infertility.

(The exception was women who had taken the drug clomiphene citrate; they had a sixty-seven percent increase in serious ovarian cancer tumors.)

The extent to which these results apply to egg donors is uncertain, however, because women experiencing problems with fertility already have a higher rate of ovarian cancer. So far, no studies have compared the cancer risks of women without fertility problems who are given hormones with the risks of women in the general population. Also, no studies have been done to determine whether ovum donors are at a higher risk for other kinds of cancer.

Informed consent for potential ovum donors is usually limited to mentioning the possibility of immediate harms. Is a donor likely to have trouble conceiving her own child? This isn't known. Will she later suffer from depression or remorse? This has not been studied. Will she increase her chances of developing ovarian cancer, breast cancer, kidney cancer, or liver cancer? The studies needed to answer this question haven't been carried out.

Knowledge of the long-term risks of being an ovum donor is almost exclusively anecdotal. The result is that even when the informed consent process is carried out in an unobjectionable manner, the "informed" part consists of such limited information that a woman who agrees to be a donor is taking unknown risks. This issue, too, needs to be emphasized in the consent process, but the anecdotal evidence suggests that it rarely is.

Personal Eugenics

Ova are now being marketed the way that sperm has been for the last twenty years. The counterpart to advertisements soliciting donors are those directed at would-be parents. Fertility clinics and "donor agencies" solicit clients with online videos and photo galleries of egg donors. Thus, just as women may shop (and pay more for) sperm they consider "superior"

in particular respects, women and couples may shop for "superior" ova.

What do they look for? Traits sought include an unproblematic family medical history (no schizophrenia, breast cancer, diabetes, sickle cell, and so on), evidence of intellectual accomplishment (admission to a highly selective college and high SAT scores serve as markers), and physical attributes such as height, weight, hair and eye color, and attractiveness.

As with the sperm market, the ovum market brings up questions about whether society is prepared to accept personal eugenic practices. We decisively reject the institutional practice of eugenics, but is the attempt to find an egg donor who embodies characteristics we would like our children to possess different in an ethically relevant way from choosing a partner with whom we would like to have children? (See the Social Context, "Shopping the Sperm Supermarket" for more discussion.)

Money is paid for donor eggs, and often the more desirable the traits the egg appears to represent, the greater is the amount of money offered. In a 2010 study, Aaron Levine reviewed more than a hundred ads in sixty-three college newspapers recruiting egg donors and found that more than half offered fees larger than the $10,000 maximum recommended in the guidelines of the American Society for Reproductive Medicine. ASRM guidelines state that compensation over $5000 above a donor's medical and living expenses "requires justification" and amounts above $10,000 "are not appropriate." So why the higher fees?

Some ads, Levine suggested, might be using a bait-and-switch tactic to encourage potential donors to make an initial contact, after which a lower fee could be negotiated. Other ads, however, appeared to be making offers designed to attract women who would donate "superior" or "extraordinary" ova. Thus, Levine discovered that every 100-point increase above a university's SAT score average was associated with a $2000 increase in the donor fee advertised in the campus newspaper. College ads, in particular, frequently exceeded the limit in the ASRM guidelines. One such ad offered $50,000 for "an extraordinary egg donor," an amount ten times that the ASRM deems "not appropriate."

Self-Regulation

Fertility clinics, Levine learned, tend to follow the ARM guidelines in their advertising. Egg-donor agencies, however, were more likely to advertise higher payments. The agencies are entrepreneurial, for-profit businesses, and they make their money from the fees they charge. Thus, they are highly motivated to secure the services of donors who will please their clients. Unlike the fertility clinics, agencies are not affiliated with organizations like ASRM: thus, they are under no obligation to follow the professional guidelines.

Several states prohibit the sales of human ova, most ignore the practice, and Virginia explicitly permits it. In 2009, California passed a law requiring that potential donors be informed of the risks as part of an informed-consent process. Nevertheless, for the most part, the states ignore the practice of recruiting ovum donors, leaving the medical and professional organizations to police the practices of their members.

Fertility clinics, assisted-reproduction physicians, and agencies that earn fees by matching donors with clients all operate in a way that is usually described as self-regulating. Critics find it easy to point to cases in which self-regulation has failed to work to protect the interests of individuals. Guidelines can be violated without real penalties, because they lack the force of law. If a physician is censured or kicked out of the professional organization, however, he can still continue to practice. In the fertility business, success in producing pregnancies, not professional status, is what counts.

Flawed Consent

Even if the guidelines are followed, anecdotal evidence suggests that the process of informed consent for ovum donors is often flawed. Too often, it seems, they are not given adequate information about the potential long-term harms they may suffer by becoming a donor. In addition, no one has a clear idea of exactly what those risks are, because relevant studies haven't been conducted.

The donation process is complicated by the fact that everyone involved—clinics, physicians, donor agencies, and donors—has a financial stake in the donation. Without a donor, the clinics, physicians, and agencies can't earn fees by providing services to their clients, and if the potential donor does not become an actual one, she is paid nothing. The clients who pay the money have their own agenda—they need donor ova to become pregnant—so their interest is in conflict with that of the potential donor.

A potential donor is likely motivated by the prospect of earning a comparatively large sum of money. That may make it more probable that she will ignore or downplay the risks of becoming a donor, that the money will serve as such a strong inducement that it will compromise her consent. Then, too, she will have the fertility clinic representative, the physician, and the egg-donor agency hoping and perhaps encouraging her to become a donor.

Envoi

Critics regard the entire ovum-donation process as one in which young women in need of money lack the protection of the law and risk being exploited by those who offer them money and encourage them to consent to become donors. As matters stand, only the moral principles and good intentions of those who recruit donors regulate the practice. This may be a barrier too weak to protect the interests of young and vulnerable women.

Advances in Reproductive Cloning

On February 3, 1997, Ian Wilmut of the Roslin Institute in Edinburgh, Scotland, made public the information that he and his research group had successfully produced a clone of an adult sheep. The younger genetic twin, the clone they named Dolly, had been born about seven months earlier and appeared to be healthy and normal in every respect.

The procedure Wilmut followed had a cookbook simplicity but was scientifically highly sophisticated. He took cells from the mammary tissue of a Finn Dorset ewe and got them to stop going through the ordinary process of cell division by culturing them in a medium with a low level of nutrients. Retrieving egg cells from a Scottish Blackface ewe, he removed their nuclei (hence the DNA) and then mixed them with the mammary cells. By passing a weak current of electricity through the mixture, Wilmut got some of the egg cells and mammary cells to fuse together. He then used a second pulse of electricity to activate the machinery responsible for cell division. (The process of transferring the nucleus of a somatic cell into an egg cell from which the nucleus has been evacuated is now called *somatic-cell nuclear transfer*. The phrase is more descriptive, but it also allows the word *cloning*, which has acquired controversial associations, to be avoided.)

Six days later, some of the fused cells had divided, becoming embryos in the way a fertilized egg develops into an embryo. Using the technology of embryo transfer, Wilmut succeeded in implanting one of the embryos in the uterus of a third sheep, another Blackface ewe. At the end of her pregnancy, the ewe gave birth to a lamb that was the genetic twin of the Finn Dorset sheep that supplied the mammary cells.

Wilmut and his group made 277 tries at fusing the nuclei of the body cells with the enucleated egg cells, but they managed to produce only twenty-nine embryos that lasted longer than six days, the usual time in vitro fertilization specialists allow for a fertilized egg to develop into an embryo before transferring it into the uterus. Of the embryos Wilmut implanted, Dolly was the sole success.

The great majority of biologists were amazed at Wilmut's achievement. Although they acknowledged that the DNA in the nucleus of a body cell contains a complete set of genes and so, in principle, could be used to produce another genetically identical individual, they didn't believe that our understanding of cells was detailed enough actually to do it. The view accepted by most researchers was that once a cell finds its place in the body, it switches off all the genes it contains, except those it needs to do its job and to reproduce itself. But to become an embryo, the genes must be switched on again. When the embryo is implanted in a uterus, they must be able to orchestrate the stunningly complicated process of development, changing the embryo into an offspring.

Wilmut demonstrated that what the majority of scientists considered only a distant possibility could be achieved in a relatively straightforward fashion. Placing the mammary cells in a culture low in nutrients seemed to return them to the state when their genetic potential is still open, and the pulse of electricity seemed to trigger them into dividing and developing. Wilmut showed that it wasn't necessary to understand the underlying biology of the process to control it. Under the right conditions, the DNA would reprogram itself to initiate and direct development.

Confirming Experiments

Wilmut's achievement was initially greeted with skepticism by some in the research community. Cloning was demonstrated as a phenomenon beyond doubt, however, in July 1998. Ryuzo Yanagimachi and his team at the University of Hawaii reported that they had produced more than fifty mouse clones. Some of the mice, moreover, were clones of clones.

Yanagimachi's technique was a variation of Wilmut's. Yanagimachi injected the genetic material from a mouse cumulus cell in the resting phase into an enucleated mouse egg and then used chemicals to get the cell to divide. After that, the cell was implanted into a surrogate mother and allowed to develop into a mouse. In one experiment, tan mice were used as genetic donors, black mice as egg donors, and white mice as gestational surrogates. The clones were all tan.

After Yanagimachi's demonstration, doubt about the reality of cloning evaporated. Scientists soon succeeded in cloning cows, goats, pigs, and cats. The first cat was cloned in 2002 only because researchers at Texas A&M failed (as others had) to clone a dog. Called cc, for "carbon copy" or "copycat," the kitten was the only successful result of attempts using eighty-seven cloned embryos transferred to gestational surrogates.

Drawbacks

Despite cc's name, cc really isn't an exact copy of her biological mother, a two-year-old calico cat named Rainbow. Although the two are genetically identical, the color and pattern of cc's coat is different. Coat color results from the separation and distribution of pigmented cells. This takes place during development and is not completely determined by genes.

Although cc is apparently healthy and normal, some cloned animals have not been so fortunate. A number die soon after birth, while others suffer from a variety of birth anomalies. Developmental delays, defective hearts, underdeveloped lungs, neurological deficits, and faulty immune systems are the more common flaws. Some cloned mice appear normal; then, as they grow, they become extremely fat. Developing calves become oversized and die prematurely.

Scientists don't know exactly what happens to cause these adverse results. Apparently, however, cloning promotes the occurrence of random changes. During normal reproduction, both egg and sperm mature before they combine, but in cloning, eggs are harvested and the DNA in cells combined with them must all be reprogrammed during a period of minutes or hours. During the process, researchers think, genes are altered and random errors occur. These cause unpredictable problems that can crop up at any time during development or after birth.

That cloning works at all is surprising to some researchers, given what needs to happen to make it possible. Still, even under the best laboratory conditions and in skilled hands, only about three percent of attempts at cloning mammals are successful. Only about one attempt in a hundred results in a viable calf.

When Dolly was born, some scientists speculated that it was likely she would age prematurely. The cell from which the nuclear DNA was removed had already undergone a number of cell divisions and, given that cells divide only about fifty times before they die, perhaps the clock for Dolly had already been ticking before she was born. Experience with cloned animals, however, has so far not shown that they age prematurely.

Dolly herself died of a lung infection on February 14, 2003. She was six years old, and the infection appeared to have nothing to do with the fact that she was a clone. Her life was terminated with a lethal injection by the veterinarians treating her when they decided that they could not control her suffering and that she was unlikely to improve. The natural life span of a domestic sheep is not clear. They are usually slaughtered for food when they are nine months old, but those kept in pastures can live ten or twelve years.

Practical Uses

Cloning was developed to be the foundation of *pharming:* the use of animals to produce drugs. The Roslin Institute is an agricultural research center, and a third of Wilmut's funding came from PPL Therapeutics, a biotechnology firm. Wilmut's aim, as well as PPL's, was to produce a flock of sheep genetically engineered to give milk containing such medically valuable and expensive substances as blood-clotting factor, insulin, and human growth hormone. If a single sheep able to secrete one of these substances in her milk could be created, cells from her could be cloned into a herd. Cloning would make it possible to produce whatever number of animal drug factories are needed, ensuring us a supply of useful substances at lower prices.

The interest in cloning cattle is to produce a line which has properties that are valued for commercial reasons. A cow that produces substantially more milk than usual, for example, could be cloned to produce a herd of dairy cows. The milk yield from such a herd would significantly reduce the cost of milk production and boost profits. Studies by the FDA in 2005 showed that milk and meat from cloned animals is safe to consume.

The research that produced cc, the cloned cat, was supported by Genetics Saving and Clone, a biotech company that aims to profit from cloning valued pets. The company is already storing, for a fee, DNA samples from pets, with the expectation that cloning technology will soon be adequate to produce a genetic replica of a beloved pet. Dogs were the first target, but when cloning them turned out to be intractable, the company turned to cats.

Critics object to the whole idea of the enterprise, pointing out that in the United States alone millions of dogs and cats are destroyed each years as an unwanted surplus. Thus, it is pointlessly cruel to create even more. Those who believe they will get an identical version of their cat or dog are simply mistaken. Cc's coat color was different from her mother's, and

very likely her behavior and personality will also be different. Developmental factors, including environmental ones, are likely to result in a very different animal.

Most people are more enthusiastic about the possibility of using reproductive cloning to establish colonies of endangered species. In 2001, scientists in Italy reported that they had successfully cloned an endangered wild sheep known as a muflon. The sheep survived and was put into a wildlife sanctuary. Another research group cloned a gaur, a wild ox, in 2002, but the calf died from an infection. Zoos around the world are investigating the possibility of cloning animals like the Siberian tiger, Sumatran tiger, several species of antelope, and the giant panda to save them from extinction. Some research facilities are saving cell samples from many species in the hope that, if they become extinct, new populations can be established.

A more distant possibility is to discover a completely preserved nucleus of an extinct animal (or piece together enough DNA fragments to form a complete set of genes), then transfer the nucleus into an enucleated egg cell and implant the embryo into the uterus of a similar species. Some researchers believe, for example, that it might be possible to resurrect the woolly mammoth by using an elephant as a gestational surrogate.

In 2002, Advanced Cell Technologies announced that it had cloned cow eggs and, when the embryos developed into fetuses, had removed kidney cells and transferred them to a sponge like matrix. The cells developed into what researchers described as a small kidney. When the kidney was implanted into the cow contributing the DNA, it produced a small amount of urine. Although no one sees this as an acceptable procedure for use with human cells, it demonstrates the possibility of growing organs for transplantation without relying on stem cells. (For the controversy over embryonic stem cells, see the Social Context, "Stem Cells," in Chapter 3.)

The possibility of using human embryonic stem cells to treat diseases, repair organs, and even grow whole organs makes cloning extremely important. Embryonic stem cells are obtained from embryos. If someone with (say) diabetes needed stem cells for treatment, then, to overcome the problem of tissue rejection, her DNA could be used to replace the nucleus in a donor egg. When the egg formed a blastocyst, the stem cells could be removed. They would be a perfect genetic match with her own tissue. This is an example of *therapeutic cloning*. That is, the cloning is for the purpose of getting materials for treatment, not for the purpose of reproduction. Because embryos must be destroyed to secure the stem cells, those who consider human embryos to have the status of persons regard even therapeutic cloning as a serious moral wrong.

Cell Conversion

In 2007, Shinya Yamanaka showed that it is possible to use a retrovirus to insert four genes into a somatic cell and convert the cell into a pluripotent state. In effect, the genes can reprogram a skin cell into an embryonic stem cell. These so-called induced pluripotent stem cells may make it unnecessary to destroy embryos to acquire stem cells; thus, the major objection to cloning for therapeutic purposes may disappear. Indeed, it may be that converted cells may make it unnecessary to rely on somatic cell nuclear transfer even for reproductive purposes. Many difficulties must be overcome, however, before either of these possibilities can be realized in any practical way. (See the Social Context "Stem Cells" in Chapter 3 for more information.)

What about Humans?

Most of the public discussion of cloning since Wilmut's announcement has focused on human *reproductive cloning*. People have been quick to realize that if sheep, mice, cattle, and cats have been cloned, there seems to be no technical reason a human can't be also.

Assuming that reproductive cloning were perfected, here are a few of the possibilities it opens up that have been discussed:

1. When one of a couple carries a gene responsible for a devastating illness, such as Tay–Sachs disease, the couple could decide to have a child and use only the genetic material from the noncarrier.

2. Women who have entered menopause as a result of chemotherapy, had their ovaries removed for therapeutic reasons, or are postmenopausal could still have a genetically connected child by employing the DNA from their somatic cells. The child would be a genetically identical twin, as well as an offspring, of the woman.

3. Similarly, men who are sterile for any reason or who no longer are capable of producing undamaged sperm (e.g., as a result of cancer surgery or radiation treatments) may still father a child.

4. The parents of a dying child could decide to have another child who will be a genetically identical replacement.

5. A woman could decide to use the DNA of a dying (or just dead) partner to have a child who would be the partner's genetic twin. A man could achieve the same end by finding a woman who would agree to be a gestational surrogate.

6. A "family" could be made up of several offspring who are genetically identical with the mother or the father. The father would also be a twin brother, and the mother a twin sister, of their offspring, although separated from them by years.

These possibilities, which many regard as potential benefits, are shadowed by other possibilities that some see as offering serious objections to human cloning.

1. Rich and egocentric people might decide to clone themselves for no reason, except to perpetuate their unique combination of genes.

2. Dictators or powerful political leaders could replace themselves with a clone, thus promoting an indefinite continuation of their influence.

3. The cellular DNA from popular figures such as athletes and movie stars might become marketed as commodities. Or because cloning would make "popular" DNA valuable, it might be stolen and used to produce children without the consent of an unwitting and unwilling donor.

Not a Photocopy

Some fears about cloning seem to reflect the mistaken belief that the clone of an individual will grow up to be exactly the same as the individual—a sort of photocopy. But of course, genetic identity doesn't result in exact similarity: we already know that identical twins, even when brought up in the same family, may turn out to be quite distinct in personality, interests, and motivations.

A child who develops in a different uterine environment, then grows up in a world filled with different people, practices, events, and experiences, is unlikely to be exactly like the person cloned. Even individuals can themselves become "different people" with experience and education.

The most serious objection to human reproductive cloning at the moment is that it would lead to so many tragic outcomes. With a success rate with mice hovering around a mere three percent the number of failed pregnancies is not likely to be better. Also, the chance of children being born with either lethal or seriously debilitating impairments is unacceptably high. We know from cloned mammals that unpredictable genetic and developmental errors occur.

No serious researcher thinks it would be anything but premature and morally indefensible to attempt to clone a human at the moment. Even if it is not wrong in principle, it would be wrong to produce children who would most likely be severely impaired, assuming that they didn't die shortly after birth.

But what of the future? In what circumstances, if any, would the cloning of humans be legitimate? Are we willing to take the risks involved in the development of a clone? Are we prepared to accept the alterations in our society that successful human cloning would produce?

Politics

Research involving cloning human embryos has been controversial from the start. On February 4, 1997, the day after Wilmut announced the cloning of Dolly, President Clinton asked the National Bioethics Advisory Committee to report to him in ninety days "with recommendations on possible Federal actions" to prevent the "abuse" of cloning. Meanwhile, on March 4, President Clinton issued an executive order banning the use of federal funds to support research leading to the cloning of humans. On June 9, the committee made its report to the president, and he immediately called for legislation banning cloning "for the purpose of creating a child."

In August 2001, President George Bush announced that he was prepared to allow human embryonic stem-cell research supported by federal funds to continue on stem cells that had already been recovered from embryos. Federal money could not be used, however, to create new embryos. Thus, the decision not only prohibited the creation of new embryos, but offered no federal support for even therapeutic cloning. In March 2009, President Barack Obama issued an executive order instructing NIH to draft guidelines lifting some of the Bush rules governing stem-cell research. The most important change was to make thirteen new human embryonic stem-cell lines eligible for research receiving federal funding.

An August 23, 2010, injunction by the Federal District Court of the District of Columbia halted federal funding, but the injunction was set aside by the United States Court of Appeals on September 9, 2010. A final resolution will depend on how the underlying lawsuit against the use of federal funding for research involving these new cell lines is decided. Obama, as well as Bush and Clinton, allowed to stand several federal regulations that explicitly prohibit reproductive cloning.

Denounced in Principle

Cloning human embryos for the purpose of reproduction continues to be denounced, even in principle, by the entire scientific and medi-cal community. Researchers have repeatedly asserted that they have no plans to carry out experiments like those which have produced other mammals. The fundamental practical interest in human cloning is in therapeutic cloning: the creation of human embryos to acquire embryonic stem cells to treat diseases and injuries. (For an analysis of these issues, see the Case Presentation "Stem Cells," in Chapter 3.)

CASE PRESENTATION

Louise Brown: The First "Test-Tube Baby"

Under other circumstances, the birth announcement would have been perfectly ordinary, the sort appearing in newspapers every day: *Born to John and Lesley Brown: a baby girl, Louise, 5 lbs. 12 ozs., 11:47 P.M., July 25, 1978, Oldham (England) General Hospital.*

But the birth of Louise Brown was far from being an ordinary event, and the announcement of its occurrence made headlines throughout the world. For the first time in history, a child was born who was conceived outside the mother's body under controlled laboratory conditions. Louise Brown was the world's first "test-tube baby."

For John and Lesley Brown, the birth of Louise was a truly marvelous event. "She's so small, so beautiful, so perfect," her mother told a reporter. Her father said, "It was like a dream. I couldn't believe it."

The joy of the Browns was understandable. From the time of their marriage in 1969, they had both very much wanted to have a child. Then they discovered that Lesley Brown was unable to conceive because of blocked fallopian tubes—the ova would not descend, so fertilization could not occur. In 1970, she had surgery to correct the condition, but the procedure was unsuccessful.

The Browns decided they would adopt a child, because they couldn't have one of their own. After two years on a waiting list, they gave up that plan. But the idea of having their own child was rekindled when a nurse familiar with the work of embryologist Robert Edwards and gynecologist Patrick Steptoe referred the Browns to them.

New Methods

For the previous twelve years, Steptoe and Edwards had been working on the medical and biochemical techniques required for embryo transfer. Steptoe developed techniques for removing a ripened ovum from a woman's ovaries, then reimplanting it in the uterus after it has been fertilized. Edwards improved the chemical solutions needed to keep ova functioning and healthy outside the body and perfected a method of external fertilization with sperm.

Using their techniques, Steptoe and Edwards had successfully produced a pregnancy in one of their patients in 1975, but it had resulted in a miscarriage. They continued to refine their procedures and were confident their techniques could produce a normal pregnancy that would result in a healthy baby.

They considered Lesley Brown a superb candidate for an embryo transfer. She was in excellent general health; at thirty-one, she was within the usual age range for pregnancy; and she was highly fertile. In 1976, Steptoe did an exploratory operation and found that her fallopian tubes were not functional and could not be surgically repaired. He removed them so he would have unimpeded access to the ovaries.

In November 1977, Mrs. Brown was given injections of a hormone to increase the maturation rate of her egg cells. Then, in a small private hospital in Oldham, Dr. Steptoe performed a minor surgical procedure. Using a laparoscope—a tube with a built-in eyepiece and light source that is inserted through a tiny slit in the abdomen—to guide him, he extracted an ovum with a suction needle from a ripened follicle.

The ovum was then placed in a small glass vessel containing biochemical nutrients and sperm secured from John Brown. Once the egg was fertilized, it was transferred to another nutrient solution. More than fifty hours later, the ovum had reached the eight-cell stage of division. Guided by their previous experience and research, Steptoe and Edwards had decided that it was at this stage an ovum should be returned to the womb. Although in normal human development the ovum has divided to produce sixty-four or more cells before it completes its descent down the fallopian tube and becomes attached to the uterine wall, they had learned that attachment is possible at an earlier stage. The stupendous difficulties in creating and maintaining the proper biochemical environment for a multiplying cell made it reasonable to reduce the time outside the body as much as possible.

Lesley Brown had been given another series of hormone injections to prepare her uterus. Two and a half days after the ovum was removed, the fertilized egg—an embryo—was reimplanted. Using a laparoscope and a hollow plastic tube (*a cannula*), Dr, Steptoe introduced the small sphere of cells into Mrs. Brown's uterus. It successfully attached itself to the uterine wall.

Success

Lesley Brown's pregnancy proceeded normally. But, because of the special nature of her case, seven weeks before the baby was due she entered the Oldham Hospital maternity ward so she could be continuously monitored. About a week before the birth was expected, the baby was delivered by cesarean section. Mrs. Brown had developed toxemia, a condition associated with high blood pressure that can lead to stillbirth.

The baby was normal, and all concerned were jubilant. "The last time I saw the baby, it was just eight cells in a test tube," Dr. Edwards said. "It was beautiful then, and it's still beautiful now." After the delivery, Dr. Steptoe said, "She came out crying her head off, a beautiful normal baby."

John Brown almost missed the great event, because no one of the hospital staff had bothered to tell him that his wife was scheduled for the operation. Only when he had been gone from the hospital for about two hours and called to talk to his wife did he find out what was about to happen.

He rushed back and waited anxiously until a nurse came out and said, "You're the father of a wonderful little girl." As he later told a reporter, "Almost before I knew it, there I was, holding our daughter in my arms."

Like many ordinary fathers, he ran down the halls of the hospital telling people he passed, "It's a girl! I've got a baby daughter."

To calm down, he went outside and stood in the rain. It was there that a reporter from a London newspaper captured Mr. Brown's view of the event. "The man who deserves all the praise is Dr. Steptoe," he said. "What a man to be able to do such a wonderful thing."

Life as Usual

On July 25, 2003, Louise Brown celebrated her twenty-fifth birthday at a party with 3000 guests, 1000 of them were others also born by in vitro fertilization (IVF). Patrick Steptoe had died in 1988, but Robert Edwards, then 77, was there to mark the occasion. So was Louise's twenty-year-old sister, Natalie, who had the distinction of being the first person born by IVF to have children of her own. Louise, who married later that year, had once wanted three or four children, but she was no longer sure she wanted to start a family of her own.

Despite dire predictions by opponents of IVF, Louise didn't turn out to be either grossly abnormal or psychologically scarred. (This is not to say that questions have not been raised about the safety of IVF; see the Briefing Session for a discussion.) The main feature distinguishing her from most of her peers turns out to be her trust fund composed of earnings from a book by her parents and from various television projects over the years. Since her birth, more than a million other babies have been born through the techniques of assisted reproduction. Such births have become so common place that they no longer attract attention.

In December 2006, three years after her enormous birthday party, Louise Brown gave birth to a boy whom she and her husband named Cameron. Some observers had started to speculate that if she waited too long, she might have to rely on the assisted-reproduction techniques required for her own birth. Presumably, this wouldn't bother her. "I want to have my own children, whatever it takes," she told a reporter from London's *Daily Mail* when she was twenty-three. "I would use the in vitro method if I couldn't have a baby."

CASE PRESENTATION
Savior Sibling

Anissa Ayala was fifteen years old in 1988 when she was diagnosed with chronic myelogenous leukemia. She received radiation and chemotherapy to destroy diseased bone marrow and blood cells, but the outcome of such treatments is that the patient's bone marrow is unable to produce enough normal blood cells to sustain life. Anissa's parents, Mary and Andy Ayala, were informed that without a bone-marrow transplant of blood-producing stem cells Anissa's chances of long-term survival were virtually zero, while with a transplant she would have a seventy to eighty percent chance.

Tests showed that neither the Ayalas nor their nineteen-year-old son, Airon, had bone marrow sufficiently compatible for them to be donors for Anissa. They then turned to a public bone-marrow registry, and for the next two years they searched for a donor. The odds of a match between two nonrelated people is only one in 20,000, and as time passed and no donor turned up, the Ayalas felt increasingly desperate. Anissa's health had stabilized, but that condition couldn't be counted on to last forever.

Radical Solution

Mary and Andy Ayala decided that the only way they could do more to help save their daughter's life was to try to have another child. Anissa's physician tried to discourage them, pointing out that the odds were only one in four that the child would have the right tissue type to be a stem-cell donor. Furthermore, the probability of their conceiving another child was very low: Andy Ayala was forty-five and had had a vasectomy sixteen years earlier; Mary was forty-two and thus well past the period of highest fertility. Nevertheless, the Ayalas decided to go ahead with their plan, and as the first step Andy Ayala had surgery to repair the vasectomy. Against all the odds, Mary Ayala became pregnant.

Response

When it became known that the Ayalas planned to have a child because their daughter needed compatible bone marrow, they became the subjects of intense media attention and received much harsh criticism. Critics claimed that they were treating the baby Mary was expecting as a means only and not as a person of unique worth. One commentator described their actions as "outrageous." Others said they were taking a giant step down the path that ultimately would lead to conceiving children merely to be sources of tissues and organs needed by others.

A few opposed this outpouring of criticism by noting that people decide to have children for many and complex reasons and sometimes for no reason at all. Also, no one observed that a reason for having a child need not determine how one regards the child. In addition, those who condemned the Ayalas often emphasized the "child-as-an-organ-bank" notion but never mentioned the relative safety of a bone-marrow transplant.

The Ayalas were hurt by the criticisms. Mary said she had wanted a third child for a number of years but had been unable to get her husband to agree. Andy admitted that he wouldn't have wanted another child if Anissa hadn't become ill, but he said he also had in mind the comfort a child would bring to the family if Anissa should die. The whole family said they would want and love the child, whether or not its bone marrow was a good match for Anissa's.

Against All Odds

In February 1990, the Ayalas found that they had beaten the odds once more. Tests of the developing fetus showed that the stem cells were nearly identical with Anissa's. During an interview after the results were known, Anissa said, "A lot of people think 'How can you do this? How can you be having this baby for your daughter?' But she's my baby sister and we're going to love her for who she is, not for what she can give me."

Then, on April 6, 1990, in a suburban Los Angeles hospital, more than a week before her due date, Mary Ayala gave birth to a healthy six-pound baby girl. The Ayalas named her Marissa Eve.

Anissa's physician, pediatric oncologist Patricia Konrad, collected and froze blood from the baby's umbilical cord. Umbilical blood contains a high concentration of stem cells, and she wanted the blood available should Anissa need it before Marissa was old enough to be a donor.

When Marissa Eve was fourteen months old and had reached an adequate weight, she was given general anesthesia and marrow was extracted from her hipbone. After preparation, the donated marrow was injected into one of Anissa's veins. The procedure was successful, and the stem cells migrated to Anissa's marrow and began to multiply. Anissa's own bone marrow began to produce normal blood cells.

Three years later, Anissa married Bryan Espinosa, and Marissa Eve was the flower girl at the wedding. Radiation treatments had destroyed Anissa's chances of having a child of her own, but she claimed that the bond between her and Marisa Eve was especially close. "Marissa is more than a sister to me," Anissa told reporter Anni Griffiths Belt. "She's almost like my child, too."

"I was struck by the extraordinary bond between the sisters," Belt said, "The fact is, neither one would be alive today without the other."

Easier Than Ever

Mary and Andy Ayala beat the odds in several ways: Andy's vasectomy was successfully reversed, Mary became pregnant without medical intervention, and Marissa Eve turned out to be a good bone-marrow match for her sister. The odds of the first two events remain about the same today, but no longer is it necessary to gamble against the odds where bone-marrow compatibility is concerned.

Using eggs and sperm, embryos can be produced in vitro by artificial insemination, then screened for compatibility with an intended bone-marrow recipient. Only those embryos compatible with the recipient will then be introduced into the uterus of the mother. Thus, the same techniques used in preimplantation genetic screening for the purpose of preventing the transmission of a heritable disease can also be employed to select for such positive traits as bone-marrow compatibility. (For a discussion see the Chapter 3, Briefing Session.)

Most often, this technique has been used to ensure that the umbilical-cord blood, which contains blood-producing stem cells, of the child is compatible with the tissue of the recipient. This procedure has been used in about 2,000 cases over the past decade. Those who object to preimplantation screening for genetic reasons also object when it is used to select for tissue donation.

CASE PRESENTATION

The Calvert Case: A Gestational Surrogate Changes Her Mind

Disease forced Crispina Calvert of Orange County, California, to have a hysterectomy, but only her uterus was removed by surgery, not her ovaries. She and her husband, Mark, wanted a child of their own, but without a uterus Crispina would not be able to bear it. For a fee of $10,000, they arranged with Anna Johnson to act as a surrogate.

Unlike the more common form of surrogate pregnancy, Johnson would have no genetic investment in the child. The ovum that would be fertilized would not be hers. Mary Beth Whitehead, the surrogate in the controversial Baby M case, had received artificial insemination. Thus, she made as much genetic contribution to the child as did the biological father.

Johnson, however, would be the gestational surrogate. In an in vitro fertilization process, ova were extracted from Crispina Calvert and mixed with sperm from Mark. An embryo was implanted in Anna Johnson's uterus, and a fetus began to develop.

Johnson's pregnancy proceeded in a normal course, but in her seventh month she announced she had changed her mind about giving up the child. She filed suit against the Calverts to seek custody of the unborn child. "Just because you donate a sperm and an egg doesn't make you a parent," said Johnson's attorney. "Anna is not a machine, an incubator."

"That child is biologically Chris and Mark's," said the Calverts' lawyer. "That contract is valid."

Critics of genetic surrogate pregnancy are equally critical of gestational surrogate pregnancy. Both methods, some claim, exploit women, particularly poor women. Further, in gestational pregnancy the surrogate is the one who must run the risks and suffer the discomforts and dangers of pregnancy. She has a certain biological claim to be the mother, because it was her body that produced the child according to the genetic information supplied by the implanted embryo.

Defenders of surrogate pregnancy respond to the first criticism by denying that surrogates are exploited. They enter freely into a contract to serve as a surrogate for pay, just as anyone might agree to perform any other service for pay. Pregnancy has hazards and leaves its marks on the body, but so do many other paid occupations. As far as gestational surrogacy is concerned, defenders say, since the surrogate makes no genetic contribution to the child, in no reasonable way can she be regarded as the child's parent.

The Ethics Committee of the American Fertility Society has endorsed a policy opposing surrogate pregnancy "for nonmedical reasons." The apparent aim of the policy is to permit the use of gestational surrogate pregnancy in cases like that of Mrs. Calvert, while condemning it when its motivation is mere convenience or an unwillingness to be pregnant. When a woman is fertile but, because of diabetes, uncontrollable hypertension, or some other life-threatening disorder, is unable to bear the burden of pregnancy, gestational surrogacy would be a legitimate medical option.

Birth and Resolution

The child carried by Anna Johnson, a boy, was born on September 19, and for a while, under a court order, Johnson and the Calverts shared visitation rights. Then, in October 1990, a California Superior Court denied Johnson the parental right she had sought. Justice R. N. Parslow awarded complete custody of the child to the Calverts and terminated Johnson's visitation rights.

"I decline to split the child emotionally between two mothers," the judge said. He said Johnson had nurtured and fed the fetus in the way a foster parent might take care of a child, but she was still a "genetic stranger" to the boy and could not claim parenthood because of surrogacy.

Justice Parslow found the contract between the Calverts and Johnson to be valid, and he expressed doubt about Johnson's contention that she had "bonded" with the fetus she was carrying. "There is substantial evidence in the record that Anna Johnson never bonded with the child till she filed her lawsuit, if then," he said. While the trial was in progress, Johnson had been accused of planning to sue the Calverts from the beginning to attempt to make the case famous so she could make money from book and movie rights.

"I see no problem with someone getting paid for her pain and suffering," Parslow said. "There is nothing wrong with getting paid for nine months of what I understand is a lot of misery and a lot of bad days. They are not selling a baby; they are selling pain and suffering."

The Calverts were overjoyed by the decision.

SOCIAL CONTEXT
Postmenopausal Motherhood

In late 1996, sixty-three-year-old Arceli Keh gave birth to a healthy baby girl. This made her the oldest woman ever to become a first-time mother.

This highly unusual event was not an accident of nature, but the result of deliberate planning and technological manipulation. Even so, Dr. Richard Paulson, the physician at the

University of Southern California infertility clinic who treated Keh, hadn't known her true age. She had lied to her previous doctors, and the age on her chart was recorded as fifty.

Fifty was already five years over the clinic's limit for in vitro fertilization, but Keh was in excellent health and did well on tests for strength and endurance. Paulson approved her for IVF, and by the time he discovered her true age, she was pregnant with an embryo formed by a donor egg fertilized with sperm provided by her sixty-year-old husband Isagani Keh.

The Kehs, who had immigrated from the Philippines, lived in Highland, California, about sixty miles east of Los Angeles. Although they had been married sixteen years, they had been unsuccessful in conceiving a child.

"I wasn't trying to make history," Arceli told a reporter for the London newspaper *The Express.* "We are working people," she said. "I only retired to have my baby." Isagani was still working as a carpenter to help pay the more than $60,000 they spent on the procedures resulting in the birth of their daughter, whom they named Cynthia.

Keh was the oldest postmenopausal woman to bear a child, but she wasn't the first. On Christmas Day, 1993, a fifty-nine-year-old British woman, identified only as Jennifer F., gave birth to twins. Jennifer F. was married and highly successful in business, but even though she was a millionaire, there came a time when she realized she regretted not having a child. By then she had undergone menopause, making it impossible for her to conceive.

Refusing to surrender her dream, Jennifer F. visited a National Health Service fertility clinic in London and asked for help. She wanted to be made pregnant with an embryo produced from her husband's sperm and a donor egg. Physicians at the clinic declined to perform the procedure, telling her she was too old to cope with the physical and emotional stress required to be a mother.

Determined to do everything possible to have a child, Jennifer F. then went to the clinic operated by Severino Antinori in Rome. Antinori agreed to accept her as a patient and performed the in vitro fertilization and embryo transfer procedure. Antinori claims he has assisted more than fifty women over the age of fifty to become pregnant.

Although both Arceli Keh and Jennifer F. attracted much media attention, other postmenopausal women had earlier become pregnant and borne children. In 1993, Geraldine Wesolowski, fifty-three, gave birth to a baby who was both her child and her grandchild. She was the gestational surrogate for her son, Mark, and his wife Susan. As a result of an accident, Susan had undergone a hysterectomy, but she and Mark were able to provide the embryo that was then transferred to Wesolowski.

A year earlier, Mary Shearing, also fifty-three, gave birth to twin girls. She was made pregnant with embryos produced by donated eggs and sperm from her thirty-two-year-old husband. Even though Mary Shearing was no longer ovulating, she and her husband had decided to have a child of their own.

Since 1987, it has been technologically possible for a postmenopausal woman to become pregnant with donor eggs, and during the last few years, the number of older (usually first-time) mothers has been increasing. In the United States in 2000, there were 255 births to women between the ages of fifty and fifty-four, a significant increase from 174 in 1999. (Statistics on births to women over the age of fifty-four are not collected by the Centers for Disease Control.)

The increase may be due partly to changes in the policies of infertility clinics. Until recently, most clinics in the United States would not accept as patients women past their early or mid-forties. Experts suspected that older women not only would have a low success rate but also would be putting their health at greater risk. A large study released in 2002 provides grounds to question both claims.

The study was carried out at the University of Southern California and involved seventy-seven postmenopausal women treated at the university's reproductive clinic from 1991 to 2001; forty-two of the women gave birth. The study showed that healthy women in their fifties using donor eggs have rates of pregnancy that are comparable to those of younger women. Further, although older women face higher rates of pregnancy-induced diabetes and hypertension, the conditions are temporary. Older women are, however, more likely to have a cesarean section than younger women.

While clinics are making it easier for postmenopausal women to attempt motherhood, critics argue that, given the scarcity of donor eggs, they ought to be reserved for younger women. It is best for a child, critics claim, to have physically and mentally active parents. Older parents may be unable to keep up with the demands of growing children, and the children will thus be cheated by not having parents who do things with them. Also, older parents are more likely to die, leaving behind young children still in need of guidance and financial support.

Defenders of granting access to fertility services to older women argue that it is pure gender bias to deny them the possibility of having a child. Men often father children well into their old age and are often admired for doing so. Charlie Chaplin was seventy-three when he had his last child, and Senator Strom Thurmond had four children during his sixties and seventies.

The actor Tony Randall became a father for the first time when he was seventy-seven. By contrast, a woman no longer ovulating, even if she has a younger husband, has no way to have a child without relying on assisted reproduction.

Also, just because a woman is relatively young does not mean she will be a better mother. On the contrary, it seems likely that an older woman with more psychological and financial security will be a better parent than many young women. Besides, younger women do not have to prove that they will be good mothers before they are allowed to have children, so why should older women? Finally, babies born to older women using eggs obtained from younger women do just as well as babies born to younger women, and now the evidence suggests that older mothers are not risking their health to a significant extent.

The number of women past menopause wishing to become pregnant is never expected to become great. Even so, the conflict between those who argue that older women are entitled to access to assisted reproduction and those who argue that access should be denied to them is likely to continue. Now that a number of children have been born to older mothers, some relevant factual questions about safety have been settled. Yet ethical and social questions about postmenopausal motherhood remain.

CASE PRESENTATION
Baby M and Mary Beth Whitehead: Surrogate Pregnancy in Court

On March 30, 1986, Elizabeth Stern, a professor of pediatrics, and her husband William accepted from Mary Beth Whitehead a baby who had been born four days earlier. The child's biological mother was Whitehead, but she had been engaged by the Sterns as a surrogate mother. Even so, it was not until almost exactly a year later that the Sterns were able to claim legal custody of the child.

The Sterns, working through the Infertility Center of New York, had first met with Whitehead and her husband

Richard in January of 1985. Whitehead, who already had a son and a daughter, had indicated her willingness to become a surrogate mother by signing up at the Infertility Center. "What brought her there was empathy with childless couples who were infertile," her attorney later stated. Her own sister had been unable to conceive.

According to court testimony, the Sterns considered Mrs. Whitehead a "perfect person" to bear a child for them. Mr. Stern said it was "compelling" for him to have children, for he had no relatives "anywhere in the world." He and his wife planned to have children, but they put off attempts to conceive until his wife completed her medical residency in 1981. In 1979, however, she was diagnosed as having an eye condition indicating that she probably had multiple sclerosis. When she learned that the symptoms of the disease might be worsened by pregnancy and that she might become temporarily or even permanently paralyzed, the Sterns "decided the risk wasn't worth it." It was this decision that led them to the Infertility Center and to Mary Beth Whitehead.

The Sterns agreed to pay Whitehead $10,000 to be artificially inseminated with Mr. Stern's sperm and to bear a child. Whitehead would then turn the child over to the Sterns, and Elizabeth Stern would be allowed to adopt the child legally. The agreement was drawn up by a lawyer specializing in surrogacy. Mr. Stern later testified that Whitehead seemed perfectly pleased with the agreement and expressed no interest in keeping the baby she was to bear. "She said she would not come to our doorstep," he said. "All she wanted from us was a photograph each year and a little letter on what transpired that year."

Birth and Strife

The baby was born on March 27, 1986. According to Elizabeth Stern, the first indication that Whitehead might not keep the agreement was her statement to the Sterns in the hospital two days after the baby's birth. "She said she didn't know if 'I can go through with it,'" Dr. Stern testified. Although Whitehead did turn the baby over to the Sterns on March 30, she called a few hours later. "She said she didn't know if she could live any more," Elizabeth Stern said. She called again the next morning and asked to see the baby, and she and her sister arrived at the Sterns' house before noon.

According to Elizabeth Stern, Whitehead told her she "woke up screaming in the middle of the night" because the baby was gone, her husband was threatening to leave her, and she had "considered taking a bottle of Valium." Stern quoted Whitehead as saying, "I just want her for a week, and I'll be out of your lives forever." The Sterns allowed Mrs. Whitehead to take the baby home with her.

Whitehead then refused to return the baby and took the infant with her to her parents' home in Florida. The Sterns obtained a court order, and on July 31 the child was seized from Whitehead. The Sterns were granted temporary custody. Then Mr. Stern, as the father of the child, and Mrs. Whitehead, as the mother, each sought permanent custody from the Superior Court of the State of New Jersey.

Trial

The seven-week trial attracted national attention, for the legal issues were without precedent. Whitehead was the first to challenge the legal legitimacy of surrogate agreement in a U.S. court. She argued that the agreement was "against public policy" and violated New Jersey prohibitions against selling babies. In contrast, Mr. Stern was the first to seek a legal decision to uphold the "specific performance" of the terms of a surrogate contract. In particular, he argued that Whitehead should be ordered to uphold her agreement and to surrender her parental rights and permit his wife to become the baby's legal mother. In addition to the contractual issues, the judge had to deal with the "best interest" of the child as required by New Jersey child-custody law. In addition to being a vague concept, the "best interest" standard had never been applied in a surrogacy case.

On March 31, 1987, Judge Harvey R. Sorkow announced his decision. He upheld the legality of the surrogate-mother agreement between the Sterns and Whitehead and dismissed all arguments that the contract violated public policy or prohibitions against selling babies.

Immediately after he read his decision, Judge Sorkow summoned Elizabeth Stern into his chambers and allowed her to sign documents permitting her to adopt the baby she and her husband called Melissa. The court decision effectively stripped Mary Beth Whitehead of all parental rights concerning this same baby, the one she called Sara.

Appeal

The Baby M story did not stop with Judge Sorkow's decision. Whitehead's attorney appealed the ruling to the New Jersey Supreme Court, and on February 3, 1988, the seven members of the court, in a unanimous decision, reversed Judge Sorkow's ruling on the surrogacy agreement.

The court held that the agreement violated the state's adoption laws, because it involved a payment for a child. "This is the sale of a child, or at the very least, the sale of a mother's right to her child," Chief Justice Wilentz wrote. The agreement "takes the child from the mother regardless of her wishes and her maternal fitness . . . ; and it accomplishes all of its goals through the use of money."

The court ruled that surrogacy agreements might be acceptable if they involved no payment and if a surrogate mother voluntarily surrendered her parental rights. In the present case, though, the court regarded paying for surrogacy as "illegal, perhaps criminal, and potentially degrading to women."

The court let stand the award of custody to the Sterns, because "their household and their personalities promise a much more likely foundation for Melissa to grow and thrive." Mary Beth Whitehead, having divorced her husband three months earlier, was romantically involved with a man named Dean Gould and was pregnant at the time of the court decision.

Despite awarding custody to the Sterns, the court set aside the adoption agreement signed by Elizabeth Stern. Whitehead remained a legal parent of Baby M, and the court ordered a lower court hearing to consider visitation rights for the mother.

The immediate future of the child known to the court and to the public as Baby M was settled. Neither the Sterns nor Mary Beth Whitehead had won exactly what they had sought, but neither had they lost all.

BRIEFING SESSION

"Oh, brave new world that has such people in it!" exclaims Miranda in Shakespeare's *The Tempest*.

This is the line from which Aldous Huxley took the title for his dystopian novel *Brave New World*. A dystopia is the opposite of a utopia, and the future society depicted by Huxley is one we're invited to view with shock and disapproval.

In Huxley's dystopia, "pregnancy" is a dirty word, sex is purely recreational, and children are produced according to explicit genetic standards in the artificial wombs of state "hatcheries." Furthermore, one's genetic endowment determines the social position and obligations one has within the society, and everyone is conditioned to believe that the role she finds herself in is the best one to have.

In significant ways, that future society is now. The new and still developing technologies of human reproduction have reached a stage in which the innovations imagined by Huxley in 1932 to make such a society possible are well within the limits of feasibility.

We have no state hatcheries and no artificial uteruses. But we do have sperm banks, donor ova, artificial insemination, frozen embryos, and surrogate pregnancies. We have it within our power to remove an ovum from a woman's body, fertilize it, then place it in her uterus so that it may develop into a child. We can remove one or more of the cells of a growing embryo and allow them to develop into separate embryos. Because we have the power to clone mammals, producing a genetically identical twin, we most likely also have the power to clone humans.

The new technology of human-assisted reproduction is so powerful, it differs only in degree from that of Huxley's dystopian world. What we have yet to do is to employ the technology as part of a deliberate social policy to restructure our world along the lines imagined by Huxley.

Yet the potentiality is there. Perhaps more than anything else, it is the bleak vision of such a mechanistic and dehumanized future that has motivated much of the criticism of current reproductive technology. The "brave new world" of Huxley is one in which traditional values associated with reproduction and family life, values based on individual autonomy, have been replaced by values of a purely social kind. In such a society, it is the good of the society or the species, not the good of individuals, that is the touchstone of justification.

The possible loss of personal values is a legitimate and serious concern. The technologies of human reproduction are sometimes viewed as machines that may be employed to pave the road leading to a world of bleakness and loss. Yet it is important to remember that these same technologies also promise to enhance the lives of those presently living and prevent potential suffering and despair.

Thousands of women (as well as a lesser number of men) unable to have children may find it possible to do so through the use of reproductive technology. It offers a means of conception when biological dysfunction makes the normal means unlikely or impossible. Women past the age of ovulation, or who have lost their ovaries to surgery, and men with a low sperm count are among those who have an opportunity where not long ago none existed.

These are all potentialities that have become actualities. But in the view of some, current methods merely mark a beginning, and the possibilities inherent in reproductive technology remain relatively unrealized. It may be possible before long, for example, to avoid sexual reproduction and use in vitro fertilization and surrogate pregnancy to reproduce clones of an individual. The technology is so powerful that, if we wish, we can employ it to change the basic fabric and pattern of our society.

Should we do that? Or will the use of the technology promote the development of a dystopia? One way of thinking about these general questions is to turn once more to Huxley.

In 1962, Huxley published a utopian novel, *Island*. Like the society in *Brave New World*, Huxley's ideal society also relies on the principles of science, but they are used to promote autonomy and personal development. For more than a hundred years, the society on the island of Pala has shaped itself in accordance with the principles of reason and science. Living is communal, sexual repression is nonexistent, children are cared for by both biological parents and other adults, drugs are used to enhance perceptual awareness, and social obligations are assigned on the basis of personal interest and ability.

Reproductive technology is one of the means the society uses to achieve its ends. It practices contraception, eugenics, and artificial insemination. Negative eugenics to eliminate genetic diseases is considered only rational. But more than this, by the use of deep freeze and artificial insemination (DF and AI), sperm from donors with superior genetic endowments are available for the use of couples who wish to improve their chances of having a child with special talents or higher-than-usual intelligence.

Huxley's ideal society is not above criticism, even from those sympathetic toward the values he endorses. Yet *Brace New World* is such a powerful cautionary tale of what might happen if science were pressed into the service of repressive political goals that it makes it difficult to imagine other possible futures in which some of the same technology plays a more benign role. *Island* is an attempt to present such an alternative future, so in thinking about the possibilities inherent in reproductive technology, fairness demands that we also consider Palinese society and not restrict our attention to the world of soma and state hatcheries.

Techniques of Assisted Reproduction

The birth of Louise Brown in 1978 (see the Case Presentation in this chapter) was a major media event. Photographs, television coverage, interviews, and news stories presented the world with minute details of the lives of the people involved and close accounts of the procedures leading to Louise's conception.

Despite the unprecedented character of the event, few people seemed surprised by it. The idea of a "test-tube baby" was one already familiar from fiction and folklore. Medieval alchemists were thought capable of generating life in their retorts, and hundreds of science fiction stories depicted a future in which the creation of life in the laboratory was an ordinary occurrence. Thus, in some ways, the birth of Louise Brown was seen as merely a matter of science and medicine catching up with imagination. Indeed, they didn't quite catch up, for the "test tube" contained sperm and an egg, not just a mixture of chemicals.

While it's doubtful that the public appreciated the magnitude of the achievement which resulted in the birth of Louise Brown, it was one of considerable significance. The first embryo transfer was performed in rabbits in 1890, but it wasn't until the role of hormones in reproduction, the nutritional requirements of developing cells, and the reproductive process itself were better understood that it became possible to consider seriously the idea of fertilizing an egg outside the mother's body and then returning it for ordinary development.

An estimated 200,000 babies are born worldwide each year through the use of assisted reproduction. The number has increased by twenty-five percent since 2000–2002 (the most recent figures), and since the birth of Louise Brown, as many as four million "test-tube babies" have entered the world. In the United States, a leader in fertility treatments, about 60,000 infants a year are born with the help of the techniques of assisted reproduction. The number of such babies doubled from 1996 to 2004, and the available evidence suggests that the increase is continuing. This is not surprising, given that, by 2010, twelve to fifteen percent of women ages 15–44 were seeking fertility treatments. The world we live in is more like the one Huxley wrote about than most people imagine.

IVF

In vitro is a Latin phrase that means "in glass," and in embryology, it is used in contrast with *in utero,* or "in the uterus." Ordinary human fertilization takes place in utero (strictly speaking, in the fallopian tubes) when a sperm cell unites with an ovum. In vitro fertilization, then, is fertilization that is artificially performed outside the woman's body—in a test tube, so to speak.

The ovum that produced Louise Brown was fertilized in vitro. But the remainder of the process involved *embryo transfer.* After the ovum from her mother's body was fertilized and had become an embryo, it was transferred—returned for in utero development.

Robert Edwards and Patrick Steptoe, who were responsible for developing and performing the techniques that led to the birth of Louise Brown, followed a process that, allowing for technical improvements, is basically the same as the one still employed.

The patient is given a reproductive hormone to cause her ova to ripen. Several mature eggs are extracted from the ovarian follicles and placed in a nutrient solution to which sperm is then added. With luck, sperm cells penetrate several ova, fertilizing them. The fertilized eggs are transferred to another nutrient solution where they undergo cell division. The embryo (also called a zygote or, by some, pre-embryo) is then transferred to the woman, who has been given injections of hormones to prepare her uterus to receive it.

Numerous modifications and extensions of Steptoe and Edwards's techniques have been introduced since 1978. It's now common to employ a nonsurgical procedure for securing ova. After hormones stimulate the ovarian follicles, ultrasound is used to locate the follicles, and a hollow needle is inserted through the vaginal wall and into a follicle. Fluid is withdrawn and egg cells are identified under the microscope. They are then fertilized with the sperm and cultured, and the resulting embryos implanted.

Also, it's now not unusual to implant two, three, or even four fertilized ova at a time. (Implanting more than two is coming to be viewed as not good medical practice.) This makes it more likely that at least one will attach to the uterine wall and so eliminates the need for a woman to have eggs removed another time. Yet the practice also has the disadvantage of increasing the chances of multiple births. (See the Case Presentation "The Octomom and the McCaughey Septuplets: The Perils of Multiple Pregnancy," earlier in this chapter.)

GIFT, ZIFT, IVC, ULER, PZD, ICSI, DNA Transfer, CD, and IUI

Gamete intrafallopian transfer, or GIFT, uses some of the same manipulative techniques as IVF. It involves inserting both ova and sperm into the fallopian tubes through a small abdominal incision, so if fertilization takes place, it does so inside the woman's body. Some regard the procedure as being more "natural" than in vitro fertilization.

Zygote intrafallopian transfer, or ZIFT, involves culturing eggs and sperm outside the body and then placing the zygotes into a woman's fallopian tubes. If the transfer is done at a particular developmental stage, it is called *pronuclear stage tubal transfer,* or PROST. Both are variants of *tubal embryo transfer,* or TET, and reflect the view that the fallopian tubes provide the most protective environment for embryo development.

Intravaginal culture, or IVC, is another attempt at naturalness. Ova are placed in a tube into which sperm cells are added, and the tube is then inserted into the vagina and kept next to the cervix by a diaphragm. Normal sexual intercourse can take place with the tube in place. Two days later, the tube is removed, the contents decanted, and any fertilized ova transferred into the uterus.

Uterine lavage embryo retrieval, or ULER, is a method for assisting pregnancy in a woman with a functioning uterus but who is either incapable of ovulation or, for some reason (e.g., she knows she is the carrier of a lethal gene), doesn't wish to use her own ova. An ovulating woman is inseminated with donor sperm. Then, after around five days, the fertilized egg is washed out of the uterus (this is the lavage) before it becomes implanted in the uterine wall. Once retrieved, the embryo is implanted in the woman being assisted. Because fertilization takes place in vivo, instead of in vitro, a potential difficulty is that the embryo may not be washed out before it becomes embedded in the uterine wall. If this happens, the donor must then decide whether to have an abortion.

Partial zona dissection, or PZD, involves using microtechniques to drill holes in the *zona,* or protective membrane surrounding an ovum, to facilitate the passage of sperm into the interior. This increases the chances of fertilization by reducing the egg's resistance to penetration, which is particularly useful when the sperm involved may be constitutionally weak.

Intracytoplasmic sperm injection, or ICSI, is a technique that can help fifty to sixty percent of infertile men become fathers. Sperm are examined microscopically and one that seems best shaped and most active is injected directly into the egg cell.

DNA transfer involves replacing the nucleus of an older egg with one taken from a younger donor egg. The aim is to take advantage of the cellular mechanisms of the younger egg, while keeping the maternal genetic material. (The technique was used in China in 2003 to make an infertile woman pregnant, although she later miscarried.) Critics charge that the technique is too similar to human cloning to be employed.

Cytoplasmic donation, or CD, involves removing the cytoplasm from a younger donor egg and injecting it into an older egg. Some data indicate that this will increase the developmental success of the recipient egg.

Intrauterine insemination (IUI) involves administering hormones to stimulate the production of ova by the ovaries and then, when ovulation occurs, injecting semen into the uterus. IUI is less expensive ($2000–3000) than IVF ($12,000–15,000), and it is more likely to be covered by insurance. The pregnancy rate is lower, however, and the hormones used in IUI are more likely to lead to a pregnancy involving multiple fetuses.

IUI is responsible for 20 percent of multiple births (8 percent of which involve triplets, quadruplets, or more), and it is a major cause of the 12.8 percent rate of premature births. (IUI resulted in the sextuplets born to Jon and Kate Gosselin and featured in the 2010 TV program *Jon & Kate Plus 8.*) If some of the multiple embryos produced by IUI are not eliminated by selective reduction, the likelihood of harm to the mother and the babies is considerable.

New techniques to assist reproduction are being developed at a rapid rate, and not all those in use are mentioned here. That so many techniques are available means that if one doesn't work, a woman may try another. Yet having so many possibilities makes it difficult for some women who wish to become pregnant to give up the attempt, even after repeated failure.

Need and Success Rates

In 2002 (the latest year for which complete data are available), the U.S. population included about 62 million women of reproductive age. About ten percent of them received fertility treatment at some point in their lives. By some estimates, at least 5 million men are infertile, and one in nine married couples has difficulty conceiving a child. In 2002 alone, about 1.2 million women sought assistance at clinics specializing in treating infertility.

In 2010, the Centers for Disease Control reported the results of the agency's study (the most recent) of the effectiveness of assisted reproductive technology as employed in 430 infertility clinics. Attempts to produce pregnancy involve one-month cycles, and during 2007 the clinics intervened in 142,435 cycles. The interventions resulted in 43,412 live births (some of them multiple), for a success rate of 30.5 percent.

Also in 2007, thirty-five percent of interventions led to pregnancy and 81.9 percent of the pregnancies resulted in live births. (These figures exclude the use of donor eggs or frozen embryos.) Single births occurred in sixty-nine percent of the cases, twins in thirty-two percent, and triplets or more in two percent. (Apart from twins, the percentage of multiple births dropped by two-thirds.)

The chance of a woman's becoming pregnant with the help of reproductive technology is roughly the same (by some estimates) as that of a normal, healthy couple attempting conception during the woman's regular monthly cycle. But of course, not all the pregnancies result in births and almost three-quarters of the women treated in infertility programs never become pregnant.

Costs

The financial cost of an attempt to become pregnant can be staggering. Each fertilization cycle costs from $12,000 to $15,000, and most women who get pregnant go through three or four cycles before pregnancy occurs. (The average cost of a single in vitro fertilization attempt was $12,400 in 2007.) Only about fifteen states require insurers to cover infertility treatments, and many people go deeply into debt to pay for them.

It is not unusual for someone to spend $25,000 to $35,000 attempting to get pregnant, and a few people spend as much as $200,000 or $300,000. By some estimates, the money spent on fertility-related medical services exceeds $3 billion to $5 billion a year. The cost of treatment has led some women to visit clinics in South Africa, Italy, or Germany, where prices are significantly lower, even though the success rate may also be lower.

Although some clinics discourage women from repeated attempts at pregnancy to improve their own success rates, others are willing to go far beyond reasonable efforts. Not only is providing fertility assistance lucrative, but some specialists are motivated by the hope that they can meet the needs of their patients. Women desperate to have a child sometimes press their physicians to employ techniques of unproven value.

Drawbacks

Cost is not the only drawback to assisted reproduction. Both the consequences of the methods used and the methods themselves are associated with a variety of moral and social difficulties.

Potential Risk to Child

An increasing number of studies indicate that a child conceived by some reproductive technologies may be at risk for serious birth defects. A study published in the *New England Journal of*

Medicine in 2002 found that babies conceived by IVF or intracytoplasmic sperm injection (ISI, see earlier) have an 8.6 percent risk of heart abnormalities, cleft palate, and undescended testicles, whereas the risk in unassisted pregnancies is 4.2 percent. A second study in the same journal found that IVF and ISI babies have 2.6 times the usual risk of low birth weight, a condition associated with heart and lung problems and poor cognitive development.

The range of risks was confirmed and extended by a 2009 Centers for Disease Control study that compared 281 IVF–ISI babies with 14,095 babies whose conception was unassisted. IVF–ISI babies were more than twice as likely to have defects in the septum of the heart (a hole between the chambers), a cleft lip or cleft palate, or an incompletely developed esophagus. Such babies were also more than four times as likely to have a malformed rectum.

We need to keep in mind, though, that the chance of any baby having some sort of birth defect is about three percent, and no study has yet been done large enough to establish the absolute risk of an IVF baby having a birth defect. The risks have been established on a comparative basis. Even so, a number of scientists think that growing embryos in the lab and manipulating sperm have consequences that are harmful to babies. In particular, IVF conditions may affect how genes are expressed and how embryonic development occurs.

The best evidence for this hypothesis comes from the prevalence of some rare diseases in IVF babies. One of the most studied is Beckwith–Wiedemann syndrome (BWS), which occurs in one of every 15,000 live births. Children with BWS have a greater chance of developing various forms of cancer (kidney cancer, in particular), show excessive growth of cells in certain organs, and display such anomalies as an oversized tongue. Researchers Andrew Feinberg and Michael DeBrun found that BWS is caused by the way a group of genes is expressed, and children with this form of gene expression have a one in two chance of developing cancer, whereas normal children have

a one in 10,000 chance. The researchers also found that the mothers of children with BWS were ten times more likely to have used IVF in getting pregnant than would be expected.

Other studies have drawn similar conclusions. One found, for example, that retinoblastoma, a cancerous eye tumor, occurs from five to seven times more often in children conceived with reproductive technology.

One current line of thought is that the culture medium in which embryos are grown contains chemicals that cause epigenetic changes—that is, changes in the way genes are expressed. The medium may add methyl groups, which act as switches to turn genes on or off. Epigenetic changes are known to cause disorders such as BWS and are also associated with low-birth-weight babies.

Studies comparing the behavior of mice born from IVF embryos with mice born without such assistance suggest that epigenetic changes can also produce behavioral differences.

Some IVF mice demonstrated memory problems, while others showed themselves lacking in normal caution and fear.

To keep the various risks in perspective, however, the actual number of children conceived by the use of reproductive technology who develop birth defects or suffer rare disease is relatively small. Also, some specialists question comparing data about IVF babies with data about babies conceived without technological assistance. Women who seek such assistance, they point out, are usually having difficulty getting pregnant, and whatever causes that difficulty may also influence their babies. Additional studies are proceeding, so new data may eventually provide a clearer picture.

Multiple Births

One of the hazards of assisted reproduction is that the fertility drugs given to women to speed up the production of ova can increase the chances that the women will become pregnant with multiple fetuses. Also, if in vitro fertilization is employed, the practice of transferring several embryos into a woman's fallopian tubes to improve the probability that at least one will implant in the uterus may result in the implanting of several embryos.

Unless selective abortion (called *fetal reduction*) is performed, a pregnancy with multiple fetuses puts the pregnancy at risk for miscarriage. A woman carrying quadruplets has a twenty-five percent chance of a miscarriage in the first trimester; a woman carrying quintuplets has a fifty percent chance.

Also, even if a miscarriage doesn't occur, a multiple pregnancy puts the infants at risk. Normal pregnancies last about forty weeks, but multiple pregnancies rarely go full term. Triplets are born around 33.5 weeks and quadruplets after thirty-one weeks. Because of their prematurity, babies born as multiples often suffer from such problems as blindness, stroke, brain damage, and impaired motor skills. Recent evidence indicates that even if impairments are not obvious, premature babies often grow up to have more difficulties in school and in life than those who were full-term babies.

The number of women taking fertility drugs tripled in the decade 1995–2005, rising from about one million to three million, and the number of multiple births *quadrupled*, from about 1980 to 2000. In 1995, 4973 children were born in groups of three or more. Triplets were most common, but quadruplets and even sextuplets were not uncommon.

A 2009 report from the National Center for Health Statistics showed that the number of multiple births has now leveled off. Twins are born at a rate of 32.1 per thousand births, and the number of triplets and other multiples declined by five percent in 2006, to 1.53 per thousand. This represents a twenty-one percent decline since 1998. Just as the increase in multiple births can be attributed to the rise in the use of reproductive technology, the decline can most likely be attributed to the guidelines that the American Society for Reproductive Medicine established in 1999. A major aim of the guidelines was to reduce the rate of triplet and higher pregnancies. Also, procedures for producing and selecting

embryos have improved over the years, reducing the need to implant several embryos to achieve a pregnancy. Although success rates in producing a pregnancy are higher with multiple embryos, studies show that the chance of having a child is better with two embryos than with three.

In 1996, seven percent of births involved triplets or higher multiples, but by 2006, the figure dropped to two percent. Even so, about one-third of births in which reproductive technology is used are multiple ones. Infertility specialists are under a great deal of pressure to produce results. The procedures they offer are expensive, and the women seeking to have a child often pressure the specialists into making them pregnant as fast as possible. The specialists also put themselves under similar pressure, because if they don't produce results, they will lose out in the competition for patients. The fertility business is a billion-dollar industry, and the incentives to violate professional guidelines are considerable.

The costs of multiple pregnancies include a social cost, along with the personal costs of the mother or the parents. As many as twenty percent of the babies in some neonatal intensive care units are babies conceived by reproductive technology and born prematurely. Society may not only have to take care of the babies when they are premature; it may also have to provide them with special educational and social programs.

That so many multiple births still occur, despite industry guidelines, raises questions about what society's response should be. Should we allow women who become pregnant with multiple fetuses to try to carry them all to term? Or should we require that any woman who wants to use assisted reproductive techniques agree beforehand to a selective reduction of fetuses? (See the Case Presentation of the Octomom and the McCaughey septuplets in this chapter.) Fertility clinics can now violate the professional guidelines for limiting the chances of multiple pregnancy without suffering a legal penalty. Perhaps giving the guidelines the force of law would solve the problems that multiple births cause to children, their mothers, their families, and the society.

Embryos, Eggs, and Transplants

An important development in assisted reproduction was the perfection of techniques for freezing embryos. One advantage of the procedure is that it eliminates the need for a woman to undergo the lengthy and uncomfortable process required to secure additional ova. If a woman fails to become pregnant in a first attempt, embryos saved from the initial fertilization can be employed in another effort.

The technique also makes it possible to delay an embryo transplant until the potential mother has reached the most favorable time in her menstrual cycle. Furthermore, because embryos survive storage very well, when a woman who wants to preserve her option to have a child undergoes chemotherapy, she may have her ova fertilized and the embryos preserved. Evidence to date indicates that embryos can be stored in a frozen condition and then unfrozen and implanted without any damage to the chromosomes.

New techniques now allow ova, as well as sperm and embryos, to be frozen and banked until needed. In 1998, Sydney Grace-Louise Murdoch became the first child born in the United States from an egg that had been frozen. Since then, several hundred children around the world have been born from frozen ova, and entrepreneurs have established fertility centers that specialize in storing the eggs of women not yet ready to have a child who worry that, by the time they are ready, they will be too old to ovulate. Also, because not every woman has a male partner or wants to use a sperm donor, banking eggs against the day that they are wanted seems a good alternative to the expense and risks of fertility treatments.

Critics charge, however, that the process of freezing eggs is so unreliable that counting on using them is a high-risk gamble. Eggs have a watery composition, and the formation of ice crystals can destroy the cell membrane or damage the chromosomes. Defenders argue that new processes avoid these problems, and that the success rate of producing a pregnancy after the eggs are thawed is about twenty percent, which is comparable to the success rate of using frozen embryos.

Ova, embryos, and sperm are not the only reproductive materials that can be successfully frozen. In 2004, a woman gave birth to a child conceived from an ovum produced by an *ovary* that had been frozen and stored for six years. The woman had been treated for breast cancer with chemotherapy, and before the treatment started, she had had an ovary removed and frozen. Years later, when the ovary was thawed and implanted under the skin of her abdomen, it began producing ova. An embryo was produced in vitro with her husband's sperm and then implanted in her uterus.

In another development in 2004, ovarian *tissue* was frozen and then successfully transplanted: Belgian physicians removed ovarian tissue from Ouarda Touirat and stored it while she was treated for lymphoma. After the effects of her chemotherapy dissipated, the tissue was reimplanted, and, without medical help, she became pregnant and had a child. In 2005, also in Belgium, physicians sewed two strips of (never-frozen) ovarian tissue donated by Sephanie Yarber's identical twin to each of her ovaries. The strips produced eggs, and Yarber became the first woman to give birth to a child by means of transplanted tissue.

Freezing eggs and ovaries and transplanting ovarian tissue raise questions about the reliability of the procedures and informed consent by participants. Are the procedures sufficiently effective to be offered to patients? Do patients understand the potential risks, as well as the benefits, of the procedures? The issues that have been most pressing and publicly discussed, however, are ones connected with frozen embryos.

Each year about 40,000 embryos are frozen at fertility clinics. Not all the embryos are implanted, and this raises what many consider to be the serious question of what should be done with them. What if a couple whose embryos are stored gets divorced? What if both die? What if the woman changes her mind about wanting to be pregnant? What if no surrogate is found?

Because more embryos are usually stored than are used to produce a pregnancy, what should be done with the leftovers? Fertility clinics typically offer the options of having excess embryos destroyed, used for research, or offered to an infertile couple. Often, though, couples cannot be traced, and centers are unwilling to give away an embryo without their permission. When embryos are unclaimed in this way or the bills for storage are left unpaid, frozen embryos are usually destroyed simply by being allowed to thaw. (A frozen embryo is only a tiny speck, because development is at the four-to eight-cell stage.)

A British law requires the destruction of unclaimed embryos after five years. The law took effect in August 1996, and in the face of some protest, about 3300 frozen embryos were destroyed. The courts had refused to set aside the law, and the prime minister ignored appeals that he intervene. Protesters held a vigil outside Westminster Cathedral, and the Vatican newspaper denounced the destruction as a "prenatal massacre."

At some fertility centers, another layer of complexity has been added by the practice of creating embryos from donated eggs and sperm from commercial sperm banks. The rationale is that donor eggs are scarce, and when more are available than are needed in a particular case, they shouldn't be wasted. Having on hand a collection of embryos that don't belong to any person or couple allows the centers to offer what fertility specialists call *embryo adoption*. This means that a woman or couple can choose ("adopt") an embryo for transfer on the basis of a description of the social and educational background and physical characteristics of the gamete donors. A couple can thus try for a resemblance between them and their potential child.

Some critics are troubled by the move from the creation of embryos in order to help particular people to the production of embryos on the speculation that someone who wants one may appear at the clinic. The practice is open to the charge that reproductive technology is a step nearer treating human embryos

as commercial products to be offered to discriminating consumers.

At present, no laws govern the preservation or destruction of frozen embryos. Fertility centers set their own policies, and the rules followed by various centers are not uniform. (The situation is changing, though, as professional organizations such as the Society for Reproductive Technologies offer guidelines that are coming to function as regulations.)

Most recently, proponents of the development of an embryonic-stem-cell technology have argued that unused embryos should be used as a source of stem cells, rather than simply discarded. Although those who ascribe no special status to embryos find the view persuasive, those who consider embryos to have the moral status of persons regard it as unacceptable.

Gestational Surrogates and Donor Ova

This is perhaps the most dramatic possibility opened up by in vitro fertilization. A woman whose uterus has been removed, making her incapable of normal pregnancy, can contribute an ovum that, after being fertilized in vitro, is implanted in the uterus of a second woman whose uterus has been prepared to receive it. The "host" or gestational surrogate then carries the baby to term.

In a similar procedure, when a woman is incapable of producing ova, as the result of disease, injury, or normal aging, a donor ovum may be fertilized in vitro and implanted into her uterus, and she then carries the child to term. Thus, postmenopausal women or many women once considered hopelessly barren may now become pregnant and give birth to a baby, even though they are genetically unrelated to the child.

Gestational surrogacy is a relatively new practice, and it opens up a number of possibilities that may have significant social consequences. That women past the natural age of childbearing can now become mothers is a stunning possibility that has already given rise to ethical and policy questions.

(For a discussion, see the Social Context "Postmenopausal Motherhood," in this chapter.) Second, women using the services of a gestational surrogate do so at present because they are unable to bear children themselves. However, it is only a short step from being unable to bear children to being *unwilling* to bear children.

Thus, it is easy to imagine that some women might choose to free themselves from the rigors of pregnancy by hiring a gestational surrogate. The employer would be the source of the ovum, which would then be fertilized in vitro and implanted as an embryo in the uterus of the surrogate. Women who could afford to do so could have their own genetic children without ever having to be pregnant.

Criticisms of Assisted-Reproduction Practices

While admitting the present and potential values of reproductive technology in assisting women who want to have children, many critics think the technology has been oversold. Despite their hopes, the majority of women who must rely on it don't become pregnant. Also, women aren't always properly informed about their chances. A particular clinic may have a success rate of twenty-five percent, but for a woman in her early forties, the rate may be only a one percent to two percent chance per month of trying. (Only about a quarter of those who seek assistance overcome their infertility.)

Critics also point out that the expense of trying to become pregnant can be quite high. Each attempt costs $12,000 or more, and several attempts are usually required for success. Further, the procedures involve anxiety and discomfort. Although the risk of injury and infection isn't great, it is real. In addition, the safety of the fertility drugs used to trigger ovulation and to prepare the uterus for implantation has been questioned. Also, there is a possibility that the high hormone levels in the blood the drugs produce may increase a woman's risk of breast cancer.

Donated ova are a scarcer commodity than sperm, and fertility clinics and egg brokers make a concerted effort to recruit donors to meet the needs of their patients and clients. Critics regard the situation as one in which young women who need money are not provided with adequate information about the risks involved and are induced to become donors, even though doing so may not be in their interest. Professional guidelines, critics say, offer insufficient protection, and the billion-dollar fertility industry should be regulated by laws. (See the Social Context "The Price of Eggs," in this chapter, for a fuller discussion.)

Benefits of IVF and Other Forms of Assisted Reproduction

Assisted reproduction is complicated, is expensive, and requires a great investment of skill, knowledge, and resources. An obvious question is, What is to be gained by it? What benefits might justify the use of the technically difficult and expensive medical procedures involved?

The most direct and perhaps most persuasive answer is that assisted reproduction makes it possible for many people to have children who wouldn't otherwise be able to do so. For those people, this is a decisive consideration. Some research shows that more than ten percent of married couples in the United States are infertile—that is, they have attempted to conceive a child for a year or longer without success. Infertility affects 6.1 million women and an estimated 4 million men. In 1995 alone, 1.2 million people sought professional help in conceiving a child.

Assisted reproduction isn't a solution to all problems of fertility, but it's the only solution possible in a large number of cases. Figures show that as many as forty-five percent of all cases of female infertility are caused by abnormal or obstructed fallopian tubes. Although normal ova are produced, they cannot move down the tubes to be fertilized. In some cases, tissue blocking the tubes can be removed or the tubes reconstructed. In other cases, however, the tubes may be impossible to repair or may be entirely absent. (Only forty to fifty percent of infertile women can be helped through surgery.) This means that the only way in which these women can expect to have a child of their own is by means of some sort of assisted reproduction. This is also true when the woman has no uterus or is postmenopausal and must rely on a donated ovum. Thus, technology offers a realistic possibility of becoming parents to many people who once had no hope of having a child.

Critics of assisted reproduction often claim there is no *right* to have a child and suggest that those unable to conceive should simply accept the fact and perhaps adopt a child. Proponents don't justify assisted reproduction in terms of rights, however. They refer primarily to the strong desire some people have to become parents, and some point out that assisted reproduction, as it is most often employed, is nothing more than a means of facilitating a natural function that can't be carried out because of some sort of biological failure.

Ethical and Social Difficulties

Several aspects of the technology of assisted reproduction and the way it can be employed are regarded by some observers as troublesome. Discussed briefly next are a few sources of uneasiness not mentioned earlier.

Incest potential

Clinics typically refuse to reveal the names of sperm donors to their clients or to the children born from sperm supplied by the clinics. Yet protecting the privacy of donors has an unintended consequence: because most clinics provide information about donors (physical appearance, height, education) and some even offer pictures, some donors are wildly popular, and their sperm may be chosen by a dozen or more potential mothers. This means that the children of these mothers will be half-siblings. If many of them live in the same geographical area, there is a small but real risk of their unknowingly engaging

in incest. The same potential exists for children conceived from donor eggs, and it is less likely only because the number of children born from donated sperm is much larger. One estimate puts the number at 30,000 a year.

Eugenics

The use of reproductive technology may encourage the development of eugenic ideas about improving the species. Rather than having children of their own, would-be parents might be motivated to seek out ova and sperm from people who possess physical and intellectual characteristics that are particularly admired. Thus, even without an organized plan of social eugenics (see Chapter 5), individuals might be tempted to follow their own eugenic notions. These include the tendency to try to have "the perfect baby," and this cheapens human life by promoting the view that human babies are commodities produced to order.

Sex Selection

Similarly, would-be parents might be inclined to exercise the potential for control over the sex of their offspring. Only males contain both an X and a Y chromosome, and their presence is detectable in the cells of the developing embryo. Determination of the sex of the embryo would allow the potential parents to decide whether they wish to have a male or female child. Consequently, a potential human being (the developing embryo) might be destroyed for what is basically a trivial reason. No fertility clinic permits sex selection, but this is a matter of policy, not law.

Weakening of Family

Reproductive technology may promote a social climate in which having children becomes severed from the family. The procedures emphasize the mechanics of conception and so minimize the significance of the shared love and commitments of the parents of a child conceived by intercourse.

Similarly, the technology dilutes the notion of parenthood by making possible peculiar relationships. For example, as many as five people may become involved in having a child, for a couple can use donor sperm and donor eggs and rely on the services of a surrogate for pregnancy. Because there is no clear sense in which the child belongs to any of them, parenthood is radically severed from conception.

Attitudes of IVF Children

In 2010, the politically conservative Institute for American Values published the results of a study based on a survey of adults 18–45 who had been conceived by the use of donor sperm. The results, as Ross Douthat reports, depict a group of people who are thankful for the technology that made their lives possible, yet feel regret about being the products of a technological and financial transaction.

IVF offspring are more likely to endorse the idea that everyone has a right to have a child, and they support the practice of assisted reproduction. (Indeed, some twenty percent say they are sperm or egg donors.) However, a substantial minority report that they are bothered by "the circumstances of my conception" and that "money was exchanged to conceive me." A larger percentage than in the general population disapprove of the practice of paying for sperm or eggs and agree with the statement "It is wrong to deliberately conceive a fatherless/ motherless child." A large minority say that if a friend were planning to get pregnant by paying for donor sperm, they would discourage her.

IVF offspring are almost twice as likely as adopted children to report envying those who knew their biological parents, twice as likely to worry that their parents "might have lied to me about important matters," and three times as likely to report feeling "confused about who is a member of my family and who is not." Not surprisingly, the children of sperm donors are also more likely than adopted children to agree that "when I see someone who resembles me, I often wonder if we are related." For similar reasons, they worry more than adopted children about becoming involved in a romantic relationship with someone who is related to them biologically.

Douthat, among others, recommends that U.S. laws be revised to give sperm and egg donation the status and protections it deserves. As a medical procedure, assisted reproduction may resemble a blood transfusion, but its social and personal consequences more closely resemble adoption. Britain, Sweden, Norway, and Switzerland are among the countries that have banned anonymous sperm and egg donation. When children who are born as a result of assisted reproduction turn 18, they have the legal right to gain access to their biological parents.

These difficulties and ones discussed earlier are not likely to be considered equally serious by everyone. Those who do not believe that human life begins at conception will hardly be troubled by the discarding of unimplanted embryos. The chance of inadvertent incest among children born from donated sperm is small. Sex choice is possible now by the use of amniocentesis, so it's not a problem unique to reproductive technology, and the same is true of the implementation of eugenic ideas.

Whether assisted reproduction leads to a weakening of the values associated with the family is partly an empirical question that only additional experience will show. Even if childbearing does become severed from current family structure, it still must be shown that this is in itself something of which we ought to disapprove. It's not impossible that alternative social structures for childbearing and childrearing might be superior to ones currently dominant in Western culture.

Little information is available about the psychological and social well-being of children born with the help of assisted reproduction. Like Louise Brown, many are on the brink of middle age, but many more are still young and growing. The Institute for American Values report suggests that more research should be done to understand the needs, attitudes, and problems of this increasingly large segment of the population. Also, drawing on the experiences of other countries, the United States should consider changing its laws to allow children born from donated sperm, eggs, or embryos to find out about their biological parentage.

Cloning and Twinning

Cloning produces individuals that are exact genetic copies of the donor from whom the DNA was obtained. Some animal cells have been cloned for more than five decades, but it wasn't until 1997 that the first mammal (a sheep) was cloned. Nothing in principle seems to stand in the way of cloning a human, but if human cloning became a practical reality, it would present serious moral and social issues. (See the Case Presentation "Hello, Dolly," in Chapter 3.)

Many issues raised in a speculative way by cloning are raised in a more immediate way by the procedure known as *twinning*. In 1993, Jerry Hall and Robert Stillman took seventeen two- to eight-cell human embryos, separated the blastomeres (the individual cells) and coated them with artificial zona pellucida (the protective coat surrounding egg cells), and then placed them in various nutrient solutions. The outcome was the production of forty-eight new embryos from the original ones.

The cells continued to divide, but development stopped after six days, partly because the embryos were abnormal—the originals were chosen just because they were defective. The work was purely experimental, and it was never intended that the embryos would be implanted.

The immediate advantage of the techniques developed by Hall and Stillman (as well as many others) is to increase the supply of implantable embryos for couples with fertility problems. If a couple's embryos, produced by in vitro fertilization, can be used to produce several more embryos, these can be used in repeated implantation attempts. Thus, the woman does not have to undergo repetitions of the unpleasant, expensive, and somewhat risky procedures involved in triggering ovulation, and then retrieving ova for in vitro fertilization.

Regarded from this point of view, the techniques may make having a child easier, cheaper, and less time-consuming for some couples.

The process used by Hall and Stillman was, strictly speaking, not actually cloning, which requires taking a somatic cell from a developed organism, extracting the DNA, and then growing an embryo from it in an enucleated egg cell. Even so, the process of *twinning* they employed showed that it would take very little more technically to use the techniques of assisted reproduction to produce a number of genetically identical humans.

Such techniques, when combined with the freezing of embryos, open up a number of social possibilities as surprising and controversial as those which cloning would make possible:

1. The production of several identical embryos would make a market in embryos possible. If a child had already been born and could be shown to have desirable qualities, the couple who had produced the embryos might sell them at high prices. It would then be possible for someone to have a child genetically identical to the one with the desirable qualities.

2. Parents could have a family in which all their children were genetic copies of one another. The oldest and the youngest would have the same genetic endowment. If several gestational mothers were employed, it would be possible to produce a dozen or more genetically identical children of the same age.

3. A couple might have a child, while also freezing an embryo twin as a spare. If the child should die, then the genetic twin could be grown from the embryo. The twin would be as much like the lost child as genetics makes possible.

4. If embryo twins were frozen and stored, they could be implanted in gestational mothers years apart. Thus, one twin might be sixty, while the other is only six.

5. Twins of an individual might be stored so that if the person needed something like

a bone-marrow or kidney transplant, the twin could be implanted in a gestational surrogate and allowed to develop. The tissue match from the twin would be perfect, and the problem of rejection would not arise.

The issues raised by twinning differ little from those raised by cloning, and twinning is already a practical reality. Some of the uses are so benign as to be hardly debatable, while others may result in such a cheapening or commercialization of human life as to be undesirable options.

Artificial Insemination

In 1909, an unusual letter appeared in the professional journal *Medical World*. A.D. Hard, the author of the letter, claimed that when he was a student at Jefferson Medical College in Philadelphia, a wealthy businessman and his wife consulted a physician on the faculty about their inability to conceive a child. A detailed examination showed that the man was incapable of producing sperm. The case was presented for discussion in a class of which Hard was member. According to Hard, the class suggested that semen be taken from the "best-looking member of the class" and used to inseminate the wife.

The letter claimed that this was done while the woman was anesthetized and that neither the husband nor the wife was told about the process. The patient became pregnant and gave birth to a son. The husband was then told how the pregnancy was produced, and, although he was pleased with the result, he asked that his wife not be informed.

The event described by Hard took place in 1884, and Hard was probably "the best-looking member of the class."

The Philadelphia case is the first recorded instance of the artificial insemination of donor sperm in a human patient, but the process itself has a much longer history. Arab horsemen in the fourteenth century inseminated mares with semen-soaked sponges, and in the eighteenth century the Italian physiologist Spallansani

documented experiments in which he fertilized dogs, reptiles, and frogs.

The Procedure

Artificial insemination is a basic technique of assisted reproduction. It is initiated when the woman's body temperature indicates that ovulation is to take place in one or two days, then is repeated once or twice more until her body temperature shows that ovulation is completed. Typically, three inseminations are performed during a monthly cycle.

The procedure is simple. The patient is usually placed in a position so that her hips are raised. A semen specimen, collected earlier through masturbation or taken from a sperm bank, is placed in a syringe attached to a catheter. The catheter is inserted into the cervical canal and the semen slowly injected into the uterus. The patient stays in her position for fifteen or twenty minutes to increase the chances that the sperm will fertilize an ovum.

The overall success rate is about eighty-five to ninety percent. Success on the first attempt is rare, and the highest rate occurs in the third month. Efforts may be made every month for as long as six months or a year. Such efforts are continued, however, only when a detailed examination shows that the woman is not suffering from some unrecognized problem preventing her from becoming pregnant.

When sperm taken from donors is used, the rate of congenital abnormalities is slightly lower than that for the general population. There is no evidence that manipulating the sperm causes any harm, but as mentioned earlier, some evidence suggests that a woman's use of reproductive technology can lead to children with a higher than usual number of genetic impairments.

Reasons for Seeking Artificial Insemination

Artificial insemination may be sought for a variety of reasons. When a man and woman are involved, the reasons are almost always associated with factors that make it impossible for them to conceive a child in the usual sexual way. About ten percent of all married couples are infertile, and forty percent of those cases are due to factors involving the male.

The male may be unable to produce any sperm cells (a condition called *asospermia*), or the number he produces may be too low to make impregnation of the female likely (a condition called *oligospermia*). In other cases, adequate numbers of sperm cells may be produced, but they may not function normally. They may not be sufficiently motile to make their way through the vaginal canal to reach the uterus. Hence, their chances of reaching and fertilizing an ovum are slight. Finally, the male may suffer from a neurological condition that makes ejaculation impossible or from a disease (such as diabetes) that renders him impotent. His sperm can be removed and used in artificial insemination.

If the female cannot ovulate or if her fallopian tubes are blocked so that ova cannot descend, artificial insemination can accomplish nothing. (See the earlier section on in vitro fertilization.) Yet there are factors affecting the female that artificial insemination can be helpful in overcoming. For example, if the female has a vaginal environment that is biochemically inhospitable to sperm, artificial insemination may be successful. Because the sperm need not pass through the vagina, their chance of surviving is better. Also, if the female has a small cervix (the opening to the uterus) or if her uterus is in an abnormal position, then artificial insemination may be used to deliver the sperm to an advantageous position for fertilization.

A couple might also seek artificial insemination for genetic reasons. Both may be carriers of a recessive gene for a genetic disorder (e.g., Tay–Sachs disease), or the male may be the carrier of a dominant gene for a genetic disorder (e.g., Huntington's disease). In either case, they may not want to run the statistical risk of their child's being born with a genetic disease, yet may also not be willing to accept prenatal testing and abortion or embryo screening.

To avoid the possibility they fear, they may choose to make use of artificial insemination with sperm secured from a donor.

The traditional recipient of artificial insemination is a married woman who, in consultation with her husband, has decided to have a child. Some physiological or physical difficulty in conceiving leads them to turn to artificial insemination.

But the traditional recipient is no longer the only recipient. Recipients now include many single women who wish to have a child and view artificial insemination as a way of taking charge of their own reproduction. In buying sperm from a sperm bank, some see an opportunity to increase the chance that their child will have genetically influenced characteristics they value. (See the Social Context "Shopping the Sperm Supermarket," in this chapter.) Also, lesbian couples are now more often deciding that one of them should become pregnant. Even if they cannot marry, they say, having a child will allow them to become a family, albeit a nontraditional one.

Sperm Donors

Sperm donors are often medical or university students. Commercial sperm banks typically recruit more widely, but effort is made to employ donors who are in excellent health, with a high level of intellectual ability. Their family histories are reviewed to reduce the possibility of transmitting a genetic disorder, and their blood type is checked to determine its compatibility with that of the recipient. Also, a potential donor must be known to be fertile. Thus, he must already be a biological parent or he must fall within the normal range in several semen analyses.

Donors are paid $50 to $200 for their services, and typically their identity is kept secret from the recipient and any resulting children. A coding system is ordinarily used both to preserve the anonymity of the donor and to ensure that the same donor is used in all inseminations.

The semen stored in sperm banks is not necessarily that of anonymous donors. For a variety of reasons, individuals may wish to have their sperm preserved and pay a fee to a sperm-bank operator for this service. For example, a man planning a vasectomy or one expecting to become sterile because of a progressive disease may store his sperm in the event that he may later want to father a child. Lance Armstrong, seven-time winner of the Tour de France, banked sperm before undergoing treatment for testicular cancer, and this enabled him to have biological children afterwards.

Issues in Artificial Insemination

Artificial insemination (AI) presents a variety of moral, legal, and social issues that have not been addressed in a thorough fashion. Legal scholars have explored some of the consequences that AI has for traditional legal doctrines of paternity, legitimacy, and inheritance. They have also made recommendations for formulating new laws (or reformulating old ones) to take into account the reality of the practice of AI.

Critics of AI have focused mostly on its potential for altering the relationship between husbands and wives and for producing undesirable social changes. They argue that AI will take the love out of sexual procreation and make it a purely mechanical process, that AI will promote eugenics and so denigrate the worth of babies that fall short of some ideal, and that AI is just another step down the road toward the society of *Brave New World*. AI, they say, has the potential for destroying the family by allowing single women and lesbian couples to have children.

Some of the issues that need close attention from philosophers concern individual rights and responsibilities. For example, does a man who has served as a sperm donor have any special moral responsibilities? He certainly must have some responsibilities. For example, it would be wrong for him to lie about any genetic diseases in his family history. But does he have any responsibilities to the child that is produced by AI employing his sperm? If

donating sperm is no different from donating blood, then perhaps he does not. But is such a comparison apt?

Can a child born as a result of AI legitimately demand to know the name of his biological father? We need not assume that mere curiosity might motivate such a request. Someone could need to know her family background in order to determine how likely it is that a potential child might have a genetic disorder. Also, some may want to be sure that they are avoiding inadvertent incest if their potential partner was also conceived by AI. Perhaps the current practice of maintaining the anonymity of sperm donors is not one that can stand critical scrutiny.

Should a woman be allowed to order sperm donated by someone who approximates her concept of an ideal person? Should she be able to request a donor from a certain ethnic group, with particular eye and hair color, a certain minimum or maximum height, physical attractiveness, with evidence of intelligence, and so on? A number of other ethical questions are easily raised about AI: Does any woman (married or single, of any age) have the right to demand AI? Should a physician make AI by donor available to a married women if her husband is opposed?

Other questions concerning the proper procedures to follow in the practice of AI are also of considerable significance. For example, how thoroughly must sperm donors be screened for genetic defects? What standards of quality must sperm as a biological material be required to satisfy? What physical, educational, or general social traits (if any) should individual donors possess? Should records be maintained and shared through an established network to prevent the marriage or mating of individuals born from AI with the same biological father?

At present, these questions have been answered only by individual physicians or clinics, if at all. No general medical or legal policies govern the practice of AI, although the professional organizations offer ethical guidelines.

Even if present practices are adequate, most people would agree that we need to develop uniform policies to regulate AI.

Ovum Donors

The use of donor ova presents virtually the same set of issues as those raised by artificial insemination. Unlike AI, however, egg donation raises questions about the exploitation of donors. Typically, they are young women who agree to donate ova because they want to earn the several thousand dollars fertility clinics are willing to pay.

To earn the money, they must put themselves through an uncomfortable process involving treatment with powerful drugs and retrieval of the eggs by a small surgical incision or a needle puncture. The immediate risk to their health is small but real. Critics point out that women who are willing to submit themselves to the process must be young and are likely to be naive and vulnerable. A need for money will thus make them ripe for exploitation. (See the Social context "The Price of Eggs," in this chapter, for a fuller discussion.)

Surrogate Pregnancy

A *gestational surrogate* (see the earlier discussion) is a "host mother," a woman who is implanted with an embryo produced by AI from the ovum of another woman. *Surrogate mothers* are women who agree to become pregnant by means of artificial insemination. The surrogate mother carries the baby to term, then turns the baby over for adoption to the couple or individual with whom she made the agreement.

Surrogate mothers are typically sought by couples who wish to have a child with whom at least the man has a genetic link and who have been unsuccessful in conceiving a child themselves. A woman unable to conceive but wanting a child may also arrange for the services of a gestational surrogate using donor sperm.

Various legal complications surround surrogate pregnancy, and at least eighteen states have passed laws regulating surrogacy arrangements. Some laws, like those in Michigan and New Jersey, make it illegal for couples to adopt a child born to a surrogate mother. The aim is to discourage surrogacy.

When surrogacy arrangements are allowed, a major problem is finding a way to pay women who agree to be surrogates. Adoption laws forbid the selling of children or even the payment of money to one of the biological parents in connection with adoption. The child must be freely surrendered. Because a child born to a surrogate mother is, in the absence of laws to the contrary, legally her child, the child must be adopted by the couple securing her services. How then can the surrogate mother be paid?

Some women have simply volunteered to be surrogate mothers in these cases, so the issue of payment would not arise. In general, however, the difficulty has been resolved by paying the mother to compensate her for her inconvenience and the loss of her time. Technically, then, she is not being paid for conceiving and bearing a child, nor is she being paid for the child, who is handed over for adoption. Hence, laws against selling a child are not violated, and the surrogate is paid from $10,000 to $25,000.

A second problem is finding a way to permit surrogacy while avoiding turning it into a commercial operation resembling the breeding of horses or show dogs. Surrogacy is often arranged by an attorney acting as a broker on behalf of a couple that wants a child. The attorney finds the surrogate and draws up a contract between her and the couple. (The contract can include such items as a prorated fee if the surrogate miscarries or a requirement that the surrogate have an abortion if prenatal tests reveal a fetal abnormality.) The surrogate must agree to relinquish her maternal rights and not stand in the way of adoption by the contracting couple. For arranging the surrogacy, as well as for drawing up the contract, the broker receives a fee of $15,000 to $20,000.

Despite the claim that a surrogate is being paid for her time and inconvenience, some critics charge that surrogacy arrangements are no more than "baby selling." To avoid this appearance, New York State passed a law with the aim of removing the profit motive from surrogacy arrangements and making them completely noncommercial. The state kept it legal for a woman to become a surrogate but made it illegal to pay a broker to handle the arrangements. Further, the state made it illegal to pay a surrogate for anything more than her medical expenses. A contract agreeing to pay a fee to a broker or to a woman acting as a surrogate would have no legal standing in court.

Some of the same reasons offered to justify assisted reproduction can also be offered for surrogate pregnancy. Fundamentally, couples who wish to have a child of their own but are unable to do so because of some uncorrectable medical difficulty experienced by the woman view surrogate pregnancy as the only hope remaining to them. Some rule out adoption because of the relative shortage of available infants, and some simply want a genetic connection between them and the child. Many people are quite desperate to have a child of their own.

Critics have charged that surrogate pregnancy is no more than a specialized form of prostitution. A woman, in effect, rents out her body for a period of time and is paid for doing so. Such a criticism rests on the assumption that prostitution is morally wrong, and this is a claim at least some would deny is correct. Furthermore, the criticism fails to take into account the differences in aims. Some surrogate mothers have volunteered their services with no expectation of monetary reward, and some women have agreed to be surrogate mothers at the request of a sister, friend, daughter, or son. Even those who are paid mention that part of their motivation is to help those couples who so desperately want a child. Far from condemning surrogate mothers as acting immorally, it

is possible to view at least some as acting in a morally heroic way by contributing to the good of others through their actions.

Perhaps the most serious objection to the use of surrogate mothers is that they are likely to be recruited from the ranks of those most in need of money. Women of upper-and middle-income groups are not likely to serve as surrogate mothers. Women with low-paying jobs or no jobs at all are obviously the prime candidates for recruiters. It might be charged, then, that women who become surrogate mothers are being exploited by those who have money enough to pay for their services.

Merely paying someone in need of money to do something does not constitute exploitation, however. To make such a charge stick, it would be necessary to show that women who become surrogate mothers are under a great deal of social and economic pressure and have no other realistic options. Furthermore, it could be argued that, within limits, individuals have a right to do with their bodies as they choose. If a woman freely decides to earn money by serving as a surrogate mother, then we have no more reason to object to her decision than we would have to object to a man's decision to earn money by working as a laborer.

As the population ages and women with careers postpone having children, the employment of surrogate mothers is likely to increase. The practice is now well established, but the ethical and social issues are far from being resolved to the general satisfaction of our society.

Ethical Theories and Reproductive Control

One of the themes of Mary Shelley's famous novel *Frankenstein* is that it is both wrong and dangerous to tamper with the natural forces of life. It is wrong because it disturbs the natural order of things, and it is dangerous because it unleashes forces beyond human control. The "monster" that is animated by Dr. Victor Frankenstein stands as a warning and reproach to all who seek to impose their will on the world through the powers of scientific technology.

The fundamental ethical question about the technology of human reproductive control is whether it ought to be employed at all. Is it simply wrong for us to use our knowledge of human biology to exercise power over the processes of human reproduction?

The natural law view, as represented by currently accepted doctrines of the Roman Catholic Church, suggests that all the techniques for controlling human reproduction that we have discussed here are fundamentally wrong.

Children may ordinarily be expected as a result of sexual union within marriage. However, if no measures are wrongfully taken to frustrate the possibility of their birth (contraception, for example), then a married couple has no obligation to attempt to conceive children by means such as artificial insemination or in vitro fertilization. Certainly, the couple has no reason to resort to anything as extreme as cloning or using donor embryos.

Indeed, many of the technological processes are themselves inherently objectionable. Artificial insemination, for example, requires male masturbation, which is prima facie wrong, since it is an act that can be considered to be unnatural, given the natural end of sex. AI, even when semen from the husband is used, tends to destroy the values inherent in the married state. It makes conception a mechanical act.

In vitro fertilization is open to the same objections. In addition, the process itself involves the destruction of fertilized ova. On the view that human conception takes place at the moment of fertilization, this means that the discarding of unimplanted embryos amounts to the destruction of human life.

On the utilitarian view, no reproductive technology is in itself objectionable. The question that has to be answered is whether the use of any particular procedure, in general or in a certain case, is likely to lead to

more good than not. In general, it is reasonable to believe that a utilitarian would be likely to approve of all the procedures we've discussed here.

A rule utilitarian, however, might oppose any or all of the procedures. If there is strong evidence to support the view that the use of reproductive technology will lead to a society in which the welfare of its members will not be served, then a rule utilitarian would be on firm ground in arguing that reproductive technology ought to be abandoned.

According to Ross's ethical theory, we have prima facie duties of beneficence. That is, we have an obligation to assist others in bettering their lives. This suggests that the use of reproductive technology may be justified as a means to promote the well-being of others. For example, if a couple desires to have a child but is unable to conceive one, then either in vitro fertilization procedures or artificial insemination might be employed to help them satisfy their shared desire. Twinning might be used to increase the number of embryos, and even cloning seems prima facie unobjectionable.

Kantian principles don't seem to supply grounds for objecting to assisted reproduction or reproductive technology in general as inherently wrong. However, the maxim involved in each action must always be one that satisfies the categorical imperative. Consequently, some instances of in vitro fertilization, artificial insemination, twinning, and cloning would no doubt be morally wrong.

The technology of reproduction is a reality of ordinary life. So far it has made our society into neither a dystopia nor a utopia. It's just one set of tools among the many that science and medicine have forged.

Yet the tools are powerful ones, and we should beware of allowing familiarity to produce indifference. The moral and social issues raised by reproductive technology are just as real as the technology. So far, we have not treated some of them with the seriousness they deserve.

Part III

Terminations

Chapter 5

Abortion

CASES AND CONTEXTS

The Conflict Begins: *Roe v. Wade*

Norma McCorvey of Dallas was unmarried, poor, and pregnant. She was twenty-one years old and wanted to have an abortion, but under Texas law in 1970, abortion was a criminal offense, except when required to save the woman's life.

McCorvey's life had been hard. She was abused both sexually and emotionally as a child, then raped at a reform school when she was a teenager. She married at sixteen, was beaten by her husband, and was involved with drugs and alcohol. Her first child, a daughter, was taken to be raised by her mother, and the father of her second child, also a daughter, assumed responsibility for the child's welfare.

When McCorvey found herself pregnant for the third time, she knew she didn't want another child. The law in California was less restrictive than the law in Texas, and McCorvey believed she could get an abortion there. Unfortunately, she lacked the money for travel and expenses. She tried to visit an illegal abortion clinic in Dallas, but found it closed down.

The Case

While still pregnant, McCorvey was approached by Linda Coffee, a public-interest attorney who had been given McCorvey's name by a lawyer specializing in adoptions. Coffee and Sarah Weddington, also an attorney, met with McCorvey and asked her if she would agree to be the plaintiff in a class-action lawsuit. The suit would be filed against Henry Wade, the district attorney of Dallas County, and would challenge the constitutionality of the Texas abortion law. McCorvey readily consented. When the papers were filed, Norma McCorvey became "Jane Roe."

Although McCorvey was the plaintiff, the case was a class-action suit that Coffee and Weddington hoped would be decided in a way that would recognize that women had a constitutional right to seek an abortion. The federal courts ruled that the Texas statute was void, but Dallas District Attorney Henry Wade appealed the District Court decision to the U.S. Supreme Court.

The legal case took time as it wound through the courts, and despite McCorvey's explicit wish not to have another child, she bowed to legal necessity and carried the fetus to term. She gave birth to a third daughter, then immediately gave up the baby for adoption.

The Decision

The Supreme Court handed down its ruling in *Roe v. Wade* on January 23, 1973. In a 7-to-2 decision, written by Justice Harry A. Blackmun, the Court found the Texas law to be unconstitutional. This ruling had the effect of decriminalizing abortion in the United States, because abortion laws in most other states differed little from the Texas statute.

The *Roe* decision did not hold that states could not regulate abortion. Rather, it placed limits on the restrictions states could impose without violating a woman's constitutionally protected right to privacy. Physicians have traditionally divided the nine months of pregnancy into three three-month trimesters, and the Court made use of these divisions to guide states in determining to what extent they could legitimately restrict abortion.

The ruling held that, during the first twelve weeks (the first trimester) of pregnancy, states cannot restrict a woman's decision to have an abortion. During the second trimester, states may place restrictions on abortion to protect the health or safety of the pregnant woman. In the final trimester, because the fetus may be considered viable and capable of an independent existence, states may restrict abortions but only in ways that still preserve the health of the pregnant woman.

From Roe to McCorvey

"Jane Roe" went back to being Norma McCorvey, but her life didn't seem to improve. A high-school dropout with no vocational training, McCorvey supported herself with various unskilled jobs, working as a waitress and a bartender. In the 1980s she began to acknowledge in public that she had been "Jane Roe," and this led to a brief flurry of attention from abortion-rights groups. She was introduced at meetings, gave interviews to the media, and gave some public talks. She became somewhat of a celebrity for a time.

Yet her celebrity didn't pay the bills, and she continued to work at low-paying jobs. Her celebrity did help her get jobs in abortion clinics, however. While she was working in a women's clinic in Dallas, the antiabortion group Operation Rescue set up an office next door and protested the clinic's activities. McCorvey was hostile to them at first, but then she began to have conversations with Philip Benham, the group's director, during her cigarette breaks. Benham, an evangelical preacher, talked to her about Christianity, and McCorvey agreed to attend church with the daughter of one of the group's members.

McCorvey converted to Christianity on her first visit to the church. She was baptized by Benham on August 8, 1995, in a swimming pool belonging to one of Benham's followers. The event, considered a major publicity coup by Operation Rescue, was videotaped and released to the media. McCorvey renounced her previous support for abortion and took a job doing word processing for Operation Rescue.

With the help of a coauthor, Andy Meisler, she went public in 1994 with the details of her story up to that time in *I Am Roe: My Life*, Roe v. Wade, *and Freedom of Choice*. With the help of another coauthor, she wrote *Won by Love*, an account of her conversion. She founded a ministry called "Roe No More," and she hopes to oppose abortion in Dallas by operating a mobile counseling center to encourage pregnant women to choose another alternative.

The Debate Continues

Linda Coffee and Sarah Weddington, McCorvey's lawyers, had achieved their aim. The *Roe* decision made it possible for most women wanting an abortion to obtain one. Yet the decision also triggered a firestorm of controversy between proponents of relatively unregulated choice ("pro-choice" advocates) and opponents of so-called abortion on demand ("pro-life" or "right-to-life" advocates) that shows no sign of dying down.

Those who favor making abortion a matter of individual decision were pleased by the *Roe* decision, but those who consider abortion a serious moral wrong were not. Many of the opponents resolved to work for a constitutional amendment prohibiting abortion or, alternatively, get the Supreme Court ruling in *Roe v. Wade* overturned.

Within the limits of regulation imposed by the *Roe* decision, opponents of abortion have taken various legal measures over the years in an attempt to slow or halt its practice. Thus, they have often succeeded in getting laws passed that impose requirements making it difficult for women to get an abortion. In response, advocates of personal choice have often charged that the laws are unconstitutional and filed suits that have ended up before the Supreme Court. *Roe v. Wade* marked the beginning of the legal skirmishes and court fights centered on abortion, but even so many years later, the end of the war is not in sight.

CASE PRESENTATION

When Abortion was Illegal: Mrs. Sherri Finkbine and the Thalidomide Tragedy

Background Note: The following case concerns an event that took place before the U.S. Supreme Court decision in Roe v. Wade *was handed down in 1973. That decision had the effect of legalizing abortion in the United States. Before the decision, most state laws permitted abortion only to save the life of the mother. The case presented here illustrates the kinds of problems faced by many women who sought an abortion for other reasons.*

In 1962, Mrs. Sherri Finkbine of Phoenix, Arizona, the mother of four children, was pregnant. Her health was good, but she was having some trouble sleeping. Rather

than talking with her doctor, she simply took some of the tranquilizers that her husband had brought back from a trip to Europe. The tranquilizers were widely used there; like aspirin or cough syrup, they could be bought over the counter in any pharmacy.

A few weeks after she began taking the tranquilizers, Sherri Finkbine read an article that discussed the great increase in the number of deformed children being born in Europe. Some of the children's arms and legs failed to develop or developed so that they had malformed hands jutting out from their shoulders. Other children were blind and deaf or had seriously defective internal organs requiring major corrective surgery. The impairments had been traced to the use in pregnancy of a supposedly harmless and widely used tranquilizer. Its active ingredient was thalidomide.

Mrs. Finkbine was worried enough to ask her doctor to find out if the pills she had been taking contained thalidomide. They did. When her doctor learned this, he told her, "The odds are so against you that I am recommending termination of pregnancy." He explained that getting approval for an abortion should not be difficult. She had good medical reasons, and all she had to do was explain them to the three-member medical board of Phoenix.

Mrs. Finkbine agreed with her doctor's advice. But then she began to think that maybe it was her duty to inform other women who may have been taking thalidomide about its disastrous consequences. She called a local newspaper and told her story to the editor. He agreed not to use her name, but on a front page, bordered in black, he used the headline "Baby-Deforming Drug May Cost Woman Her Child Here."

The story was picked up by the wire services, and Mrs. Finkbine's identity soon became known. The medical board had already approved her request for an abortion, but because of the great publicity that her case received, the members grew skittish and canceled their approval. The Arizona abortion statute legally sanctioned abortion only when it was required to save the life of the mother. The board was afraid that their decision might be challenged in court and that it couldn't stand up to the challenge.

Sherri Finkbine became the object of a great outpouring of antiabortion feelings. *Il Osservatore Romano*, the official Vatican newspaper, condemned her and her husband as murderers. Although she received some letters of support, others were abusive. One writer said, "I hope someone takes the other four children and strangles them, because it is all the same thing." Another wrote from the perspective of the fetus: "Mommy, please dear Mommy, let me live. Please, please, I want to live. Let me love you, let me see the light of day, let me smell a rose, let me sing a song, let me look into your face, let me say Mommy."

Sherri Finkbine tried to obtain a legal abortion outside her own state, but she was unable to find a doctor who would help her. Eventually, she got on a plane to Sweden and consulted a physician at a Swedish hospital. After a rigorous investigation by a medical board, Sherri Finkbine received the abortion she had traveled so far and struggled so hard to get.

Sherri Finkbine's problem was solved. Even so, she continued to express sympathy for the thousands of pregnant women who had taken thalidomide but lacked the money to go to another country for an abortion. Whether they wanted to or not, state abortion laws forced them to continue with pregnancies that would end with the birth of seriously impaired children. She considered such restrictive laws inhumane.

SOCIAL CONTEXT
A Statistical Profile of Abortion in the United States

January 2011 marked the thirty-eighth anniversary of the Supreme Court decision legalizing abortion in the United States. Yet nearly four decades after the decision, abortion has not become a standard, uncontroversial medical procedure, as many abortion-rights advocates expected.

Even though some 1.2 million abortions are performed every year in the United States, Americans remain ambivalent and divided on abortion's moral acceptability. To an extent, abortion has become even less accepted than it was during the 1980s and 1990s.

The data that follow present a statistical profile of abortion in the United States. The picture

that emerges reveals a strong commitment to the idea that abortion should remain a legal procedure, combined with a lesser, yet still strong, belief that abortion should be illegal.

Despite the enduring and often sharp political conflicts over abortion, public support for keeping the procedure legal, although perhaps stringently regulated, remains high. Abortion as a procedure is not going to go away, yet neither are the moral and political issues associated with it.

(The data cited here may sometimes be inconsistent from section to section. Some statistics are for the latest year for which complete data are available, while other numbers are for more recent years for which data are incomplete. The discrepancies are few and small, and don't substantially alter the general picture.)

How Many Abortions?

About twenty-two percent of all pregnancies among American women end with an abortion, according to a 2010 estimate. When the pregnancies aren't intended, this percentage rises to forty percent. Each year, more than twenty out of every 1000 women aged 15–44 have an abortion, and half of those who have an abortion have had one before.

In 2005 (the most recent statistics), 1.21 million abortions were performed. This was a decrease from 1.31 million in 2000, and reflects what may be a relatively constant number.

Public health experts estimate that during the 1950s and 1960s, before the 1973 Supreme Court decision in *Roe v. Wade* that legalized abortion, 200,000 to 1.2 million illegal abortions were performed each year. The number of abortions increased after the procedure was made legal, peaking at 1.6 million in 1990. Since then, abortions have been declining, measured both as an absolute number and as a percentage of women of childbearing age who have them. It's beginning to look as if the number of abortions has stabilized at between 1.0 and 1.3 million a year.

The reasons for this stabilization (if it's real) are unclear, but some believe it's connected with the aging of the population, the wider availability of contraception, and fewer unwanted pregnancies. Others think the decline reflects a change of attitude toward abortion, as well as changes in society that make it more difficult for a woman to secure an abortion. As evidence, they point to protests at clinics, the shrinking number of abortion providers, and stiffer regulation by the states.

While the number of abortions is likely to vary slightly from year to year, experts think it is unlikely that any increase will reach the 1996 high point. Some suggest that a less accepting public attitude toward abortion will keep the number even lower than might otherwise be expected.

Who Has an Abortion?

Age. More than half (52%) of women who have an abortion are in their twenties. Women ages 20–24 account for 33% of all abortions, and teenagers account for another 18%.

Race. European Americans have 36% of the abortions performed in the United States, African Americans, 30%, and Hispanics, 25%.

Religion. Of women who have abortions, 37% say they are Protestants and 28% identify themselves as Catholics.

Marital status. About 45% of all abortions are obtained by women who have never been married.

Children. More than 61% of abortions are among women who have previously given birth to at least one child.

Rape. Each year, about 12,000 women have abortions as a result of rape.

Why Abortion?

- Seventy-five percent of women say they are choosing to have an abortion because having a child would interfere with their education, work, or other responsibilities.

- Seventy-five percent say that they cannot afford to have a (or another) child for financial reasons.

- Fifty percent say they don't want to be a single parent or that they aren't getting along with their husband or partner and don't want to face the problems of adding a child to the situation.

Contraception and Abortion

Some critics of abortion claim that its availability encourages women to use it as a form of birth control. The statistics suggest, however, that the situation is more complicated than that. Nearly all women seeking an abortion have (at some time) used some form of contraception, and the majority used it during the month in which they became pregnant. The intention of the majority to avoid becoming pregnant is most often thwarted by their failure to use contraception properly and consistently.

- Eight percent of women having abortions have never used any form of birth control. Those who are young, poor, African American, unmarried, or poorly educated are most likely never to have used contraception.

- Fifty-four percent of women having abortions used some method of contraception during the month in which they became pregnant.

- Seventy-six percent of pill users and forty-nine percent of condom users said they were inconsistent in the way they used the methods. Those who said they used them correctly were, respectively, thirteen percent and fourteen percent.

Obtaining an Abortion

Drug-Induced Abortion

In 2000, the federal Food and Drug Administration approved the drug RU-486 (mifepristone) for inducing abortion, permitting women in the earlier stages of pregnancy to avoid a surgical abortion. About 560,000 drug-induced abortions were performed in 2006.

Safety

- Less than one percent of women who have abortions experience major complications.

- The risk of death associated with abortion increases with the length of pregnancy: up to 8 weeks, 1 death per million; 16–20 weeks, 1 per 29,000; 21+ weeks, 1 per 11,000.

- The risk of death associated with childbirth is 11 times as high as the risk associated with abortion.

Timing

The great majority of abortions (eighty-eight percent) take place during the first twelve weeks of pregnancy. About fifty percent of the women who have an abortion after the fifteenth week of pregnancy say the delay was

WHEN WOMEN HAVE ABORTIONS	
Before the 9th week	61.8%
9–10 weeks	17.1
11–12 weeks	9.1
13–15 weeks	6.2
16–20 weeks	4.2
21+ weeks	1.4

caused by problems in getting the money or in finding someone to perform the procedure. Teenagers are much more likely than older women to have an abortion after the fifteenth week.

Providers

- During the period 2000–2005, the number of hospitals, clinics, and physicians providing abortion declined by twelve percent.

- Eighty-seven percent of counties in the United States lacked an abortion provider in 2005.

- Thirty-five percent of all women 15–44 lived in a county without an abortion provider in 2005.

- In 2005, the cost of a surgical abortion in the tenth week of pregnancy carried out with local anesthesia in a clinic or doctor's office ranged from $90 to $1800. The average cost was $413.

Public Payment

- Federal law prohibits the use of Medicaid funds (the state–federal program for the poor) to pay for abortion, except in cases in which the mother's life is endangered or the pregnancy is the result of rape or incest.

- Some states (17) allow public funds to be used to pay for abortion when a woman meets a low-income requirement.

- Publicly funded family planning services prevent an estimated 1.3 million unplanned pregnancies a year. On the basis of the rate at which unplanned pregnancies are terminated, more than 632,000 abortions a year are thus avoided.

Ambivalence Toward Abortion

That the country has mixed feelings about abortion is revealed in a May 2009 poll by the Gallup Organization. The poll also shows a slight swing in a conservative direction. When people were asked, "With respect to the abortion issue, would you consider yourself to be pro-choice or pro-life?" those answering pro-life rose to 51% from the 44% reported in 2005. Those describing themselves as pro-choice declined from 48% to 42%. This is the first time a majority of U.S. adults have identified themselves as pro-life since Gallup first asked the question in 1995.

This conservative shift was not accompanied, however, by a significant increase in the number of people wanting to see abortion outlawed. In 2009, only 23% endorsed the view that abortion should be illegal, while 53% said it should be legal under some circumstances. Another 22% said it should be legal in any circumstance. Thus about 75% of the population favors maintaining abortion's legal status.

In a second 2009 Gallup poll, 75% of the people surveyed expressed the view that abortion should be "always" or "sometimes" legal and only 23% endorsed the notion that it should always be "illegal." Once again, it seems that about three-quarters of the population accepts the legitimacy of abortion for at least some reasons.

Abortion and New Medical Technology

To some extent, the ambivalence about abortion and the public clash of opinions about its moral legitimacy may be due to the development of new reproductive and life-sustaining technology, as well as to an increase in awareness of the character of the fetus.

When a genetic disease like Tay–Sachs is present in a family, in vitro fertilization and the

ABORTION SHOULD BE . . .	
Always legal	22%
Sometimes legal	53%
Always illegal	23%

Source: Gallup Poll, May 2–5, 2009

selection of an embryo free of the disease for implantation can avoid a problem that might lead to abortion. While for some, discarding unused embryos created by in vitro fertilization is equivalent to abortion, most people are more comfortable with the idea of destroying embryos than of aborting a fetus.

Reproductive technology has also made more familiar the concept of "selectively reducing" one or more developing fetuses in a multiple pregnancy resulting from the use of fertility drugs. For some, selective reduction is simply abortion by another name, but for others it is a procedure necessary to give the remaining fetuses a better chance to develop normally.

Also, statistics indicate that more than half the population (seventy percent) aren't troubled by preventing a pregnancy through the use of a "morning after" drug like Plan B or ending a pregnancy by using a drug like RU-486. This may be because most people don't think of a fertilized egg as a fetus until development in the uterus is well underway. Thus, they don't equate it with a baby.

The other relevant development in technology is the ability to keep alive babies who are so premature that, in important aspects, they are still developing fetuses. A baby is considered full term if it is born forty weeks after conception, but a state-of-the-art neonatal unit staffed with trained and experienced people can save the lives of infants who have had only twenty-three or twenty-four weeks of development.

These babies often do not do well and suffer serious lifelong problems. (See Chapter 6.) Even so, the fact that such small babies can survive outside the uterus has led many people to become more restrained in their endorsement of abortion or to favor restrictions on when it

ABORTION AND WOMEN'S CHARACTERISTICS	
Age (rate per 1000 women)	
Under 15	1
15–19	24
20–24	46
25–29	32
30–34	19
35–39	10
40–44	3
Race/Ethnicity (percent of all abortions)	
White	14%
Hispanic	21%
African American	38%
Race/Ethnicity and Marital Status (rate per 1000 women)	
White, married	6
White, unmarried	26
African American, married	20
African American, unmarried	71
Hispanic, married	12
Hispanic, unmarried	52

Source: Centers for Disease Control and Prevention, 2006

can be performed. After all, the second trimester ends at around twenty-five weeks. (See the discussion of the *Webster* decision in "Social Context: Supreme Court Abortion Decisions After *Roe v. Wade*" later in this chapter.)

The Difficult Middle

The abstract and absolute positions represented by statements like "A woman has a right to choose to have an abortion for any reason at all" and "A fertilized egg is as much a person as a born child and has just as much right to life" have become less representative of the beliefs of most people over the last few decades. The majority of people tend toward the view that the most reasonable position on abortion lies somewhere between these extremes.

To sum up in a phrase, Americans appear to think abortion should be "safe, legal, and rare." But of course, agreement to such a general proposition doesn't translate into agreement about what restrictions are appropriate. Although, abstract positions may have blurred for most people, debates over particular policies remain as divisive and acrimonious as ever.

SOCIAL CONTEXT

The Morning-After Pills (Plan B and Ella): Emergency Contraception and Politics

Every year, American women have three million unintended pregnancies. One-quarter of all pregnancies end in abortion, and when the pregnancy is unintended, the percentage increases to almost one-half (forty-nine percent). One in three young women under the age of twenty becomes pregnant, and eighty percent of those pregnancies are unintended. More than 25,000 women a year become pregnant as a result of sexual assault.

One way to decrease the number of abortions performed each year would be to decrease the number of unwanted pregnancies, and this could happen if women had available a drug they could use to prevent pregnancy even *after* intercourse.

Also, women who have been raped can gain immediate reassurance from such a drug.

Plan B

The emergency contraceptive called Plan B is one such drug. (Plan A is some form of ordinary contraception, including abstinence. The newer drug ella has advantages over Plan B that will be discussed later.) More properly, Plan B is a treatment regimen that consists of taking two pills containing high doses (.75 mg) of the birth-control drug levonorgestrel synthetic version of the hormone progesterone. To be effective, the first pill must be taken within seventy-two hours of having sex and the second twelve hours later. (The optimal time to take the first dose is within the first twenty-four hours after sex, and the sooner, the better.) When both doses are taken within the effective period, the chance of preventing a pregnancy becomes eighty-nine percent.

The major side effects of the double dose of Plan B are nausea and vomiting. From one- to two-thirds of women taking the drug experience nausea for about two days, and some twelve to twenty-two percent have episodes of vomiting. An antinausea drug taken at the same time as the contraceptives can reduce the side effects.

Plan B (and drugs like it) prevent pregnancy by delaying or preventing ovulation, inhibiting fertilization, or preventing a fertilized egg from implanting itself in the wall of the uterus. Several drugs that function in this way were already available before Plan B was proposed, and physicians knew that they could provide their patients with emergency contraception by using high doses of FDA-approved birth-control pills. (The drug RU-486 can also prevent pregnancy if used early enough; see "Social Context: The Abortion Pill.")

Because there is no way to tell when an egg becomes fertilized after intercourse, Plan B blurs the line between contraception and abortion. A majority of Americans have no objections to contraception or to very early abortion, so they tend to see emergency contraception as a legitimate way to prevent an unintended pregnancy. Those opposed to contraception or to abortion, however, reject the use of Plan B.

Alaska, California, Hawaii, Oregon, and Washington allow pharmacists to provide emergency contraception in the form of a double dose of birth-control pills without a doctor's prescription. In about thirty other countries, including Britain and France, pharmacists can also dispense drugs similar to Plan B without a prescription if the client declares an urgent need for them.

Emergency contraceptive drugs are available over the counter (OTC) in Norway and Sweden, and proponents of Plan B were hopeful that the FDA would approve

Barr Laboratories' application to make the regimen available in the same way throughout the U.S. Women's groups, in particular, saw Plan B as a way to give women more control over their reproductive potential by freeing them from accidental pregnancies. In 2000, emergency contraception is estimated to have prevented 51,000 abortions and perhaps a similar number of additional unwanted pregnancies.

Conflict

When the FDA received reports that standard birth-control drugs were being prescribed by doctors for emergency contraception, the agency invited manufacturers to submit proposals for relabeling the drugs for this use. The Women's Capital Corporation had been established to manufacture Plan B so that it would be available to women, and in 2003 it applied to the FDA for approval to sell Plan B OTC. Barr Laboratories acquired the assets of the Women's Capital Corporation that same year and took over the task of getting FDA approval.

Although Plan B was approved as safe and effective by the FDA in 1999, it was available only by prescription. The Barr application to sell Plan B as an OTC drug proposed that no age restriction be placed on who could buy it. The application was reviewed by an independent FDA advisory panel of scientists and physicians, and the panel voted 23–4 for approval.

The FDA had always taken the advice of its advisory panels, but this time the panel's recommendation was overruled by upper-level FDA officials. Plan B was controversial, and abortion opponents were lobbying administration officials to pressure the FDA to turn down Barr's application. Although the FDA's own scientific panel had already concluded that Plan B was a contraceptive agent, not an abortion drug, this finding was rejected by many social conservatives. They also objected to making the drug available OTC, because it might encourage sexual activity among young teens who might otherwise be kept in check by the fear of pregnancy. The United

States Conference of Catholic Bishops was among several groups that lobbied federal officials to use their influence to prevent the FDA from approving Barr's application.

On the other side of the reproductive divide, the American Medical Association, American College of Gynecologists and Obstetricians, American Academy of Family Physicians, and American Academy of Pediatricians endorsed OTC sales of Plan B as in the best medical interest of women. OTC sales also were supported by Planned Parenthood and a number of women's health groups, which lobbied for its approval and gained support from a number of members of Congress.

Plan B was the only one of twenty-three applications to change a drug from prescription-required status to OTC to be turned down in the period 1994–2004. When the application was rejected, however, the political controversy over the drug didn't end. Rumors soon surfaced that Steven Galson, the head of the FDA's drug-review center, had told staff members that it didn't matter what the independent advisory panel's recommendation was, because the decision would be made by top officials at the agency. He later denied making such a statement, but it was Galson himself who made the final decision about Plan B.

After the Plan B application was turned down, several members of Congress asked the Government Accountability Office (GAO) to conduct a review of what had taken place at the FDA. The GAO investigation discovered that the decision to reject the application was made before the FDA's own scientific review of the application was finished. This supported the charge that inappropriate influence had been at work in the drug-evaluation process.

The GAO report also characterized the FDA's grounds for rejecting the proposal as "novel." Galson claimed he had made the "non-approved" decision on the ground that only twenty-nine of the 585 participants in Barr's clinical trial of Plan B were between the ages of 14 and 16. Younger teenagers,

Galson said, might act differently from older teenagers. In particular, they might engage in riskier sex if they knew that an emergency contraceptive was easily available. Thus, he claimed, Barr needed to supply more data to show that young adolescents could use the drug properly.

What the GAO pointed out was that the FDA had always used the behavior of older adolescents to predict the behavior of younger ones, including predictions about how they were likely to use OTC drugs. Galson's reason for rejecting Plan B was "novel" because it was the opposite of the reasoning used by the FDA in all other cases.

New Application: 16+

Barr responded to the FDA's claim that not enough teens ages 14–16 were included in the initial study of Plan B by filing a new application in July 2004. It requested that the company be able to sell the drug OTC to females *older* than 16.

The FDA's own rules required it to act on Barr's application by January. However, it failed to take any action until August 2005, more than a year later. The agency then announced that it was delaying approval to allow time for public comment. This action provoked additional charges that political ideology within the FDA was derailing what should be a science-based decision.

Despite such protests, in February 2005 the FDA announced that, although Barr's application was scientifically sound, the agency needed to delay its decision *indefinitely* while it considered whether it had the regulatory authority to approve Barr's plan to sell Plan B OTC and whether the plan to limit sales to those over 16 could be enforced.

In September 2005, Susan Wood, director of the FDA's Office of Women's Health resigned to protest the agency's decision. "I feel very strongly that this shouldn't be about abortion politics," she said. "This is a way to prevent pregnancy and thereby prevent abortion. This should be something that we should all agree on." She told a reporter that she could no longer serve at the FDA "when scientific and clinical evidence, fully evaluated and recommended by approval by the professional staff here, has been overruled."

2006 Applications: 18+

Various members of Congress expressed outrage over the FDA's decision to do nothing about Plan B, but the stalemate continued until August 2006. Andrew von Eschenbach, acting commissioner of the FDA, was about to appear before congressional committees that would decide whether to recommend him for a regular appointment, when he announced that he had asked Barr for a complete plan for limiting sales of Plan B to women over 16. The announcement elicited a positive reaction from those who had been critical of the agency for dragging its feet on Plan B.

Later that month, however, the FDA announced that it had met with representatives of Barr Laboratories and asked the company to submit a new application that would make Plan B available OTC to women *18 or older*. Those younger than 18 would need a prescription to gain access to the drug. Also, Plan B would be available only at pharmacies and clinics holding a federal drug license. The FDA signaled to the company that its price for approving Plan B as an OTC drug was to make it available only to adults.

2009 Application: 17+ and No Prescription

In 2009, Judge Edward R. Korman of the New York Federal District Court ruled that the FDA's decision to limit access to Plan B to those 18 or older was determined by politics, not science. He gave the agency thirty days to lower the limit to age 17.

The FDA announced that it would appeal the decision, and it invited the drug's manufacturer to submit a plan to market Plan B

"without a prescription to women seventeen years of age or older." The announcement was praised by organizations promoting the reproductive autonomy of women and condemned by conservative groups on the grounds that easier access to Plan B would encourage more unprotected sex and more abortions.

The Pill Called Ella

In June 2010, a federal scientific advisory panel unanimously recommended that the FDA approve an emergency contraceptive drug called ella. Unlike Plan B, which must be taken within a seventy-two-hour period in order to be effective, ella remains effective up to five days after unprotected sex. Also, the effectiveness of Plan B declines with time, whereas ella is as effective on the fifth day as on the first. Ella blocks the effects of progesterone, the female hormone that triggers ovulation. The drug is similar in chemical structure to RU-486 (the "abortion pill"), but the exact mechanism of its action is still not known.

The lack of knowledge about how ella operates makes it controversial. Abortion opponents claim that it prevents a fertilized egg from implanting in the uterus and so must be regarded as a drug that *terminates* conception. The manufacturer claims, in contrast, that the drug works by delaying ovulation and so *prevents* conception. Some scientists suggest that it may do both. Unlike RU-486, the ella did not end established pregnancies in animal studies.

Ella was developed in the United States, although it is manufactured by HRA Pharma, a French company. It was approved for sale in Europe in 2009. Even if the FDA approves it for sale in the United States, most experts think it will have little effect on reducing the number of unwanted pregnancies. Women who have unprotected sex have a 1 in 20 chance of becoming pregnant. If they take Plan B within the prescribed time, this chance drops to 1 in 40, and if ella is used, the risk drops to 1 in 50. Thus, ella is not likely to make much of a practical difference.

Envoi

Many groups aiming to give women more control over their reproductive potential imagined a time when a pill would be available to allow women to prevent a pregnancy after a sexual encounter they had not wanted or for which they hadn't been prepared. They imagined a future in which a woman of childbearing age wouldn't have to consult a doctor or show proof of age to a pharmacist, but merely walk into a convenience store, a bar, or a gas station and buy a pill that would provide the protection from pregnancy that she wanted. With both Plan B and ella, this remains a distant prospect.

SOCIAL CONTEXT
The "Abortion Pill"

Sandra Crane, as we'll call her, decided she had missed her period. She was thirty-one years old, and ordinarily her menstrual cycle was as regular as clockwork. Because she was now a week overdue, she was sure she must be pregnant.

The feeling was familiar. She had two children already: six-year-old Jennifer and two-year-old Thomas. She and her husband had decided not to have any more kids, so if she got pregnant, she'd take steps to end the pregnancy.

Sandra Crane paid a visit to her gynecologist's office the next day, and the day after that Dr. Krantz's nurse practitioner called and told Sandra that the test was positive. She was likely to be about two weeks pregnant. Sandra explained that she wanted the pregnancy ended as soon as possible, and the nurse made an appointment for her to see a doctor at the Women's Clinic. Sandra discussed her decision with Dr. Tina Merida, then returned for a second visit. She was given two tablets to swallow—a 600-milligram dosage of Mifeprex, a drug better known by the generic names RU-486 and mifepristone—and told to come back in two days.

When Sandra returned to the clinic, she was given a 400-milligram oral dose of misoprostol. The drug, a prostaglandin, began to act three days later. It made her uterus contract, and she began to experience cramping and bleeding. Soon, however, the uterine lining was expelled, just as if she were having a miscarriage. Sandra felt some discomfort, but the process differed little from an unusually heavy menstrual period.

After a day of rest, she felt almost her usual self again. Two weeks later, she returned to the clinic for an examination to make sure the abortion was complete.

Background

RU-486 was developed by the French endocrinologist Étienne-Émile Baulieu. The drug works by blocking the action of progesterone, the hormone that prepares the uterine wall for the implantation of a fertilized egg. The dose of misoprostol (a kind of prostaglandin) taken two or three days later then induces uterine contractions that expel the sloughed-off lining, including the zygote or fetus.

To be safest and most effective, RU-486 must be taken during the first five to seven weeks of pregnancy. Most physicians urge that it be taken as early as possible, although some research suggests that its use might be extended even to the tenth week of pregnancy.

If RU-486 is taken soon after sexual intercourse, it blocks the action of progesterone, and as a result, a fertilized egg won't be able to implant itself in the uterine wall. Hence, the drug also has the possibility of serving as a "morning-after pill" for preventing pregnancy, even after fertilization. But the drug's major use lies in its power to induce an abortion. In initial testing, 100 women volunteers less than a month pregnant were given RU-486. Of these, eighty-five percent aborted within four days, without reporting the pain or psychological difficulties that can accompany surgical abortion. The later use of prostaglandin injections in conjunction with the drug increased the speed of the process. An oral dose of misoprostol later replaced the injection. Women tolerated this better, and the price was significantly lower.

Additional clinical trials in France and the use of the drug by more than 1.5 million women showed it to be safe and 95.5 percent effective. With the use of misoprostol, the effectiveness rises to 96.9 percent. Some women taking the drug bleed excessively, and a proportion do not abort as expected (about three percent, according to a French study) and require surgical intervention. For these reasons, the drug is intended for use only under close medical supervision.

Conflict

The drug was developed in 1980 by the pharmaceutical company Roussel-Uclaf and approved for use in France in September 1988. A month later, in response to a boycott of the company's products by abortion opponents, Roussel took the drug off the market. This provoked public protests, and Health Minister Claude Evin notified the company that if it did not release the drug, the government, which owned 36.25 percent of the company, would permanently transfer the patent to another company. "From the moment the governmental approval of the drug was granted, RU-486 became the moral property of women, not just the property of the drug company," Evin said. Two days later the company resumed marketing the drug.

United States

Roussel licensed the drug for use in China, Sweden, and Britain, but its plans to market the drug in the United States were abandoned because of opposition from abortion opponents. The general position was stated by a representative of the National Right to Life Committee, who characterized the use of RU-486 as "chemical warfare against an entire class of innocent humans."

The Population Council, a nonprofit research organization committed to making medical abortion available to U.S. women, was frustrated by Roussel's decision and persuaded the company to grant it a license to manufacture and distribute the drug in the United States. The Council conducted another clinical trial, getting results similar to those of the French study. The data were presented to the FDA, and in September 2000 the agency recognized RU-486 as safe and effective and approved it as a prescription drug.

Reactions to the approval were predictably mixed. Abortion opponents denounced the FDA decision, calling RU-486 a "baby poison" and vowing to lobby for legislation to prohibit its use. Pro-choice advocates praised the decision, saying the drug would allow women to keep abortion decisions private. Also, women living in rural areas without easy access to surgical abortion would now have a safe option.

In Practice

Only some of the hopes that pro-choice advocates pinned on RU-486 have materialized. Many physicians still prefer the speed and reliability of surgical abortions. A procedure takes only a few minutes, and then the patient is on the way to recovery. RU-486 is limited to use during the first seven weeks of pregnancy, and once a woman is given the drug, the protocol approved by the FDA requires that she return to the office two more times. The process takes about three weeks.

Many physicians who thought they were likely to prescribe RU-486 soon came to realize that abortion is regulated by a bewildering complexity of state laws. Many of the laws were lobbied for by abortion opponents who wanted to make it difficult for a women to get an abortion, and the approval of RU-486 didn't make it possible for physicians to ignore the laws.

Some states require, for example, that a physician performing abortions have an ultrasound machine, life-support equipment, and an operating suite available. Other states have laws stipulating specific standards the facility must satisfy, including hall width, temperature of running water, and amount of ventilation.

At least thirteen states require counseling before an abortion is performed and dictate a waiting period. Some states require that the fetal tissue be inspected, and others demand that it be disposed of by cremation or burying. The laws of some states regulate abortion in general, but those in other states specifically mention drug-induced abortion.

Under these circumstances, it's not surprising that the availability of RU-486 did not have the impact on abortion that those pressing to make the drug available had anticipated. Of the 1.3 million abortions performed in the United States in 2006, about 560,000 were drug induced. This is a significant number, but some women's groups had expected that virtually all abortions would become drug induced. To what extent the situation would be different without state laws passed to discourage abortion is a matter of speculation.

Unexplained Deaths

Chemical abortion continues to face a challenge that calls into question its future as a common medical procedure. The trouble began when researchers discovered that between January 2005 and March 2006 seven pregnant women died who had been given the combination of RU-486 and misoprostol. Five of the women died of toxic shock due to infection by the bacterium *Clostridium sordellii*. Four of them died in California. There was no obvious explanation for the infections. One hypothesis was that the pills were contaminated, and another, more alarming one, was that misoprostol itself was responsible for the infections.

The protocol approved by the FDA in 2000 required that, after getting RU-486, women return to the clinic in two days to get an oral dose of misoprostol. Soon after the FDA approval, however, Planned Parenthood and other clinics instructed women to skip the second visit and take the misoprostol at home as a vaginal

suppository. This way of administering the drug turned out to be just as effective, allowed a lower dose of misoprostol to be used, and required fewer visits to the clinic. Thus, vaginal insertion of the drug was both more convenient and less expensive than the oral dosing required by the FDA protocol.

Some researchers suggest that it was this shift to vaginal insertion that was responsible for most of the deaths. In inserting misoprostol, they hypothesized, women might accidentally contaminate the pill with fecal bacteria. Other researchers suggested that the drug itself was to blame for the deaths. They hypothesize that misoprostol might lower the effectiveness of the immune system, thus making pregnant women less able to fight off a *Clostridium sordellii* infection. (For unclear reasons, pregnant women, seem unusually vulnerable to this infection.)

Although comparatively small, the number of deaths was seen as statistically significant. The combination of RU-486 and misoprostol was used in about 560,000 out of 1.3 million abortions in 2006, and the deaths associated with the drug combination meant that a woman using it had a 1-in-100,000 chance of dying. This risk is low, but it is ten times greater than the one-in-a million risk of dying from a surgical abortion. A drug-induced abortion is also five to ten times as likely to fail and require follow-up surgery, and the greater the length of the pregnancy, the greater is the risk of failure.

For these and similar reasons, the majority of physicians who performed abortions continued to prefer to use surgical methods. Also, in many cases insurers insisted that clinics and physicians return to using the FDA protocol requiring that misoprostol be administered orally in a physician's office. That no deaths in Europe were reported as attributable to the drug combination suggested that the deaths in the United States were connected with bacterial contamination.

Planned Parenthood, the largest abortion provider in the United States, funded a study to determine what factors might be responsible for the potentially lethal infections associated with the RU-486 and misoprostol combination. The study analyzed the records of 227,823 women who had abortions at Planned Parenthood clinics from January 2005 to June 2008. The study, published in 2009 in the *New England Journal of Medicine*, found that ninety-two serious infections were present in this group, but that when the misoprostol was given vaginally or by mouth (dissolved before swallowing) and antibiotics were routinely prescribed, the infection rate dropped to 0.06 per 1,000 abortions from the previous 0.93 per 1,000.

The study suggests that the drug combination can be safely used and that antibiotics can reduce the chance of infection to an even lower level. It is not clear, however, that the findings will significantly alter the way abortion providers operate. Some physicians are reluctant to prescribe antibiotics as a matter of routine, because the rate of infection is already so low. (The drugs were used by about 184,000 women in 2009.) Also, in developing countries, where drug-induced abortion is more likely to be used antibiotics are often not available or are too expensive to be used for anything but life-threatening infections.

Envoi

The dream of many women's health groups in the 1980s was that RU-486 would make abortion safe, private, and easily secured by all women who wanted it. Despite the commitment of these groups and their long political struggles, the dream had been more approximated than realized.

TIMELINE

April 2003: The Women's Capital Corporation, license holder for manufacturing Plan B, applies to the FDA for OTC approval.

October 2003: Barr Laboratories buys the assets of the Women's Capital Corporation and assumes responsibility for the application.

December 2003: FDA's independent advisory committee votes in favor of allowing Plan B to be sold OTC.

May 2004: FDA decides that women under age 16 might not be able to use Plan B and rejects Barr's application.

July 2004: Barr applies to allow OTC sales only for women over age 16.

August 2005: FDA delays approval to allow public comment.

November 2005: FDA indefinitely delays a decision on Plan B to determine whether limiting OTC sales in the way Barr proposed was practical and enforceable.

August 2006: FDA asks Barr for a complete plan for limiting OTC sales of Plan B to women over age 16. Later, it asks Barr for an application that will limit OTC sales to women over age 18.

August 2009: FDA agrees to accept a New York Circuit Court decision and approve an application to sell Plan B to people ages 17 and older without a doctor's prescription.

SOCIAL CONTEXT
The "Partial-Birth Abortion" Controversy

In 1995, debate began to rage around abortion performed after twenty weeks of gestation, often focusing on a specific surgical procedure used to terminate a pregnancy. Technically known as intact dilation and extraction, the procedure was named "partial-birth abortion" by those opposed to abortion.

The debate, still raging after more than a dozen years, is characterized to an unusual extent by a lack of information and a reliance on misinformation by participants on both sides. Instead of laying out the issues as the opponents present them, it is more useful to begin by considering some of the facts relevant to evaluating the various positions taken.

Late-Term Abortion

While abortion opponents often portray "abortion doctors" as employing brutal procedures to destroy viable fetuses in order to satisfy the whims of pregnant women, those favoring abortion rights often present women as opting for such measures in only rare and extreme cases. The best estimates available suggest that neither picture is accurate.

The length of a normal pregnancy is forty weeks. More than half (59.1%) of all abortions are performed less than nine weeks after conception, and more than a quarter (29%) are performed in weeks nine through twelve. Indeed, 98.6% of all abortions are performed within twenty weeks of conception. Thus, late-term abortion, defined as abortion after twenty weeks, is relatively rare, accounting for only 1.4% of all abortions.

No statistics are available on the reasons women have late-term (instead of early) abortions. The best information comes from the congressional testimony of physicians who perform abortions. They suggest that one group of women has abortions because the woman's own health is threatened by pregnancy. For example, the pregnancy may have triggered an autoimmune disease, or the woman may have developed cancer and need treatment with chemotherapy and radiation.

A second group has late-term abortions because the fetus has developed a severe defect. For example, ultrasound may reveal that the growing child's cerebral hemispheres have failed to develop. If the pregnancy continues, the child that is born not only will lack all cognitive capacity, but will die within a few days or weeks.

The third and largest group comprises those who have failed to get an early abortion for a variety of mostly social reasons. The group includes teenagers in psychological denial about being pregnant until they (or a parent) had to face the undeniable fact. Also included are indigent women, who may be homeless, mentally retarded, or socially unskilled. Drug users, who engage in their own form of denial, are included in this third group, as are women

with menstrual periods so irregular that they don't suspect they are pregnant until several months have passed.

Proponents of abortion rights tend to overlook this third group and focus instead on the other two. Being able to cite the pressing need of a pregnant woman to save her life or the cruelty of forcing a pregnant woman to carry to term a fetus with a serious developmental defect makes it easier for them to defend their case.

Opponents of abortion, by contrast, tend to discuss late-term abortion as if it were the general rule, rather than very much the statistical exception. When 98.6 percent of all abortions are performed before twenty weeks, it is misleading to condemn all abortion by focusing on the 1.4 percent as representative. They also tend to ignore powerful reasons for having a late-term abortion, preferring to use cases producing the strongest negative emotional response.

Fetal Viability

Abortion opponents have focused on fetal viability as the crucial grounds for outlawing late-term abortion. In making their case, they have suggested that late abortions involve killing babies that otherwise would live and thrive. This has made the debate over late-term abortion particularly contentious, for determinations of viability cannot be made in definite and reliable ways.

Perinatologists (specialists in newborns) say that too many factors are involved in determining viability to make reliable generalizations about which fetuses will live and which will die at any given stage of development. In addition to characteristics such as a fetus's weight and the developmental stage of the organs, factors like the health of the mother, her socioeconomic status, and her access to health care also play a role. So do the race and gender of the fetus. In development, a white fetus generally lags a week behind an African American one of the same age and a male fetus lags the same amount behind a female.

The viability of a fetus is also connected with the state of medical technology and

TIMING OF ABORTIONS	
Before the 9th week	59.1%
9–10 weeks	19.0
11–12 weeks	10.0
13–15 weeks	6.2
16–20 weeks	4.2
21+ weeks	1.4

management. At the time of the *Roe v. Wade* decision in 1973, fetal viability was around 26 weeks, but now it is closer to 24, with 21–22 weeks being barely possible. A *micropremie* weighs 500 to 600 grams (a bit over a pound) and is hardly larger than the palm of a man's hand. Babies of this age and size, even if they survive, are likely to have irreversible physical and mental deficits. (See Chapter 10.)

The American College of Obstetrics and Gynecology estimates that lees than four percent of babies are born during weeks 23 to 25 of the normal 40-week gestation period, and their survival is conditional on the factors mentioned. Some experts doubt that even with aggressive intervention and intensive care, more than about one percent of 25-week fetuses would survive. Some hospitals and state laws make 23 or 24 weeks the cutoff point for elective abortions, while others follow a more restrictive policy and make 20 weeks the limit. After the cutoff, a factor such as the health and safety of the mother or a fetal abnormality must be present to justify an abortion.

How viable a fetus is and how likely it is to survive without serious and permanent mental and physical deficits is a clinical judgment that can be made only case by case. A claim to the effect that thousands or even hundreds of viable fetuses are destroyed by abortion is not supported by the evidence.

Methods

Opponents of abortion have focused attention on a method to perform late-term abortion known as intact dilation and extraction.

The procedure involves using a drug to dilate (widen) the pregnant woman's cervix, then manipulating the fetus by hand until it can be pulled through the birth canal. Usually, to ease the passage and make the procedure easier on the woman, the fetal brain is extracted by suction so that the skull can be collapsed (fenestrated). It is this procedure that abortion opponents have called "partial-birth abortion," a name coined for rhetorical purposes and not one used in medicine.

Intact dilation and extraction may also be performed by injecting digoxin into the uterus to stop the fetal heart. After the death of the fetus, the woman is induced into labor with a hormone injection and the fetus is delivered vaginally. Some obstetricians consider this form of the procedure too psychologically stressful for the woman. Others believe it is sufficiently well tolerated to make it the preferred method.

The third or classic method of dilation and extraction does not involve removing an intact fetus. After a woman's cervix is dilated, instruments are used to dismember the fetus and extract the parts through the birth canal. The fetus is killed either by a prior injection or by the process itself. Ultrasound may be used to guide the instruments, and the procedure may take twenty minutes or longer.

Surgeons who prefer intact dilation and extraction point to the time and risks associated with the classic procedure. The woman's uterus may be damaged by an instrument or punctured by a sharp bone fragment. It is safer for the woman if the intact fetus is pulled out by hand.

About eighty-six percent of abortions performed after twenty weeks are done by one of these three procedures. "Any procedure done at this stage is pretty gruesome," said one high-risk-pregnancy specialist.

Early Federal Attempts to Ban

In 1996, Congress passed legislation banning late-term abortion, along with intact dilation and extraction, but the bill was vetoed by President Clinton on the ground that it made no provision for protecting the health of the pregnant woman.

A second attempt at passing legislation began a year later. The House passed a bill by a margin large enough (295–136) to override a presidential veto. The Senate passed a similar ban, but by a margin (64–36) short of the votes needed to survive a veto. President Clinton announced he would veto any bill that did not allow an abortion to protect the health of a pregnant woman, but both the House and Senate bills would protect only the *life* of the pregnant woman. Abortion opponents claimed that allowing an exception for health would be virtually equivalent to no regulation at all, given the nebulous nature of claims about health, particularly mental health.

The final version of the Senate bill was revised to reflect a proposal framed and endorsed by the American Medical Association. In the first endorsement of any position on abortion, the AMA proposal made it clear that dilation and *evacuation*, the procedure most often used in early abortions, was not banned. Also, the proposal protected physicians from criminal penalties if they had to perform a dilation and extraction because of unforeseen circumstances during a delivery. Finally, the proposal allowed physicians accused of violating the ban to appear before a state medical board instead of a trial court.

In contrast with the AMA, the American College of Obstetricians and Gynecologists and the American Academy of Pediatrics both opposed any ban on dilation and extraction. Some saw a danger in the AMA's position, suggesting that it invited politicians to make decisions about what medical procedures are appropriate.

State Attempts to Ban

Impatient with the slowness of Congress in passing a law banning "partial-birth abortion," about twenty-two states had passed their own laws by 1997. By 2005, however, all these laws had been ruled unconstitutional by the courts.

The most common flaw was that the language of the laws was so broad that it would also apply to abortions performed before the fetus could even be viable. Also, like the original bill passed by Congress, the laws made no exception to protect the pregnant woman's health.

Ohio Decision

In 1995, the Ohio legislature passed a law banning all abortion past the point of fetal viability. Viability was presumed to occur twenty-four weeks after conception. The only exception to the ban was for abortions a physician decided needed to be performed to "prevent the death of the pregnant woman or a serious risk of the substantial and irreversible impairment of a major bodily function of the pregnant woman."

The law also included a provision making it a crime for a physician to end a pregnancy "by purposely inserting a suction device into the skull of a fetus to remove its brain."

In *Voinovich v. Women's Medical Professional Corporation*, a case brought to challenge the law, the U.S. Sixth Circuit Court of Appeals in Cincinnati ruled that the law unconstitutionally restricted a woman's right to abortion by defining the prohibited procedure so broadly that it had the consequence of banning the most common method of performing a surgical abortion during the second trimester.

The ruling was appealed to the Supreme Court. In a 1998 decision (6–3), the Court refused to hear the case, letting the Appeals Court decision stand. In the dissenting opinion, Justice Thomas made clear that the dissenters' concern was not with late-term abortion, but with whether the prohibition of late-term abortion except to protect the life and health of the mother could limit the health that was protected to physical health and exclude mental health. In the 1973 decision *Roe v. Bolton*, the Court had held that physicians may consider "emotional" and "psychological" factors in deciding whether an abortion after fetal viability is necessary to preserve the health of the pregnant woman.

Nebraska Decision

A 2000 ruling by the United States Supreme Court on a Nebraska law resulted in nullifying more than thirty state laws. The 1997 Nebraska law banned "an abortion procedure in which the person performing the abortion partially delivers vaginally a living unborn child before killing the unborn child and completing the delivery." The phrase "partial delivery" was defined as "deliberately and intentionally delivering into the vagina a living unborn child or a substantial proportion thereof."

In a 5–4 vote, the Supreme Court held that the government cannot prohibit physicians from employing an abortion procedure that may be the most medically appropriate way of terminating some pregnancies. The Nebraska law, the Court decided, did not contain provisions for protecting the health and safety of the mother. Justice Stevens wrote in the majority opinion that it was "impossible for me to understand how a state has any legitimate interest in requiring a doctor to follow any procedure other than the one he or she reasonably believes will best protect the woman" in exercising her constitutional right to abortion.

Partial-Birth Abortion Ban Act of 2003

Many observers believed that the Supreme Court decision effectively declared that all legislation, state or federal, aimed at regulating abortion by outlawing procedures would be unconstitutional. Even so, in 2003, Congress passed the Partial-Birth Abortion Ban Act. The law makes it a crime for a doctor to perform an abortion in which "the entire fetal head" or "any part of the fetal trunk past the navel" is outside the woman's uterus at the time the fetal life is terminated.

Opponents of the law immediately challenged it in court, so the law did not take effect. In 2005, the Eighth Circuit U.S. Court of Appeals in St. Louis ruled that the law was unconstitutional. The act, the court held, contained an exception to protect a pregnant woman's life, but it made no exception to protect her health. This decision was in keeping with the court's ruling overturning the 1997 Nebraska law.

Congress, in an attempt to avoid having the law overturned on just this ground, appended to the law a "finding" claiming that the "partial-birth" procedure is never needed to protect the health of a pregnant woman and that "there is no credible medical evidence that partial-birth abortions are safe or are safer than other abortion procedures." Both these claims have been challenged in court by expert medical testimony. One doctor testified, for example, that the fertility of some women could be preserved by avoiding such complications as the puncturing of the uterus by bone fragments.

The Bush administration immediately appealed the St. Louis ruling to the Supreme Court (*Gonzales v. Carhart*). The Court agreed to hear the case, and in 2007 it upheld the constitutionality of the Partial-Birth Abortion Ban Act of 2003. This came as a surprise to many observers, because the Court's 2000 decision had overturned a Nebraska law that was essentially the same as the 2003 Act.

Need for a Law?

Many observers believe there was never a need for laws banning late-term abortion. In keeping with the *Roe v. Wade* decision granting states the power to regulate abortion to protect the interest of the fetus after the first trimester, and in keeping with the *Webster* decision (see the Social Context "Supreme Court Decisions After *Roe v. Wade*" in this chapter), more than forty states passed laws banning abortion after fetal viability. The problem of determining viability, however, is vexing and perhaps unsolvable, but an additional law banning late-term abortion, even if constitutional, would not help resolve the issue.

Advocates for abortion rights and even some opponents of abortion have expressed the view that the controversy over late-term abortion is primarily a way to keep abortion issues at the forefront of political discussion and to pressure politicians to modify their endorsement of elective abortion. Some have also seen the controversy as a way to raise money for all antiabortion activities.

Although, these analyses may be inaccurate, or even cynical, it seems fair to say that the debate over late-term abortion introduces no new ethical issues into the discussion. The old problems remain as complex and perhaps intractable as before.

SOCIAL CONTEXT
Supreme Court Abortion Decisions After *Roe v. Wade*

The conflict over abortion has been expressed, in part, in a continuing series of legal skirmishes that have produced a number of Supreme Court decisions seeking to define abortion rights and limits. To get some sense of the way in which laws, regulations, and practices have changed since the *Roe* decision in 1973, it is useful to review a few Court decisions. They give a sense of the direction taken by public policy on abortion.

Roe v. Bolton (1973)

The Court rejected the requirement that abortions had to be performed in hospitals, thus opening the way for abortion clinics. The Court also found that physicians could consider emotional and psychological factors connected with the health of a pregnant woman in deciding whether an abortion after the first trimester was justifiable.

Planned Parenthood v. Danforth (1976)

The Missouri law requiring a husband's consent for an abortion was struck down. Also, parents of minor, unmarried girls were found not to have an absolute veto over their daughter's decision to have an abortion.

Maher v. Roe (1977)

The Court ruled that states don't have a constitutional obligation to pay for abortions for the poor. Hence, states can decide whether they want to include abortion funding in their contribution to the Medicaid program.

Harris v. McRae (1980)

The Court upheld the Hyde Amendment, a federal law banning the use of federal Medicaid funds to pay for abortions. Hence, a woman who wants an abortion but is unable to pay for it must obtain the money from some other source. States may choose to provide the funds, but they have no constitutional obligation to do so.

City of Akron v. Akron Center for Reproductive Health (1983)

The Court struck down a law requiring that women seeking an abortion receive counseling that includes the statement that "the unborn child is a human life from the moment of conception," then wait a minimum of twenty-four hours before reaffirming their decision.

Webster v. Reproductive Health Services (1989)

The Missouri law in the *Webster* case is similar to laws the Court had ruled unconstitutional. However, the law was carefully crafted by pro-life advocates to avoid the specific difficulties that had led the Court to reject the law in *Webster*. The preamble of the law asserts that "life begins at conception," but at issue were three provisions restricting abortion: (1) Public employees, including physicians and nurses, are forbidden to perform an abortion, except when necessary to save a woman's life. (2) Tax-supported facilities, including public hospitals, cannot be used to perform abortions, unless one is necessary to save a woman's life. (3) Physicians are required to conduct tests to determine the viability of a fetus if they have reason to believe the woman has been pregnant for at least twenty weeks.

On July 3, 1989, in a 5-to-4 decision, the Supreme Court upheld the constitutionality of the law. Chief Justice William Rehnquist, writing for the majority, held that the Court did not have to rule against the claim that life begins at conception, for such language is only an expression of a permissible value judgment. Furthermore, "Nothing in the Constitution requires States to enter or remain in the business of performing abortions. Nor . . . do private physicians and their patients have some kind of constitutional right of access to public facilities for the performance of abortions."

So far as viability is concerned, Rehnquist saw a problem not with the Missouri law, but with *Roe v. Wade*'s "rigid trimester analysis of a pregnancy." He found the Missouri law more sensitive to the issue of viability than the trimester rule, which holds that the state can regulate abortion in the second trimester (i.e., during the second three-month period) to protect a woman's health and regulate it more stringently, down to prohibiting it, in the last trimester.

Justice Harry A. Blackmun, the author of the majority opinion in *Roe v. Wade*, wrote the dissenting opinion in *Webster*. He regarded the Court's decision as an outright attack on Roe. Rehnquist, he argued, failed to consider the case for viability on appropriate grounds—namely, the right to privacy or autonomy, on which *Roe* was decided. Instead, Rehnquist misread the Missouri law in a way that seemed to conflict with the trimester structure established in *Roe* to balance the state's interest in maternal health and potential life against the right to privacy.

Abortion opponents hoped that the Court would use the *Webster* case to overturn *Roe v.*

Wade. The Court stopped short of that, but the *Webster* decision made it clear that the Court was willing to approve restrictions on abortion of a sort that it had held unconstitutional until then. Various new state and local regulations were then formulated and passed into law.

Planned Parenthood v. Casey (1992)

The Pennsylvania Abortion Control Act was framed with the intention of making abortions more difficult to secure. It set forth the following restrictions: (1) A physician must inform a woman seeking an abortion about the procedure and its risks, the stage of her pregnancy, and the alternative of carrying the fetus to term. (2) The woman must wait at least twenty-four hours after receiving this information before having an abortion. (3) A girl under the age of eighteen must secure the informed consent of at least one parent before having an abortion, and a parent must accompany the girl to counseling. Alternatively, consent may be sought from a court. (4) A married woman must (except under certain circumstances) sign a statement that she has notified her husband of her intention to have an abortion.

The 5-to-4 Court ruling upheld most sections of the law, but it rejected the provision requiring a married woman to notify her husband of her intention. In the view of some, however, the most important result of the *Casey* decision was to reaffirm a constitutional right to an abortion, while introducing a new legal standard for testing the constitutional legitimacy of abortion regulations.

The Court considered the law's provisions in terms of whether they had the purpose or result of imposing an "undue burden" on a woman seeking an abortion. The Court defined a burden as "undue" if it places a "substantial obstacle in the path of a woman seeking an abortion before the fetus attains viability." Only the spousal notification requirement, the Court held, imposed such a burden. The undue-burden standard thus made clear the Court's view that laws attempting to prohibit abortions outright or reduce the frequency of abortions by making them extraordinarily difficult to obtain are unconstitutional.

The Court explicitly endorsed *Roe v. Wade* as having established "a rule of law and a component of liberty that we cannot renounce." It held that Roe has acquired such a "rare precedential force" that it could be repudiated only "at the cost of both profound and unnecessary damage to the Court's legitimacy and to the nation's commitment to the rule of law."

Until the *Webster* decision, abortion was considered a fundamental right that could not be restricted, except to serve a compelling state interest. Thus, during the first two trimesters of pregnancy, almost all restrictions were considered unconstitutional. After *Webster*, abortion opponents saw that it might be possible to impose more and heavier regulation. However, although the "undue-burden" standard introduced in *Casey* permits considerable regulation during that period, it does not allow the practice to be regulated so heavily as to make it virtually unavailable.

Madsen v. Women's Health Center (1994)

In 1993, a Florida Circuit Court issued an injunction to protect access to the clinic operated by the Aware Woman Center for Choice in Melbourne, Florida. Demonstrators from Operation Rescue and related organizations were made subject to the injunction. The order imposed a 300-foot protected zone around the clinic, forbade the display of signs that could be seen from inside the clinic, and barred demonstrators from making excessive noise.

The case was appealed, and in a 6-to-3 ruling the Supreme Court upheld the basic provisions of the injunction. It approved an approximately thirty-six-foot buffer zone to keep protesters away from the clinic's entrance and parking lot and off a public right-of-way. The buffer zone "burdens no more speech than necessary to accomplish the government's interest," Justice Rehnquist wrote.

Schenck v. Pro-Choice Network (1997)

In a New York State case in which a group opposed to abortion appealed an injunction ordering them to cease blockading the entrances to a clinic and stop harassing and intimidating the women seeking an abortion, the Supreme Court, in a 6-to-3 decision, upheld the lower court's decision to keep the protesters from blocking doorways and driveways.

The Court struck down (6–3) a section of the New York law that established a "floating" fifteen-foot buffer zone between protesters and people entering or leaving a clinic, because the indefinite character of the zone raised the prospect of suppressing more speech than necessary to protect the state's interest in public safety. Yet the Court upheld (6–3) a section of the injunction allowing only two protesters at a time to come within a fixed fifteen-foot buffer zone to talk to women in a nonthreatening way and to "cease and desist" and to withdraw outside the zone if asked to do so.

The Court's tacit endorsement of a fixed buffer zone around abortion clinics is significant, because about 300 of the 900 abortion clinics in the country are protected by buffer zones spelled out in court injunctions. Both the Florida and New York rulings are considered important indicators of the Court's view of the Freedom of Access to Clinic Entrances Act, which is designed to provide federal remedies, including criminal penalties, to restrict violent protests at abortion clinics.

Hill v. Colorado (2000)

In a 6-to-3 ruling, the Court held that a Colorado law aimed at protecting abortion clinic physicians, patients, and visitors from harassment by protestors did not violate the protestors' First Amendment rights to free expression. The law holds that within 100 feet of any health care facility, no one can approach anyone closer than eight feet to talk or pass out leaflets, unless the person approached permits it.

Stenberg v. Carhart (2000)

A Nebraska law directed at prohibiting late-term (past twenty weeks) abortion banned any "abortion procedure in which the person performing the abortion partially delivers vaginally a living unborn child before killing the unborn child and completing the delivery." In a 5–4 vote, the Court held that the government cannot prohibit physicians from employing whatever abortion procedure may be the most medically appropriate. Also, in trying to regulate abortion, the law failed to include any provisions for protecting the health and safety of the pregnant woman. Justice Stevens wrote in the majority opinion that it is "impossible for me to understand how a state has any legitimate interest in requiring a doctor to follow any procedure other than the one he or she reasonably believes will best protect the woman" in exercising her constitutional right to abortion.

Gonzales v. Carhart (2007)

Congress passed the *Partial-Birth Abortion Ban Act* in 2003, making it a crime to perform an abortion in which "the entire fetal head" or "any part of the fetal trunk past the navel" is outside the woman's uterus at the time fetal life is ended. The law was challenged before it went into effect, and a federal Appeals Court rulings in St. Louis found it to be unconstitutional. The rulings were immediately appealed to the Supreme Court, which upheld the law in a 5–4 decision. The ruling effectively negated the impact of the 2000 Nebraska decision, which had found unconstitutional a law with virtually the same prohibitions as the 2003 Partial-Birth Abortion Ban Act.

BRIEFING SESSION

Hardly more than three decades ago, most Americans considered abortion a crime so disgusting that it was rarely mentioned in public. Back-alley abortionists with dirty hands and unclean instruments were real enough, but they were also the villains of cautionary tales to warn women against being tempted into the crime. Abortion was the dramatic stuff of novels and movies portraying "girls in trouble" or women pushed to the brink. To choose to have an abortion was to choose to be degraded.

The Supreme Court decision in *Roe v. Wade* changed all that in 1973. The decision had the effect of legalizing abortion, and since then abortion has gained an ambivalent acceptance from a majority of the population. Yet controversy over the legitimacy of abortion continues to flare. Indeed, no other topic in medical ethics has attracted more attention or so polarized public opinion. The reason is understandable: in the abortion question, major moral, legal, and social issues are intertwined to form a problem of great subtlety and complexity.

Before focusing on some of the specific issues raised by abortion, it is useful to have in hand some of the relevant factual information about human developmental biology and the techniques of abortion.

Human Development and Abortion

Fertilization occurs when an ovum is penetrated by a sperm cell and the nuclei of the two unite to form a single cell containing forty-six chromosomes. This normally occurs in the fallopian tube (or oviduct), a narrow tube leading from the ovary into the uterus (womb). The fertilized ovum—zygote, or conceptus—continues its passage down the fallopian tube, and during its two- to three-day passage it undergoes a number of cell divisions that increase its size. (Rarely, the zygote does not descend but continues to develop in the fallopian tube, producing an ectopic pregnancy. Because the tube is so small, the pregnancy has to be terminated surgically.) After reaching the uterus, a pear-shaped organ, the zygote floats free in the intra-uterine fluid. Here it develops into a *blastocyst*, a ball of cells surrounding a fluid-filled cavity.

By the end of the second week, the blastocyst becomes embedded in the wall of the uterus. At this point and until the end of the eighth week, it is known as an embryo. During the fourth and fifth weeks, organ systems begin to develop, and the external features take on a definitely human shape. During the eighth week, brain activity usually becomes detectable. At this time, the embryo comes to be known as a fetus.

Birth generally occurs about nine months after fertilization or, to be more accurate, around forty-plus weeks. It is customary to divide this time into three three-month (thirteen-week) periods or trimesters.

At present, pregnancy can be diagnosed as early as seven to ten days after fertilization. Also, improvements in ultrasound imaging allow the gestational sac surrounding the embryo to be detected in its earliest stages. Hence, a woman may be found to be pregnant even before she has missed an expected period.

Abortion is the termination of pregnancy. It can occur because of internal biochemical factors or as a result of physical injury to the woman. Terminations from such causes are usually referred to as "spontaneous abortions," but they are also commonly called miscarriages.

Abortion can also be a deliberate process resulting from human intervention. The methods used in contemporary medicine depend to a great extent on the stage of the pregnancy. The earliest intervention involves the use of drugs (such as RU-486 or the hormones in birth control pills) to prevent the embedding of the blastocyst in the uterine wall.

Because the new tests and ultrasound make it possible to detect pregnancy as early as a

week or ten days after fertilization, a pregnancy can be terminated at that point. A physician dilates (widens) the cervix (the narrow opening to the uterus), then uses a hand-operated syringe to suction out the contents of the uterus.

Subsequent intervention during the first trimester (up to about twelve weeks) commonly employs the same technique of uterine or vacuum aspiration. After the cervix is dilated, a small tube is inserted into the uterus and its contents are emptied by suction. The procedure is known as dilation and evacuation. The classical abortion procedure is dilation and curettage. The cervix is dilated, and its contents are gently scraped out by the use of a curette, a spoon-shaped surgical instrument. The procedure has been almost wholly replaced by evacuation in developed countries.

After twelve weeks, when the fetus is too large to make the other methods practical, the most common abortion technique involves dilating the cervix and extracting the fetus. (See the Social Context "The 'Partial-Birth Abortion' Controversy," earlier in this chapter, for discussion.)

These facts about pregnancy and abortion put us in a position to discuss some of the moral problems connected with them. We won't be able to untangle the skein of issues wrapped around the abortion question. We'll only attempt to state a few of the more serious ones and to indicate the lines of argument that have been offered to support positions taken with respect to them; afterward we'll sketch out some possible responses that might be offered on the basis of the ethical theories we discuss in Part V, "Foundations of Bioethics."

The Status of the Fetus

It is crucial for the application of the principles of any moral theory that we have a settled opinion about the objects and subjects of morality. Although principles are generally stated with respect to rational individuals, every theory recognizes that there are people who in fact cannot be considered rational agents. For example, mental and physical incapacities may diminish or destroy rationality. But ethical theories generally recognize that we still have duties to people who are so incapacitated.

The basic problem that this raises is this: Who or what is to be considered a person? Are there any characteristics that we can point to and say that it is by virtue of possessing these characteristics that an individual must be considered a person and thus accorded moral treatment?

The abortion issue raises this question most particularly with regard to the fetus. (We will use the term "fetus," for the moment, to refer to the developing organism at any stage.) Just what is the status of the fetus in the world? We must find a satisfactory answer to this question, some writers have suggested, before we can resolve the general moral problem of abortion.

Let's consider the possible consequences of answering the question one way or the other. First, if a fetus is a person, it has a serious claim to life. We must assert the claim on its behalf, for, like an unconscious person, the fetus is unable to do so. The claim of the fetus as a person must be given weight and respect in deliberating about any action that would terminate its life. Perhaps only circumstances as extreme as a threat to the life of the mother would justify abortion.

Assuming that the fetus is a person, then, an abortion would be a case of killing and something not to be undertaken without reasons sufficient to override the fetus's claim to life. In effect, only conditions of the same sort that would justify our killing an adult person (e.g., self-defense) would justify our killing a fetus. Thus, the moral burden in every case would be to demonstrate that abortion is not a case of wrongful killing.

By contrast, if a fetus is not a person in a morally relevant sense, then abortion need not be considered a case of killing equivalent to the killing of an adult. In one view, it might be said that an abortion is not essentially different from an appendectomy. According to this way of

thinking, a fetus is no more than a complicated clump of organic material, and its removal involves no serious moral difficulty.

In another view, it could be argued that, even though the fetus is not a person, it is a potential person, and thus is a significant and morally relevant property. The fetus's very potentiality makes it unique and distinguishes it from a diseased appendix, a cyst, or any other kind of organic material. Thus, because the fetus can become a person, abortion does present a moral problem. A fetus can be destroyed only for serious reasons. Thus, preventing a person from coming into existence must be justified to an extent comparable to the justification required for killing a person. (Some have suggested that the justification does not have to be identical because the fetus is only a potential person. The justification we might present for killing a person would thus serve only as a guide for those who might justify abortion.)

So far we have used the word "fetus," and this usage tends to obscure the fact that human development is a process with many stages. Perhaps it is only in the later stages of development that the entity becomes a person. But exactly when might this happen?

The difference between a fertilized ovum and a fully developed baby just a few minutes before birth are considerable. The ovum and the blastocyst seem just so much tissue. But the embryo and the fetus present more serious claims to being persons. Should abortion be allowed until the fetus becomes visibly human, or until the fetus shows heartbeat and brain waves, or until the fetus can live outside the uterus (becomes viable)?

The process of development is continuous, and so far it has proved impossible to find differences between stages that can be generally accepted as morally relevant. Some writers on abortion have suggested that it is useless to look for such differences, because any place where the line is drawn will be arbitrary. Others have claimed that it is possible to draw the line by relying on criteria that can be rationally defended. A few have even argued that a reasonable set of criteria for determining who shall be considered a person might even deny the status to infants.

Pregnancy, Abortion, and the Rights of Women

Pregnancy and fetal development are normal biological processes, and most women who choose to have a child carry it to term without unusual difficulties. However, it is important to keep in mind that even a normal pregnancy involves changes and stresses that are uniquely burdensome. Once the process of fetal growth is initiated, a woman's entire physiology is altered by the new demands placed on it and by the biochemical changes taking place within her body. For example, the metabolic rate increases, the thyroid gland grows larger, the heart pumps more blood to meet fetal needs, and a great variety of hormonal changes take place. The growing fetus physically displaces the woman's internal organs and alters the size and shape of her body.

As a result of such changes, the pregnant woman may suffer a variety of ailments. More common ones include severe nausea and vomiting ("morning sickness"), muscle cramps, abdominal pain, anemia, tiredness, and headaches. For many women, such complaints are relatively mild or infrequent; for others, they are severe or constant. Nausea and vomiting can lead to dehydration and malnutrition so serious as to be life threatening. Women who suffer from diseases such as diabetes are apt to face special health problems as a result of pregnancy.

Partly because of hormonal changes, women are also more likely to experience psychological difficulties when pregnant, such as emotional lability (mood swings), severe depression, and acute anxiety. Such conditions are often accompanied by quite realistic concerns about the loss of freedom associated with becoming a parent, compromised job status, loss of sexual attractiveness due to the change in body shape, and the pains and risks of childbirth.

The woman who intends to carry a child to term is also likely to have to alter her behavior in many ways. She may have to curtail the time she spends working, take a leave of absence, or even quit her job. Any career plans she has are likely to suffer. She may be unable to participate in social activities to the extent that she previously did, and forced to give up some entirely. In addition, if she recognizes an obligation to the developing fetus and is well informed, she may have to alter her diet, stop smoking, and strictly limit the amount of alcohol she consumes.

In sum, the physical and emotional price paid by a woman for a full-term pregnancy is high. Even a normal pregnancy, one that proceeds without any special difficulties, exacts a toll of discomfort, stress, restricted activity, and worry.

Women who wish to have a child are generally willing to undergo the rigors of pregnancy to satisfy this desire. But is it a woman's duty to nurture and carry to term an unwanted child? Pregnancies resulting from rape and incest are the kinds of dramatic cases frequently mentioned to emphasize the seriousness of the burden imposed on women. But the question is also important when the conditions surrounding the pregnancy are more ordinary.

Suppose that a woman becomes pregnant unintentionally and decides that having a child will be harmful to her career or her way of life. Or suppose she simply does not wish to subject herself to the pains of pregnancy. Does a woman have a moral duty to see to it that the developing child comes to be born?

A number of writers have taken the position that women have an exclusive right to control their own reproductive function. In the view of these writers, such a right is based upon the generally recognized right to control what is done to our bodies. Since pregnancy is something that involves a woman's body, the woman concerned may legitimately decide whether to continue the pregnancy or terminate it. The decision is hers alone, and social or legal policies that restrict the free exercise of her right are unjustifiable.

Essentially the same point is sometimes phrased by saying that women own their bodies. Because their bodies are their own "property," women alone have the right to decide whether to become pregnant and, if pregnant unintentionally, whether to have an abortion.

Critics have pointed out that this general line of argument, taken alone, does not support the strong conclusion that women should be free from all constraints in making abortion decisions. Even granting that women's bodies are their own property, we nevertheless recognize restrictions on exercising property rights. We have no right to shoot trespassers, and we cannot endanger our neighbors by burning down our house. Similarly, if any legitimate moral claims can be made on behalf of the fetus, then the right of women to decide whether to have an abortion may not be unrestricted.

Some philosophers (e.g., Judith Jarvis Thomson) have taken the view that, although women are entitled to control their bodies and make abortion decisions, the decision to have an abortion must be supported by weighty reasons. They have suggested that, even if we grant that a fetus is a person, its claim to life cannot be given unconditional precedence over the woman's claim to control her own life. She is entitled to autonomy and the right to arrange her life in accordance with her own concept of the good. It would be wrong for her to destroy the fetus for a trivial reason, but legitimate and adequate reasons for taking the life of the fetus might be offered.

Others, by contrast, have argued that when a woman becomes pregnant, she assumes a responsibility for the life of the fetus. It is, after

all, completely dependent on her for its continued existence. She has no more right to take its life in order to seek her own best interest than she has to murder someone whose death may bring benefits to her.

Therapeutic Abortion

Abortion is sometimes required to save the life of the mother or in order to provide her with medical treatment considered essential to her health. Abortion performed for such a purpose is ordinarily regarded as a case of self-defense. For this reason, it is almost universally considered to be morally unobjectionable. (Strictly speaking, the Roman Catholic view condemns abortion in all of its forms. It does approve of providing medical treatment for the mother, even if this results in the death of the fetus, but the death of the fetus must never be intended.)

If the principle of preserving the life and health of the mother justifies abortion, then what conditions fall under that principle? If a woman has cancer of the uterus and her life can be saved only by an operation that will result in the death of the fetus, then this clearly falls under the principle. But what about psychological conditions? Is a woman's mental health relevant to deciding whether an abortion is justified? What if a psychiatrist believes that a woman cannot face the physical rigors of pregnancy or bear the psychological stresses that go with it without developing severe psychiatric symptoms? Would such a judgment justify an abortion? Or is the matter of psychological health irrelevant to the abortion issue?

Consider, too, the welfare of the fetus. Suppose that prenatal tests indicate that the developing child suffers from serious abnormalities. (This was the case of the "thalidomide babies.") Is abortion for the purpose of preventing the birth of such children justifiable?

It might be argued that it is not, that an impaired fetus has as much right to its life as an impaired person. We do not, after all, consider it legitimate to kill people who become seriously injured or suffer from diseases that render them helpless. Rather, we care for them and work to improve their lives—or at least we ought to.

Some might argue, however, that abortion in such cases is not only justifiable, but a duty. It is our duty to kill the fetus to spare the person it will become a life of unhappiness and suffering. We might even be said to be acknowledging the dignity of the fetus by doing what it might do for itself if it could—what any rational creature would do. Destroying such a fetus would spare future pain to the individual and his or her family and save the family and society from an enormous expense. Thus, we have not only a justification to kill such a fetus, but also the positive obligation to do so.

In this chapter, we will not deal explicitly with the issues that are raised by attempting to decide whether it is justifiable to terminate the life of an impaired fetus. Because such issues are directly connected with prenatal genetic diagnosis and treatment, we discuss them more fully in Chapter 10. Nonetheless, in considering the general question of the legitimacy of abortion, it is important to keep such special considerations in mind.

Abortion and the Law

Abortion in our society has been a legal issue as well as a moral issue. Until the Supreme Court decision in *Roe v. Wade*, nontherapeutic abortion was illegal in virtually all states. The Webster decision (see the Social Context "Supreme Court Decisions After *Roe v. Wade*," in this chapter) is a recent indication that the Court is willing to accept more state restrictions than previously, but even so, abortions are far from being illegal. However, even though groups still lobby for a constitutional amendment to protect a fetus's "right to life" and prohibit elective abortion, the position has little popular support.

The rightness or wrongness of abortion is a moral matter, one whose issues can be resolved only by appealing to a moral theory. Different theories may yield incompatible answers, and even individuals who accept the same theory may arrive at different conclusions.

Such a state of affairs raises the question of whether the moral convictions or conclusions of some people should be embodied in laws that govern the lives of all people in the society. The question can be put succinctly: Should the moral beliefs of some people serve as the basis for laws that will impose those beliefs on everyone?

This question cannot be answered in a straightforward way. To some extent, which moral beliefs are at issue is a relevant consideration. So, too, are the political principles that we are willing to accept as basic to our society. Every ethical theory recognizes that there is a scope of action that must be left to individuals as moral agents acting freely on the basis of their own understanding and perceptions. Laws requiring the expression of benevolence or gratitude, for example, seem peculiarly inappropriate.

Yet, one of the major aims of a government is to protect the rights of its citizens. Consequently, a society must have just laws that recognize and enforce those rights. In a very real way, then, the moral theory we hold and the conclusions arrived at on the basis of it will determine whether we believe that certain types of laws are justified. They are justified when they protect the rights recognized in our moral theories—when political rights reflect moral rights. (See the Briefing Session in Chapter 8 for a fuller discussion of moral rights and their relation to political rights.)

An ethical theory that accords the status of a person to a fetus is likely to claim also that the laws of the society should recognize the rights of the fetus. A theory that does not grant the fetus this position is not likely to regard laws forbidding abortion as justifiable.

Ethical Theories and Abortion

Theories like those of Mill, Kant, Ross, and Rawls attribute autonomy, or self-direction to individuals. An individual is entitled to control his or her own life, and it seems reasonable to extend this principle to apply to one's own body. If so, then a woman should have the right to determine whether or not she wishes to have a child. If she is pregnant with an unwanted child, then, no matter how she came to be pregnant, she might legitimately decide on an abortion. Utilitarianism also suggests this answer, though on consequential grounds. In the absence of other considerations, if it seems likely that having a child will produce more unhappiness than an abortion would, then an abortion would be justifiable.

If the fetus is considered to be a person, however, the situation is different for some theories. The natural law view holds that the fetus is an innocent person and that direct abortion is never justifiable. Even if the pregnancy is due to rape, the fetus cannot be held at fault and made to suffer through its death. Even though she may not wish to have the child, the mother has a duty to preserve the life of the fetus.

For deontological theories like those of Kant and Ross, the situation becomes more complicated. If the fetus is a person, it has an inherent dignity and worth. It is an innocent life that cannot be destroyed except for the weightiest moral reasons. Those reasons may include the interests and wishes of the woman, but deontological theories provide no clear answer as to how these factors are to be weighed.

For utilitarianism, by contrast, even if the fetus is considered a person, the principle of utility may still justify an abortion. Killing a person is not, for utilitarianism, inherently wrong. (Yet it is compatible with rule utilitarianism to argue that permitting elective abortion as a matter of policy would produce more unhappiness than forbidding abortion altogether. Thus, utilitarianism does not offer a definite answer to the abortion issue.)

As we have already seen, both utilitarianism and deontological theories can be used to justify therapeutic abortion. When the mother's life or health is at stake, the situation may

be construed as one of self-defense. Both Kant and Ross recognize that we each have a right to protect ourselves, even if it means taking the life of another person. For utilitarianism, preserving one's life is justifiable, for being alive is a necessary condition for all forms of happiness.

We have also indicated that abortion "for the sake of the fetus" can be justified by both utilitarianism and deontological theories. If by killing the fetus we can spare it a life of suffering, minimize the sufferings of its family, and preserve the resources of the society, then abortion is legitimate on utilitarian grounds. In the terms of Kant and Ross, destroying the fetus might be a way of recognizing its dignity. If we assume that it is a person, then by sparing it a life of indignity and pain, we are treating it in the way that a rational being would want to be treated.

The legitimacy of laws forbidding abortion is an issue that utilitarianism would resolve by considering their effects. If such laws promote the general happiness of the society, then they are justifiable. Otherwise, they are not. In general, Kant, Ross, Rawls, and natural law theory recognize intrinsic human worth and regard as legitimate laws protecting that worth, even if those holding this view are only a minority of the society. Thus, laws discriminating against blacks and women, for example, would be considered unjust on the basis of these theories. Laws enforcing equality, by contrast, would be considered just.

But what about fetuses? The Roman Catholic interpretation of natural law would regard the case as exactly the same. As full human persons, they are entitled to have their rights protected by law. Those who fail to recognize this are guilty of moral failure, and laws permitting abortion are the moral equivalent of laws permitting murder.

For Kant and other deontologists, the matter is less clear. As long as there is substantial doubt about the status of the fetus, it is not certain that it is legitimate to demand that the rights of fetuses be recognized and protected by law. It is clear that the issue of whether or not the fetus is considered a person is most often taken as the crucial one in the abortion controversy.

The battle over abortion is certain to continue in the courts, the streets, the media, and classrooms. The issues are of great social importance, yet highly personal and explosively emotional. The best hope for a resolution continues to rest with the condemnation of violence and an emphasis on the traditional strategies of verbal persuasion, rational argument, and the appeal to basic moral principles.

After The Concert

It happened after a concert. Sixteen-year-old Mary Pluski had gone with three of her friends to hear Bruce Springsteen at Chicago's Blanton Auditorium. After the concert, in a crowd estimated at 11,000, Mary became separated from the other three girls. She decided that the best thing to do was to meet them at the car.

But when she got to the eight-story parking building, Mary realized she wasn't sure what level they had parked on. She thought it might be somewhere in the middle, so she started looking on the fourth floor. While she was walking down the aisles of cars, two men in their early twenties, one white and the other black, stopped her and asked if she were having some kind of trouble.

Mary explained the situation to them, and one of the men suggested that they get his car and drive around inside the parking building. Mary hesitated, but both seemed so polite and genuinely concerned to help that she decided to go with them.

Once they were in the car, however, the situation changed. They drove out of the building and toward the South Side. Mary pleaded with them to let her out of the car. Then, some seven miles from the auditorium, the driver stopped the car in a dark area behind a vacant building. Mary was then raped by both men.

Mary was treated at Allenworth Hospital and released into the custody of her parents. She filed a complaint with the police, but her troubles were not yet over. Two weeks after she missed her menstrual period, tests showed that Mary was pregnant.

"How do you feel about having this child?" asked Sarah Ruben, the Pluski family physician.

"I hate the idea," Mary said. "I feel guilty about it, though. I mean, it's not the child's fault."

"Let me ask a delicate question," said Dr. Ruben. "I know from what you've told me before that you and your boyfriend have been having sex. Can you be sure this pregnancy is not really the result of that?"

Mary shook her head. "Not really. I use my diaphragm, but I know it doesn't give a hundred percent guarantee."

"That's right. Now, does it make any difference to you who the father might be, so far as a decision about terminating the pregnancy is concerned?"

"If I were sure it was Bob, I guess the problem would be even harder," Mary said.

"There are some tests we can use to give us that information," Dr. Ruben said. "But that would mean waiting for the embryo to develop into a fetus. It would be easier and safer to terminate the pregnancy now."

Mary started crying. "I don't want a child," she said. "I don't want any child. I don't care who's the father. It was forced on me, and I want to get rid of it."

"I'll make the arrangements," said Dr. Ruben.

1. If abortion can be justified in a case of rape, can a similar argument be used to justify it in a case in which the pregnancy was unintended?

2. Suppose the fetus is a person. Can abortion be justified on the grounds that a woman has a right to decide whether she wants to carry the child to term?

3. Is depriving the fetus of a future justified by the conditions under which the fetus was conceived?

DECISION SCENARIO **3**

A Procedure by Another Name

In March 1995, Tammy Watts had been pregnant for eight months and was excited by the prospect of becoming a mother for the first time. Then her world fell apart. A routine ultrasound revealed that her baby had trisomy 13, a chromosomal abnormality that causes severe deformities and no hope of survival for the child.

Tammy Watts' child was dying inside her, and this put her own life at risk. Because she could not help her child and feared for her own life, she chose to have the procedure known as intact dilation and extraction. This is the procedure called "partial-birth abortion" by abortion opponents.

"Losing my baby at the end of my pregnancy was agonizing," Watts said in congressional testimony in 1995. "But the way the right deals with the procedure makes it even worse. When I heard [President] Bush mention 'partial-birth abortion' during the [presidential] debates, I thought, 'How dare you stand there and tell flat-out lies?' There is no such thing as this procedure."

Watts' testimony was accompanied by additional testimony from Viki Wilson, who had a late-term abortion because the brain of the fetus she was carrying was developing outside the skull. More testimony was given by Vikki Stella, whose fetus had developed without a brain (was anencephalic) and had seven other serious abnormalities.

The women all testified that they owed their own health to a late-term abortion and that a continuation of their ultimately futile pregnancies would have led to threats to their lives posed by strokes, blood clots, and infection. "No women have these procedures for trivial reasons," Stella testified. "They have them because it's their own choice."

1. "Partial-birth abortion" is a term coined by opponents of late-term abortion for its rhetorical power. Does the use of the term make it difficult to engage in informed public discussions of the relevant issues? (The so-called Partial-Birth Abortion Act of 2003 gave the term and the definition in the act a legal status.)

2. Stella testified that women did not choose late-term abortion for "trivial reasons." Statistics indicate, however, that some women with normally developing fetuses seek late-term abortions because, for whatever reason, they failed to seek an early abortion. Does this fact undercut the argument the three women are making in their testimony?

3. Does the testimony indicate that there is sufficient reason not to make late-term abortion illegal. (For a discussion of the Partial-Birth Abortion Act of 2003, see the Social Context "The 'Partial-Birth Abortion' Controversy," in this chapter.)

DECISION SCENARIO **4**

A Pregnant Mental Child

Clare Macwurter was twenty-two years old chronologically, but mentally she remained a child. As a result of her mother's prolonged and difficult labor, Clare had been deprived of an adequate blood-oxygen supply during her birth. The consequence was that she suffered irreversible brain damage.

Clare enjoyed life and was generally a happy person. She couldn't read, but she liked listening to music and watching television, although she could rarely understand the stories. She was physically attractive and, with the help of her parents, she could care for herself.

Clare was also interested in sex. When she was seventeen, she and a fellow student at the special

school they attended had been caught having intercourse. Clare's parents had been told about the incident, but after Clare left the school the following year, they took no special precautions to ensure that Clare would not become sexually involved with anyone. After all, she stayed at home with her mother every day, and, besides, it was a matter they didn't much like to think about.

The Macwurters were both surprised and upset when Clare became pregnant. At first they couldn't imagine how it could have happened. They recalled that on several occasions Clare had been sent to stay at the house of Mr. Macwurter's brother and his wife while Mrs. Macwurter went shopping.

John Macwurter at first denied that he had had anything to do with Clare's pregnancy. But during the course of a long and painful conversation with his brother, he admitted that he had had sexual relations with Clare.

"I wasn't wholly to blame," John Macwurter said. "I mean, I know I shouldn't have done it. But still, she was interested in it, too. I didn't really rape her. Nothing like that."

The Macwurters were at a loss about what they should do. The physician they consulted told them that Clare would probably have a perfectly normal baby. But of course, Clare couldn't really take care of herself, much less a baby. She was simply unfit to be a mother. Mrs. Macwurter, for her part, was not eager to assume the additional responsibilities of caring for another child. Mr. Macwurter would be eligible to retire in four more years, and the couple had been looking forward to selling their house and moving back to the small town in Oklahoma where they had first met and then married. The money they had managed to save, plus insurance and a sale of their property, would permit them to place Clare in a long-term care facility after their deaths. Being responsible for another child would both ruin their plans and jeopardize Clare's future well-being.

"I never thought I would say such a thing," Mrs. Macwurter told her husband, "but I think we should arrange for Clare to have an abortion."

"That's killing," Mr. Macwurter said.

"I'm not so sure it is. I don't really know. But even if it is, I think it's the best thing to do."

Mrs. Macwurter made the arrangements with Clare's physician for an abortion to be performed. When Mr. Macwurter asked his brother to pay for the operation, John Macwurter refused. He explained that he was opposed to abortion and so it would not be right for him to provide money to be used in that way.

1. Could Thomson's defense of abortion be employed here to show that the proposed abortion is permissible?

2. Why would Noonan oppose abortion in this case? What alternatives might he recommend? What if it were likely that the baby would be impaired? Would this alter the situation for Noonan?

3. Do the traits Warren lists as central to the concept of personhood require that we think of Clare Macwurter as not being a person in a morally relevant sense?

4. Why would Marquis oppose this abortion?

DECISION SCENARIO 5

Fetal Reduction

Mrs. Lois Bishop (as we will call her) learned that she was carrying twins at the same time she learned that one of the twins had Down syndrome.

"There's no question in my mind," she said. "I want to have an abortion. I had the tests done in the first place to do what I could to guarantee that I would have a normal, healthy child. I knew from the first that there was a possibility that I would have to have an abortion, so I'm prepared for it."

Her obstetrician, Dr. George Savano, nodded. "I understand that," he said. "You are certainly within your rights to ask for an abortion, and I can arrange for you to have one. But there is another possibility, an experimental one, that you might want to consider as an option."

The possibility consisted of the destruction of the abnormally developing fetus. In the end, it was the possibility that Mrs. Bishop chose. A long, thin needle was inserted through Mrs. Bishop's abdomen and guided into the heart of the fetus. A solution was then injected directly into the fetal heart.

Although there was a risk that Mrs. Bishop would have a miscarriage, she did not. The surviving twin continued to develop normally, and Mrs. Bishop had an uneventful delivery.

Dr. Savano was criticized by some physicians as "misusing medicine," but he rejects such charges. Mrs. Bishop also has no regrets, for if the procedure had not been performed, she would have been forced to abort both twins.

1. What sort of utilitarian argument might be offered to justify Dr. Savano's experimental procedure in this case?

2. Would Marquis consider the destruction of the fetus with Down syndrome immoral? After all, it may be argued that persons with Down syndrome do not have "a future like ours."

3. The procedure leads to the death of a developing fetus, so one might say that it is morally equivalent to abortion. Are there any morally relevant factors that distinguish this case from more ordinary cases involving abortion?

DECISION SCENARIO **6**

A Family Tragedy

For months, doctors told eleven-year-old Visna (as we'll call her) and her parents that her abdominal pains were nothing but indigestion. Then, in July 1998, the truth finally emerged: Visna was twenty-seven weeks' pregnant.

Visna's family had emigrated from India to the Detroit suburb of Sterling Heights, Michigan, only the previous summer. Her parents found factory jobs and rented a two-bedroom apartment, and Visna shared one of the rooms with Hari, her sixteen-year-old brother. Sometime during the winter after their arrival, Visna told her parents, Hari raped her, but this emerged only after Visna, who had turned twelve, was found to be pregnant.

As soon as Visna's parents learned her condition, they made plans to take her to Kansas for an abortion. Visna would have to have a late-term abortion, and because Michigan law bans almost all abortions after twenty-four weeks, her family would have to take her out of state. But their plans were frustrated when they were leaked to a family court judge. Charges of parental negligence were filed by prosecutors against her parents, and the court immediately removed Visna from her family and made her a ward of the state.

At a court hearing, Visna's doctor argued that if her pregnancy were allowed to continue, it could cause her both physical and psychological damage. A psychologist testified that, because Visna was a Hindu, if she were forced to have an illegitimate child, it would make her unfit for marriage by another Hindu. Her parents also expressed their worry that if Visna had a child, the child might suffer from genetic abnormalities and, in particular, might be mentally retarded, because her brother would be the father.

At the end of the hearing, the prosecution announced that it was convinced that pregnancy might endanger Visna's life and dropped the negligence charge against her parents. Visna was reunited with her family, and her parents pursued their original plan of taking her to Kansas. In Wichita, Dr. George Tiller, who was later shot to death by a pro-life activist, stopped the fetus's heart and used drugs to induce labor, thus performing a "partial-birth" abortion.

1. In what circumstances, if any, should late-term abortions be legally permitted?

2. Should some sort of hearings board or court be established to decide on the legitimacy of cases of late-term abortion?

3. Is there a difference between late-term abortion and infanticide?

4. Assuming that late-term abortion is sometimes indistinguishable from infanticide, does that imply that late-term abortion is never justified?

DECISION SCENARIO **7**

Unexpected News

Helen and John Kent waited nervously in the small consulting room while Laurie Stent, their genetic counselor, went to tell Dr. Charles Blatz that they had arrived to talk to him.

"I regret that I have some bad news for you," Dr. Blatz told them. "The karyotyping that we do after amniocentesis shows a chromosomal abnormality."

He looked at them, and Helen felt that she could hardly breathe. "What is it?" she asked.

"It's a condition known as trisomy 21, and it produces a birth defect we call Down syndrome. You may have heard of it under the old name of mongolism."

"Oh, God," John said. "How bad is it?"

"Such children are always mentally retarded," Dr. Blatz said. "Some are severely retarded and others just twenty or so points below average. They have some minor physical deformities, and they sometimes have heart damage. They typically don't live beyond their thirties, but by and large they seem happy and have good dispositions."

Helen and John looked at each other with great sadness. "What do you think we should do?" Helen asked. "Should I have an abortion, and then we could try again?"

"I don't know," John said. "I really don't know. You've had a hard time being pregnant these last five months, and you'd have to go through that again. Besides, there's no guarantee this wouldn't happen again."

"But this won't be the normal baby we wanted," Helen said. "Maybe in the long run we'll be even unhappier than we are now."

1. Explain the nature of the conflict between the positions taken by Noonan and Warren that arises in this case.

2. If one accepts Thomson's view, what factors are relevant to deciding whether an abortion is justifiable in this instance?

3. Does feminist ethics suggest any way of dealing with this situation?

DECISION SCENARIO **8**

A Matter of Convenience

Ruth Perkins is twenty-four years old, and her husband, Carl Freedon, is four years older. Both are employed, Ruth as an executive for Laporte Gas Transmission and Carl as a systems analyst at a St. Louis bank. Their combined income is more than $240,000 a year.

Perkins and Freedon live up to their income. They have an eleven-room house with a tennis court in a high-priced suburb, they both dress well, and Carl is a modest collector of sports cars (three MG-TDs). Both like to travel, and they try to get out of the country at least twice a year—to Europe for a month in the summer and to Mexico or the Caribbean for a couple of weeks during the winter.

Perkins and Freedon have no children. They agreed when they were married that children would not be a part of their plan for life together. They were distressed when Ruth became pregnant and at first refused to face the problem. They worried about it for several months, considering arguments for and against abortion. At last they decided that Ruth should have an abortion.

"I don't see why I have to go through with this interview," Ruth said to the woman at the Morton Hospital Counseling Center.

"It's required of all who request an abortion," the counselor explained. "We think it's better for a person to be sure what she is doing so she won't regret it later."

"My husband and I are certain," Ruth said. "A child doesn't fit in at all with our lifestyle. We go out a lot,

and we like to do things. A child would just get in the way."

"A child can offer many pleasures," the woman said.

"I don't doubt it. If some want them, that's fine with me. We don't. Besides, we both have careers that we're devoted to. I'm not about to quit my job to take care of a child, and the same is true of my husband."

"How long have you been pregnant?"

Ruth looked embarrassed. "Almost six months," she said. "Carl and I weren't sure what we wanted to do at first. It took a while for us to get used to the idea."

"You don't think you waited too long?"

"That's stupid," Ruth said. She could hardly keep her voice under control. "I didn't mean that personally. But Carl and I have a right to live our lives the way we want. So far as we are concerned, a six-month fetus is not a person. If we want to get rid of it, that's our business."

"Would you feel the same if it were a child already born?"

"I might," Ruth said. "I mean, a baby doesn't have much personality or anything, does it?"

"I take it you're certain you want the abortion."

"Absolutely. My husband and I think it's the right thing for us. If others think we're wrong . . . well, it's their right to think what they please."

1. How might Warren's arguments be used to support Perkins' position?

2. Could someone who accepts Thomson's arguments consider abortion justified in this case?

3. If Brown's criticism of Marquis is correct, does this mean that abortion for any reason is justified?

Whose Life?

Daniel Bocker was worried. The message his secretary had taken merely said "Go to see Dr. Tai at 3:30 today." He hadn't been asked if 3:30 was convenient for him, and he hadn't been given a reason for coming in.

Mr. Bocker knew it would have to do with his wife, Mary. She had been suffering a lot of pain during her pregnancy, and the preceding week she had been examined by a specialist that Dr. Tai, her gynecologist, had sent her to see. The specialist had performed a thorough examination and taken blood, tissue, and urine samples, but he had told Mary nothing.

"Thank you for coming in," Dr. Tai said. "I want to talk to you before I talk to your wife, because I need your help."

"The tests showed something bad, didn't they?" Mr. Bocker said. "Something is wrong with the baby."

"The baby is fine, but there is something wrong with your wife, something very seriously wrong. She has what we call uterine neoplasia."

"Is that cancer?"

"Yes it is," said Dr. Tai. "But I don't want either of you to panic about it. It's not at a very advanced stage, and at the moment it's localized. If an operation is performed very soon, then she has a good chance to make a full recovery. The standard figures show about 80% success."

"But what about the baby?"

"The pregnancy will have to be terminated," Dr. Tai said. "And I should tell you that your wife will not be able to have children after the operation."

Mr. Bocker sat quietly for a moment. He had always wanted children; for him, a family without children was not a family at all. He and Mary had talked about having at least three, and the one she was pregnant with now was the first.

"Is it possible to save the baby?" he asked Dr. Tai.

"Mrs. Bocker is only in her fourth month; there is no chance that the child could survive outside her body."

"But what if she didn't have the operation? Would the baby be normal?"

"Probably so, but the longer we wait to perform the operation, the worse your wife's chances become. I don't want to seem to tell you what to do, but my advice is for your wife to have an abortion and to undergo the operation as soon as it is reasonably possible."

"But she might recover, even if she had the child and then had the operation, mightn't she?"

"It's possible, but her chances of recovery are much less. I don't know what the exact figures would be, but she would be running a terrible risk."

Mr. Bocker understood what Dr. Tai was saying, but he also understood what he wanted.

"I'm not going to encourage Mary to have an abortion," he said. "I want her to have a child, and I think she wants that, too."

"What if she wants to have a better chance to live? I think the decision is really hers. After all, it's her life that is at stake."

"But it's not just her decision," Mr. Bocker said. "It's a family decision, hers and mine. I'm not going to agree to an abortion, even if she does want one. I'm going to try to get her to take the extra risk and have the child before she has the operation."

1. Would the doctrine of double effect justify taking steps to treat Mrs. Bocker's illness, even at the cost of terminating her pregnancy?

2. Would both Noonan and Thomson see the situation as one in which considerations of self-defense are relevant?

3. It is sometimes said that the father of a child also has a right to decide whether an abortion is to be performed. Would Daniel Bocker be justified in urging his wife to take the risk of having the child?

Reducing Abortion by Making It Legal?

A study published in 2009 by the Gutmacher Institute and the World Health Organization showed that a decline in the number of abortions took place worldwide during the period 1995–2003. (This period offered the most recent set of complete data.) The number fell from forty-six million in 1995 to thirty-two million in 2003.

The factor most responsible for the decline was access to contraception. The study also found that abortion occurs about as often in countries in which it is illegal as it does in countries that permit it. The aspect of abortion affected most by its legal status was its safety. "Where abortion is illegal, it is likely to be unsafe, performed under unsafe conditions by poorly trained providers," one of the researchers said.

In Uganda, abortion is illegal and sex education is limited to programs teaching abstinence. The estimated abortion rate for 2003 in Uganda was fifty-four per 1,000 women, about twice the U.S. rate of twenty-one per 1,000 for that year. The lowest abortion rate is in Western Europe (twelve per 1,000), where contraception is easily available and abortion is legal.

1. Can an argument be made that, paradoxically, those who oppose abortion ought to endorse its legal status and promote the use of contraception?

2. Why would those who endorse a natural law view (e.g., Roman Catholics) find this argument impossible to support?

3. Does the fact that abortion occurs about as often when it is illegal as when it is legal and that when abortion is illegal it is considerably more unsafe support the conclusion that abortion should be legal?

Baby Owens: Down Syndrome and Duodenal Atresia

On a chilly December evening in 1976, Dr. Joan Owens pushed through the plate glass doors of Midwestern Medical Center and walked over to the admitting desk. Dr. Owens was a physician in private practice and regularly visited Midwestern to attend to her patients.

But this night was different. Dr. Owens was coming to the hospital to be admitted as a patient. She was pregnant, and shortly after 9:00 she began having periodic uterine contractions. Dr. Owens recognized them as the beginnings of labor pains. She was sure of this not only because of her medical knowledge but also because the pains followed the same pattern they had before her other three children were born.

While her husband, Phillip, parked the car, Dr. Owens went through the formalities of admission. She was not particularly worried, for the birth of her other children had been quite normal and uneventful. But the pains were coming more frequently now, and she was relieved when she completed the admission process and was taken to her room. Phillip came with her, bringing her small blue suitcase of personal belongings.

At 11:30 that evening, Dr. Owens gave birth to a 4.5-pound baby girl. The plastic bracelet fastened around her wrist identified her as Baby Owens.

Bad News

Dr. Owens was groggy from exhaustion and from the medication she had received. But when the baby was shown to her, she saw at once that it was not normal. The baby's head was misshapen and the skin around her eyes strangely formed.

Dr. Owens recognized that her daughter had Down syndrome.

"Clarence," she called to her obstetrician. "Is the baby mongoloid?"

"We'll talk about it after your recovery," Dr. Clarence Ziner said.

"Tell me now," said Dr. Owens. "Examine it!"

Dr. Ziner made a hasty examination of the child. He had already seen that Dr. Owens was right and was doing no more than making doubly certain. A more careful examination would have to be made later.

When Dr. Ziner confirmed Joan Owens's suspicion, she did not hesitate to say what she was thinking. "Get rid of it," she told Dr. Ziner. "I don't want a mongoloid child."

Dr. Ziner tried to be soothing. "Just sleep for a while now," he told her. "We'll talk about it later."

Four hours later, a little after 5:00 in the morning and before it was fully light, Joan Owens woke up. Phillip was with her, and he had more bad news to tell. A more detailed examination had shown that the child's small intestine had failed to develop properly and was closed off in one place—the condition known as duodenal atresia. It could be corrected by a relatively simple surgical procedure, but until surgery was performed the child could not be fed. Phillip had refused to consent to the operation until he had talked to his wife. Joan Owens had not changed her mind: she did not want the child.

"It wouldn't be fair to the other children to raise them with a mongoloid," she told Phillip. "It would take all of our time, and we wouldn't be able to give David, Sean, and Melinda the love and attention they need."

"I'm willing to do whatever you think best," Phillip said. "But what can we do?"

"Let the child die," Joan said. "If we don't consent to the surgery, the baby will die soon. And that's what we have to let happen."

Phillip put in a call for Dr. Ziner, and when he arrived in Joan's room, they told him of their decision. He was not pleased with it.

"The surgery has very low risk," he said. "The baby's life can almost certainly be saved. We can't tell how retarded she'll be, but most DS children get along quite well with help from their families. The whole family will grow to love her."

"I know," Joan said. "And I don't want that to happen. I don't want us to center our lives around a defective child. Phillip and I and our other children will be forced to lose out on many of life's pleasures and possibilities."

"We've made up our minds," Phillip said. "We don't want the surgery."

"I'm not sure the matter is as simple as that," Dr. Ziner said. "I'm not sure we can legally just let the baby die. I'll have to talk to the director and the hospital attorney."

Applying for a Court Order

At 6:00 in the morning, Dr. Ziner called Dr. Felix Entraglo, the director of Midwestern Medical Center, and Isaac Putnam, the head of the center's legal staff. They agreed to meet at 9:00 to talk over the problem presented to them by the Owenses.

They met for two hours. It was Putnam's opinion that the hospital would not be legally liable if Baby Owens were allowed to die because her parents refused to give consent for necessary surgery.

"What about getting a court order requiring surgery?" Dr. Entraglo asked. "That's the sort of thing we do when an infant requires a blood transfusion or immunization and his parents' religious beliefs make them refuse consent."

"This case is not exactly parallel," said Mr. Putnam. "Here we're talking about getting a court order to force parents to allow surgery to save the life of a defective infant. The infant will still be defective after the surgery, and I think a court would be reluctant to make a family undergo significant emotional and financial hardships when the parents have seriously deliberated about the matter and decided against surgery."

"But doesn't the child have some claim in this situation?" Dr. Ziner asked.

"That's not clear," said Mr. Putnam. "In general, we assume that parents will act for the sake of their child's welfare, and when they are reluctant to do so we look to the courts to act for the child's welfare. But in a situation like this . . . who can say? Is the Owens baby really a person in any legal or moral sense?"

"I think I can understand why a court would hesitate to order surgery," said Dr. Entraglo. "What sort of life would it be for a family when they had been pressured into accepting a child they didn't want? It would turn a family into a cauldron of guilt and resentment mixed in with love and concern. In this case, the lives of five normal people would be profoundly altered for the worse."

"So we just stand by and let the baby die?" asked Dr. Ziner.

"I'm afraid so," Dr. Entraglo said.

The Final Days

It took twelve days for Baby Owens to die. Her lips and throat were moistened with water to lessen her suffering, and in a small disused room set apart from the rooms of patients, she was allowed to starve to death.

Many nurses and physicians thought it was wrong that Baby Owens was forced to die such a lingering death. Some thought it was wrong for her to have to die at all, but such a protracted death seemed needlessly cruel. Yet they were cautioned by Dr. Entraglo that anything done to shorten the baby's life would probably constitute a criminal action. Thus, fear of being charged with a crime kept the staff from administering any medication to Baby Owens.

The burden of caring for the dying baby fell on the nurses in the obstetrics ward. The physicians avoided the child entirely, and it was the nurses who had to see to it that she received her water and was turned in her bed. This was the source of much resentment among the nursing staff, and a few nurses refused to have anything to do with the dying child. Most kept their ministrations to an absolute minimum.

But one nurse, Sara Ann Moberly, was determined to make Baby Owens's last days as comfortable as possible. She held the baby, rocked her, and talked soothingly to her when she cried. Doing all for the baby that she could do soothed Sara Ann as well.

But even Sara Ann was glad when Baby Owens died. "It was a relief to me," she said. "I almost couldn't bear the frustration of just sitting there day after day and doing nothing that could really help her."

SOCIAL CONTEXT

The Baby Doe Cases

In Bloomington, Indiana, in 1982, a child was born with Down syndrome and esophageal atresia. The parents and the physicians of the infant, who became known as Baby Doe, decided against the surgery that was needed to open the esophagus and allow the baby to be fed. The decision was upheld by the courts, and six days after birth Baby Doe died of starvation and dehydration.

A month later, in May 1982, the secretary of Health and Human Services (HHS) notified hospitals that any institution receiving federal funds could not lawfully "withhold from a handicapped infant nutritional sustenance or medical or surgical treatment required to correct a life-threatening condition if (1) the withholding is based on the fact that the infant is handicapped and (2) the handicap does not render treatment or nutritional sustenance contraindicated."

Baby Doe Hot Line

Ten months later, acting under instructions from President Reagan, an additional and more detailed regulation was issued. Hospitals were required to display a poster in NICUs and pediatric wards indicating that "discrimination" against handicapped infants was a violation of federal law. The poster also listed a toll-free, twenty-four-hour "hot-line" number for reporting suspected violations. In addition, the regulations authorized representatives of HHS to take "immediate remedial action" to protect infants. Further, hospitals were required to permit HHS investigators access to the hospital and to relevant patient records.

A group of associations, including the American Academy of Pediatrics, brought suit against HHS in an attempt to stop the regulations from becoming legally effective. Judge Gerhard Gesell of the U.S. District Court ruled, in April 1983, that HHS had not followed the proper procedures in putting the regulations into effect and so they were invalid. In particular, the regulations were issued without notifying and consulting with those affected by them, a procedure that is legally required to avoid arbitrary bureaucratic actions. The judge held that, although HHS had considered relevant factors in identifying a problem, it had failed to consider the effects of the use of the hot-line number. An "anonymous tipster" could cause "the sudden

descent of Baby Doe squads" on hospitals, and "monopolizing physician and nurse time, and making hospital charts and records unavailable during treatment, can hardly be presumed to produce quality care of the infant."

Furthermore, Judge Gesell held, the main purpose of the regulations was apparently to "require physicians treating newborns to take into account wholly medical risk–benefit considerations and to prevent parents from having any influence upon decisions as to whether further medical treatment is desirable." The regulations explored no other ways to prevent "discriminatory medical care." In his conclusion, Judge Gesell held that federal regulations dealing with imperiled newborns should "reflect caution and sensitivity" and that "wide public comment prior to rule-making is essential."

HHS responded to the court decision by drafting another regulation (July 5, 1983) that attempted to resolve the procedural objection that invalidated the first. Sixty days was allowed for the filing of written comments. Since the substance of the regulation was virtually the same, the proposal was widely contested, and on January 12, 1984, another set of regulations was published. They too became an object of controversy.

Baby Jane Doe

Meanwhile, a second Baby Doe case had become the focus of public attention and legal action. On October 11, 1983, an infant who became known as Baby Jane Doe was born in Port Jefferson (Long Island), New York. Baby Jane Doe suffered from meningomyelocele, anencephaly, and hydrocephaly. (See Briefing Session, this chapter, for an explanation of these conditions.) Her parents were told that without surgery she might live from two weeks to two years, but with surgery she might survive twenty years. However, she would be severely retarded, epileptic, paralyzed, and likely to have constant urinary and bladder infections. The parents consulted with neurologists, a Roman Catholic priest, nurses, and social workers. They decided surgery was not in the best interest of the child and opted, instead, for the use of antibiotics to prevent infection of the exposed spinal nerves. "We love her very much," her mother said, "and that's why we made the decision we did."

Lawrence Washburn, Jr., a lawyer who for a number of years had initiated lawsuits on behalf of the unborn and impaired, somehow learned that Baby Jane Doe was being denied surgery and entered a petition on her behalf before the New York State Supreme Court. Because Washburn was not related to the infant, his legal standing in the case was questionable, and the court appointed William Weber to represent the interest of Baby Jane Doe. After a hearing, the judge ruled that the infant was in need of surgery to preserve her life and authorized Weber to consent.

This decision was reversed on appeal. The court held that the parents' decision was in the best interest of the infant. Hence, the state had no basis to intervene. The ruling was then appealed to the New York Court of Appeals and upheld. The court held that the parents' right to privacy was invaded when a person totally unrelated and with no knowledge of the infant's condition and treatment entered into litigation in an attempt to challenge the discharge of parental responsibility. However, the main grounds for allowing the ruling to stand were procedural, for the suit had not followed New York law requiring that the state intervene in the treatment of children through the family court.

In the cases of both Baby Doe and Baby Jane Doe, the federal government went to court to demand the infants' medical records. The government charged that decisions against their treatment represented discrimination against the handicapped. However, the courts consistently rejected the government's demands. In June 1985, the Supreme Court agreed to hear arguments to decide whether the federal laws that protect the handicapped against discrimination also apply to the treatment of imperiled newborns who are denied life-prolonging treatment.

Final Regulations

On May 15, 1985, the third anniversary of the death of Baby Doe, HHS's final "Baby Doe" regulation went into effect. The regulation was an implementation of an amendment to the Child Abuse Prevention and Treatment Act that was passed into law in October 1984 and the result of negotiations among some nineteen groups representing right-to-life advocates, the disabled, the medical professions, and members of Congress.

The regulation extended the term "medical neglect" to cover cases of "withholding of medically indicated treatment from a disabled infant with a life-threatening condition." Withholding treatment, but not food and water, was not "medical neglect" in three kinds of cases:

1. The infant is chronically and irreversibly comatose.

2. The provision of such treatment would merely prolong dying, not be effective in ameliorating or correcting all the infant's life-threatening conditions, or otherwise be futile in terms of the survival of the infant.

3. The provision of such treatment would be virtually futile in terms of the survival of the infant, and the treatment itself under such circumstances would be inhumane.

The regulation defined "reasonable medical judgment" as "a medical judgment that would be made by a reasonably prudent physician knowledgeable about the case and the treatment possibilities with respect to the medical conditions involved." State child-protection service agencies were designated as the proper organizations to see to it that infants were not suffering "medical neglect," and, in order to receive any federal funds, such agencies were required to develop a set of procedures to carry out this function. Parents, physicians, and hospitals were thus no longer the direct subjects of the regulation.

Supreme Court Decision

On June 9, 1986, the Supreme Court, in a 5-to-3 ruling with one abstention, struck down the Baby Doe regulations. The Court held that there was no evidence that hospitals had discriminated against impaired infants or had refused treatments sought by parents. Accordingly, there was no basis for federal intervention.

Justice John Paul Stevens, in the majority opinion, stressed that no federal law requires hospitals to treat impaired infants without parental consent. Nor does the government have the right "to give unsolicited advice either to parents, to hospitals, or to state officials who are faced with difficult treatment decisions concerning handicapped children." Furthermore, state child-protection agencies "may not be conscripted against their will as the foot soldiers in a Federal crusade."

Hospitals and those directly involved in neonatal care were generally relieved by the Supreme Court decision. In their arguments before the Court, they had claimed that federal "Baby Doe squads arriving within hours after birth" had second-guessed the agonizing decisions made by parents and physicians and that this had "a devastating impact on the parents."

The Court decision once again placed the responsibility for making decisions about withholding life-sustaining treatment from imperiled newborns on families and physicians acting in consultation. Some hospitals use review committees to recommend whether infants ought to be treated, but what powers these committees should have and who should be on them continue to be a matter of dispute.

CASE PRESENTATION

Baby K: An Anencephalic Infant and a Mother's Request

The female child known in court records as Baby K was born in 1993 at Fairfax Hospital in Falls Church, Virginia. She was born with the catastrophic impairment called anencephaly. Her brain lacked both cerebral hemispheres, and she would never be capable of even a rudimentary form of thought. Only her brain stem was intact, and it would keep her breathing for a while.

The standard treatment for anencephalic infants is to make them comfortable, provide them with nourishment, and then wait until their organ systems fail and death ensues. Death usually comes within a few hours, days, or weeks from respiratory failure, because the brain stem does not adequately regulate breathing.

Baby K remained alive much longer than most babies with her impairment, primarily because of her mother's insistence that the baby's periodic respiratory crises be treated aggressively, including the use of a mechanical ventilator to breathe for her. The mother was described in one court document as "acting out of a firm Christian faith that all life should be protected."

At the age of sixteen months, Baby K lived, not at home with her mother, but in an extended-care facility so that she could receive the constant attention she needed. She left the nursing home only to have respiratory treatment at Fairfax Hospital. After her second admission, the hospital went to the federal district court to seek a ruling that it would not violate any state or federal law by refusing to provide Baby K with additional treatment. Physicians at the hospital held that further treatment would be futile, and a hospital ethics committee decided that withholding aggressive treatment would be legitimate. Nevertheless, the court ruled that the hospital had to provide the care required to preserve the infant's life.

Ruling Appealed

The hospital appealed the district court ruling to the U.S. Court of Appeals. The appeal was supported by Baby K's father (who was not married to her mother) and by a court-appointed guardian. However, the court ruled 2-to-1 that the 1986 Federal Emergency Medical Treatment and

Active Labor Act required the hospital to provide treatment for Baby K. The court held that, although providing assisted breathing for an anencephalic infant might not be expected to produce a medical benefit, the law, as passed by Congress, made no exceptions for situations in which the "required treatment would exceed the prevailing standard of medical care."

The appeals court's extension of the Emergency Medical Treatment Act to the Baby K case surprised most observers. The law was passed to keep private hospitals from "dumping" to public facilities patients with emergency problems (including pregnant women in labor) but no money and no health insurance to pay for the cost of their care. (The act is usually referred to as an antidumping law.) However, payment was not an issue in the Baby K case, for her mother was fully insured as a member of the Kaiser Permanente health maintenance organization.

According to the mother's attorney, Ellen Flannery, the court simply applied the law in a straightforward manner. "There's no dispute that the appropriate treatment for acute respiratory distress is ventilation," she said. "The care is not physiologically futile. It will achieve the result required by the mother, and that is to stabilize the baby." The physicians in the case, she claimed, based their decision on their judgment about the quality of life such a child might have, and the law does not address such issues.

Others saw the consequences of extending the law as threatening the power of physicians, hospitals, and ethics committees to have a say in decisions about treating infants with profound birth anomalies. Arthur Kohrman, head of the American Academy of Pediatrics ethics committee, was quoted as saying, "This is a profoundly important case, because it strips away the ability of physicians to act as moral agents and turns them into instruments of technology. [Anencephalic] babies are born dying, and the issue is not prolonging their death but supporting it in a humane and dignified way."

Robert Veatch, head of the Kennedy Institute for Bioethics, testifying on behalf of the mother, expressed the view that courts should not defer their judgment to that of physicians. "These are religious and philosophical judgments on which physicians have no more expertise than parents," he said. The impact that the extension of the antidumping law to cases of severe birth impairment may have on treatment decisions is not yet obvious. As the appeals court pointed out, Congress made no exceptions with respect to providing care above the accepted standard in cases judged to be futile. The law might be amended by Congress to include exceptions.

Potential Results

If the law is not amended, decisions to provide no more than standard treatment for impaired infants may turn out to have no effect in particular cases. When emergency medical attention is requested by a parent, the emergency treatment law may require that an earlier decision about limiting treatment be set aside.

BRIEFING SESSION

If we could speak of nature in human terms, we would often say that it is cruel and pitiless. Nowhere does it seem more heartless than in the case of babies born into the world with severe physical impairments and deformities. The birth of such a child transforms an occasion of expected joy into one of immense sadness. It forces the child's parents to make a momentous decision at a time when they are least prepared to reason clearly: Should they insist that everything be done to save the child's life? Or should they request that the child be allowed an easeful death?

Nor can physicians and nurses escape the burden that the birth of such a child delivers.

Committed to saving lives, can they condone the death of that child? What will the physician say to the parents when they turn to him or her for advice? No one involved in the situation can escape the moral agonies that it brings.

To see more clearly what the precise moral issues are in such cases, we need to consider some of the factual details that may be involved in them. We also need to mention other kinds of moral considerations that may be relevant to deciding how an impaired newborn child is to be dealt with by those who have the responsibility to decide.

Genetic and Congenital Impairments

The development of a child to the point of birth is an unimaginably complicated process, and there are many ways in which it can go wrong. Birth defects are the leading cause of infant mortality in the United States. Although some can be successfully treated, many more either are fatal or lead to a lifetime of often serious disability.

Two kinds of errors are most frequently responsible for producing impaired children:

1. *Genetic errors.* The program of information that is coded into DNA (the genetic material) may be in some way abnormal because of the occurrence of a mutation. Consequently, when the DNA code is "read" and its instructions followed, the child that develops will be impaired. The defective gene may have been inherited, or it may be due to a new mutation. Single-gene defects are typically inherited. For example, phenylketonuria (PKU) results when the gene that encodes the enzyme phenylalanine hydroxylase that breaks down the amino acid phenylalanine is missing or faulty. Phenylalanine is produced when protein metabolizes, and if it is not broken down, the buildup results in brain damage. Other birth defects are produced by a combination of inherited genes and mutations. Most of these defects are not well understood and occur in a sporadic (i.e., unpredictable) way.

2. *Congenital errors.* "Congenital" means only "present at birth," and since genetic defects have results that are present at birth, the term is misleading. Ordinarily, however, the phrase is used to designate errors that result during the developmental process. The impairment, then, is not in the original code of genes, but results either from genetic damage or from the reading of the code. The "manufacture and assembly" of the materials that constitute the child's development are affected.

We know that many factors can influence fetal development. Radiation (such as X-rays), drugs (such as thalidomide), chemicals (such as mercury), and nutritional deficiencies (such as lack of folic acid) can all cause changes in an otherwise normal process. Also, biological disease agents, such as certain viruses or spirochetes, may intervene in development, altering the machinery of the cells, interfering with the formation of tissues, and defeating the carefully programmed process that leads to a normal child. In about half the cases in which a baby is born with an impairment, however, the cause is not known.

Specific Impairments

Once an impaired child is born, the medical and moral problems are immediate. Let us consider now some of the defects commonly found in newborn children. Our focus will be more on what they are than on what caused them, for, as far as the moral issue is concerned, how the child came to be impaired is of no importance.

Down Syndrome

This is a chromosomal disorder first identified in 1866 by the English physician J. L. H. Down. Normally, humans have twenty-three pairs of chromosomes, but Down syndrome results from the presence of an extra chromosome. The condition is called trisomy 21, for, instead of a twenty-first pair of chromosomes, the affected person has a twenty-first triple. (Less often, the syndrome is produced when the string of chromosomes gets twisted and chromosome pair number 21 sticks to number 15.)

In ways not wholly understood, the normal process of development is altered by the extra chromosome. The child is born with retardation and various physical abnormalities. Typically, the latter are relatively minor and include such features as a broad skull, a large tongue, and an upward slant of the eyelids. It is this last feature that led to the name "mongolism" for the condition, a name no longer in use in medicine.

Down syndrome occurs in about one of every 800 births. The risk of a baby's being born with the condition rises with the age of the mother, although it is not known why this is so. In young women, the syndrome occurs at a rate of one in every 2000 births; in women over 40, it increases to one in one hundred, and in women over 50, it rises to one in twelve. In 1984, researchers discovered that certain chromosomes sometimes contain an extra copy of a segment known as the *nucleolar organizing region*. This abnormality seems linked to Down's syndrome, and families in which either parent has the abnormality are twenty times more likely to have an afflicted child. Researchers hope to use such information to develop a reliable screening test.

There is no cure for Down syndrome—no way to compensate for the abnormality of the development process. Those with the defect generally have an IQ of about 50–80 and usually require the care and help of others. They can learn basic tasks and can follow routines. Despite their impairment, people with Down syndrome can live semi-independent lives and usually seem to be quite happy. Because they frequently have heart abnormalities and other problems, people with Down syndrome used to die in their twenties and thirties. With close medical attention, they now live into their fifties and beyond. In the United States, the life expectancy of someone with Down syndrome is 56. (See the following section for an account of prenatal tests for the syndrome.)

Spina Bifida

Spina bifida is a general name for birth impairments that involve an opening in the spine. In development, the spine of the child with spina bifida fails to fuse properly, and often the open vertebrae permit the membrane covering the spinal cord to protrude to the outside. The membrane sometimes forms a bulging, thin sac that contains spinal fluid and nerve tissue. When nerve tissue is present, the condition is called *myelomeningocele*. This form of spina bifida is a very severe one and often has a harsh prognosis.

Complications arising from spina bifida must often be treated surgically. The opening in the spine must be closed, and in severe cases the sac must be removed and the nerve tissue inside placed within the spinal canal. Normal skin is then grafted over the area. The danger of an infection of the meninges (meningitis) is great; thus, treatment with antibiotics is also necessary.

Furthermore, a child with spina bifida is likely to require orthopedic operations to attempt to correct the deformities of the legs and feet that occur because of muscle weakness and lack of muscular control due to nerve damage. The bones of such children are thin and brittle, and fractures are frequent.

A child born with spina bifida is virtually always paralyzed to some extent, usually below the waist. Because of the nerve damage, the child will have limited sensation in the lower part of the body. This means he will have no control over his bladder or bowels. The lack of bladder control may result in infection of the bladder, urinary tract, and kidneys because the undischarged urine may serve as a breeding place for microorganisms. Surgery may help with the problems of bowel and urinary incontinence.

The incidence of spina bifida is between one and ten per 1000 births. Roughly 2000 babies a year are born with the disorder. For reasons that remain speculative, among whites the rate is three times higher in families of low socioeconomic status than in families of higher socioeconomic status. The rate in the black population is less than half that in the white population. In 1994, the federal government began requiring the addition of folic acid to enriched grain products, and a 2005 study showed that, during the period 1995–2002, there was a significant decrease in the prevalence of spina bifida and anencephaly. (See the discussion that follows.) Folic acid is a B vitamin found in green vegetables, beans, and orange juice, but how it might work to provide a protective effect is unknown. Spina bifida is almost always accompanied by hydrocephaly.

Hydrocephaly

"Hydrocephaly" literally means "water on the brain." When, for whatever reason, the flow of fluid through the spinal canal is blocked, the cerebro-spinal fluid produced within the brain cannot escape. Pressure buildup from the fluid can cause brain damage, and if it is not released, the child will die. Although hydrocephaly is frequently the result of spina bifida, it can have several other causes and can occur late in a child's development. Treatment requires surgically inserting a thin tube, or shunt, to drain the fluid from the skull to the heart or abdomen, where it can be absorbed. The operation can save the baby's life, but physical and mental damage is frequent. Placing the shunt and getting it to work properly are difficult tasks that may require many operations. If hydrocephaly accompanies spina bifida, it is treated first.

Anencephaly

This term literally means "without brain." In this invariably fatal condition, the cerebral hemispheres of the brain are totally absent. The defect is related to spina bifida, for in some forms the bones of the skull are not completely formed and leave an opening through which brain material bulges to the outside. There is never hope for improvement by any known means.

Esophageal Atresia

In medical terms, an atresia is the closing of a normal opening or canal. The esophagus is the muscular tube that extends from the back of the throat to the stomach. Sometimes the tube forms without an opening, or it does not completely develop so that it does not extend to the stomach. The condition must be corrected by surgery in order for the child to get food into its stomach. The chances of success in such surgery are very high.

Duodenal Atresia

The duodenum is the upper part of the small intestine. Food from the stomach empties into it. When the duodenum is closed off, food cannot pass through and be digested. Surgery can repair this condition and is successful in most cases.

Problems of Extreme Prematurity

A normal pregnancy lasts approximately forty weeks. Infants born after only twenty-six weeks of growth or less typically fail to live. Those born in the weeks after that time have extremely low birth weights. About half of those weighing from 1 to 1.5 pounds fail to survive, and those who do have a multiplicity of problems resulting from the fact that their bodies have simply not had the time to develop adequately to cope with the demands of life outside the uterus.

The undeveloped lungs of premature infant are inefficient and prone to infections. The mechanical ventilation needed to assist their breathing may result in long-term lung damage. Extremely premature infants are subject to cerebral hemorrhages ("brain bleeds") that may lead to seizures, blindness, deafness, retardation, and a variety of less noticeable disabilities. (For a discussion of extremely premature infants and the moral issues they present with respect to withholding or withdrawing treatment, see the Social Context "The Dilemma of Extreme Prematurity," in this chapter.)

Testing for Impairments

Genetic impairments are inherited; they are the outcome of the genetic endowment of the child. A carrier of defective genes who has children can pass on the genes. Congenital impairments are not inherited and cannot be passed on.

With proper genetic counseling, individuals belonging to families in which certain diseases "run" can assess the risk that their children might be impaired by examining patterns of inheritance. Also, some genetic diseases can be diagnosed before birth (or even in the embryo) by detecting the presence of the gene.

(See Chapter 8 for a discussion of screening for genetic diseases.) Some developmental anomalies, such as the chromosomal abnormality resulting in Down syndrome, can be detected by examining genetic material during fetal development. Large abnormalities in the developing fetus (such as anencephaly, or "missing brain") can often be detected by the use of images produced by ultrasound (sonography).

Amniocentesis and CVS

Until recently, the most used and most reliable methods of prenatal diagnosis were amniocentesis and chorionic villus sampling (CVS). Both involve direct cell studies. In amniocentesis, the amnion (the membrane surrounding the fetus) is punctured with a needle and some of the amniotic fluid is removed for examination. The procedure cannot be usefully and safely performed until fourteen to sixteen weeks into the pregnancy. Until that time, the amount of fluid is inadequate.

The risk to the woman and to the fetus from the procedure is relatively small, usually less than one percent. (The risk that the procedure will result in a miscarriage is about one in 200.) If amniocentesis is performed eleven to twelve weeks after conception, there is a small increase in the probability that the child will have a deformed foot.

Chorionic villus sampling (CVS) involves retrieving hair-like villi cells from the developing placenta. The advantage of the test is that it can be employed six to ten weeks after conception. Although the procedure is as safe as amniocentesis, a 1994 study by the Centers for Disease Control found that infants whose mothers had undergone CVS from 1988 to 1992 had a 0.03 percent risk of missing or undeveloped fingers or toes. A later study questioned this finding and found no reason to believe that the risk of fetal damage is greater than normal.

Amniocentesis came into wide use only in the early 1960s. At first, it was restricted mostly to testing fetuses in cases in which there was a risk of Rh incompatibility. When the mother lacks a group of blood proteins called the Rhesus (or Rh) factor, and the fetus has it, the immune system of the mother may produce antibodies against the fetus. The result for the fetus may be anemia, brain damage, and even death.

It was soon realized that additional information about the fetus could be gained from further analysis of the amniotic fluid and the fetal cells in it. The fluid can be chemically assayed, and the cells can be grown in cultures for study. An examination of the DNA can show whether there are any known abnormalities that are likely to cause serious physical or mental defects.

Some disorders (such as Tay–Sachs disease) can be detected by chemical analysis of the amniotic fluid. However, some of the more common genetic diseases, such as PKU, Huntington's, and muscular dystrophy, require an analysis of the genetic material. Because only males have a Y chromosome, it's impossible to examine fetal cells without also discovering the gender of the fetus.

Amniocentesis and CVS do pose slight hazards. Accordingly, neither is regarded as a routine procedure to be performed in every pregnancy. There must be some indication that the fetus is at risk from a genetic or developmental disorder. One indication is the age of the mother. Down syndrome is much more likely to occur in fetuses conceived in women over the age of thirty-five. Because the syndrome is produced by a chromosome abnormality, an examination of the chromosomes in the cells of the fetus can reveal the defect.

Alphafetoprotein

A test for Down syndrome introduced in the 1980s employs a blood sample taken from the pregnant woman. The sample is examined for the presence of three fetal proteins. About sixteen to eighteen weeks after gestation, fetuses with Down syndrome are known to produce abnormally small quantities of estriol and alphafetoprotein and abnormally large amounts of chorionic gonadotropin. The levels of the proteins, plus such factors as the woman's age, can be used to determine the statistical probability of a child with the syndrome. This test avoids the risks of amniocentesis and CVS.

A blood test for the presence of alphafetoprotein can also indicate the likelihood of neural tube defects characteristic of spina bifida. Ultrasound can then be used to confirm or detect these or other developmental anomalies.

New Noninvasive Tests

A 2005 study of 117 cases of Down syndrome occurring in some 38,000 pregnant women found that a combination of three noninvasive tests at eleven to thirteen weeks of gestation was eighty-seven percent accurate in predicting whether the fetus had Down syndrome. The tests were an ultrasound examination of the thickness of the fetal neck (nuchal translucency) and two blood tests. The first was a test for pregnancy-associated plasma protein A(PAPP-A), and the second was a test for beta human chorionic gonadotropin (HCG). If a second ultrasound to detect the presence or absence of a fetal nasal bone is added, the detection rate of Down syndrome rises to ninety-seven percent.

An estimated six percent of all live births, some 200,000 infants a year, require intensive neonatal care. The afflictions singled out for special mention are those which are most often the source of major moral problems. Those correctable by standard surgical procedures present no special moral difficulties. But even they are often associated with other impairments, such as Down syndrome, that make them important factors in moral deliberations.

Ethical Theories and the Problem of Birth Impairments

A great number of serious moral issues are raised by impaired newborns. Should they be given only ordinary care, or should special efforts be made to save their lives? Should they be given no care and allowed to die? Should they be killed in a merciful manner? Who should decide what is in the interest of the child? Might acting in the interest of the child require not acting to save the child's life?

A more basic question that cuts even deeper than these concerns the status of the newborn. It is virtually the same as the question raised in Chapter 9 about the fetus—namely, Are severely impaired newborns persons? It might be argued that some infants are so severely impaired that they should not be considered persons in a relevant moral sense. Not only do they lack the capacity to function, but they lack even the potentiality for ordinary psychological and social development. In this respect, they are worse off than most maturing fetuses.

If this view is accepted, then the principles of our moral theories do not require that we act to preserve the lives of impaired newborns. We might, considering their origin, be disposed to show them some consideration and treat them benevolently—perhaps in the same way we might deal with animals that are in a similarly hopeless condition. We might kill them or allow them to die as a demonstration of our compassion.

One major difficulty with this view is that it is not at all clear which impaired infants could legitimately be considered nonpersons. Birth defects vary widely in severity, and, unless one is prepared to endorse infanticide generally, it is necessary to have defensible criteria for distinguishing among newborns. Also, one must defend a general concept of a person that would make it reasonable to regard human offspring as occupying a different status.

By contrast, it might be claimed that the fact that a newborn is a human progeny is sufficient to consider it a person. Assuming that this is so, the question becomes, How ought we to treat a severely impaired infant person? Just because they are infants, impaired newborns cannot express wishes, make claims, or enter into deliberations. All that is done concerning them must be done by others.

A utilitarian might decide that the social and personal cost (the suffering of the infant, the anguish of the parents and family, the monetary cost to the family and society) of saving the life of such an infant is greater than the social and personal benefits that can be expected. Accordingly, such a child should not be allowed to live, and it should be killed as painlessly as possible to minimize its suffering. Yet a rule utilitarian might claim, on the contrary, that the rule "Save every child where possible" would, in the long run, produce more utility than disutility.

The natural law position of Roman Catholicism is that even the most defective newborn is a human person. Yet this view does not require that extraordinary means be used to save the life of such a child. The suffering of the family, great expense, and the need for multiple operations would be reasons for providing only ordinary care. Ordinary care does not mean that every standard medical procedure that might help should be followed. It means only that the defective newborn should receive care of the same type provided for a normal infant. It would be immoral to kill the child or to cause its death by withholding all care.

If the infant is a person, then Kant would regard it as possessing an inherent dignity and value. But the infant in its condition lacks the capacity to reason and to express its will. How, then, should we, acting as its agents, treat the infant? Kant's principles provide no clear-cut answer. The infant does not threaten our own existence, and we have no grounds for killing him. But, it could be argued, we should allow the child to die. We can imaginatively put ourselves in the place of the infant. Although it would be morally wrong to will our own death (which, Kant claimed, would involve a self-defeating maxim), we might express our autonomy and rationality by choosing to refuse treatment that would prolong a painful and hopeless life. If this is so, then we might act in this way on behalf of the defective child. We might allow the child to die. Indeed, it may be our duty to do so. A similar line of argument from Ross's viewpoint might lead us to decide that, although we have a prima facie duty to preserve the child's life, our actual duty is to allow him to die.

Another basic question remains: Who is to make the decision about how an impaired newborn is to be treated? Traditionally, the assumption has been that this is a decision best left to the infant's parents and physicians. Because they can be assumed to have the highest concern for the infant's welfare and the most knowledge about its condition and prospects, they are the ones who should have the primary responsibility for deciding her fate. If there is reason to believe that they are not acting in a responsible manner, then it becomes the responsibility of the courts to guarantee that the interests of the infant are served.

Hardly any responsible person advocates heroic efforts to save the lives of infants who are most severely impaired, and hardly anyone advocates not treating infants with relatively simple and correctable impairments. The difficult cases are those which fall somewhere along the continuum. Advances in medical management and technology can now save the lives of many infants who earlier would have died relatively quickly, and yet we still lack the power to provide those infants with a life that we might judge to be worthwhile. Yet a failure to treat such infants does not invariably result in their deaths, and a failure to provide them with early treatment may mean that they are even more impaired than they would be otherwise.

No one believes that we currently have a satisfactory solution to this dilemma. It is important to keep in mind that it is not a purely intellectual problem. The context in which particular decisions are made is one of doubt, confusion, and genuine anguish.

Envoi

In 1973, R. S. Duff and A. G. M. Campbell shocked the public by reporting that during a thirty-month period forty-three infants at the Yale–New Haven Hospital had been permitted to die. Each of the children suffered from one or more severe birth defects. Although the staff of the hospital took no steps to end the lives of the infants, treatment was withheld from them.

Such decisions had been made for years in hospitals throughout the world. Sometimes they were made by physicians acting alone and sometimes by physicians in consultation with families. But almost never had the situation been discussed openly and publicly.

Now there is more openness about the whole complex of moral and human problems presented by impaired newborns. There is a greater willingness to consider the possibility that saving the life of a child might not be the right act to perform—that it may even be our duty to assist the child's dying. The time of covert decisions and half-guilty conferences has passed. The issues are there, they are known to be there, and they must be faced.

We must also face questions about how we as a society will respond to the needs of children who are severely impaired and the associated needs of their families and caregivers. Medicine has become progressively more successful at keeping alive infants who might once have died, but as these infants grow older, they are likely to have an array of medical, social, educational, and pshychological problems. We have taken only small steps toward the goal of integrating impaired children and adults into our society.

We have done almost nothing to recognize that the people who care about, and (typically) care for, impaired children need help. The constant worry of aging parents responsible for a seriously impaired adult child is captured in the question "Who will take care of her when we are dead?" This is a question that we as a society have not answered.

Chapter 7

Euthanasia and Assisted Suicide

CASES AND CONTEXTS

Karen Quinlan: The Debate Begins

At two in the morning on Tuesday, April 14, 1975, Mrs. Julie Quinlan was awakened by a telephone call. When she hung up she was crying. "Karen is very sick," Mrs. Quinlan said to her husband, Joseph. "She's unconscious, and we have to go to Newton Hospital right away."

The Quinlans thought their twenty-one-year-old adopted daughter might have been in an automobile accident. But the doctor in the intensive-care unit told them that wasn't so. Karen was in a critical comatose state of unknown cause and was being given oxygen through a mask taped over her nose and mouth. She had been brought to the hospital by two friends who had been with her at a birthday party. After a few drinks, she had started to pass out, and her friends decided she must be drunk and put her to bed. Then someone checked on her later in the evening and found that Karen wasn't breathing. Her friends gave her mouth-to-mouth resuscitation and rushed her to the nearest hospital.

Blood and urine tests showed that Karen had not consumed a dangerous amount of alcohol. They also showed the presence of .6 milligram of aspirin and the tranquilizer Valium. Two milligrams would have been toxic, five lethal. Why Karen stopped breathing was mysterious. But it was during that time that part of her brain died from oxygen depletion.

After Karen had been unconscious for about a week, she was moved to St. Clare's Hospital in nearby Denville, where testing and life-support facilities were better. Dr. Robert J. Morse, a neurologist, and Dr. Arshad Javed, a pulmonary internist, became her physicians. Additional tests were made. Extensive brain damage was confirmed, and several possible causes of the coma were ruled out.

No Longer the Same

During the early days, the Quinlans were hopeful. Karen's eyes opened and closed, and her mother and her nineteen-year-old sister, Mary Ellen, thought that they detected signs that Karen recognized them. But Karen's condition began to deteriorate. Her weight gradually dropped from 120 pounds to 70 pounds. Her body began to contract into a rigid fetal position, until her five-foot-two-inch frame

was bent into a shape hardly longer than three feet. She was now breathing mechanically, by means of an MA-1 respirator that pumped air through a tube in her throat. By early July, Karen's physicians and her mother, sister, and brother had come to believe it was hopeless to expect her ever to regain consciousness.

Only her father continued to believe it might be possible. But when he told Dr. Morse about some encouraging sign he had noticed, Dr. Morse said to him, "Even if God did perform a miracle so that Karen would live, her damage is so extensive she would spend the rest of her life in an institution." Mr. Quinlan then realized that Karen would never again be as he remembered her. He now agreed with Karen's sister: "Karen would never want to be kept alive on machines like this. She would hate this."

Need to Go to Court

The Quinlans' parish priest, Father Thomas Trapasso, had also assured them that the moral doctrines of the Roman Catholic Church did not require the continuation of extraordinary measures to support a hopeless life. Before making his decision, Mr. Quinlan asked the priest, "Am I playing God?" Father Thomas said, "God has made the decision that Karen is going to die. You're just agreeing with God's decision, that's all."

On July 31, after Karen had been unconscious for three and a half months, the Quinlans gave Drs. Morse and Jared their permission to take Karen off the respirator. The Quinlans signed a letter authorizing the discontinuance of extraordinary procedures and absolving the hospital from all legal liability. "I think you have come to the right decision," Dr. Morse said to Mr. Quinlan.

But the next morning Dr. Morse called Mr. Quinlan. "I have a moral problem about what we agreed on last night," he said. "I feel I have to consult somebody else and see how he feels about it." The next day, Dr. Morse called again. "I find I will not do it," he said. "And I've informed the administrator at the hospital that I will not do it."

The Quinlans were upset and bewildered by the change in Dr. Morse. Later they talked with the hospital attorney and were told by him that, because Karen was over twenty-one, they were no longer her legal guardians. The Quinlans would have to go to court and be appointed to guardianship. After that, the hospital might or might not remove Karen from the respirator.

Mr. Quinlan consulted attorney Paul Armstrong. Because Karen was an adult without income, Mr. Quinlan explained, Medicaid was paying the $450 a day it cost to keep her alive. The Quinlans thus had no financial motive in asking that the respirator be taken away. Mr. Quinlan said that his belief that Karen should be allowed to die rested on his conviction that it was God's will, and it was for this reason that he wanted to be appointed Karen's guardian.

Legal Arguments

Mr. Armstrong filed a plea with Judge Robert Muir of the New Jersey Superior Court on September 12, 1975. He explicitly requested that Mr. Quinlan be appointed Karen's guardian so that he would have "the express power of authorizing the discontinuance of all extraordinary means of sustaining her life."

Later, on October 20, Mr. Armstrong argued the case on three constitutional grounds. First, he claimed that there is an implicit right to privacy guaranteed by the Constitution and that this right permits individuals or others acting for them to terminate the use of extraordinary medical measures, even when death may result. This right holds, Armstrong said, unless there are compelling state interests that set it aside.

Second, Armstrong argued that the First Amendment guarantee of religious freedom extended to the Quinlan case. If the court did not allow them to act in accordance with the doctrines of their church, their religious liberty would be infringed. Finally, Armstrong appealed to the "cruel and unusual punishment" clause of the Eighth Amendment. He claimed that "for the state to require that Karen Quinlan be kept alive, against her will and the will of her family, after the dignity, beauty, promise, and meaning of earthly life have vanished, is cruel and unusual punishment."

Karen's mother, sister, and a friend testified that Karen had often talked about not wanting to be kept alive by machines. An expert witness, a neurologist, testified that Karen was in a "chronic vegetative state" and that it was unlikely that she would ever regain consciousness. Doctors testifying for St. Clare's Hospital and Karen's physicians agreed with this. But, they argued, her brain still showed patterns of electrical activity, and she still had a discernible pulse.

Thus, she could not be considered dead by legal or medical criteria.

On November 10, Judge Muir ruled against Joseph Quinlan. He praised Mr. Quinlan's character and concern, but he decided that Mr. Quinlan's anguish over his daughter might cloud his judgment about her welfare, so he should not be made her guardian. Furthermore, Judge Muir said, because Karen is still medically and legally alive, "the Court should not authorize termination of the respirator. To do so would be homicide and an act of euthanasia."

Appeal

Mr. Armstrong appealed the decision to the New Jersey Supreme Court. On January 26, 1976, the court convened to hear arguments, and Mr. Armstrong argued substantially as before. But this time the court's ruling was favorable. The court agreed that Mr. Quinlan could assert a right of privacy on Karen's behalf and that whatever he decided for her should be accepted by society. It also set aside any criminal liability for removing the respirator, claiming that if death resulted, it would not be homicide, and that, even if it were homicide, it would not be unlawful. Finally, the court stated that if Karen's physicians believed that she would never emerge from her coma, they should consult an ethics committee to be established by St. Clare's Hospital. If the committee accepted their prognosis, then the respirator could be removed. If Karen's present physicians were then unwilling to take her off the respirator, Mr. Quinlan was free to find a physician who would.

Six weeks after the court decision, the respirator still had not been turned off. In fact, another machine, one for controlling body temperature, had been added. Mr. Quinlan met with Morse and Jared and demanded that they remove the respirator. They agreed to "wean" Karen from the machine, and soon she was breathing without mechanical assistance. Dr. Morse and St. Clare's Hospital were determined that Karen would not die while under their care. Although she was moved to a private room, it was next door to the intensive-care unit. They intended to put her back on the respirator at the first sign of breathing difficulty.

Because Karen was still alive, the Quinlans began a long search for a chronic-care hospital. Twenty or more institutions turned them away, and physicians expressed great reluctance to become involved in the case. Finally, Dr. Joseph Fennelly volunteered to treat Karen, and on June 9 she was moved from St. Clare's to the Morris View Nursing Home.

The End—After Ten Years

Karen Quinlan continued to breathe. She received high-nutrient feedings and regular doses of antibiotics to ward off infections. During some periods she was more active than at others, making reflexive responses to touch and sound.

On June 11, 1985, at 7:01 in the evening, ten years after she lapsed into a coma, Karen Quinlan finally died. She was thirty-one years old.

Her father died of cancer on December 10, 1996, at the Karen Quinlan Center of Hope, a hospice Joseph and Julia Quinlan had founded in 1980 with money they received from the film and book rights to their daughter's story. Joseph Quinlan continued to support the right of patients and their families to discontinue the use of life-sustaining technologies, but he opposed all forms of physician-assisted suicide.

SOCIAL CONTEXT
When the Diagnosis Is Death

Unlike our computers, our bodies aren't equipped with a tiny light that stops glowing when they stop functioning. Thus, no society has ever been quite sure when to declare someone dead. Some cultures in the Middle East don't consider people dead until three days after their hearts stop beating.

Parents are often faced with a terrible situation in which, in outward appearance, their child is still alive. Their son's blood is circulating, his temperature is normal, and his chest moves in and out. Yet what they are seeing is an illusion of life created by drugs and machines. Fifty years earlier, the parents wouldn't have had to deal with the emotional and conceptual challenge of accepting the fact that their son is dead and that stopping his treatment is the right thing to do.

Death as a Practical Matter

"When is someone dead?" didn't become a practical question until the rise of intensive-care medicine in the 1950s and the increasing success of organ transplantation in the 1970s. People began to ask, "If a physician switches off the ventilator that is keeping a patient's body supplied with oxygen, is this homicide?" and "If a surgeon removes the heart from a breathing patient, has she killed him?"

These questions became more than academic exercises for a few surgeons who were

arrested and charged with homicide, and finding answers became more urgent for personal and practical reasons. If surgeons couldn't remove organs from a body with a beating heart without fearing a trial and a prison sentence, they would no longer perform transplants.

Discussions during the 1970s and 1980s about determining criteria for death led to the development of four basic ideas about what it means to be dead:

1. *Cardiopulmonary.* A person is dead when her heart stops beating and she is no longer breathing. This is the traditional definition of death as "the permanent cessation of breathing and blood circulation." It is akin to what people have in mind when they say, "He died twice while they were operating on him."

2. *Whole Brain.* Death is "the irreversible cessation of all brain functions." A person is dead when his brain displays no organized electrical activity and even the brain stem, which controls basic functions such as breathing and blood pressure, is electrically silent.

3. *Higher Brain.* Death is the permanent loss of consciousness. An individual in an irreversible coma is dead, even though her brain stem continues to regulate her heartbeat and blood pressure.

4. *Personhood.* Death occurs when someone ceases to be a person. Relevant to deciding whether this has happened is information about the absence of mental activities such as reasoning, remembering, experiencing an emotion, anticipating the future, and interacting with others.

These ideas remain the definitions at the focus of current debates.

Death as a Diagnosis

The definition of death in the 1985 federal Universal Determination of Death Act is a straightforward endorsement of the first two concepts:

An individual who has sustained either (1) irreversible cessation of circulatory and respiratory functions or (2) irreversible cessation of all functions of the entire brain, including the brain stem, is dead.

This definition is embodied in the laws of all fifty states, but that we accept both concepts can be confusing. Many people don't see how someone whose body is still working can be declared dead. But many others don't see how someone can be declared dead unless a doctor tests him to make sure that he is brain dead. The key to eliminating such confusions is recognizing that death is a diagnosis governed by two sets of criteria. In some circumstances, cardiopulmonary criteria are appropriate, while in others, brain death criteria are. Neither set trumps the other.

Diagnosis

A physician makes a diagnosis by confirming the hypothesis that the patient's disorder best fits into a particular category. Thus, a five-year-old girl who has a fever, light sensitivity, and a red, pustular rash has chicken pox. Symptoms and signs define the "chicken pox" category, and the data about the little girl confirm the hypothesis that these criteria are met. The same is so when "death" is the diagnostic category.

Cardiopulmonary

The cardiopulmonary criteria dictate that a patient is dead when his circulatory and respiratory functions have irreversibly ceased. To determine whether the data support this hypothesis, the physician examines the patient. She may feel for a pulse in the carotid or femoral artery and use a stethoscope to listen for heart and lung sounds. She may use an ophthalmoscope to see if the blood in the vessels in the retinas has broken into the stagnant segments which indicate that the blood isn't circulating. (This criterion is called the *boxcars sign*.) She may also perform an electrocardiogram to determine whether the heart is displaying any electrical activity. Using such data, the physician may conclude that the cardiopulmonary criteria are satisfied. That is, death is her diagnostic conclusion.

Whole Brain

The diagnosis of death by means of whole-brain criteria follows similar diagnostic logic, but two restrictions govern the use of such criteria. First, they don't apply to encephalic infants or children under two. Encephalic infants are born without brain hemispheres, and because they lack even the potential for consciousness, it makes no sense to test for its loss. Also, young children develop at such different rates neurologically that clinical and imaging tests can't be used to make reliable predictions. For these groups, only cardiopulmonary criteria are appropriate for determining death.

Second, before a physician pronounces someone in a coma dead, he must rule out reversible causes. He must establish that drugs, an internal chemical imbalance (as in diabetes), or hypothermia isn't the cause of the coma. Patients with these conditions may show clinical signs of death, yet recover consciousness. For example, fugu—puffer-fish liver—is a delicacy in Japan, but if a diner eats too much, its poison (a tetrodotoxin) may induce a state in which his pulse and respiration are so slow that they are difficult to detect. Some people have come awake to find themselves naked, cold, and shivering in the morgue. (It seems likely that others didn't come awake at the right time.) Thus, it's crucial for the examining physician to be sure that a patient hasn't consumed something that might cause a reversible coma.

Once these preliminary conditions are met, the physician examines the patient to determine whether her brain stem has suffered irreversible damage. She is removed briefly from a ventilator, at least once and often twice, to see if an increase in carbon dioxide in her blood will trigger her body to breathe. If it doesn't, then damage to the brain stem is indicated.

The physician tests other reflexes controlled by the brain stem. He strokes the back of the patient's throat to check her gag reflex, shines a light in her eyes to see if her pupils contract, touches her eyeball to test for a blink response, and sticks her with a needle to look for a pain response. He may turn her head to the side to see if her eyes move with it—the *"doll's eyes" sign.*

Clinical observations like these are the prime data used to determine death. Often, however, an MRI or a CT scan is obtained to look for the amount and location of the brain damage, and an electroencephalogram (EEG) is employed to confirm the clinical judgment that the patient's brain has undergone irreversible structural damage. (The brain probably will show some electrical activity, because isolated groups of cells remain active, but there must be no pattern of organized activity.) These tests are most likely to be used when a patient is young or was not expected to die from his injury or disease. The physician relies on the data they produce to decide whether they support the hypothesis that the patient's brain has suffered an irreversible loss of all functions. If so, death is the diagnosis.

Success

The cardiopulmonary criteria in the Uniform Determination of Death Act are traditional, but the brain-death criteria are modeled on those in the 1968 report of the Harvard Medical School's Ad Hoc Committee to Examine the Definition of Brain Death. The Committee was explicit about why a definition was needed: "Our primary purpose," the report stated, "is to define irreversible coma as a new criterion for death," because the cardiopulmonary criteria "can lead to controversy in obtaining organs for transplantation." Also, the Committee wanted to avoid wasting resources on patients who are unable to benefit from life-support measures and to spare their families the financial and emotional costs of supporting them.

More than ninety-nine percent of the people who die in hospitals are pronounced dead by traditional cardiopulmonary criteria. Those declared dead by brain-death criteria are always patients receiving intensive care. Once they are declared dead, they are taken off life support or, with the consent of their families, their organs are removed for transplantation.

The Harvard Committee was successful in both its aims. The concept of brain death freed many families from the doubt and guilt involved in deciding to remove someone from intensive care. The concept also improved the success rate of transplants by allowing surgeons to use undamaged organs from bodies kept functioning by intensive measures.

Higher Brain Function and PVS

Some would like to see society adopt the third concept and define death as the "irreversible loss of *higher* brain function." This would expand the criteria for determining death to include those in a persistent vegetative state (PVS).

Those diagnosed with PVS have damaged cerebral hemispheres, and this results in their not being aware of themselves or their surroundings. They are incapable of thinking or intentional movement, but if their brain stems are undamaged, their autonomic nervous system continues to control their reflexes.

Thus, PVS patients can breathe and excrete, their hearts beat, their muscles respond to stimuli, and they cycle through regular sleep–wake patterns. Although their eyelids may blink and their eyes move, they lack the brain capacity needed to see. They are like digital cameras with a functioning optical system but no microprocessor: information is supplied, but can't be used. Some PVS patients may smile or produce tears that run down their cheeks, but these are reflexes that are only accidentally connected with what's happening around them.

After six months to a year, PVS patients are not likely to recover even the most rudimentary form of consciousness. They aren't like patients diagnosed as "minimally conscious," who have some episodes of awareness and a small, yet real, possibility of waking up. PVS patients remain vegetative for as long as they live, which may be for decades. Karen Quinlan lived for almost ten years, and Nancy Cruzan was allowed to die after seven. Terri Schiavo slipped into a coma in 1990 and died in 2005, only after a protracted legal battle by her parents to keep her husband from ordering her removed from life support. (See the Case Presentation "Terri Schiavo," in this chapter.)

PVS patients require total care. They must be fed through a surgically implanted gastric tube, hydrated with IV fluids, bathed and toileted, kept on special mattresses and turned to avoid pressure sores, given antibiotics to prevent infections, and provided with around-the-clock nursing care.

If the "irreversible loss of higher brain function" were accepted as the third legal definition of death, PVS patients could be declared dead and no longer given life-support measures, including gastric feeding and IV hydration. Such acceptance wouldn't require a court decision or even a request from the family.

Adopting this criterion would mean that as many as fifty thousand PVS patients in the United States could be removed from life support. (No one is sure of the exact number of PVS patients.) This would result in immense savings, because it costs about one hundred thousand dollars a year to provide care for a PVS patient. The money, proponents of adopting the criterion argue, could be better spent on extending the lives of those who are conscious and play a role in the lives of their family and society.

Unlikely

The whole-brain definition of death was accepted in our society with little fuss. To most people, it made intuitive sense that someone whose brain isn't functioning at all and will never function again can't be alive. The criterion also seemed cut and dried: the EEG shows that the brain is electrically silent.

The higher brain definition is unlikely ever to be accepted. It lacks the precision and certainty that makes the whole-brain definition uncontroversial. Given the same data from brain scans and clinical tests, doctors can disagree about when higher brain functions have been permanently lost. Studies show further that PVS is frequently misdiagnosed, so many patients who are capable of recovery might fall victim to a bad diagnosis.

Also, the families of some PVS patients believe that, no matter how long the odds, the patient may eventually wake up from the coma. The thinking of these families is also probably representative of that of a large part of the population, even those who know no one with PVS.

Loss of Personhood

The definition of death as the loss of personhood has a resonance with most people. We understand what a friend means when she says her mother's progressive dementia has so destroyed her as a person that she might as well be dead.

We see how a woman with a degenerative neurological disorder like Alzheimer's or Huntington's may reach a later stage in which she has lost so much cognitive and emotional functioning that she may no longer be thought of as a person. If we could agree that she has lost whatever is essential to being a person, then, given the "loss of personhood" definition of death, it would be morally permissible for us to withdraw life support.

Understandable or not, the definition isn't likely to gain the support it would need to be adopted as a legal criterion. Exactly what attributes are required to qualify as a person is open to dispute, and we're unlikely to get general agreement on exactly when someone has lost so many of them that she has lost her personhood. Diagnosing death might thus come to be seen as arbitrary. Worse, critics charge, it could open the road to abuse: the old, the poor, and the poorly functioning might stop measuring up to personhood and not be given needed support.

A large number of people will always believe that an individual they care about, no matter how mentally and physically impaired, is the same person as before. Looking like a person and having a history as a person are seen by many as sufficient for being a person. This attitude is not likely to change.

Circle Completed

We end where we began: death can be defined as the permanent failure of heartbeat and respiration or as the permanent failure of the whole brain. These definitions, it is widely agreed, have served us well. That they are seen as objective and precise gives them a strength that the other two definitions can't match. Leaving well enough alone seems to most observers to be our best option.

We can hope that as the concept of brain death becomes more familiar, people faced with a situation in which a loved one has been diagnosed as brain dead won't have to suffer the pain of an unrealistic hope based on doubt. Whether diagnosed by cardiopulmonary criteria or whole-brain criteria, the diagnosis is the same death.

CASE PRESENTATION

Elizabeth Bouvia's Demand to Starve: A Request for Assisted Suicide?

On September 3, 1983, Elizabeth Bouvia was admitted, at her own request, to Riverside General Hospital in Riverside, California. She sought admission on the grounds that she was suicidal. She was twenty-six years old, a victim of cerebral palsy, and almost totally paralyzed. She had the partial use of one arm, could speak, and could chew her food if someone fed it to her. In addition to her paralysis, she suffered almost constant pain from arthritis.

Despite the severity of her handicap, Mrs. Bouvia had earned a degree in social work, been married, and lived independently with the assistance of relatives and others. Then matters became particularly difficult for her. She had not been successful in an attempt to have a child, her husband left her, and she lost the state grant that paid for her special transportation needs.

After her admission, Mrs. Bouvia announced to the hospital staff that she wished to starve herself to death. She asked to be provided with hygienic care and painkilling medicines but no food. She explained that she wanted the hospital to be a place where she would "just be left alone and not bothered by friends or family or anyone else" so that she could "ultimately starve to death" and be free from her "useless body."

Mrs. Bouvia refused to eat the solid food offered to her, and her attending physician stated that if she did not eat, he would have her declared mentally ill and a danger to herself. She could then be force-fed. She responded by calling local newspapers and asking for legal assistance. The American Civil Liberties Union agreed to provide her an attorney, and Richard Stanley Scott became her legal representative.

Mr. Scott convinced her to allow herself to be fed while he made efforts to secure a court order restraining the hospital from either discharging her or force-feeding her. At the court hearing, Mrs. Bouvia testified as to her reasons for refusing nourishment:

> I hate to have someone care for every personal need . . . it's humiliating. It's disgusting, and I choose to no longer do that, no longer to be dependent on someone to take care of me in that manner. . . . I am choosing this course of action due to my physical limitation and disability.

Dr. Donald E. Fisher, head of psychiatry at the hospital, testified that he would force-feed Mrs. Bouvia, even if the court ordered him not to.

On behalf of his client, Mr. Scott argued that her decision to refuse nourishment was "exactly medically and morally analogous to the patient deciding to forgo further kidney dialysis," knowingly accepting death as the consequence.

Judge John H. Hews refused to grant the restraining order. He expressed the view that Mrs. Bouvia was a competent, rational, and sincere person whose decision was based on her physical condition and not upon her recent misfortunes. Nevertheless, allowing her to starve herself to death in the hospital would "have a profound effect" on the staff, other patients, and other handicapped people. Mrs. Bouvia, Judge Hews held, was "not terminal" and might expect to live another fifteen to twenty years. Accordingly, he held that "the established ethics of the medical profession clearly outweigh and overcome her own rights of self-determination" and "force-feeding, however invasive, would be administered for the purpose of saving the life of an otherwise nonterminal patient and should be permitted. There is no other reasonable option." In effect, in Judge Hews's view, Mrs. Bouvia had a right to commit suicide but she did not have the right to have others assist her.

Mrs. Bouvia later refused to eat, and Judge Hews authorized the hospital to feed her against her will. Her attorney argued that this was an unlawful invasion of her privacy and appealed to the California Supreme Court. The court unanimously refused to grant a hearing on the appeal, thus allowing the lower court ruling to stand.

In February 1986, Mrs. Bouvia was back in court. Through her attorney, she sought an injunction to stop High Desert Hospital of Lancaster, California, where she had become a patient, from using a nasogastric tube to feed her against her wishes. In a public statement, she asserted that she had no intention to attempt to starve herself to death but wished only to receive a liquid diet. The hospital's physicians and lawyers maintained that a liquid diet would be a form of starvation and that the law precluded them from agreeing to her demand. The eventual court decision was again in favor of Mrs. Bouvia, and in April the feeding tube was removed.

Elizabeth Bouvia eventually decided that she would begin to eat. The hospital resumed feeding her, and when her health was considered stable once more, she was released. She announced at the time of her release that she had changed her mind about dying, but in 1987 she again reversed herself. She tried starving herself to death but gave up the effort when doctors told her it might take several weeks. She felt she could not endure such side effects as the constant vomiting caused by taking painkilling medications without food. "Starving myself would take too long," she said. "I wish there were a quicker way."

She moved to Los Angeles and took up residence in a small cell-like room at the L.A. County–USC Medical Center. The cost of the room, more than $800 a day, was paid for by MediCal, the California version of the Medicaid program for those unable to pay for medical care. Her father and two sisters visited her a couple of times a year, and friends visited about once a week. Mostly, though, she remained in her bed and watched TV. "The thought of being here another ten years, I just can't fathom," she told a reporter. "I would rather be dead than lie here."

No one seems to know whether Elizabeth Bouvia is still lying in bed and waiting to die. On May 11, 2008, the *Los Angeles Times* mentioned that she was still alive, and in January 2010 the same newspaper referred to her in a story about the death of a judge in one of her court cases. Alive or dead, her initial plan to starve herself to death and the decision by Judge Hews that "the established ethics of the medical profession" outweighed her right to self-determination have continued to be an important part of the background in the debate about physician-assisted suicide.

The Cruzan Case: The Supreme Court Upholds the Right to Die

In the early morning of January 11, 1983, twenty-five-year-old Nancy Cruzan was driving on a deserted county road in Missouri. The road was icy and the car skidded, then flipped over and crashed. Nancy was thrown from the driver's seat and landed face down in a ditch by the side of the road.

An ambulance arrived quickly, but not quickly enough to save her from suffering irreversible brain damage. Nancy never regained consciousness, and her physicians eventually concluded that she had entered into what is known medically as a persistent vegetative state, awake but unaware. The higher brain functions responsible for recognition, memory, comprehension, anticipation, and other cognitive functions had all been lost.

Her arms and legs were drawn into a fetal position, her knees against her chest, and her body stiff and contracted. Only loud sounds and painful stimuli evoked responses, but even those were no more than neurological reflexes.

"We've literally cried over Nancy's body, and we've never seen anything," her father, Joe Cruzan, said. "She has no awareness of herself."

Nancy was incapable of eating, but her body was sustained by a feeding tube surgically implanted in her stomach. She was a patient at the Missouri Rehabilitation Center, but no one expected her to be rehabilitated. She could only be kept alive.

"If only the ambulance had arrived five minutes earlier—or five minutes later," her father lamented.

The cost of Nancy Cruzan's care was $130,000 a year. The bill was paid by the state. Because she was a legal adult when her accident occurred, her family was not responsible for her medical care. Had she been under twenty-one, the Cruzans would have been responsible for her medical bills, as long as they had any financial resources to pay them.

Eight Years Later

In 1991, eight years after her accident, Nancy was almost thirty-three years old, and her physicians estimated that she might live another thirty years. She was like some 10,000 other Americans who are lost in the dark, dimensionless limbo lying between living and dying. Those who love them can think of them only with sadness and despair. Given a choice between lingering in this twilight world and dying, most people find it difficult to imagine anyone would choose not to die.

Hope eventually faded even for Nancy Cruzan's parents. They faced the fact she would never recover her awareness, and the time came when they wanted their daughter to die, rather than be kept alive in her hopeless condition. They asked that the feeding tube used to keep her alive be withdrawn. Officials at the Missouri Rehabilitation Center refused, and Joe and Louise Cruzan were forced to go to court.

Lower Court Decisions

During the court hearings, the family testified that Nancy would not have wanted to be kept alive in her present condition. Her sister Christy said Nancy had told her that she never wanted to be kept alive "just as a vegetable." A friend testified that Nancy had said that if she were injured or sick she wouldn't want to continue her life, unless she could live "halfway normally." Family and friends spoke in general terms of Nancy's vigor and her sense of independence.

In July 1988, Judge Charles E. Teel of the Jasper County Circuit Court ruled that artificially prolonging the life of Nancy Cruzan violated her constitutional right. He wrote, "There is a fundamental right expressed in our Constitution as 'the right to liberty,' which permits an individual to refuse or direct the withholding or withdrawal of artificial death-prolonging procedures when the person has no cognitive brain function."

Missouri Attorney General William Webster said Judge Teel's interpretation of the Missouri living-will law was much broader than the legislature intended and appealed the ruling. In November 1988, in a 4-to-3 decision, the Missouri Supreme Court overruled the decision of the lower court: Nancy Cruzan's parents would not be allowed to disconnect the feeding tube.

The court focused on the state's living-will statute. The law permits the withdrawing of artificial life-support systems in cases in which individuals are hopelessly ill or injured and there is "clear and convincing evidence" that this is what they would want done. The act specifically forbids the withholding of food and water. Judge Teel's reasoning in the lower court decision was that the surgically implanted tube was an invasive medical treatment and that the Missouri law permitted her parents, as guardians, to order it withdrawn.

The Missouri Supreme Court held that the evidence as to what Nancy Cruzan would have wanted did not meet the "clear and convincing" standard required by the law. Also, the evidence did not show that the implanted feeding tube was "heroically invasive" or "burdensome." In the circumstance, then, the state's interest in preserving life should override other considerations.

The court found "no principled legal basis" to permit the Cruzans "to choose the death of their ward." Thus, "in the face of the state's strongly stated policy in favor of life, we choose to err on the side of life, respecting the right of incompetent persons who may wish to live despite a severely diminished quality of life." William Colby, the Cruzans' attorney, appealed the ruling to the U.S. Supreme Court, and for the first time the Court agreed to hear a case involving "right to die" issues.

Supreme Court Decision

On June 25, 1990, the Supreme Court issued a landmark ruling. In a 5-to-4 decision, it rejected Colby's argument that the Court should overturn as unconstitutional the State of Missouri's stringent standard requiring "clear and convincing evidence" as to a comatose patient's wishes. The decision came as a cruel disappointment to Nancy Cruzan's parents, because it meant that they had lost their case.

Yet, for the first time in U.S. judicial history, the Court recognized a strong constitutional basis for living wills and for the designation of another person to act as a surrogate in making medical decisions on behalf of another. Unlike the decisions in *Roe v. Wade* and *Quinlan,* which found a right of privacy in the Constitution, the Court decision in *Cruzan* appealed to a Fourteenth Amendment "liberty interest." The interest involves being free to reject unwanted medical treatment. The Court found grounds for this interest in the common-law tradition, according to which, if one person even touches another without consent or legal justification, then battery is committed.

The Court regarded the latter finding as the basis for requiring that a patient give informed consent to medical treatment. The "logical corollary" of informed consent, the Court held, is that the patient also possesses the right to withhold consent. A difficulty arises, though, when a patient is in no condition to give consent. The problem becomes one of knowing what the patient's wishes would be.

Justice Rehnquist, in the majority opinion, held that the Constitution permits states to decide on the standard that must be met in determining the wishes of a comatose patient. Hence, Missouri's rigorous standard that requires "clear and convincing proof" of the wishes of the patient was allowed to stand. The Court held that it was legitimate for the state to err on the side of caution, "because an erroneous decision not to terminate treatment results in the maintenance of the status quo," while an erroneous decision to end treatment "is not susceptible of correction."

Justice William Brennan dissented strongly from this line of reasoning. He pointed out that making a mistake about a comatose patient's wishes and continuing treatment also has a serious consequence. Maintaining the status quo "robs a patient of the very qualities protected by the right to avoid unwanted medical treatment."

Justice Stevens, in another dissent, argued that the Court's focus on how much weight to give previous statements by the patient missed the point. The Court should have focused on the issue of the best interest of the patient. Otherwise, the only people eligible to exercise their constitutional right to be free of unwanted medical treatment are those "who had the foresight to make an unambiguous statement of their wishes while competent."

One of the more significant aspects of the decision was that the Court made no distinction between providing nutrition and hydration and other forms of medical treatment. One argument on behalf of the state was that providing food and water was not medical treatment. However, briefs filed by medical associations made it clear that determining the formula required by a person in Nancy Cruzan's condition and regulating her feeding are medically complex procedures. The situation is more comparable to determining the contents of an intravenous drip than to giving someone food and water.

The Missouri living-will statute explicitly forbids the withdrawal of food and water. However, the law was not directly at issue in the *Cruzan* case, because Nancy Cruzan's accident occurred before the law was passed. The Court's treatment of nutrition and hydration as just another form of medical treatment has since served as a basis for challenging the constitutionality of the Missouri law, as well as laws in other states containing a similar provision.

The Supreme Court decision placed much emphasis on the wishes of the individual in accepting or rejecting medical treatment. In doing so, it underscored the importance of the living will as a way of indicating our wishes if something should happen to render us incapable of making them known directly. In some states, though, living wills have a legal force only when the individual has a terminal illness (Nancy Cruzan did not) or when the individual has been quite specific about what treatments are unwanted. Because of such limitations, some legal observers recommend that individuals sign a durable power of attorney designating someone to make medical decisions for them if they become legally incompetent.

The Court decision left undecided the question of the constitutionality of assisted suicide. Some state courts have held that, although individuals have a right to die, they do not have a right to the assistance of others in killing themselves. While more than twenty states have passed laws against assisted suicide, only Oregon has made it legal for physicians to prescribe drugs to help patients end their lives.

A Final Court Ruling

What of Nancy Cruzan? The State of Missouri withdrew from the case, and both the family's attorney and the state-appointed guardian filed separate briefs with the Jasper County Circuit Court asking that the implanted feeding tube be removed. A hearing was held to consider both her medical condition and evidence from family and friends about what Nancy Cruzan would wish to be done. On December 14, 1990, Judge Charles Teel ruled that there was evidence to show that her intent, "if mentally able, would be to terminate her nutrition and hydration," and he authorized the request to remove the feeding tube.

Even after the tube was removed, controversy did not end. About twenty-five protesters tried to force their way into Nancy Cruzan's hospital room to reconnect the feeding tube. "The best we can do is not cooperate with anyone trying to starve an innocent person to death," one of the protest leaders said.

Twelve days after the tube was removed, on December 26, 1990, Nancy Cruzan died. Her parents, sisters, and grandparents were at her bedside. Almost eight years had passed since the accident that destroyed her brain and made the remainder of her life a matter of debate.

"We all feel good that Nancy is free at last," her father said at her graveside.

The *Cruzan* decision, by acknowledging a "right to die" and by finding a basis for it in the Constitution, provides states with new opportunities to resolve the issues surrounding the thousands of cases as tragic as Nancy Cruzan's.

CASE PRESENTATION
Terri Schiavo

Michael Schiavo claimed that around four in the morning on February 26, 1990, he was awakened by a dull thud. Startled, he jumped out of bed, and it was then that he discovered his wife Terri sprawled on the floor. Michael knelt down and spoke to her, but she was obviously unconscious. He called 911, but by the time the paramedics arrived and resuscitated Terri, she had suffered damage from which she would never recover.

Teresa Marie Schindler was born on December 31, 1963, in Huntingdon Valley, Pennsylvania. Although overweight during her childhood, she lost fifty pounds in her senior year in high school, and most of the rest of her life she struggled to keep her weight down. She and Michael Schiavo met when she was in her second semester at Bucks County Community College. They married in 1984 and soon moved to St. Petersburg, Florida. Michael worked as a restaurant manager, and Terri got a job as a clerk with an insurance company. Terri's parents, Robert and Mary Schindler, also moved to Florida to be near their daughter and son-in-law. Relations between the parents and the young couple were friendly.

After Terri collapsed at home, she was rushed to the nearest hospital and treated for an apparent heart attack. A blood assay done at the hospital showed that she was suffering from a potassium imbalance, and her doctors thought that this had probably triggered the heart attack. The potassium imbalance, some physicians later suggested, might have been the result of bulimia, the eating disorder that had troubled her life since high school. The cycle of overeating, purging, and dieting characteristic of the disorder can produce a change in the electrolytes in the blood. Because this change disrupts the electrical signals controlling the heart, it may produce cardiac arrest. Terri had continued to work at losing weight in Florida, and at the time of her collapse she weighed only 120 pounds.

Diagnosis

Whatever the reason for Terri's collapse, she failed to regain consciousness. Once she was out of immediate danger, the hospital neurologists performed a series of tests and examinations: Did she respond to a simple command like "Squeeze my hand"? Did her eyes track moving objects? Did her pupils respond to light? Did she show any sign of recognizing Michael or her parents? The answers to these questions were always no.

Terri's neurological responses were distinctly abnormal, and she showed no signs of cognitive functioning. In addition, CT scans of her brain revealed that the disruption of the oxygen supply to her brain caused by the cardiac arrest had damaged the cerebral cortex. The more primitive parts of her brain were undamaged, but the parts responsible for even the most basic forms of thinking and self-awareness had been destroyed.

The neurologists, after reviewing all the evidence, reached the conclusion that Terri Schiavo had suffered damage to her brain that was both severe and irreversible. She was diagnosed as being in a persistent vegetative state.

Persistent Vegetative State

Persistent vegetative state (PVS) is a specific diagnosis, not to be confused with brain death. People diagnosed with PVS have damaged or dysfunctional cerebral

hemispheres, and this results in their not being aware of themselves or their surroundings. They are incapable of thinking and of deliberate or intentional movement. When the brain stem is undamaged, as it was in Terri's case, the autonomic nervous system and a range of bodily reflexes remain intact. (See the Social Context "When the Diagnosis Is Death," in this chapter.)

PVS patients are still able to breathe and excrete; their hearts beat, and their muscles behave reflexively. The patients cycle through regular sleep–wake patterns, but although their eyelids may blink and their eyes move, they lack the brain capacity to see. (They resemble a digital camera with a functioning optical system but no microprocessor—information is supplied, but it can't be used.) Some PVS patients may smile or tears may run down their cheeks, but these events are reflexive and thus are connected with circumstances in which smiling or crying would be appropriate only in an accidental way.

If a patient's brain is injured but not substantially destroyed, the patient may remain in a vegetative state for only a short time. Such a recovery is unusual, however. After a vegetative state lasts four weeks, neurologists consider it *persistent.* In most cases of PVS, if a change for the better has not occurred after three months, it's not likely to occur at all. When PVS lasts for six months, only about half of those with the diagnosis ever acquire any sort of interactive consciousness. Even then, it is only interactive consciousness of the "Squeeze my hand" variety. Such higher functions as talking or answering questions do not occur. (A study by Cambridge University scientists in September 2006 showed that MRI images might be used to make more reliable diagnoses. The study obtained images of conscious people asked to imagine walking around a room in their house or watching a tennis match, then compared them with the images of a brain of a patient who was given the same instructions. The same areas of the patient's brain lighted up. This suggested that her brain was responding to the command, but whether she was having any subjective experience can't be known. Nor is it clear whether the patient or others like her are likely to recover any interactive abilities.)

After six months, PVS patients virtually never recover even the most rudimentary form of consciousness. They remain vegetative as long as they live, which may be for decades. (Karen Quinlan lived almost ten years after lapsing into unconsciousness: see the Case Presentation

"Karen Quinlan: The Debate Begins," in this chapter.) PVS patients require complete care, including feeding through a gastric tube surgically implanted in the stomach and hydration through an IV line, for the remainder of their lives. Because they are prone to infections, they must be carefully monitored and given IV antibiotics prophylactically. They must be kept on special mattresses and moved regularly to prevent the development of bedsores, ulcers caused by the breakdown of the skin and underlying tissue from the constant pressure of the body's weight on the same area.

Neither Brain Dead nor Minimally Conscious

PVS patients have no higher level brain functioning, but they are not brain dead. To be considered brain dead, a patient must be diagnosed as lacking in any detectable brain activity. This means that even the brain stem (which keeps the heart beating and the lungs functioning) must show no functional or electrical activity.

PVS patients are also not in a *minimally conscious state*. Those who fit into this diagnostic category show at least some episodes of awareness. Their eyes may track movement from time to time, though not always. They may respond to commands like "Squeeze my hand for yes" by squeezing for no.

Neurologists consider this category an appropriate diagnosis when the available evidence supports the idea that the patient displays some glimmer of consciousness at least some of the time. Brain scans of minimally conscious patients, for example, show that their language areas respond when a loved one speaks to them. PVS patients display none of these characteristics. Also, minimally conscious patients have a much higher expectation of recovering more consciousness than do PVS patients. Even so, the expectation of any recovery is low, and if any recovery does occur, it is likely to be only slight.

Michael as Guardian

Michael Schiavo, as Terri's husband, became her legal guardian as soon as she was diagnosed as mentally incompetent. In 1992, he sued his wife's gynecologists for malpractice to get the money to pay for her private care. The theory behind the suit was that they had failed to detect the potassium imbalance that led to her heart

attack, which, in turn, led to the loss of oxygen that caused her brain damage. (After Terri Schiavo died, an autopsy showed no evidence that she had suffered a heart attack.) Michael won the suit. He was awarded $750,000 earmarked for Terri's extended care and another $300,000 to compensate him for his loss and suffering.

In 1993, a year later, Michael and his wife's parents, Robert and Mary Schindler, had a disagreement over the care Terri was receiving. Michael later claimed that the disagreement was really over money and that the Schindlers wanted to force him to give them a share of his $300,000 malpractice award. They filed a suit asking the court to remove Michael as Terri's guardian and appoint them in his place. The court found no reason to hold that the care Michael was providing Terri was inadequate, and the suit against him was dismissed.

Treatment Decisions: The Legal Battles

The course of events involving the struggle over the fate of Terri Schiavo became intricate and confusing after the falling-out between Michael and the Schindlers. The clearest way to follow the dispute is to consider the events in chronological order.

1994. Four years after Terri's PVS diagnosis, Michael met with the doctors taking care of her to ask about the likelihood of her ever regaining consciousness. He learned from them that this was unlikely ever to happen. Michael then told the long-term care facility where she was a patient that he didn't want her to be resuscitated if she suffered a heart attack or if some other life-threatening event occurred. (This is known as a "do not resuscitate," or DNR, order.)

Relations between Michael and the Schindlers continued to deteriorate, particularly after Michael and his girlfriend Jodi Centonze had two children together. (The Schindlers had originally encouraged Michael to move on with his life, and he started a relationship with Centonze only after Terri had been in a nursing home for four years.) Supporters of the Schindlers denounced Michael as an adulterer who was not fit to act as Terri's guardian.

1998–2003. Four years after Michael had authorized the DNR order and eight years after Terri was diagnosed as being in a PVS, Michael, in his role as Terri's guardian, filed a petition asking Florida's Pinellas–Pasco Circuit Court to authorize him to order the removal of her gastric tube and allow her to die. Michael argued that, even though Terri had left no written instructions, several times she had expressed to him the view that she would not want to be kept alive in her present condition. Robert and Mary Schindler opposed Michael's petition, claiming that Terri was capable of recovering consciousness.

The court found in favor of Michael, but between 1998 and 2003 the Schindlers continued to engage in legal maneuvers to block Michael's efforts to allow Terri to die. They filed civil suits against him, as well as accusations of abuse. They sought support from prolife groups and members of the religious right, urging them to appeal to elected officials for help in keeping Terri alive. In violation of a court order, they showed a videotape of Terri that convinced many viewers that she had some cognitive function.

When Terri's feeding tube was removed under court order on October, 15, 2003, the Florida state legislature quickly passed "Terri's Law" allowing the governor to order the tube replaced. Governor Jeb Bush signed the order, and President George Bush made a public statement praising the action.

Religious conservatives claimed that Terri's Law was the result of their prayer vigils, broadcasts on Christian radio, and thousands of email messages to Florida legislators. Some saw the result as a model for an approach they might take to get laws passed in other states to forbid removing feeding tubes, to allow prayer in school, and to post the Ten Commandments in courts and other public places. Terri's Law, some said, was a victory for conservatives nationally, for it showed that it was possible to use legislation to take away much of the power of the courts.

Vigils and demonstrations continued around Woodside Hospice, where Terri was a patient. Fundamentalist religious conservatives, both Catholic and Protestant, vied for media attention. Most had special agendas, some connected with promoting religious values, others with promoting disability rights. Still others seemed to focus only on Terri and the prospect of her death. Very few counterdemonstrators appeared in what was often a hostile, angry environment. Michael Schiavo was compared to Hitler and called a murderer.

Starting in 2001, the Schindlers began to file accusations of abuse against Michael. From 2001 to 2004, they made nine accusations that included neglect of hygiene, denial of dental care, poisoning, and physical harm. All were investigated by the Florida Department of Children and Families. (Agency reports released in 2005 concluded that there were no indications of any harm, abuse, or neglect.) The Schindlers continued to make clear their opinion that Terri's condition was not the result of a heart attack. In their view, Michael tried to strangle her but failed to kill her. They offered no evidence for this view, other than their speculation that Michael eventually established a relationship with another woman.

2005. When Terri's Law was ruled unconstitutional by a state court, the Florida attorney general appealed the case to the Florida Supreme Court, which upheld the lower court ruling. When the Schindlers appealed the decision to the U.S. Supreme Court, the case was again refused. On March 18, 2005, the Florida Circuit Court once more ordered the gastric tube removed.

Various members of the U.S. Congress were approached by a number of members of the religious right and asked to intervene in the Florida case. Speaker of the House Tom DeLay, a Texas Republican, said that the removal of Terri's feeding tube would be "an act of medical terrorism." One of the Schindlers' spiritual advisors said, "We pray that this modern-day crucifixion will not happen."

March 16. Congress initiated a debate over what could be done to allow the Schindlers to prevent Terri's feeding tube from being removed. The White House indicated that if Congress passed such a bill, the president would sign it.

March 18. While the debate was proceeding, Terri's feeding tube was removed, for the third time, in accordance with Judge Greer's order. The Schindlers visited Terri in the hospice afterward. They were accompanied by one of their spiritual advisors, Father Malinowski, who later said he had taken a scrap from a robe worn by Mother Teresa and touched Terri's throat, forehead, and cheek with it.

March 21. The House and Senate passed a bill that allowed the Schindlers' case against removing Terri's feeding tube to be heard in a federal court. They were thus given another opportunity to achieve what they had failed to accomplish in the state courts. "Every hour is incredibly important to Terri Schiavo," said House Majority Leader DeLay.

Senator Bill Frist, Republican of Tennessee, the Senate majority leader, said that Congress had to act on the bill because "These are extraordinary circumstances that center on the most fundamental of human values and virtues: the sanctity of human life." Frist, a transplant surgeon as well as a senator, had earlier claimed to be able to tell from the videotape of Terri that she was not in a persistent vegetative state. He received much criticism from the medical community for making a diagnosis without examining the patient or the medical records.

A number of legislators denounced the legislation. Representative Christopher Shays of Connecticut, one of four Republicans in the House to vote against it, objected that "this Republican party of Lincoln has become a party of theocracy."

President Bush signed the bill into law at his ranch in Texas around one in the morning. The next day, at a public appearance in Tucson, he praised Congress for "voting to give Terri's parents another chance to save their daughter's life." The statement was met with a roar of approval from the crowd of Republican supporters.

March 23–26. The bill passed by Congress and signed into law permitted the Schindlers to file a sequence of petitions and appeals in the federal courts. On Wednesday, March 23, they filed an emergency request with the U.S. Supreme Court to replace Terri's feeding tube. Republican leaders of the House and the Senate filed briefs in support of the Schindlers. The brief signed by Senator Frist argued that "the Court cannot permit Mrs. Schiavo to die" before the claims of her parents are reviewed by federal courts. But on Thursday, March 24, the Supreme Court rejected the Schindlers' petition.

In Florida, Governor Bush suggested on Wednesday, March 23, that he might send state agents to forcibly replace Terri's gastric tube. Judge Greer issued an emergency order barring the state from "taking possession of Theresa Marie Schiavo."

On Thursday, March 24, Governor Bush appealed the ruling. In court documents, he charged that Terri's medical condition might be due to abuse by her husband and filed an affidavit by a neurologist claiming that she had been misdiagnosed as being in a persistent vegetative state. The Schindlers also filed a petition on the same grounds.

The court-appointed neurologist who examined Terri rejected the possibility of a misdiagnosis. Judge Greer then turned down the petitions of both Governor Bush and the Schindlers. On the same day, a higher state court and the Florida Supreme Court also rejected appeals of the rulings.

A federal 11th Circuit Court of Appeal panel in Atlanta refused to reconsider the case. Further, Chief Judge J. L. Edmundson, a conservative Republican, wrote that federal courts had no jurisdiction in the case and that the law enacted by Congress and signed by President Bush allowing the Schindlers to seek a federal court review was unconstitutional. "If sacrifices to the independence of the judiciary are permitted today," Judge Edmundson wrote, "precedent is established for the constitutional transgressions of tomorrow." Having been turned down by the Appeals Court, the Schindlers made another emergency appeal to the U.S. Supreme Court. For the fifth time, however, the Supreme Court refused to intervene in the case. The Schindlers had reached the end of the legal line.

March 27–30. Reporter Rick Lyman described the mood of the protesters who maintained their post across the street from Woodside Hospice as one that was more somber and subdued than it had been earlier. Not Dead Yet, a disability rights organization that focuses on end-of-life issues, blocked the driveway leading to the hospice. A member of the group said that it hoped to make society change its view that a life with a severe disability is not worth living. One man at the scene blew a ram's horn from time to time, another chanted, and a young woman prayed into her cupped hands, then released the prayer toward the hospice.

Signs expressed in shorthand the views that protesters had often spelled out in interviews and speeches: *Hey, Judge. Who Made You God? Murder Is Legal in America, Hospice or Auschwitz?* Even Governor Bush wasn't immune from criticism, because he had said there was nothing else he could do within the law: *Where's Jeb?* Some protestors became angry, shouting "Nazi!" and "Murder!" but the Schindlers made it known that they wanted the crowd to remain calm.

Several protesters tried to carry cups of water into the hospice to give to Terri, but they were turned back by the police. Because Terri was unable to swallow, the attempts were symbolic. Some protesters continued to hold prayer vigils.

The End

On the morning of Thursday, March 31, 2005, just after nine o'clock, Terri Schiavo died at Woodside Hospice. Michael was at her bedside and cradled her head as life slipped away and she stopped breathing. At Michael's request, neither her parents nor her brother or sister was present, although all of them had paid her a last visit at the hospice. Thirteen days had passed since Terri's feeding tube had been withdrawn. The end came, as is typical in such cases, as a result of dehydration.

The acrimony toward Michael by the Schindlers and their supporters did not end with Terri's death. "After these recent years of neglect at the hands of those who were supposed to care for her, she is finally at peace with God for eternity," Terri's sister, Suzzane Vitadamo, said in a public statement. "His [Michael's] heartless cruelty continued until the very last moment," said a priest who had sided with the Schindlers.

Michael Schiavo neither appeared in public nor made any statement. His lawyer, speaking on his behalf, said that "Mr. Schiavo's overriding concern here was to provide for Terri a peaceful death with dignity. This death was not for the siblings and not for the spouse and not for the parents. This was for Terri."

Autopsy

Three months after Terri Schiavo's death, on June 15, 2005, the results of the extensive autopsy that was performed on her body were made public. The results revealed that her brain had shrunk to less than half its normal weight due to the destruction caused by a loss of oxygen ("anoxic-ischemic encephalopathy"). No treatment nor the passage of time could ever have restored Terri to even the lowest level of awareness or motor control. Her brain had shriveled and forever lost those capacities. The autopsy showed that the original diagnosis of persistent vegetative state had been correct.

The autopsy failed to find any signs of trauma or strangulation, undercutting the assertion by the Schindlers that Michael had abused Terri and thus was responsible for her condition. Also, no evidence was found suggesting that she had been neglected or received inadequate or inappropriate care.

What the autopsy could not establish, however, was the cause of the cardiac arrest that resulted in the oxygen deprivation that caused Terri's brain damage. "No one observed her taking diet pills, binging and purging or consuming laxatives," the autopsy report observes, "and she apparently never confessed to her family or friends about having an eating disorder." What is more, says the report, her potassium level was measured only after she had been treated with a number of drugs known to lower potassium in the blood, and this makes suspect the main piece of evidence supporting the idea that she suffered from bulimia. Thus, the evidence that Terri suffered "a severe anoxic brain injury" is certain, but what caused it is not. "The manner of death will therefore be certified as undetermined," the report concludes.

The Battles Continue

Incredibly, the conflict over Terri Schiavo did not end with her death. The Schindlers attempted to have independent experts witness the autopsy, but the Pinellas County Medical Examiner refused their request. Videotapes, photographs, and tissue samples from the autopsy were made available by the agency's office, however.

The Schindlers also petitioned a court for the right to determine the disposition of their daughter's body. They said that they wanted her to be buried in Pinellas County so that they could visit her grave. The court rejected the petition, holding that Michael Schiavo had the right to make such decisions.

Terri Schiavo's body was cremated on April 1, 2005. Michael's lawyer announced that Michael's plan was to bury Terri's ashes in Huntingdon Valley, Pennsylvania, where she had grown up and where they had met so many years earlier. In January 2006, Michael married Jodi Centonze, the woman he had met in 1994, four years after Terri had been placed in a nursing home. The newly married couple and their two children continued to live in Florida.

Jack Kevorkian: Moral Leader or Doctor Death?

On August 5, 1993, Thomas W. Hyde, Jr., a thirty-year-old Michigan construction worker with a wife and a two-year-old daughter, was taken inside a battered white 1968 Volkswagen bus parked behind the apartment building in the Detroit suburb of Royal Oak, where sixty-five-year-old retired pathologist Dr. Jack Kevorkian lived.

Dr. Kevorkian fitted a respiratory mask over Hyde's face and connected the plastic tubing leading from the mask to a short cylinder of carbon monoxide gas. Dr. Kevorkian placed a string in Hyde's hand. At the opposite end of the string was a paper clip crimping the plastic tubing and shutting off the flow of gas. Hyde jerked on the string, pulled loose the paper clip, then breathed in the carbon monoxide flowing into the mask. Twenty minutes later, he was dead.

Mr. Hyde suffered from amyotrophic lateral sclerosis (Lou Gehrig's disease), a degenerative and progressive neurological disorder. He was paralyzed, unable even to swallow, and, without suctioning, he would have choked to death on his own saliva. He reported that he was in great pain, and like hundreds before him, he approached Dr. Kevorkian to help him end his life.

In a videotape made on July 1, 1993, Mr. Hyde said to Dr. Kevorkian, "I want to end this. I want to die." Dr. Kevorkian agreed to help, and Mr. Hyde became the twentieth person since 1990 whom Dr. Kevorkian had assisted in committing suicide.

Trial

After the death of Thomas Hyde, Dr. Kevorkian was arrested and charged with violating the 1992 Michigan law that had been enacted specifically to stop his activities. The law applies to anyone who knows that another person intends to commit suicide and who either "provides the physical means" or "participates in a physical act" by which the suicide is carried out. However, the law explicitly excludes those administering medications or procedures that may cause death "if the intent is to relieve pain or discomfort."

On May 2, 1994, a jury found Dr. Kevorkian innocent of the charge of assisting suicide. As one juror said, "He

convinced us he was not a murderer, that he was really trying to help people out." According to another, Dr. Kevorkian had acted to relieve Mr. Hyde's pain, and that is allowed by the law.

Several jurors expressed skepticism and resentment at the attempt to legislate behavior falling within such a private sphere. "I don't feel it's our obligation to choose for someone else how much pain and suffering they can go through," one said. "That's between them and their God."

After the decision, Dr. Kevorkian reiterated his position that people have a right to decide when to end their lives. He acted, he said, to protect that right. "I want that option as I get older, and I want it unencumbered, unintimidated, free with my medical colleagues," he said. "So I did it for myself, too, just as any competent adult would want to do."

Kevorkian always insisted that he practiced physician-assisted suicide only in accordance with stringent safeguards. "You act only after it is absolutely justifiable," he said. "The patient must be mentally competent, the disease incurable." He maintained that other physicians should determine that a candidate for assisted suicide was incurable and that a psychiatrist assess the patient's mental state and determine that he or she was competent. In practice, Kevorkian did not proceed in this fashion, because other physicians refused to cooperate with him.

Critics. Critics charged that without the safeguard of a psychiatric evaluation, patients who sought out Kevorkian to help them kill themselves were likely to be suffering from depression. Hence, they couldn't be regarded as having made an informed, rational decision to end their lives.

Other critics worried that if physicians are allowed to play a role in terminating the lives of patients, that role could expand. Physicians might begin by assisting those who ask their help, but then move on to making their own decisions about who should live. Or they might even be recruited to carry out a government policy identifying those who should be "assisted" in dying. The potential for abuse is so serious that physicians should not be associated in any way with procedures intended to end the lives of patients.

Finally, some critics, though disagreeing with Kevorkian, believed he had successfully pointed out a major flaw in the health care system: the medical profession is so committed to preserving life that it has not developed ways of dealing with death in cases in which it is inevitable. Rather than help people kill themselves, critics said, physicians ought to surrender the idea of treatment and concentrate on making those with terminal illnesses pain free so that they can spend their remaining time receiving the comfort of their families and friends.

It was in keeping with such an aim that hospitals and other institutions set up hospices to provide nursing care and support for the dying. Even after decades, however, hospices remain at the margins of the medical establishment, and physicians associated with them are given little respect by their colleagues.

A Charge of Murder. In 1998, the Michigan Department of Consumer and Industry Services, the state agency responsible for licensing physicians, charged that Jack Kevorkian was practicing medicine without a license by assisting forty-two people in committing suicide. (Kevorkian said that he had assisted about 120 people.)

Although the agency had issued a cease-and-desist order, Kevorkian continued to help terminally ill people die. That same year, the Michigan legislature passed a law making assisting in suicide a crime, but Kevorkian announced that he would continue his activities despite the law.

In September 1998, Dr. Kevorkian administered a lethal injection to Thomas Youk, a fifty-two-year-old man in an advanced stage of the motor neuron disease amyotrophic lateral sclerosis (ALS). For the first time, Kevorkian, by his own direct action, caused the death of a person, thus moving from physician-assisted suicide to active euthanasia.

Kevorkian videotaped the event and offered the tape to the CBS program *Sixty Minutes,* which broadcast excerpts from the tape on national television on November 22. About 15.6 million households watched the program.

Kevorkian said he had given the tape to CBS in the hope that it would lead to his arrest and become a test case for assisted suicide and active euthanasia.

"I want a showdown," Kevorkian told a reporter. "I want to be prosecuted for euthanasia. I am going to prove that this is not a crime, ever, regardless of what words are written on paper."

On November 25, the prosecutor of Oakland County, Michigan, filed first-degree murder charges against Jack Kevorkian. David G. Gorcyca, the prosecutor, said that Dr. Kevorkian's actions clearly fit the definition of premeditated murder and that the consent of the man killed was no legal defense.

On April 13, 1999, Jack Kevorkian was found guilty of second-degree murder and sentenced to a prison term of ten to twenty-five years. "This trial was not an opportunity for a referendum," Judge Jessica Cooper said at the sentencing.

Follow-up

Kevorkian was denied parole in 2005, but in June 2007, after eight years in prison, he was paroled on the grounds of good behavior. Kevorkian had already announced that once he was free, he would not go back to assisting people in committing suicide, but would, rather, campaign to change laws to make such a practice legal. He kept this resolution, and since his parole, he has given lectures on college campuses, run for Congress, and published books advocating the view that people who are terminally ill should be allowed to decide when to end their lives and secure the help of a physician in achieving this goal.

Jack Kevorkian continues to be a figure in the public's consciousness. In April 2010, the movie *You Don't Know Jack,* directed by Barry Levinson and starring Al Pacino as the title character, was broadcast on HBO. The movie presented Kevorkian as a quirky but serious crusader for his ideas. Those sympathetic to the views espoused by Kevorkian believe he did more than anyone else to force society to face an issue that it has chosen to ignore. His critics believe he made a circus of what should be a serious and deliberative discussion.

On March 24, 1998, an anonymous woman in her mid-eighties became the first person known to choose physician-assisted suicide under an Oregon law authorizing physicians to prescribe drugs that terminally ill patients can use to end their lives.

The woman, who lived in Portland, died shortly after swallowing a lethal dose of barbiturates, which she washed down with a glass of brandy. She was suffering from metastatic breast cancer and had been given less than two months to live. In an audiotape she made two days before her death, she said she "looked forward" to her coming suicide, because "I will be relieved of all the stress I have." She said she had grown tired of fighting cancer and had trouble breathing and walking. "I can't see myself living a few more months like this," she said. She died about half an hour after taking the prescribed drugs.

She may not have been the first person to commit suicide under the provisions of the law. The law allows for strict privacy, and the woman's death was made public, with her consent, by an advocacy group that supports the law.

The Law

Oregon's 1994 "Written Request for Medication to End One's Life in a Humane and Dignified Manner," or Death With Dignity Act, is the first physician-assisted suicide measure passed by any state. The law does not permit a physician to play an active role in ending a patient's life. The major provision of the measure is that it allows physicians to prescribe lethal drugs for terminally ill patients without risking criminal prosecution.

The law spells out a set of conditions that must be met by patients and physicians:

1. A primary-care physician and a consulting physician must both agree that the patient has six months or less to live.

2. The patient must make two oral requests (at least forty-eight hours apart) for drugs to use to terminate his or her life.

3. The patient must wait at least fifteen days after the initial oral request, then make a written request to the physician.

4. If either physician thinks the patient has a mental disorder or is suffering from impaired judgment from depression, they must recommend the patient for counseling.

5. The patient can terminate the request at any time during the process.

6. The physician prescribing the drugs must inform the patient of such feasible alternatives as hospice care, comfort care, and pain control.

Under the law, a physician is not permitted to assist a patient to die by any means more active than prescribing a drug that can cause death and indicating the manner in which the drug can be used. Hence, such practices as lethal injections remain as illegal as before.

A Long Time Coming

In 1994, the Oregon law was approved by the slight margin of fifty-two to forty-eight percent of voters. Opponents of the law immediately challenged it in court. The legal wrangles took three years; then, in 1997, the opponents mounted an effort to have it repealed through a voter initiative. The effort failed, and the law was approved once more—this time by sixty percent of the voters.

Despite voter approval, physicians were uncertain about what might happen to them if they acted in accordance with the law and assisted a patient in killing himself. Thomas Constantine, then the head of the Drug Enforcement Administration, responding to pressure by two conservative members of Congress, announced that the agency would impose severe sanctions on any physician who prescribed lethal doses of drugs. Constantine claimed that prescribing drugs for use in suicide wasn't a legitimate medical use under the federal drug laws. The DEA cannot cancel a physician's license to practice medicine, but it can withdraw a physician's license to prescribe drugs. Thus, the DEA threat to physicians was very real.

The DEA warning kept the law from being implemented until June 1998. Attorney General Janet Reno said that the DEA threat to prosecute physicians had been issued without her knowledge or consent. Because the DEA is a branch of the Justice Department, Reno's statement removed a legal roadblock. Overruling Constantine, Reno said that the drug laws were intended to block illicit drug dealing and that there was no evidence that Congress ever meant for the DEA to play a role in resolving the moral problems presented by the Oregon law.

The law explicitly protects only physicians from prosecution. Hence, it leaves in doubt the legal status of nurses. Many terminally ill patients are paralyzed or too weak to take prescribed medications without assistance. Nurses typically help patients take prescribed medications, but what if they help the patient take a lethal dose of drugs? Does this make them liable for legal prosecution?

Also, from a moral point of view, if a nurse is opposed to euthanasia or suicide, does the general responsibility he has to assist a patient require him to help the patient take a lethal drug? Nurses in Oregon are facing these questions, although few (if any) have had to deal with them in a practical way.

Some Oregon pharmacists also have trouble with the physician-assisted suicide law. Because they must fill the prescriptions written by physicians, the law makes them, to an extent, participants in the suicide. Some have argued that drugs prescribed for potential use in a suicide should be labeled as such on the prescription. That way pharmacists who object to assisted suicide can avoid becoming involved in one. The prescription could be filled by some other pharmacist.

Physicians object to this proposal, though. They point out that if prescriptions were labeled as potential suicide agents, the patient's confidentiality would be violated. Particularly in small towns, if word got out, the families of those who chose assisted suicide might become the targets of criticism or demonstrations by opponents of assisted suicide.

In March 1998, Oregon state officials decided to make physician-assisted suicide available to low-income residents under the state's Medicaid program. The state will have to bear the full cost, however, because, by law, federal funds cannot be used to pay for physician-assisted suicide.

Critics claim that this use of state funds is a tacit endorsement of suicide, but supporters claim that it is only an extension of the "comfort care" already covered by Medicaid. Many who believe state mental-health services are underfunded think that supporting physician-assisted suicide is a serious mistake. It suggests to patients that death is the only help available to them.

Is the Law Needed?

Proponents of the Oregon law would like to see other states pass similar legislation. They point out that terminally ill people who decide to end their lives are often frustrated in carrying out their wishes, even though the society has endorsed, in principle, a "right to die."

The federal Patient Self-Determination Act requires hospitals to inform patients that they have the right to refuse or discontinue treatment and that by means of living wills and powers of attorney for health care, they can put their decisions into practice. The Supreme Court in the *Cruzan* decision (see the Case Presentation "The Cruzan Case: The Supreme Court Upholds the Right to Die," in this chapter) implicitly acknowledged a "right to die," by allowing the withdrawal of life-sustaining treatment when "clear and compelling evidence" shows that this reflects an individual's wish. Yet, despite the legal possibility of exercising control over medical care during the last stages of one's life, various barriers stand in the way of actual control.

Right to Discontinue Care

Surveys of physicians and health care workers show that many are not aware of laws allowing them to withhold or discontinue such care as mechanical ventilation, kidney dialysis, and even feeding tubes. Many believe that once a treatment has been started, it is illegal to discontinue it. Courts have repeatedly upheld the right of individuals to decide that, at a certain point in their treatment, they do not want to be provided with food or water, yet in one survey forty-two percent of health care workers rejected this right as an option patients could choose.

Oral Instructions

Many physicians and hospitals simply ignore the oral instructions patients give them about discontinuing their care. In one study of more than 4000 seriously ill patients, researchers found that although a third of the patients asked not to be revived by cardiopulmonary resuscitation, fifty percent of the time "Do not resuscitate" was never written in their charts.

Advance Directives

The living wills or powers of attorney made out by patients may not be followed. In a 1997 study of 4804 terminally ill patients, only 688 had written directives, and just 22 of these contained instructions explicit enough to guide the care they received. Even these instructions were ignored about half the time, and physicians knew about the patient's instructions only about a quarter of the time.

Also, advance directives are sometimes not included among the documents constituting a patient's medical chart. In another study, when seventy-one patients were moved to a nursing home, twenty-five of them had living wills that were not sent with them.

As a result, despite the efforts patients may make to control what happens to them at the end of their lives, they may be forced to accept decisions about their care made by physicians or nurses in accordance with their own values or institutional policies.

Patient vs. Family

Families may override the wishes expressed by patients in their living wills. Even though the views of the patient take legal precedence over those of a relative, in practice a physician or hospital may do as the relative wishes. Families never sue because of the overtreatment of a patient, but they do because of withholding or discontinuing treatment.

Laws like the one in Oregon are viewed by many as the only way patients can be sure that they can exercise control in the final days of their lives. Many fear that if they enter a hospital, they won't be able to trust nurses and physicians to know their wishes and to respect them.

Various polls suggest that a majority of the American people favor a policy of voluntary physician-assisted suicide. When physicians have been charged with aiding the death of a terminally ill patient at the patient's request, they have typically been found not guilty or been given suspended sentences. People who cannot control their illness often take some comfort in being able to control their escape from it.

How Many Cases?

The Oregon law is written so that only Oregon residents can ask physicians to assist them in suicide under the stipulated conditions. Thus, sick people have not migrated to the state with the idea of getting a physician's help in killing themselves.

Although the way is clear for any terminally ill Oregon resident to seek help in dying, relatively few people have done so. State officials reported that in 1998, the first year under the new law, fifteen people ended their lives with drugs legally prescribed for that purpose. (There were 29,000 deaths in Oregon that year.) The average age of the eight men and seven women was seventy.

The most recent figures available show that from 1998 to 2009 only 460 people ended their lives with assistance. The average age was seventy-one, but the range was from twenty-five to ninety-six. According to a state report, those choosing physician-assisted suicide were "not disproportionately poor, uneducated, uninsured, fearful of the financial consequences of their illnesses," or "lacking end-of-life care." The primary factor mentioned by individuals was "the importance of autonomy and personal control." Neither financial worries nor the pain of a long illness was mentioned by them as a decisive factor.

The average time to unconsciousness after taking the prescribed drugs was five minutes (with a range of one to thirty-eight), and the average time to death was twenty-five minutes.

That relatively few have taken advantage of the Oregon law may support the idea of those favoring it that most people simply want to know that if they are terminally ill and in pain, a way out is available to them. To this extent, then, the Oregon experience may encourage other states to allow physician-assisted suicide.

Supreme Court Leaves the Matter to the States

In November 2001, Attorney General John Ashcroft reversed the course taken by Janet Reno and sent a letter to the DEA authorizing agents to take legal action against physicians prescribing drugs for the purpose of ending the lives of terminally ill patients. Ashcroft held that "prescribing, dispensing or administering federally controlled substances to assist suicide" is "not a legitimate medical purpose." Ashcroft's successor, Alberto Gonzales, accepted the same view. Oregon filed suit against the Justice Department, and eventually the case went to the U.S. Supreme Court. In January 2006, the Court upheld the decisions of two lower courts and ruled six to nine that the Justice Department had acted without legal authority in attempting to restrict the actions of Oregon physicians.

The ruling was made on the narrow administrative ground that the regulation of medical practice is a state, not a federal, matter. The ruling left open the possibility that Congress could pass a law explicitly forbidding the use of drugs by physicians who are assisting in a suicide. However, because the ruling held that the regulation of medical practice is a state issue, it also opened the way for the states to pass assisted-suicide laws.

In March 2009, Washington became the second state to pass a ballot initiative allowing physician-assisted suicide. (The "Death with Dignity" law received sixty percent of the vote.) The law is modeled closely on the Oregon law, including the age requirement, waiting period, and certification by two physicians that the patient has no more than six months to live. Since the law went into effect, sixty-three people have filled prescriptions for lethal medication, but only thirty-six died as a result of taking the drugs.

In December 2009, a state court in Montana ruled that it was not illegal for a physician to prescribe lethal medications for terminally ill patients under certain conditions. The state, however, has neither passed any laws nor put into place the regulatory mechanisms that would allow physicians to escape legal challenges for assisting patients in ending their lives.

Other states are also struggling with the issue. Massachusetts is considering a measure allowing assisted suicide, but the bill is surrounded with controversy. A Connecticut physicians' group has filed a lawsuit to get the state to clarify the legal position of doctors who prescribe lethal drugs to terminally ill patients who request them.

CASE PRESENTATION

The Awakening: A Brief Miracle

In 1995, Donald Herbert was thirty-four years old and a member of the Buffalo, New York, fire rescue squad. On the morning of December 29 of that year, he raced into a burning apartment building and began searching the attic for potential victims. The smoke was thick, but he wore a breathing apparatus.

Suddenly, without warning, the roof of the burning building collapsed. Herbert's breathing mask was knocked off, and he was buried under flaming debris. His fellow firefighters realized what had happened, but by the time they could reach him, he had been without oxygen for at least six minutes. His rescuers pulled him through a window, then rushed him to the Erie County Medical Center.

Herbert's condition was critical. In addition to oxygen deprivation, he had suffered severe head trauma. He remained in a coma for two and a half months. He regained consciousness in 1996, but his speech was slurred, he couldn't feed himself, his vision appeared to be damaged, and he was confined to a bed or wheelchair. He didn't know his age or what his job had been. He seemed unable to recognize his wife and children or his relatives and old friends. Because he could not care for himself, Herbert was removed to Baker Manor, a nursing home in a Buffalo suburb.

Awakening

On a Saturday morning in May 2005, Donald Herbert suddenly recovered his memory. "I want to talk to my wife," Herbert said to a nursing home employee. The employee called his home, but it was his thirteen-year-old son

who answered. "That can't be," Herbert said. "He can't talk, he's just a baby."

Herbert was soon surrounded by his wife Linda, his four sons, various relatives, and several old friends. For fourteen hours, they hugged and kissed him, talked to him, and rejoiced in his recovery. Herbert asked questions, especially about his sons. "He wouldn't go to sleep," his mother-in-law said. "He stayed up all night talking to his sons."

"How long have I been gone?" he asked.

"We told him almost ten years," his uncle Simon Manka recalled. "He said, 'Holy Cow!' He thought it had been three months." While Herbert was unconscious, cell phones became common, e-mail use spread worldwide, the attack of 9/11 occurred, and the United States went to war in Iraq. His oldest son turned twenty-four, and many of his fellow firefighters retired.

Mr. Manka told reporters that Herbert recognized several family members and friends and called them by name. He was completely different than he had been. "He was asking questions, and he'd recognize a voice." He recognized the voices of the members of the rescue crew he'd served with, even though he couldn't see the people.

Hearing her husband speak was "completely overwhelming," Linda Herbert said. "We are still trying to cope with this incredible experience."

A Change

Three days after his startling recovery, Donald Herbert began to become less animated. He still engaged in conversation, but his periods of clarity became less frequent.

He spent most of his time sleeping, and his family and friends made an effort not to tire him.

His doctor, Jamil Ahmed, said that Herbert's condition had been close to a persistent vegetative state, one in which he appeared to be awake but was unaware of what was going on around him. He seemed to have laid down some memories during this period, however, because he was able to recognize the names of some of the nursing home staff. The big change in Herbert took place three months after his medication was changed. The drug combination that he took had shown beneficial results in patients with more recent brain injuries. The combined drugs are more often used individually to treat patients with Parkinson's disease, attention deficit disorder, and depression.

On February 22, 2006, Donald Herbert died. He never left the nursing home, but he continued to interact to a limited degree with his family and friends until the end of his life. As recently as the week before his death, he was playing catch with his youngest son. Herbert developed pneumonia that weekend, and although he was treated with antibiotics, he failed to recover.

"He was never as good as he was when he first woke up," Michael Lombardo said. "But he was pretty good right up to the end."

Cases of people with severe brain damage making what seem to be miraculous recoveries of self-consciousness and memory occur from time to time, but they are extremely rare. When such cases are publicized, they encourage people who love someone diagnosed with a severe brain injury to believe that recovery is likely. Sadly, these hopes are almost never realized.

BRIEFING SESSION

Death comes to us all. We hope that when it comes it will be swift and allow us to depart without prolonged suffering, our dignity intact. We also hope that it will not force burdens on our family and friends, making them pay both financially and emotionally by our lingering and hopeless condition.

Such considerations give euthanasia a strong appeal. Should we not be able to snip the thread of life when the weight of suffering and hopelessness grows too heavy to bear? The answer to this question is not as easy as it may seem, for hidden within it are a number of complicated moral issues.

Just what is euthanasia? The word comes from the Greek for "good death," and in English it has come to have the meaning "easy death." But this does little to help us understand the concept. For consider these questions:

If we give ourselves an easy death, are we committing suicide? If we assist someone else to an easy death (with or without that person's permission), are we committing murder? Anyone who opposed killing (either of oneself or of others) on moral grounds might also consider it necessary to object to euthanasia.

It may be, however, that the answer to both questions is no. But if it is, then it is necessary to specify the conditions that distinguish euthanasia from both suicide and murder. Only then would it be possible to argue, without contradiction, that euthanasia is morally acceptable but the other two forms of killing are not.

Someone who believes that suicide is morally legitimate would not object to euthanasia carried out by the person herself, but he would still have to deal with the problem posed by the euthanasia/murder issue.

Active and Passive Euthanasia

We have talked of euthanasia as though it involved directly taking the life of a person, either one's own life or the life of another. However, some philosophers distinguish between "active euthanasia" and "passive euthanasia," which in turn rests on a distinction between killing and letting die.

To kill someone (including oneself) is to take a definite action to end his or her life (e.g., administering a lethal injection). To allow someone to die, by contrast, is to take no steps to prolong that person's life when those steps seem called for—failing to give a needed injection of antibiotics, for example. Active euthanasia, then, is direct killing and is an act of commission. Passive euthanasia is an act of omission.

This distinction is used in most contemporary codes of medical ethics (e.g., the American Medical Association's Code of Ethics) and is also recognized in the Anglo-American tradition of law. Except in special circumstances, it is illegal to deliberately cause the death of another person. It is not, however, illegal (except in special circumstances) to allow a person to die. Clearly, one might consider active euthanasia morally wrong while recognizing passive euthanasia as morally legitimate.

Some philosophers, however, have argued that the active–passive distinction is morally irrelevant with respect to euthanasia. Both are cases of causing death, and it is the circumstances in which death is caused, not the manner of causing it, that is of moral importance.

Furthermore, the active–passive distinction is not always clear cut. If a person dies after special life-sustaining equipment has been withdrawn, is this a case of active or passive euthanasia? Is it a case of euthanasia at all?

Voluntary, Involuntary, and Nonvoluntary Euthanasia

Writers on euthanasia have often thought it important to distinguish among voluntary, involuntary, and nonvoluntary euthanasia. *Voluntary euthanasia* includes cases in which a person takes his or her own life, either directly or by refusing treatment. But it also includes cases in which a person deputizes another to act in accordance with his wishes.

Thus, someone might instruct her family not to permit the use of artificial support systems should she become unconscious, suffer from brain damage, and be unable to speak for herself. Or someone might request that he be given a lethal injection after suffering third-degree burns over most of his body, suffering uncontrollable pain, and being told he has little hope of recovery.

Finally, assisted suicide, in which the individual requests the direct help of someone else in ending his life, falls into this category. (Some may think that one or more of the earlier examples are also cases of assisted suicide. What counts as assisted suicide is both conceptually and legally unclear.) That the individual explicitly consents to death is a necessary feature of voluntary euthanasia.

Involuntary euthanasia consists in ending the life of someone contrary to that person's wish. The person killed not only fails to give consent, but expresses the desire not to be killed. No one arguing in favor of nonvoluntary euthanasia holds that involuntary euthanasia is justifiable. Those who oppose both voluntary and nonvoluntary euthanasia often argue that to permit either runs the risk of opening the way for involuntary euthanasia.

Nonvoluntary euthanasia includes those cases in which the decision about death is not made by the person who is to die. Here the person gives no specific consent or instructions, and the decision is made by family, friends, or physicians. The distinction between voluntary and nonvoluntary euthanasia is not always a clear one. Physicians sometimes assume that people are "asking" to die even when no explicit request has been made. Also, the wishes and attitudes that people express when they are not in extreme life-threatening medical situations may be too vague for us to be certain that they would choose death when they are in such a situation. Is "I never want to be hooked up to one of those machines" an adequate indication that the person who says this does not want to be put on a respirator should she meet with an accident and fall into a comatose state?

If the distinctions made here are accepted as legitimate and relevant, we can distinguish eight cases in which euthanasia becomes a moral decision:

1. Self-administered euthanasia
   a. active
   b. passive

2. Other-administered euthanasia
   a. active and voluntary
   b. active and involuntary
   c. active and nonvoluntary
   d. passive and voluntary
   e. passive and involuntary
   f. passive and nonvoluntary

Even these possibilities don't exhaust the cases euthanasia presents us with. For example, notice that the voluntary–nonvoluntary distinction doesn't appear in connection with self-administered euthanasia in our scheme. Yet it might be argued that it should, for a person's decision to end his life (actively or passively) may well not be a wholly voluntary or free decision. People who are severely depressed by their illness and decide to end their lives, for example, might be thought of as not having made a voluntary choice.

Hence, one might approve of self-administered voluntary euthanasia, yet think that the nonvoluntary form should not be permitted. It should not be allowed not because it is necessarily morally wrong, but because it would not be a genuine decision by the person. The person might be thought to be suffering from a psychiatric disability. Indeed, the current debate about physician-assisted suicide turns, in part, on just this issue.

Defining "Death"

The advent of new medical technologies, pharmaceutical agents, and modes of treatment raises the question of when we should consider someone dead. Suppose someone's heartbeat, blood pressure, respiration, and liver and kidney functions can be maintained within the normal range of values by medical intervention. Should we still include this individual among living persons, even though she is in an irreversible coma or a chronic vegetative state?

If we consider the individual to be a living person, we need to decide how she ought to be treated. Should she be allowed to die or be maintained by medical means? This is the kind of question faced by families, physicians, and the courts in the *Quinlan* and *Cruzan* cases (see the Case Presentations "Karen Quinlan: The Debate Begins," and "The Cruzan Case: The Supreme Court Upholds the Right to Die," in this chapter), and it is one faced every day in dozens of unpublicized, though no less agonizing, cases.

But what if an unconscious individual lacking higher cortical functioning is no longer a living person? Could a physician who disconnected a respirator or failed to give an antibiotic be said to have killed a person? If nutrition and hydration are withheld from a brain-dead individual or even if the individual is given a lethal injection, is it reasonable to say that this is a case of killing? Perhaps the person died when her brain stopped functioning at a certain level. Or perhaps she died when she lapsed into coma.

A practical question that advances in medicine have made even more pressing is when or whether a comatose individual may be regarded as a source of transplant organs. If the individual remains a living person, it may be morally wrong (at least prima facie) to kill him to obtain organs for transplant. But what if the comatose individual is not really alive? What if he is dead already and no longer a person? Then there seem to be no reasonable grounds for objecting to removing his organs and using them to save the lives of those who need them. (See Chapter 7 for a discussion of organ donation.)

Questions like the ones raised here have prompted various attempts to define the notion of death. In the view of many commentators, the traditional notion of death is no longer adequate to serve as a guide to resolving issues about the treatment of individuals who, through disease or accident, have fallen into states in which many of their basic physiological functions can be maintained by medical means, although they remain comatose or lacking in higher-brain function.

Until recently, the traditional notion of death has been enshrined in laws defining crimes such as homicide and manslaughter. Given the change in medical technology, actions such as removing a respirator, which might once have been regarded as criminal for causing the death of a person, perhaps should now be viewed in a different way. Perhaps a person may be dead already, even though major physiological systems are still functioning.

Four major notions or concepts of death have emerged during the last two decades. We'll list each of them, but it's important to keep in mind that there is a difference between specifying the concept of death (or, as it is sometimes put, defining "death") and stating the criteria for determining that the concept fits in particular cases. The situation is analogous to defining "the best team" as the team winning the most games and then providing criteria for determining what counts as winning a game.

The concepts are merely sketched and the criteria for applying them only hinted at:

1. *Traditional.* A person is dead when he is no longer breathing and his heart is not beating. Hence, death may be defined as the permanent cessation of breathing and blood flow. This notion is sometimes known as the "cardiopulmonary" or "heart–lung criterion" for death.

2. *Whole brain.* Death is regarded as the irreversible cessation of all brain functions. Essentially, this means that there is no electrical activity in the brain, and even the brain stem is not functioning. Application of the concept depends on the use of electroencephalographic or imaging data.

3. *Higher brain.* Death is considered to involve the permanent loss of consciousness. Hence, someone in an irreversible coma or chronic vegetative state would

be considered dead, even though the brain stem continued to regulate breathing and heartbeat. Clinical, electroencephalographic, and imaging data are relevant to applying the concept. So, too, are statistics concerning the likelihood of the individual's regaining consciousness.

4. *Personhood.* Death occurs when an individual ceases to be a person. This may mean the loss of features that are essential to personal identity or (in some formulations) the loss of what is essential to being a person. Criteria for personal identity or for being a person are typically taken to include a complex of such activities as reasoning, remembering, feeling emotion, possessing a sense of the future, interacting with others, and so on. The criteria for applying this concept have more to do with the way an individual functions than with data about his brain.

Technology makes it necessary to take a fresh look at the traditional notion of death, but technology also provides data that have allowed for the development of new notions. It would be pointless, for example, to talk about brain death without having some means to determine when the concept might be satisfied.

The whole-brain concept of death was proposed in the 1981 *Report of the President's Commission for the Study of Ethical Problems in Medicine* and included in the Uniform Death Act. As a consequence, state laws employing the traditional concept of death generally have been modified in keeping with the whole-brain concept.

The whole-brain concept has the advantage of being relatively clear cut in application. However, applying the concept is not without difficulty and controversy. In the view of some, the concept is too restrictive and so fails to resolve some of the difficulties that prompted the need for a new concept. For example, both Karen Quinlan and Nancy Cruzan (see the Case Presentations "Karen Quinlan: The Debate Begins," and "The Cruzan Case: The Supreme Court Upholds the Right to Die," in this chapter) would have been considered alive by the whole-brain criteria. However, those who favor concepts of death based on the loss of higher brain function or the loss of personhood might argue that both cases were ones in which the affected individuals were, in the respective technical senses, dead.

Furthermore, critics charge, the whole-brain concept is not really as straightforward in its application as it might seem. Even when there appears to be a complete lack of cognitive functioning and even when basic brain-stem functions appear to have disappeared, a brain may remain electrically active to some degree. Isolated cells or groups of cells continue to be alive, and monitoring of the brain yields data that are open to conflicting interpretations.

The higher brain and personhood concepts face even greater difficulties. Each must formulate criteria that are accepted as nonarbitrary and as sufficient grounds for deciding that an individual is dead. No one has yet solved either of these problems for either of these concepts. The fact that there can be controversy over whole-brain death indicates how much harder it is to get agreement about when higher brain functions are lost. Also, securing agreement on criteria for determining when an entity either becomes or ceases to be a person is a conceptual difficulty far from being resolved to the satisfaction of most philosophers. (For more on this topic, see the discussion of defining death in the Social Context) "When the Diagnosis is Death," in this chapter.)

Advance Directives

Like so many issues in bioethics, euthanasia has traditionally been discussed only in the back rooms of medicine. Often, decisions about whether to allow a patient to die are made by physicians acting on their own authority. Such decisions do not represent so much an arrogant claim to godlike wisdom as an acknowledgment of the physician's obligation to do what is best for the patient.

Most physicians admit that allowing or helping a patient to die is sometimes the best assistance that can be given. Decisions made in this fashion depend on the beliefs and judgment of particular physicians. Because these may differ from those of the patient concerned, it is quite possible that the physician's decision may not reflect the wishes of the patient.

But covert decisions made by a physician acting alone are becoming practices of the past as euthanasia is discussed more widely and openly. Court cases, such as *Quinlan* and *Cruzan*, have both widened the scope of legally permissible actions and reinforced the notion that an individual has a right to refuse or discontinue life-sustaining medical treatment. Such cases have also made it clear that there are limits to the benefits that can be derived from medicine—that, under some conditions, individuals may be better off if everything that technologically can be done is not done. Increasingly, people want to be sure that they have some say in what happens to them should they fall victim to hopeless injury or illness.

One indication of this interest is that the number of states permitting individuals to sign "living wills" or advance directives has now increased to include all fifty states. The first living-will legislation was the "Natural Death Act" passed by the California legislature on August 30, 1977. The act is generally representative of all such legislation. It permits a competent adult to sign a directive that will authorize physicians to withhold or discontinue "mechanical" or "artificial" life-support equipment if the person is judged to be "terminal" and if "death is imminent."

The strength of advance directives is that they allow a person to express in an explicit manner how he or she wishes to be treated before treatment is needed. In this way, the autonomy of the individual is recognized. Even though unconscious or comatose, a person can continue to exert control over his or her life. This, in turn, means that physicians need not and should not be the decisive voice in determining the continuation or use of special medical equipment.

Critics of advance-directive legislation have claimed that it does not go far enough in

Whose Life Is It Anyway

A study published in the March 2002 issue of the *Journal of the American Geriatric Society* found that sixty percent of the 1185 Medicare patients surveyed at five teaching hospitals told their doctors to focus on making them comfortable rather than on extending their lives. Yet evidence indicated that more than one-third of the people expressing this wish had it ignored. They were treated more and lived longer than the two-thirds whose wishes were respected. Either their doctors forgot about their preferences, or they deliberately ignored them.

protecting autonomy and making death easier (where this is what is wanted). They point out that the directive specified in the California bill and most others would have made no difference in the case of Karen Quinlan. She had not been diagnosed as having a "terminal condition" at least two weeks prior to being put on a respirator, yet this is one of the requirements of the act. Consequently, the directive would have been irrelevant to her condition.

Nor, for that matter, would those people be allowed to die who wish to if their disease or injury does not involve treatment by "artificial" or "mechanical" means. Thus, a person suffering from throat cancer would simply have to bear the pain and wait for a "natural" death. Finally, at the moment, some states explicitly exclude nutrition and hydration as medical treatments that can be discontinued. The Supreme Court in the *Cruzan* case accepted the notion that the nutrition received by Nancy Cruzan through a feeding tube implanted in her stomach was a form of medical treatment that could be withdrawn. However, the Court did not rule on the Missouri law that forbids withdrawal. Until this law or some other like it is successfully challenged in court, an advance directive does not necessarily guarantee that such treatment will be discontinued, even when requested.

Limitations of such kinds on living wills have led some writers to recommend that individuals sign a legal instrument known as a durable power of attorney. In such a document,

an individual can name someone to act on his behalf should he become legally incompetent to act. Hence, unlike the advance directive, a durable power of attorney allows a surrogate to exercise control over novel and unanticipated situations. For example, the surrogate may order the discontinuation of artificial feeding, something that an advance directive might not permit.

The widespread wish to have some control over the end of one's life is reflected in a federal law that took effect in 1991. The Patient Self-Determination Act is sometimes referred to as a "medical Miranda warning."

The act requires that hospitals, nursing homes, and other health-care facilities receiving federal funding provide patients, at the time of admission, with written information about relevant state laws and the rights of citizens under those laws to refuse or discontinue treatment. Patients must also be told about the practices and policies at that particular institution so that they can choose a facility willing to abide by their decisions. The institutions must also record whether a patient has provided a written "advance directive" (e.g., a living will or power of attorney for health care) that will take effect should the patient become incapacitated.

Another sign of change is the recent concern with the medical circumstances in which people die. The medical ideal of a "hospital death," one in which the patient's temperature, pulse rate, and respiration are brought within normal limits by medication and machinery, is being severely challenged. This is reflected in the policy of the AMA which holds that it may be morally appropriate to withhold "all means of life-prolonging medical treatment," including artificial feeding, from patients in irreversible comas.

A new ideal of natural death also seems to be emerging. In this view, the kind of support a dying patient needs is psychological counseling and contact with family and friends rather than heroic medical efforts. An acceptance of death as a normal end of life and the development of new means of caring for the dying may ease the problem of euthanasia. If those who face imminent death are offered an alternative to either euthanasia or an all-out medical effort to preserve their lives, they may choose that alternative. "Death with dignity" need not always mean choosing a lethal injection.

Ethical Theories and Euthanasia

Roman Catholicism explicitly rejects all forms of euthanasia as being against the natural law duty to preserve life. The religion considers euthanasia as morally identical with either suicide or murder. This position is not so rigid as it may seem, however; the principle of double effect (see Part V, "Foundations of Bioethics") makes it morally acceptable to give medication for the relief of pain—even if the indirect result of the medication will be to shorten the life of the recipient. The intended result is not the death of the person but the relief of suffering. The difference in intention is thus considered to be a morally significant one. Those not accepting the principle of double effect would be likely to classify the administration of a substance that would relieve pain but also cause death as a case of euthanasia.

Furthermore, on the Catholic view there is no moral obligation to continue treatment when a person is medically hopeless. It is legitimate to allow people to die as a result of their illness or injury, even though their lives might be lengthened by the use of extraordinary means. In addition, we may legitimately make the same decisions about ourselves that we make about others who are in no condition to decide. Thus, without intending to kill ourselves, we may choose measures for the relief of pain that may secondarily hasten our end. Or we may refuse extraordinary treatment and let "nature" take its course—let "God's will" determine the outcome. (See Part V, "Foundations of Bioethics," for a fuller discussion of the Roman Catholic position on euthanasia and extraordinary means of sustaining life.)

At first sight, utilitarianism would seem to endorse euthanasia in all of its forms. Whenever suffering is great and the condition of the person is one without legitimate medical hope, the principle of utility might be invoked to approve putting the person to death. After all, in such a case we seem to be acting to end suffering and to bring about a state of affairs in which happiness exceeds unhappiness. Thus, whether the person concerned is ourself or another, euthanasia would seem to be a morally right action.

A utilitarian might argue in this way, but it is not the only way in which the principle of utility could be applied. It could be argued, for example, that since life is a necessary condition for happiness, it is wrong to destroy that condition because, by doing so, the possibility of all future happiness is lost. Furthermore, a rule utilitarian might well argue that a rule like "The taking of a human life is permissible when suffering is intense and the condition of the person permits no legitimate hope" would be open to abuse. Consequently, in the long run the rule would actually work to increase the amount of unhappiness in the world. Obviously, it is not possible to say that there is such a thing as "the utilitarian view of euthanasia." The principle of utility supplies a guide for an answer, but it is not itself an answer.

Euthanasia presents a considerable difficulty for Kant's ethics. For Kant, an autonomous rational being has a duty to preserve his or her life. Thus, one cannot rightly refuse needed medical care or commit suicide. Yet our status as autonomous rational beings also endows us with an inherent dignity. If that status is destroyed or severely compromised, as it is when people become comatose and unknowing because of illness or injury, then it is not certain that we have a duty to maintain our lives under such conditions. It may be more in keeping with our freedom and dignity for us to instruct others either to put us to death or to take no steps to keep us alive should we ever be in such a state. Voluntary

EUTHANASIA

When a person has a disease that cannot be cured, do you think that doctors should be allowed by law to end that patient's life by some painless means if the patient and his or her family request it?

Support: 71%

Do Not Support: 27%

Based on national telephone survey of 1,003 adults conducted on May 10–13, 2007. Half were asked the question above. Gallup Organization, May 31, 2007.

euthanasia may be compatible with (if not required by) Kant's ethics.

By a similar line of reasoning, it may be that nonvoluntary euthanasia might be seen as a duty that we have to others. We might argue that by putting to death a comatose and hopeless person we are recognizing the dignity that person possessed in his or her previous state. It might also be argued that a human being in a vegetative state is not a person in the relevant moral sense. Thus, our ordinary duty to preserve life does not hold.

According to Ross, we have a strong prima facie obligation not to kill a person except in justifiable self-defense—unless we have an even stronger prima facie moral obligation to do something that cannot be done without killing. Since active euthanasia typically requires taking the life of an innocent person, there is a moral presumption against it. However, another of Ross's prima facie obligations is that we keep promises made to others. Accordingly, if someone who is now in an irreversible coma with no hope of recovery has left instructions that in case of such an event she wishes her life to be ended, then we are under a prima facie obligation to follow her instructions. Thus, in such a case we may be justified in overriding the presumption against taking an innocent life.

What if there are no such instructions? It could be argued that our prima facie obligation of acting beneficently toward others requires us to attempt to determine what someone's wishes would be from what we know about him as a person. We would then treat him the way that we believe that he would want us to. In the absence of any relevant information, we might make the decision on the basis of how a rational person would want to be treated in similar circumstances. Of course, if anyone has left instructions that his life is to be maintained, if possible, under any circumstances, then we have a prima facie obligation to respect this preference also.

Part IV

Resources

Chapter 8

Organ Transplants and Scarce Medical Resources

CASES AND CONTEXTS

Did Steve Jobs Cheat?

Steve Jobs is the legendary cofounder of Apple, Inc., and the creative inspiration behind such innovative technology as personal computers with a graphical interface and, more recently, the iPod, iPhone, and iPad. He is a major figure in the world's financial community and has a personal net worth estimated to be around $6 billion.

Yet Steve Jobs is also human, and like everyone else, he is subject to illnesses. In 2004, he was diagnosed with pancreatic cancer, a disease that in the United States alone kills about 25,000 people a year. His doctors found, however, that Jobs had an islet-cell neuroendocrine tumor, one of the few forms of pancreatic cancer that can be treated with some success. Most forms of pancreatic cancer progress so rapidly that by the time they are diagnosed, treatment is ineffective. Islet-cell tumors are slow growing, however, so treatment has a decent chance of succeeding.

In July 2004, Steve Jobs was operated on to remove the tumor. His surgeons employed the Whipple procedure (or pancreaticoduodenectomy), which involves removing part of the pancreas, as well as a portion of the small intestine, the gallbladder, the bile duct, and, sometimes, part of the stomach. Jobs received no chemotherapy or radiation treatments, and a few months after the surgery he returned to his position at Apple.

Even though Jobs was back at work, he didn't seem completely well. He lost a significant amount of weight and began suffering from digestive problems. He appeared so thin and frail that his health became a matter of financial importance, because investors began to speculate openly about whether Jobs would be able to continue to guide Apple and maintain its profits. Even with the stock price of Apple threatened, Jobs remained unwilling to discuss his health in public or release statements about it. As speculation continued to mount, however, he said that his weight loss was due to enzyme imbalances, and later on he said he seemed physically frail because he was suffering from a severe case of the flu.

Speculation did not end, however. As news of Jobs' operation for pancreatic cancer leaked out, some observers began to interpret his fragile appearance as evidence that he still had cancer. The most likely scenario appeared to be that the islet-cell tumor had metastasized to his liver, something that would not be unusual. Neither Jobs, his wife, nor an Apple representative would make any public comment about this possibility. In January 2009, however, Jobs announced that he would take a six-month leave for health reasons.

Liver Transplant

In June 2009, reports began to surface that Jobs, who was then fifty-four years old, had received a liver transplant two months earlier. Jobs himself refused to comment, but people who had been briefed by members of Apple's board of directors confirmed to reporters that Jobs had received a liver transplant in Tennessee. Although the name of the hospital wasn't released, it didn't take long for it to leak out that the surgery had taken place at the Methodist University Hospital Transplant Institute in Memphis. The transplant program, which performs about 120 liver transplants a year, eventually issued a press release, with Jobs' permission, confirming that Jobs had been a patient at the Institute. He had received a liver from a deceased donor in April 2009.

At that time, Jobs was living in the San Francisco area, which is more than two thousand miles from Memphis. Why, then, many people began to ask, did he go to a hospital in Memphis for a liver transplant? Was it because, by going to Memphis, he was somehow able to use his wealth to manipulate the transplant system and get a donor liver he didn't deserve? Donor livers are a scarce resource. Nationwide, around 16,000 people are on the waiting list for a new liver and only about 5000 of them will receive one. So, people asked, isn't it suspicious that Steve Jobs just happened to end up with one? At first sight, some said, it looks like Jobs may have used his great wealth to cheat the system.

Getting a Liver Transplant

A 1984 U.S. law makes it illegal to buy or sell organs, so Jobs couldn't have bought a liver and had it transplanted at Methodist University Hospital. Nor is the organ distribution system set up so that people can jump to the front of the line. The 127 transplant centers in the United States all follow the same set of rules for allocating organs. The rules are formulated by the United Network for Organ Sharing (UNOS), an independent agency that works under a contract with the federal government. UNOS regularly audits transplant centers to make sure that they adhere to the definitions that define the categories that allow the centers to say that one patient is sicker or more in need of a transplant than some other patient.

Patients on the waiting list for a liver are characterized in terms of features such as human leukocyte antigen (HLA) profile (human leukocyte antigens, are proteins on cell surfaces), and physical size (a liver from a large man won't do for a small child), and these features are used to help determine who is a suitable candidate for a transplant organ.

Patients are also characterized by how sick they are. Liver transplant candidates are given a Model for End-Stage Liver Disease (MELD) score that determines where they rank on the transplant list. The score ranges from 6 to 40, and the higher the score, the sicker is the patient. The higher score also means the patient ranks higher on the transplant list. (When patients have the same MELD score, the one who has been on the list longer is ranked higher.)

UNOS also maintains the waiting list for transplant organs and works with the nation's fifty-eight regional organ procurement organizations (OPOs). When an organ becomes available, an OPO consults the UNOS waiting list for a suitable recipient in the relevant geographical region. Because organs begin to deteriorate as soon as they lose their blood supply, the distance they can be transported and remain viable is limited. Thus, organs are distributed first to local candidates, then to more distant ones. This means that someone local may get a liver, even though his MELD score is not as high as someone farther away.

Contrary to the belief of many, there is no national waiting list, only regional ones. Regions vary considerably in both geographical area and population size. Thus, regions like New York and Los Angles have ten to fifteen times the populations of regions like St. Louis and Memphis. This means that someone needing a transplant is more likely to get one more quickly in (say) Memphis or St. Louis than in New York, Los Angeles, or San Francisco.

The national average waiting time for a transplant liver is over a year, and in regions with dense populations, the time can be more than three years. The waiting time in the Memphis region from 2002 to 2007 was four months. Thus, someone on the waiting list and needing a liver transplant was likely to have to wait a much shorter time in the Memphis region than in the San Francisco region. Those with lower MELD scores are also more likely to get a donor liver more quickly than even those with higher scores in more densely populated regions. More organs may be available in high-population areas, but the demand is also greater. (Indeed, the demand for livers regularly exceeds the supply.)

Money also plays a role in who gets a transplant. A transplant organ can't be bought, but unless a patient has the means (cash or insurance) to pay for the surgery, the organ-acquisition fees, the hospital stay, and the drugs and medical care needed after the surgery, the patient will not make it to the transplant list. A liver transplant costs about $600,000, so an estimated one-third of people needing one cannot qualify on financial grounds alone. Despite the health care reform laws scheduled to take effect in 2011–2012, it is doubtful that this figure will change. Even though more people will have basic medical insurance, such coverage does not typically pay for organ transplants.

Multicenter Registration

If you are shopping in a supermarket and are in a hurry, you look for the fastest checkout line. Often your choice is wrong, and you find yourself wishing you were in line A instead of line B. If you have to wait in line at all, it would be ideal if you could wait in all the lines at the same time—or at least all that seem to be moving fast.

In 2003, UNOS began requiring transplant centers to notify candidates for organ transplants that they can be evaluated and registered (be put on the waiting list) at more than one center. Also, they can transfer the waiting time built up at one center to any other center. Thus, in principle, candidates for a liver transplant can register at multiple centers and so be put on multiple regional waiting lists. This will give them a better chance to get an organ faster than if they had to wait in only one line—particularly if that line happened to be in a heavily populated region like New York or San Francisco.

Everyone is eligible to register at multiple centers, but as with so much else in life, what can be done in principle is difficult or impossible for most people to do in practice. To start with, every center typically requires that anyone who wants to register for a transplant at that center be evaluated by that center. Such a workup may cost $10,000 or more, and most insurance companies are not likely to pay for multiple evaluations. Hence, individuals who want to register with several centers must be able to pay the additional evaluation costs themselves.

In addition, even when an insurance policy covers the costs of a transplant, the insurance company typically requires that the transplant be performed at a particular transplant center. This is because the company has negotiated a price with that center, so the company will refuse to pay the full cost (or perhaps any of the cost) for a transplant carried out at another center. Thus, usually the only people who can take advantage of multicenter registrations are those who can afford to pay the $600,000 or more for a transplant.

Steve Jobs

Whether Steve Jobs registered at several transplant centers has not been made public. Multicenter registration would explain, though, why someone who lives in the San Francisco area received a liver transplant at a Memphis hospital. Waiting times for specific organs at transplant centers are public information. As mentioned earlier, the national average waiting time for a donor liver is 12.3 months, but the waiting time at the Methodist University Hospital Transplant Center is 3.8 months. It would have

made sense for Steve Jobs to register with the Memphis center. As Michael Poreyko, director of liver transplants at Vanderbilt University observed, a person with access to a private jet could probably reach any transplant center in the United States during the six-hour window that a donor liver remains viable and suitable for transplant.

Steve Jobs has a net worth measured in billions. He would have no difficulty paying for the evaluations required to get onto the waiting lists at as many transplant centers as he wished. He would have no trouble paying for the transplant out of his own pocket. He would have no difficulty getting access to a private plane to deliver him to a center as soon as a donor liver became available and his MELD score qualified him to be the recipient.

Needing a Transplant While Rich

It is not reasonable to believe that Steve Jobs did anything wrong in getting his liver transplant. Nothing at all suggests that he cheated or pushed his way to the front of the line. What the case of Steve Jobs makes clear, however, is that the organ transplant system is structured to favor the rich. Only they can afford to pay for the multiple evaluations required to register at several transplant centers, and only they have access to a private plane to rush them to a center when an organ becomes available. Finally, only the rich can afford to pay for a transplant if their insurance won't cover the costs at a particular center.

Nothing suggests that Steve Jobs did anything wrong, but a great deal of evidence suggests that he is rich.

CASE PRESENTATION
The Prisoner Who Needed a Heart

We'll call him Ken Duke. That's not his name, but the California Department of Corrections doesn't make public the names of prisoners under its jurisdiction.

Ken Duke was a bad man. Not a murderer, not that bad, but a dangerous thief. The first California conviction that got him sent to prison was for armed robbery. After serving only part of his sentence, Duke had done enough time and behaved well enough to merit parole. He would

still have to report to his parole officer, but otherwise he was a free man.

That didn't last long. In 1996, a mere eight months after the prison bus dropped Ken Duke off in Los Angeles, he was again arrested for armed robbery in Los Angeles county. He was convicted of the crime in March 1997 and sentenced to serve a fourteen-year term in prison. Under California law, Duke wouldn't be eligible for a second crack at parole until 2008.

Bad Luck

Ken Duke was a bad man, but he also had some bad luck. Somewhere along the line, either on the street or in prison, he picked up a viral infection that damaged his heart. He lived with the damage without much of a problem for a while, but as time passed, Duke's heart steadily deteriorated. The heart muscle weakened, and the heart lost its pumping effectiveness. It grew in size in an attempt to compensate for its loss of function. He was given drugs to strengthen his heartbeat.

Even so, Duke's blood circulation slowed, and without a steady blood flow to carry away wastes, fluid built up in his lungs, reducing their effectiveness. His feet and ankles swelled, and he became so out of breath that even slight exertions, like walking across his cell, became impossible. He had to sleep with his head and shoulders raised to be able to breathe. Ken Duke was only thirty-one years old, but he was sick and feeble, suffering from congestive heart failure.

Unique Status

Duke was transferred from the Vacaville prison hospital in Northern California to the Stanford University Medical Center, one of the nation's leading medical facilities. His condition was assessed by the Stanford physicians assigned to care for him, and they were unanimous in their conclusion: If Ken Duke didn't get a heart transplant, he would die.

Treating Duke the way they would any other patient, the Stanford physicians listed Duke with the United Network for Organ Sharing as a candidate for a donor heart. His medical condition was so precarious that he was assigned to the category of those most urgently in need of a transplant.

At the time Ken Duke's name was entered on the UNOS waiting list, about 4000 other Americans were also waiting for a donor heart. Duke was unique, though; not only was he the only prisoner on the heart transplant list; he was the only prisoner who had ever been on the list.

The United Network for Organ Sharing, the agency responsible for framing the general rules for allocating transplant organs, explicitly refuses to distinguish between prisoners and other people, so far as qualifying for an organ is concerned. *The UNOS Ethics Committee Position Statement Regarding Convicted Criminals and Transplant Evaluation* holds that "one's status as a prisoner" should not preclude anyone "from consideration for a transplant." Whether people, prisoner or not, actually receive a transplant depends on their medical condition and the availability of a transplant organ. It also depends on whether they have the resources to pay for the cost of the transplant. Duke had the State of California to pay.

On January 3, 2002, Ken Duke received a heart transplant. The surgery and the hospital stay cost California about $200,000. This was not the final cost of Duke's treatment, however. He would have to remain on immunosuppressive drugs for the rest of his life, receive regular medical checkups, and most likely be hospitalized for one or more episodes of rejection. The total medical costs were estimated to be about $1 million, the same as for any other heart transplant patient.

Outcry

News of Ken Duke's transplant sparked a controversy that spread throughout the country. Why was a convicted prisoner getting a heart transplant paid for by the state, when thousands of people were in need of transplants but unable to get them because they lacked the resources to pay for them? Was it fair to give a lawbreaker a scarce, expensive, lifesaving resource while simultaneously denying the same resource to law-abiding but low-income and uninsured citizens? Many people were angered that Ken Duke was given what so many others desperately needed to save their lives but could not afford.

This anger was articulated by *Los Angeles Times* columnist Steve Lopez. "What is this telling people?" Lopez asked. "What's the message here to the public? You know, you had two robbery convictions, you're in jail, you get sick, you're going to the top of the line, buddy." Most people, such as his father, who has heart disease, Lopez says, will never get the kind of care represented by a medical center like Stanford.

They also won't get a heart transplant just because they need one. "I had this conversation with a woman who calls me and says, my brother needs a heart transplant, and he could not get on the list. And they said, 'Well, you're going to have to raise $150,000.' And he says, 'Well, I don't have $150,000.' They're practically having bake sales."

A Special Right?

California prison officials believed they had no choice about getting a heart transplant for Ken Duke, no matter how much it cost and no matter how angry and unhappy it made the public. Duke, in the view of the officials, seemed to have both the Constitution and court decisions interpreting it on his side.

In 1976, the U.S. Supreme Court had ruled that failing to provide prisoners with "adequate medical care" would violate the Eighth Amendment of the Constitution, which guarantees that people who are incarcerated will not be subjected to "cruel and unusual punishment." Also, in 1995 a federal District Court ordered correction officials to list an inmate for a kidney transplant. The officials had originally turned down the inmate's request, but he sued the state, winning not only the right to be listed for a kidney transplant but also a $35,000 settlement.

If the California Department of Corrections had failed to provide Duke with a heart transplant, corrections official said, he would have died, and his estate could have sued the state. The estate almost certainly would have won the suit, because it would have the court rulings interpreting the Eighth Amendment on its side.

Some consider the federal courts' interpretation of the Amendment as, in effect, recognizing a right to medical care that has not been recognized for those who are not prisoners. "Inmates have a Constitutional right that you and I don't have," Steve Green, a California corrections official, told a reporter. "The right to health care."

Critics argue that the legal view that states must provide prisoners with "adequate medical care" has been too generously interpreted by corrections officials. Does "adequate" care mean that every available form of medical care that might be of value in extending the life of a prisoner must be employed? Or perhaps "adequate care" means only care that is basic and does not require the use of expensive and scarce resources. Perhaps it means only the sort of care that is available to people of modest means and no health insurance. They can afford ordinary surgery, but they certainly can't afford the initial and continuing costs of a heart transplant.

Ken Duke did well initially, then died in December 2003, almost a year after his transplant.

CASE PRESENTATION
Playing God with Dialysis

In 1966, Brattle, Texas, had a population of about 10,000. Brattle County had another 20,000 people, living on isolated farms deep within the pine forests, or in crossroads towns with a filling station, a feed store, one or two white frame churches, and maybe twenty or twenty-five houses. Brattle was the market town and county seat, the place all the farmers, their wives, and children went to on Saturday afternoon.

Brattle was also the medical center, because it had the only hospitals in the county. One of them, Conklin Clinic, was hardly more than a group of doctors' offices. But Crane Memorial Hospital was quite a different sort of place. Occupying a relatively new three-story brick building in downtown Brattle, the hospital offered new equipment, a well-trained staff, and high-quality medical care.

This was mostly due to the efforts of Dr. J. B. Crane, Jr. The hospital was dedicated to the memory of his father, a man who had practiced medicine in Brattle County for almost fifty years. Before Crane became a memorial hospital, it was Crane Clinic. But J. B. Crane, Jr., after returning from Johns Hopkins Medical School, was determined to

expand the clinic and transform it into a modern hospital. The need was there, and private investors were easy to find. Only a year after his father's death, Dr. Crane was able to offer Brattle County a genuine hospital.

It was only natural that when the county commissioner decided that Brattle County should have a dialysis machine, he would turn to Dr. Crane's hospital. The machine was bought with county funds, but Crane Memorial Hospital would operate it under a contract agreement. The hospital was guaranteed against loss by the county, but the hospital was also not permitted to make a profit on dialysis. Furthermore, although access to the machine was not restricted to county residents, residents were to be given priority.

Dr. Crane was not pleased with this stipulation. "I don't like to have medical decisions influenced by political considerations," he told the commissioner. "If a guy comes in and needs dialysis, I don't want to tell him that he can't have it because somebody else who doesn't need it as much is on the machine and that person is a county resident."

"I don't know what to tell you," the commissioner said. "It was county tax money that paid for the machine, and the County Council decided that the people who supplied the money ought to get top priority."

"What about the kind of case that I mentioned?" Dr. Crane asked. "What about somebody who could wait for dialysis who is a resident, as opposed to somebody who needs it immediately who's not a resident?"

"We'll just leave that sort of case to your discretion," the commissioner said. "People around here have confidence in you and your doctors. If you say they can wait, then they can wait. I know you won't let them down. Of course, if somebody died while some outsider was on the machine . . . well, that would be embarrassing for all of us, I guess."

Dr. Crane was pleased to have the dialysis machine in his hospital. Not only was it the only one in Brattle County, but none of the neighboring counties had even one. Only the big hospitals in places like Dallas, Houston, and San Antonio had the machines. It put Crane Memorial up in the top rank.

Dr. Crane was totally unprepared for the problem when it came. He hadn't known there were so many people with chronic renal disease in Brattle County. But when news spread that there was a kidney machine available at Crane Memorial Hospital, twenty-three people applied for the dialysis program. Some were Dr. Crane's own patients or patients of his associates on the hospital staff. But a number of them were referred to the hospital by other physicians in Brattle and surrounding towns. Two of them were from neighboring Lopez County.

Working at a maximum, the machine could accommodate fourteen patients. But the staff decided that maximum operation would be likely to lead to dangerous equipment malfunctions and breakdowns. They settled on ten as the number of patients that should be admitted to the program.

Dr. Crane and his staff interviewed each of the program's applicants, reviewed their medical history, and got a thorough medical workup on each. They persuaded two of the patients to continue to commute to Houston, where they were already in dialysis. In four cases, renal disease had already progressed to the point that the staff decided that the patients could not benefit sufficiently from the program to make them good medical risks. In one other case, a patient suffering intestinal cancer and in generally poor health was rejected as a candidate. Two people were not in genuine need of dialysis but could be best treated by a program of medication.

That left fourteen candidates for the ten positions. Thirteen were from Brattle County and one from Lopez County.

"This is not a medical problem," Dr. Crane told the commissioner. "And I'm not going to take the responsibility of deciding which people to condemn to death and which to give an extra chance at life."

"What do you want me to do?" the commissioner asked. "I wouldn't object if you made the decision. I mean, you wouldn't have to tell everybody about it. You could just decide."

"That's something I won't do," Dr. Crane said. "All of this has to be open and aboveboard. It's got to be fair. If I decide, then everybody will think I am favoring my own patients or just taking the people who can pay the most money."

"I see what you mean. If I appoint a selection committee, will you serve on it?"

"I will. As long as my vote is the same as everybody else's."

"That's what I'll do, then," the Commissioner said.

The Brattle County Renal Dialysis Selection Committee was appointed and operating within the week. In addition to Dr. Crane, it was made up of three people chosen by the commissioner. Amy Langford, a Brattle housewife in her mid-fifties whose husband owned the largest automobile and truck agency in Brattle County, was one member. The Reverend David Johnson was another member. He was the only African American on the committee and the pastor of the largest predominantly African American church in Brattle. The last member was Jacob Sims, owner of a hardware store in the nearby town of Silsbee. He was the only member of the committee not from the town of Brattle.

"Now, I'm inclined to favor this fellow," said Mr. Sims at the selection committee's first meeting. "He's twenty-four years old, he's married, and he has a child two years old."

"You're talking about James Nelson?" Mrs. Langford asked. "I had some trouble with him. I've heard that he used to drink a lot before he got sick, and from the looks of his record, he's had a hard time keeping a job."

"That's hard to say," said Reverend Johnson. "He works as a pulpwood hauler, and people who do that change jobs a lot. You just have to go where the work is."

"That's right," said Mr. Sims. "One thing, though. I can't find any indication of his church membership. He says he's a Methodist, but I don't see where he's told us what his church is."

"I don't either," said Mrs. Langford. "And he's not a member of the Masons or the Lions Club or any other sort of civic group. I wouldn't say he's made much of a contribution to this community."

"That's right," said Reverend Johnson. "But let's don't forget that he's got a wife and baby depending on him. That child is going to need a father."

"I think he is a good psychological candidate," said Dr. Crane. "That is, I think if he starts the program he'll stick to it. I've talked with his wife, and I know she'll encourage him."

"We should notice that he's a high school dropout," Mrs. Langford said. "I don't think we can ever expect him to make much of a contribution to this town or to the county."

"Do you want to vote on this case?" asked Mr. Sims, the chairman of the committee.

"Let's talk about all of them, then go back and vote," Reverend Johnson suggested.

Everyone around the table nodded in agreement. The files were arranged by date of application, and Mr. Sims picked up the next one from the stack in front of him.

"Alva Algers," he said. "He's a fifty-three-year-old lawyer with three grown children. His wife is still alive, and he's still married to her. He's Secretary of the Layman's Board of the Brattle Episcopal Church, a member of the Rotary Club and the Elks. He used to be a scoutmaster."

"From the practical point of view," said Dr. Crane, "he would be a good candidate. He's intelligent and educated and understands what's involved in dialysis."

"I think he's definitely the sort of person we want to help," said Mrs. Langford. "He's the kind of person that makes this a better town. I'm definitely in favor of him."

"I am, too," said Reverend Johnson. "Even if he does go to the wrong church."

"I'm not so sure," said Mr. Sims. "I don't think fifty-three is old—I'd better not, because I'm fifty-two myself. Still, his children are grown; he's led a good life. I'm not sure I wouldn't give the edge to some younger fellow."

"How can you say that?" Mrs. Langford said. "He's got a lot of good years left. He's a person of good character who might still do a lot for other people. He's not like that Nelson, who's not going to do any good for anybody except himself."

"I guess I'm not convinced that lawyers and members of the Rotary Club do a lot more good for the community than drivers of pulpwood trucks," Mr. Sims said.

"Perhaps we ought to go on to the next candidate," Reverend Johnson said.

"We have Mrs. Holly Holton, a forty-three-year-old housewife from Mineral Springs," Mr. Sims said.

"That's in Lopez County, isn't it?" Mrs. Langford asked. "I think we can just reject her right off. She didn't pay the taxes that bought the machine, and our county doesn't have any responsibility for her."

"That's right," said Reverend Johnson.

Mr. Sims agreed, and Dr. Crane raised no objection.

"Now," said Mr. Sims, "here's Alton Conway. I believe he's our only African American candidate."

"I know him well," said Reverend Johnson. "He owns a dry-cleaning business, and people in the black community think very highly of him."

"I'm in favor of him," Mrs. Langford said. "He's married and seems quite settled and respectable."

"I wouldn't want us to take him just because he's black," Reverend Johnson said. "But I think he's got a lot in his favor."

"Well," said Mr. Sims, "unless Dr. Crane wants to add anything, let's go on to Nora Bainridge. She's a thirty-year-old divorced woman whose eight-year-old boy lives with his father over in Louisiana. She's a waitress at the Pep Cafe."

"She is a very vital woman," said Dr. Crane. "She's had a lot of trouble in her life, but I think she's a real fighter."

"I don't believe she's much of a churchgoer," said Reverend Johnson. "At least she doesn't give us a pastor's name."

"That's right," said Mrs. Langford. "And I just wonder what kind of morals a woman like her has. I mean, being divorced and working as a waitress and all."

"I don't believe we're trying to award sainthood here," said Mr. Sims.

"But surely moral character is relevant," said Mrs. Langford.

"I don't know anything against her moral character," said Mr. Sims. "Do you?"

"I'm only guessing," said Mrs. Langford. "But I wouldn't say that a woman of her background and apparent character is somebody we ought to give top priority to."

"I don't want to be the one to cast the first stone," said Reverend Johnson. "But I wouldn't put her at the top of our list either."

"I think we had better be careful not to discriminate against people who are poor and uneducated," said Dr. Crane.

"I agree," said Mrs. Langford. "But surely we have to take account of a person's worth."

"Can you tell us how we can measure a person's worth?" asked Mr. Sims.

"I believe I can," Mrs. Langford said. "Does the person have a steady job? Is he or she somebody we would be proud to know? Is he a churchgoer? Does he or she do things for other people? We can see what kind of education the person has had and consider whether he is somebody we would like to have around."

"I guess that's some of it, all right," said Mr. Sims. "But I don't like to rely on things like education, money, and public service. A lot of people just haven't had a decent chance in this world. Maybe they were born poor or have had a lot of bad luck. I'm beginning to think that we ought to make our choices just by drawing lots."

"I can't approve of that," said Reverend Johnson. "That seems like a form of gambling to me. We ought to choose the good over the wicked, reward those who have led a virtuous life."

"I agree," Mrs. Langford said. "Choosing by drawing straws or something like that would mean we are just too cowardly to make decisions. We would be shirking our responsibility. Clearly, some people are more deserving than others, and we ought to have the courage to say so."

"All right," said Mr. Sims. "I guess we'd better get on with it, then. Simon Gootz is a forty-eight-year-old baker. He's got a wife and four children. Owns his own bakery—probably all of us have been there. He's Jewish."

"I'm not sure he's the sort of person who can stick to the required diet and go through the dialysis program," Dr. Crane said.

"I'll bet his wife and children would be a good incentive," said Mrs. Langford.

"There's not a Jewish church in town," said Reverend Johnson. "So of course we can't expect him to be a regular churchgoer."

"He's an immigrant," said Mr. Sims. "I don't believe he has any education to speak of, but he did start that bakery and build it up from nothing. That says a lot about his character."

"We can agree that he's a good candidate," said Mrs. Langford.

"Let's just take one more before we break for dinner," Mr. Sims said. "Rebecca Scarborough. She's a sixty-three-year-old widow. Her children are all grown and living somewhere else."

"She's my patient," Dr. Crane said. "She's a tough and resourceful old woman. I believe she can follow orders and stand up to the rigors of the program, and her health in general is good."

Reverend Johnson said, "I just wonder if we shouldn't put a lady like her pretty far down on our list. She's lived a long life already, and she hasn't got anybody depending on her."

"I'm against that," Mrs. Langford said. "Everybody knows Mrs. Scarborough. Her family has been in this town for ages. She's one of our most substantial citizens. People would be scandalized if we didn't select her."

"Of course, I'm not from Brattle," said Mr. Sims. "And maybe that's an advantage here, because I don't see that she's got much in her favor except being from an old family."

"I think that's worth something," said Mrs. Langford.

"I'm not sure it's enough, though," said Reverend Johnson.

After dinner at the Crane Memorial Hospital cafeteria, the selection committee met again to discuss the seven remaining candidates. It was past ten o'clock before their final decisions were made. James Nelson, the pulpwood truck driver; Holly Holton, the housewife from Mineral Springs; and Nora Bainridge, the waitress, were all rejected as candidates. Mrs. Scarborough was rejected also. The lawyer, Alva Algers; the dry cleaner, Alton Conway; and the baker, Simon Gootz, were selected to participate in the dialysis program. Others selected were a retired secondary school teacher, an assembly-line worker at the Rigid Box Company, a Brattle County Sheriff's Department patrolman, and a twenty-seven-year-old woman file clerk in the office of the Texas Western Insurance Company.

Dr. Crane was glad that the choices were made so the program could begin operation. But he was not pleased with the selection method and resolved to talk to his own staff and with the county commissioner about devising some other kind of selection procedure.

Without giving any reasons, Mr. Sims sent a letter to the county commissioner resigning from the Renal Dialysis Selection Committee. Mrs. Langford and Reverend Johnson also sent letters to the commissioner. They thanked him for appointing them to the committee and indicated their willingness to continue to serve.

CASE PRESENTATION
Transplants for the Mentally Impaired?

Sandra Jensen was born with a deformed heart, but it wasn't until she was thirty-five that it began to make her so sick that she needed a heart–lung transplant to extend her life. She was young and otherwise healthy, but transplant centers at both Stanford University and the University of California, San Diego, rejected her as a candidate.

Sandra Jensen also had Down syndrome, and the transplanters doubted that she had sufficient intelligence to care for herself after the surgery. She would have to follow the complicated routine of taking doses of dozens of medications daily that is the lot of every transplant recipient. If she failed to adhere to the postoperative requirements, she would die, and the organs that might have saved the life of one or two other people would be wasted.

William Bronston, a state rehabilitation administrator and a friend of Jensen, became her advocate. He pointed out that she had demonstrated a high level of intellectual functioning. She was a high school graduate who worked with people with Down syndrome, and she had lived on

her own for several years. She spoke for the disabled in California and attended the Washington signing by George H. Bush of the Americans with Disabilities Act in 1990.

Thanks to strong lobbying by Bronston and the threat of adverse publicity, Stanford reversed its decision. On January 23, 1996, in a five-hour operation, Ms. Jensen became the first seriously mentally retarded person in the United States to receive a major organ transplant.

More than a year later, on May 4, 1997, after her health began deteriorating, Ms. Jensen entered Sutter General Hospital in San Francisco. She had been admitted to the hospital several times before because of her reaction to the immunosuppressive drug. But this time was the last, and she died there on May 25, 1997. "Every day was always precious and lived well by her," her friend William Bronston said.

Prompted by Ms. Jensen's struggle to be accepted for a transplant, the California Assembly passed a bill to prohibit transplant centers from discriminating against impaired people needing a transplant.

SOCIAL CONTEXT
Acquiring and Allocating Transplant Organs

Organ transplantation is perhaps the most dramatic example of how the high technology of contemporary medicine can extend or improve the lives of hundreds of thousands of people. Developments in surgical techniques, improvements in organ preservation, and the advent of new immunosuppressive drugs have made organ transplantation into a standard surgical therapy.

Yet behind the wonder and drama of transplant surgery lies the troubling fact that the need for transplant organs seriously and chronically outstrips the supply. Thus, against a background of a chronic shortage, physicians, surgeons, and committees must make judgments that will offer an opportunity for some while destroying the last vestige of hope for others.

Although transplanting kidneys began as early as the 1950s, the list of organs now transplanted with a significant degree of success has been expanded over the last twenty years to include corneas, bone marrow, bone and skin, livers, lungs, pancreases, intestines, and hearts. All involve special problems, but we will limit discussion to solid organs—those like the heart and liver, which are complete functional units.

Worldwide, more than 200,000 kidney transplants have been performed, and about ninety-four percent of the organs are still functioning one year later. (Some recipients are still alive after almost forty years.) Thomas Starzl and his team successfully transplanted the first liver in 1967, and the rate of survival after three years is about seventy-five percent. Also in 1967, Christiaan Barnard transplanted a human heart, and now around seventy-five percent of these procedures are considered successful. Lung transplants, though still a relatively new procedure, have a fifty-five percent three-year survival rate. New techniques of management and the development of drugs to suppress part of the immune response have done much to increase the success rate of transplants, but additional improvements will probably require improvements in the ability to control tissue rejection. (See the Briefing Session for more details.)

Costs

A major social and moral difficulty of transplant surgery is that it is extremely expensive. For example, a kidney transplant may cost about $40,000, a heart transplant about $150,000, and a liver transplant in the range from $200,000 to $300,000. The immunosuppressive drugs needed to prevent rejection of a transplanted organ cost from $10,000 to $20,000 a year, and they must be taken for the remainder of the patient's life. Despite the high costs of transplantation, it may offer cost savings over dialysis and medical treatments. Further, combined costs constitute less than one percent of all health care costs.

Questions have been raised in recent years about what restrictions, if any, should be placed on access to transplants. Should society deny them to everyone, pay for all who need them but cannot afford them, or pay for only some who cannot pay? Medicare, Medicaid, and most, but not all, insurance companies pay for organ transplants and at least part of the continuing drug and treatment costs. The End-Stage Renal Disease Program covers kidney transplants for everyone, yet people needing any other sort of transplant who don't qualify for public programs and lack appropriate insurance must find some way of raising the money. Otherwise, hospitals are not likely to provide them with an organ. Every transplant candidate, in Starzl's phrase, must pass a wallet biopsy to qualify.

No one knows yet what impact the new health care laws will have on organ transplantation when they take effect in 2011. Everyone (with some exceptions) will be required to have insurance, but because of the costs involved, most people are not likely to have insurance that will pay for a heart, liver, lung, or any other kind of organ transplant. This means that the great majority of people will still be in the position of having to pass Starzl's wallet biopsy before they qualify for the transplant waiting list.

Availability

The second major problem, after cost, is the availability of donor organs. The increase in the number of transplant operations performed during the last thirty years has produced a chronic scarcity of organs. About 25,000 people a year receive transplants at the nation's 278 transplant centers, but about 10,000 more die while waiting for organs. To put this in perspective, this is about three times the number of people who died on the September 11, 2001, terrorist attack on the World Trade Center.

At any given time, about 100,000 people are on the transplant waiting list. Each year, 35,000–40,000 additional people register to get organs. For each organ transplanted, three more people sign up, and those on the waiting list die at a rate of ten a day.

People in need of a kidney or pancreas can rely on dialysis or insulin injections to treat their diseases, but those in need of a liver, heart, or lung have limited alternative treatments available. Artificial livers remain experimental, and left-ventricular-assist devices can help only some heart patients. For those waiting for livers, lungs, or hearts, the lack of a suitable transplant organ spells almost certain death. Given the currently limited supply of organs, we face two key questions: How can the supply be increased? How are those who will actually receive organs to be selected from the pool of candidates?

Increasing Supply

An obvious answer to the first question is that the supply of organs can be increased by increasing donations. Exactly how many organs that could be used for transplant aren't retrieved from those declared dead is unclear. According to one estimate, between 6900 and 10,700 potential donors are available, but because the next of kin either is not asked to donate or refuses to donate, or because of the circumstances of death or the condition of the organs, only about thirty-seven to fifty-seven percent of potential donors become actual donors.

At a time when the need for donors is increasing, their actual number is decreasing. In 2008, for the first time in the history of the Organ Procurement and Transportation Network, the number of both deceased and live donors declined from the previous year. (This necessarily led to a decline in the number of transplants.) The number of live donors began to decline in 2004, and each year since for which there are figures shows that the decline is continuing. Some way to reverse the trend in organ donors is desperately needed.

Required Request and Required Response Laws

The federal Uniform Anatomical Gift Act of 1984 served as a model for state laws, and virtually all states have enacted laws to promote the increase of organ donation. Some states have "required response" laws requiring people to declare, upon renewing their driver's license, whether they wish to become organ donors, and most states make it easy for people to decide to become donors by printing organ donation cards on the backs of driver's licenses. State laws based on the act spell out a person's right to donate all or part of his body and to designate a person or institution as a recipient. A federal law passed in 1987 mandates that organ donor cards be included with tax refund checks.

Even with the support of such laws, transplant centers have been reluctant to intrude on a family's grief by asking that a deceased patient's organs be donated. Even if a patient has signed an organ donation card, the permission of the immediate family is required, in most cases, before the organs can be removed. In 1991, a federal appeals court ruled in favor of an Ohio woman who argued that the coroner who had removed her husband's corneas during an autopsy and donated them to the Cincinnati Eye Bank had violated her property rights. Her property interest in her husband's body was found to be protected under the due process clause of the Fourteenth Amendment.

In an attempt to overcome the reluctance of physicians to request organ donations, a 1986 federal law requires that hospitals receiving Medicare or Medicaid payments (ninety-seven percent of the nation's hospitals) identify patients who could become organ donors at death. The law also requires that hospitals discuss organ donations with the families of such patients and inform them of their legal power to authorize donations. Although this "required request" law has been in effect for more than twenty years, because of difficulties in administering it, including overcoming the reluctance of physicians to approach worried or bereaved families, the law has led to only a modest (about ten percent) increase in the supply of transplant organs.

Non-Heart-Beating Donors

An approach devised at the University of Pittsburgh involves acting on the requests of patients (or their representatives) to remove their organs when their hearts stop beating, even though they may not yet be brain dead. (See Chapter 7 for a discussion of criteria for determining death.) Hence, someone on a ventilator wanting to be weaned off the machine may ask that her organs be used for transplant, should the withdrawal result in her death. The ventilator is removed in an operating room, and three minutes after the patient's heart has stopped beating, the transplant organs are removed. In practice, most donor candidates are not like the one described. They have suffered severe brain damage but are not brain dead, and permission has been obtained from their families.

Critics of the practice have raised questions about using the cessation of heartbeat as a proper criterion for death. (Perhaps the patient could be resuscitated. Is three minutes long enough to wait?) Some have also wondered if the practice doesn't put pressure on mentally competent, but seriously ill, patients to give up the struggle for their lives by volunteering to become organ donors. Similarly, critics have charged, by providing a rationalization, the practice may make it too easy for the parents or other representatives of comatose patients on life support to decide to withdraw support and end the person's life.

Organ Protection Before Obtaining Consent

Another innovative but controversial approach employed by some medical centers involves injecting organ-protective drugs and preservatives into patients who die in or on the way an emergency room. The organs are not removed from the body (although some surgical steps may be taken), but by making sure the organs have a good blood supply and so are protected from damage, physicians gain additional time to seek permission from the families. Otherwise, the organs would deteriorate and be useless for transplantation.

Critics of this practice claim that hospitals do not always determine that a patient is dead before injecting drugs with the aim of preserving the organs. Thus, physicians can cause harm to still-living patients. Others claim that the practice borders on desecration and denies dignity to individuals whose dead bodies are subjected to an invasive procedure without their prior consent. Further, critics say, we have no generally accepted ideas about what it is legitimate to do to a newly dead body to provide benefit to others.

Defenders of the practice say it gives families time to recover from the shock of learning about the death of a loved one and allows them to make a more considered decision. In this respect, the practice is more humane than asking a family for permission to take an organ from a loved one right at the time they learn of the loved one's death. Also, taking steps to preserve the organs of a dead body enables us to use them to save the lives of others, for organs deteriorate rapidly.

Using organs from non-heart-beating cadavers and preserving the organs of the newly dead before securing consent are both practices that aim to provide a way to fill the gap between the number of transplant organs obtainable from brain-dead individuals and the number needed by those awaiting a transplant. Although 12,000 to 20,000 people are declared brain dead every year, 100,000 are in need of transplants.

Selling Organs

Another possibility for increasing the organ supply is to permit organs to be offered for sale. Before death, an individual might arrange payment for the posthumous use of one or more of his organs. Or after his death, his survivors might sell his organs to those needing them. In a variation of this proposal, donors or their families might receive tax credits, or a donor might be legally guaranteed that if a family member or friend required a transplant organ, that person would be given priority in the distribution. Under either plan, there would be a strong incentive to make organs available for transplant.

The public reaction to any plan for marketing organs has been strongly negative. People generally regard the prospect of individuals in need of transplants bidding against one another in an "organ auction" or offering a kidney for sale on eBay as ghoulish and morally repugnant, and this attitude extends to all forms of the market approach. (A government-regulated market with fixed prices is likely to be preferable to an open market.) In 1984, the National Organ Transplantation Act made the sale of organs for transplant illegal in the United States. At least twenty other countries, including Canada, Britain, and most of Europe, have similar laws.

A third possibility would be to allow living individuals to sell their non-vital organs to those in need of transplants. Taking hearts from living people would be illegal, as it would involve homicide by the surgeon who removed them. However, kidneys occur in pairs, and we already permit individuals to donate one of them—indeed, we celebrate those who do. Also, surgeons can now remove a lobe of a donor's liver and transplant it into a recipient with relative safety. It is thus only a short step from the heroic act of giving away a kidney or the lobe of a liver to the commercial act of selling it.

Kidney donors can now have a kidney removed laparoscopically, allowing them to avoid traditional open surgery that involves a twelve inch incision, the removal of a rib, and three to six weeks of recuperation. This means that donors make a faster recovery and avoid some of the pain of the open procedure. Donors face odds of one in 20,000 of dying from surgical complications, but the risk of dying as a result of having only one kidney is extremely small. People with one kidney are slightly more likely to develop high blood pressure than those with two. No long-term studies of kidney donors have been done, however, so whether they suffer adverse effects ten or twenty years afterward is not established.

Even less is known about liver-lobe donors. The procedure started about fifteen years ago with a parent donating a liver segment to a child and has now expanded to include adult-to-adult donation. After a month or so, the lobes of the donor and recipient grow back to roughly normal size. The risk of death to the donor is not well established, but it is thought to be about one in 10,000.

Allowing the sale of an organ would be in keeping with the generally acknowledged principle that people ought to be free to do as they wish with their own bodies. We already permit the sale of blood, plasma, bone marrow, ova, and sperm. Also, the kidney shortage is so severe that it cannot be solved without using kidneys from living donors. Similarly, people with end-stage liver disease have no alternative to a transplant, and the need for livers outstrips the supply. Paying kidney and liver-lobe donors for their organs would thus save lives.

The most telling disadvantage to allowing such transactions as a matter of social policy, however, is that it would be the poor who would be most likely to suffer from it. It is all too easy to imagine a mother wishing to improve the lives and opportunities of her children deciding to sell a kidney to help make that possible.

That the economically advantaged should thrive by literally exploiting the bodies of the poor seems morally repulsive to most people. (The 1984 Organ Transplant Act was in direct response to the operations of the International Kidney Exchange, which was established in Virginia for the purpose of selling kidneys from living donors. The donors were predominantly indigent.) It is not a wholly persuasive answer to object that someone should be permitted to do as he wishes with his body to provide for the welfare of his family. If selling a liver lobe and putting his own life and health at risk is the only option open to someone with that aim, this in itself constitutes a prima facie case for major social reform.

"Everyone Makes a Fee, Except for the Donor"

Despite strong public sentiment against selling organs, a telephone poll conducted by the United Network for Organ Sharing and the National Kidney Foundation showed that forty-eight percent of the people interviewed favored some form of "donor compensation." Under the Transplant Act, there can be none.

The law does permit payments associated with removing, preserving, transporting, and storing human organs. As a result, a large industry has developed around organ transplants. Sixty-nine procurement organizations, operating in federally defined geographical regions, collect organs from donors and transport them to the 278 hospitals with transplant facilities.

A procurement agency may be paid about $25,000 for its services. This amount includes fees for ambulance trips to pick up and deliver the organ, fees to the hospital for the use of the operating room where the organ is removed, costs of tissue matching and blood testing, and overhead expenses for the agency and its personnel.

In addition, costs involved in a transplant may include fees paid to local surgeons to prepare the patient for organ removal and fees paid to a surgical team coming into town to remove the organ. Such fees typically amount to several thousand dollars. Hospitals pay for the organs they receive, but they pass on their costs and more. Hospitals charge, as a rough average, $16,000 to $18,000 for a kidney or a heart and $20,000 to $22,000 for a liver. According to one study, hospitals may mark up the cost of an organ by as much as 200 percent to cover costs that patients are unable to pay or that exceed the amount the government will reimburse. A donor of several organs can produce considerable income for the transplanting hospital.

Some critics of current transplant practices have pointed out that everyone, except the donor makes a fee from donated organs. Yet matters show little sign of changing. A representative of the National Kidney Foundation proposed to a congressional committee that the law be changed to allow a relatively small amount of money (perhaps $2000) to be given to the families of organ donors as a contribution to burial expenses. The recommendation was not acted on, and similar proposals are no more likely to meet with success.

Given current transplant practices, it is understandable why donor families can sometimes become bitter. When Judy Sutton's daughter Susan killed herself, Mrs. Sutton donated Susan's heart and liver and so helped save the lives of two people. Mrs. Sutton then had to borrow the money to pay for Susan's funeral. "Susan gave life even in death," Mrs. Sutton told a reporter. "It's wrong that doctors make so much money off donors. Very wrong."

Presumed Consent

A possibility widely discussed as a means of increasing the number of transplant organs is adopting a policy of "presumed consent." That is, a state or federal law would allow hospitals to take it for granted that a recently deceased person has tacitly consented to having any needed organs removed, unless the person had indicated otherwise or unless the family objects. The burden of securing consent would be removed from physicians and hospitals, and the burden of denying consent would be imposed on individuals or their families. To withdraw consent would require a positive action.

A policy of presumed consent has been adopted by several European countries. Critics of the policy point out that this has not, in general, done much to reduce the shortage of transplant organs in those countries. Although legally empowered to remove organs without a family's permission, physicians continue to be reluctant to do so. It is doubtful that a policy of presumed consent would be any more successful in this country. Also, if families are to be given the opportunity to deny consent, they must be notified of the death of the patient, and in many cases this would involve not only complicated practical arrangements, but also a considerable loss of time. Thus, it is doubtful that presumed consent would do a great deal to increase the number of usable transplant organs.

Altruistic Donation

Many argue that the present system of organ procurement by voluntary donation for altruistic reasons is the best system. It appeals to the best in people rather than to greed and self-interest, it avoids exploiting the poor, and it's efficient. Families who donate organs can gain some satisfaction from knowing that the death of a loved one brought some benefit to others.

Living Donors

Some centers have relaxed or eliminated rules requiring that a living donor belong to the same family as the recipient. This practice allows those who wish to act in a generous and commendable fashion to directly benefit a friend, a coworker, or a complete stranger. Living donors now constitute more than 50% of all kidney donors, and the number of unrelated donors is around 2000, ten times the number in 1996. The importance of living donors can be appreciated by considering that if only one in every 3000 people donated a kidney, the kidney shortage would be solved. Also, recipients of a kidney from a living donor have a one-year survival rate of 98% and a ten-year survival rate of 90%. Recipients with kidneys from deceased donors have rates of 94% and 80%, respectively.

Kidneys, as mentioned earlier, are no longer the only organs transplanted from living donors. A healthy liver rapidly regenerates, and lobes have been transplanted with success. More recently, lung segments have been added to the list. While the history of using living kidney donors shows that the risk to them is relatively slight, experience with liver and lung segment donors isn't sufficiently extensive to be statistically meaningful. Early data suggest that the risks they pose to the donor are sufficiently low to justify the procedures, particularly when the life of a recipient is at stake.

Although the use of living donors can help reduce the chronic scarcity of some organs, the practice is not without critics. Thomas Starzl, the developer of liver transplants, refused to use living kidney donors, because too often the person in a family who "volunteers" to be a donor does so only because of the pressures of family dynamics. In effect, Starzl charges, consent cannot be voluntary. Those favoring the practice argue that Starzl's criticism is not a reason to reject living donors so much as a

reason to design a system of securing informed consent that will protect vulnerable individuals. When the informed consent process is reliable, they hold, living donors of both kidneys and liver lobes (perhaps even lung lobes) ought to be allowed.

The chronic shortage of transplant organs probably cannot be relieved by any one of the proposals mentioned here. Some combination of them might come close to solving the problem. Most likely, however, we must wait for a technological solution. If genetic engineering made it possible to breed pigs with organs invisible to the human immune system, the shortage of transplant organs would be ended. Some critics worry that the use of animal transplants, even if successful, might be dangerous. Viral sequences incorporated into pig DNA might mutate or cross over in genetic recombination and produce viruses as deadly and uncontrollable as the AIDS virus. Also, some question the breeding and use of animals solely to serve human wants and needs. The long-term solution, some believe, is that a powerful stem-cell technology, in addition to tissue engineering, may one day allow us to grow replacement kidneys, hearts, and livers that are compatible with an individual's immune system, making the use of immunosuppressive drugs unnecessary. At the moment, although this is imaginable, it is little more than science fiction.

Organ Allocation

Whatever the future may promise, the fact remains that at present the supply of transplant organs is limited and the demand far exceeds the supply. Thus, the key question today is, How are organs to be distributed when they become available? Currently, no national policies or procedures supply a complete answer to this question. In general, with some exceptions, such decisions are made in accordance with policies adopted by particular regional or hospital-based transplant programs.

Typically, a transplant center employs a screening committee made up of surgeons, physicians, nurses, social workers, and a psychologist to determine whether a candidate for a transplant should be admitted to the waiting list. Medical need—whether the candidate might benefit from the transplant—is the first consideration, but it is far from the only one. A committee's decisions may also be based on the patient's general medical condition, age, and ability to pay for the operation, as well as whether he has the social support needed to assist him during recovery, shows evidence of being able to adhere to a lifetime regimen of antirejection drugs, and belongs to the constituency that the center is committed to serving. Factors like race and gender are considered irrelevant, but in practice the individual's "social worth" (education, occupation, accomplishments) may also be taken into account.

Some large transplant centers employ a scoring system that involves assigning values to a list of what the center considers relevant factors. Those with the highest score are accepted as candidates and given a priority ranking. If their medical condition worsens, they may later be moved up in the ranking. At most centers, this process is carried out in a more informal fashion.

Once a patient is admitted to a center's waiting list, the allocation rules of the federally funded United Network for Organ Sharing also apply. UNOS policies stipulate the ways in which organs are distributed. Until recently, when an organ became available within one of the nine UNOS regions of the country, the institutions in the region had first claim on it, without respect to the needs of patients in other regions. In practice, few organs ever left the region in which they were donated. UNOS now stipulates that an organ must go to a patient with the greatest need, no matter what the region, assuming the organ can be transported in good condition to the patient.

The policy creates something like a national waiting list. Proponents say that it will get more organs to the patients who need them most, while critics charge that it means that the greatest number of organs go to the largest transplant centers, because the largest number of patients in acute need are there. Eventually, then, a number of centers will have to close. Some observers view this positively, for not all centers do enough transplants to gain the experience needed to offer patients the best outcomes possible.

Some of the factors considered by transplant centers in admitting a patient to the waiting list have been criticized by many as morally irrelevant. A patient's social worth and ability to pay are rejected by most critics, but opinion is divided over how much weight should be given to factors such as alcoholism, drug abuse, and poor health habits. Because of the shortage of organs, people needing transplants as a result of "lifestyle diseases" caused in part by obesity, smoking, or alcohol abuse would be automatically excluded as candidates by some. By contrast, others would ask only that such people demonstrate a willingness to change their behavior. At present, transplant centers have much leeway in deciding which candidates to accept.

A good example of an effort to formulate acceptable guidelines for making decisions about allocating organs is the Massachusetts Task Force on Organ Transplantation. The group issued a unanimous report that included the following recommendations:

1. Transplant surgery should be provided "to those who can benefit most from it in terms of probability of living for a significant period of time with a reasonable prospect for rehabilitation."

2. Decisions should not be based on "social worth" criteria.

3. Age may be considered as a factor in the selection process, but only to the extent that age is relevant to life expectancy and prospects for rehabilitation. Age must not be the only factor considered.

4. If not enough organs are available for all those who might benefit from them, final

selections should be made by some random process (e.g., a lottery or a first-come, first-served basis).

5. Transplants should be provided to residents of New England on the basis of need, regardless of their ability to pay, as long as this does not adversely affect health-care services with a higher priority. Those who are not residents of New England should be accepted as transplant candidates only after they have demonstrated their ability to pay for the procedure.

Organ transplantation continues to face two crucial problems: the chronic shortage of organs and the inability of some people needing a transplant to pay for one. The shortage problem might eventually be solved by developments in biotechnology, but the financial problem could be solved immediately by a change in social policy. Why should the society be willing to fund a kidney transplant for someone without insurance or adequate financial resources, yet refuse to fund someone needing a liver or heart transplant?

CASE PRESENTATION
Drug Lottery: The Betaseron Shortage

Multiple sclerosis (MS) is a neurological disorder affecting almost 300,000 Americans. Its symptoms include fatigue, dizziness, slurred speech, vision loss, numbness, tingling sensations, and muscle spasticity that affects coordination and makes walking difficult. The disease strikes adults from twenty to forty years old. It is progressive and, in extreme cases, can lead to paralysis.

About one-third of those with the disease have a form known as relapsing–remitting multiple sclerosis. They can live free of symptoms for months, then have an attack during which their symptoms return and they may be confined to a wheelchair for weeks. Typically, the symptoms are worse than they were during the previous episode, and as the attacks continue to occur, people become progressively more disabled.

The hopes of some sufferers were raised in 1993 when the FDA announced its approval of a new drug that had been shown in clinical trials to reduce the frequency of attacks by about thirty percent in early stages of the relapsing–remitting form of the disease. What's more, magnetic resonance imaging indicated that brain changes associated with the symptoms were fewer than those seen in untreated patients. The drug was a genetically engineered form of interferon known as interferon beta IB with the trade name Betaseron. An injectable drug, it promised to help an estimated 100,000 to 175,000 people with MS. It was the first drug that

promised to slow the course of the disease, rather than merely treat its symptoms.

By the fall of 1993, immediately after FDA approval, MS patients throughout the country were pressuring their physicians to prescribe the drug for them. Most physicians were happy to do so, but the problem was that there wasn't enough Betaseron to meet the needs of the patients who might benefit from it. Berlex Laboratories, the developer of the drug, had been caught by surprise by the FDA's fast-track approval process and so was not in a position to manufacture large quantities of the drug rapidly. Further, because Betaseron can be manufactured only in a fermentation process using genetically engineered *E. coli* bacteria, production of the drug could not be speeded up to meet demand.

Berlex's response to the situation was to establish a lottery, the first of its kind, as a means of determining who would receive the drug. The lottery was open only to those with relapsing–remitting MS who were certified by their doctors to be in the earlier stages of the disease and able to walk at least one hundred yards unassisted. Some 67,000 people applied for the drug by the September 15 deadline, and another 7000 applied after the deadline.

As people applied, they were assigned randomly to positions on a waiting list by a computer program. Enough doses of the drug were available to help 17,000 people immediately. Those receiving higher numbers would have to wait for additional supplies to be manufactured.

Berlex was especially concerned that those treated with Betaseron receive an uninterrupted course of the drug. "A lot of patients on and off therapy is no good for anybody," Jeffrey Latts, a Berlex vice president said. "We felt it was better for some patients to get continuous therapy rather than intermittent therapy."

Before announcing the lottery, Berlex officials talked with patient groups, drug distribution experts, and physicians. Patients tended to favor a lottery, but physicians were generally not happy with the idea of giving up control over choosing which patients might benefit from the drug.

"We felt it was important to keep this process completely clean," Latts said about the lottery. "I personally can guarantee that no one got moved up, no matter how influential. We said, 'No, Governor, we can't,' and 'I'm sorry, Senator, it's not possible.' We heard rumors that someone was offering to pay for a lower number, but we have records of what number went to what patient where."

Despite Berlex's commitment to fairness, some patients did receive Betaseron without going through the lottery. Some 3500 doses of the drug were sent to one hundred medical centers, and the centers decided how to distribute them. "I feel guilty that I was chosen and other people weren't," said a fifty-seven-year-old lawyer who was one of those who got the drug without entering the lottery. "But not guilty enough not to take it. When you've had MS for many years, you just look for some ray of hope."

Some patients not meeting the lottery guidelines pressured their physicians into certifying them as in the early stages of the disease, permitting them to qualify for the lottery. An even larger number objected to being excluded from the lottery, claiming that they had as much right as anyone to get whatever benefit they could from Betaseron. Most physicians, however, rejected this point of view. They considered it wrong to give the drug to patients for whom it had not been proved effective when there was an inadequate supply of the drug for patients for whom its effectiveness had been demonstrated.

Along with the lottery, Berlex Laboratories introduced a second program with the aim of ensuring access to Betaseron by those who might benefit from it. The cost of the drug was $989 a month, putting it out of the financial reach of many people. To address this problem, Berlex provided the drug free to those who were uninsured and earned less than $20,000 a year. For those uninsured and earning up to $50,000, it employed a sliding scale of charges. Medicaid and most private insurance companies paid for the drug, but Medicare did not. To encourage patients to adhere to the best treatment schedule, Berlex committed itself to providing free drugs to all patients for the eleventh and twelfth months.

By 1994, the shortage of Betaseron was over. While some physicians and patients were unhappy with the lottery approach, most observers considered it the best model to follow in the event of future drug shortages. Given that many new drugs are likely to be the product of genetic engineering, the next shortage may lie not far in the future.

BRIEFING SESSION

Few of us have as much as we desire of the world's goods. Usually, this is because we don't have enough money to pay for everything we want. We have to make choices. If we wish to spend a month in Paris, we can't afford a new car. Even when an abundance of goods is available, we can't buy everything we want. Sometimes, even when we have the money, we can't buy some item because the supply is inadequate or nonexistent. A manufacturer, for example, might not be turning out a new phone fast enough to meet the demand for it. Or, to take a different sort of case, we can't buy fresh figs in Minnesota in January, because they simply aren't available.

In some circumstances, we can't acquire an item because its supply is limited and our society has decided that it falls into the category of things that require more than money to acquire. The item may then be rationed on the basis of priorities. During wartime, for example, the military is supplied with all the food it needs, and food for civilians is rationed. Thus, even those able to pay for a pound of butter may not be permitted to buy it.

Medical goods and services include medications, care by physicians, visits to the emergency room, stays in hospitals, surgical operations, MRIs, diagnostic laboratory tests, in vitro fertilization, bone-marrow transplants, blood transfusions, genetic screening, respirators, . . . and so on. Not everyone who wants these goods and services or even everyone who needs them can get them. To acquire them in our society, except in special circumstances, you must have the means of paying for them. This means having cash or adequate insurance coverage or being covered by a government entitlement program. You can't get so much as a CT scan unless you can demonstrate your ability to pay. (Emergency services to get you medically stable must be provided by hospitals receiving federal money.)

In the case of some medical goods and services, however, the need and ability to pay are not enough. That was the way it was with dialysis machines at the beginning. That's the way it sometimes is when there is a shortage of a crucial vaccine. That's the way it always is when we have to decide who gets the next donor liver, heart, or kidney that becomes available.

These are decisions about distributing scarce resources. Most of this chapter will focus on the distribution of transplant organs. Aside from the distribution of health care itself, parceling out donated organs to people likely to die unless they receive them is the most pressing medical distribution problem in our society. The issues that arise in distributing transplant organs are not, in principle, different from those which arise in connection with any scarce commodity.

Transplant organs are of particular concern, however—not only because they can save and extend lives and so ought not be wasted, but because we have no way of eliminating the shortage. We can't simply crank up production, the way we can with drugs and diagnostic equipment. Nor is there an equivalent of building more hospitals or training more physicians and nurses.

Transplants, Kidneys, and Machines

The story of Robin Cook's novel *Coma* takes place in a large Boston hospital at the present time. What sets the novel apart from dozens of others with similar settings and characters is the fact that the plot hinges on the operations of a large-scale black market in transplant organs. For enormous fees, the criminals running the operation will supply corneas, kidneys, or hearts to those who can pay.

Cook claims that the inspiration for his novel came from an advertisement in a California newspaper. The anonymous ad offered to sell for $5000 any organ that a reader wanted to buy. In this respect, Cook's novel seems rooted firmly in the world we know today and is not merely a leap into the speculative realms of science fiction.

Organ transplants have attracted a considerable amount of attention in the last few years. Not only are transplants dramatic, often offering last-minute salvation from an almost certain death, but the very possibility of organ transplants is bright with promise. We can easily imagine a future in which any injured or diseased organ can be replaced almost as easily as the parts on a car. The present state of biomedical technology makes this more than a distant dream, although not a current reality. Kidneys, hearts, lungs, livers, intestines, and pancreases are now transplanted as a matter of routine, and perhaps before long the list will be extended to include ovaries, testes, spleens, gallbladders, esophagi, and stomachs. The basic problem with organ transplants is the phenomenon of tissue rejection by the immune system.

Controlling Rejection

Alien proteins trigger the body's defense mechanisms. In pioneering work with kidneys, the proteins in the transplanted tissues were matched as carefully as possible with those of the recipient; then powerful immunosuppressive drugs were used in an effort to allow the host body to accommodate itself to the foreign tissue. These drugs left the body open to infections that it could normally cope with without much difficulty.

Use of the drug cyclosporine dramatically improved the success of organ transplants when it was first used almost three decades ago. Cyclosporine selectively inhibits only part of the immune system and leaves enough of it functional to fight off most of the infections that were once fatal to large numbers of transplant recipients. Also, although tissue matching is important, particularly for kidneys, matches do not have to be as close as before and may be dispensed with altogether.

Now 90% to 96% of transplanted kidneys function after one year; in the 1970s, only about 50% did. Since 1970, the one-year survival rate for children with liver transplants has increased from 38% to more than 75%, and there is good reason to believe that if children survive for as long as one year, they have a genuine chance to live a normal life. About 88% of heart transplant recipients now live for at least one year, a major increase over the 20% of the 1970s. Lung transplants have a success rate of about 84% when an organ is from a decreased donor and 100% when the lung segment is from a living donor (for complete statistics, see United Network for Organ Sharing website).

Allocation and Scarcity

Because of the relatively high rate of success in organ transplants, the need for organs (kidneys in particular) is always greater than the supply. (The black-market operation in Cook's novel is thus not wholly unrealistic.) In such a situation, where scarcity and need conflict, it is frequently necessary to decide who among the candidates for a transplant will receive an available organ.

Relatively objective considerations such as the "goodness" of tissue matching, the size of the organ, and the general medical condition of the candidates may rule out some individuals.

But it does happen that choices have to be made. Who should make such choices? Should they be made by a physician, following her own intuitions? Should they be made by a committee or board? If so, who should be on the committee? Should a patient have an advocate to speak for his interest—someone to "make a case" for his receiving the transplant organ? Should the decision be made in accordance with a set of explicit criteria? If so, what criteria are appropriate? Are matters such as age, race, gender, and place of residence irrelevant? Should the character and accomplishments of the candidates be given any weight? Should people be judged by their estimated "worth to the community"? Should the fact that someone is a parent be given any weight?

What if one is a smoker, an alcoholic, or obese? Are these conditions to be considered "medical" or "behavioral" risk factors that may legitimately be employed to eliminate someone as a candidate for a transplant? Or are they to be treated as aspects of people's chosen "lifestyle" that cannot be used as a basis for denying them an organ needed to save their lives?

These are just some of the questions relevant to the general issue of deciding how to allocate medical goods in situations in which the available supply is surpassed by a present need. Transplant organs are an example of one type of goods. (See the Social Context: "Acquiring and Allocating Transplant Organs," in this chapter.) Even so, most of the ethical issues raised by the distribution of organs also arise when we have to consider how we're going to parcel out such goods and services as hospital beds, physician consultations, nursing care, physical therapy, medications, diagnostic MRIs, chemotherapy, coronary angiography, or any of the hundreds of other resources used in delivering medical care. All resources, economists remind us, are limited, so we must always face the problem of how to distribute them. It was a shortage of machines, rather than organ transplantation, that first called public attention to the issue of medical resource allocation.

Seattle and Kidney Machines

The shortage occurred most dramatically in the early 1960s when the Artificial Kidney Center in Seattle, Washington, initiated an effective large-scale treatment program for people with renal diseases. Normal kidneys filter waste products from the blood that have accumulated as a result of ordinary cellular metabolism—salt, urea, creatinine, potassium, uric acid, and other substances. These waste products are sent from the kidneys to the bladder, where they are then secreted as urine. Kidney failure, which can result from any of a number of diseases, allows waste products to build up in the blood, possibly causing high blood pressure and even heart failure, tissue edema (swelling), and muscular seizure. Unremedied, the condition results in death.

When renal failure occurs, hemodialysis is a way of cleansing the blood of waste products by passing it through a cellophane-like tube immersed in a chemical bath. The impurities in the blood pass through the membrane and into the chemical bath by osmosis, and the purified blood is then returned to the patient's body.

At the beginning of the Seattle program, there were many more candidates for dialysis than units ("kidney machines") to accommodate them. As a response to this situation, the Kidney Center set up a committee to select patients who would receive treatment. (See the Case Presentation "Playing God with Dialysis," in this chapter, for an account of how such a committee might work.) In effect, the committee was offering some people a better chance for life than they would have without access to dialysis equipment.

As other centers and hospitals established renal units, they faced the same painful decisions that Seattle had. Almost always there were many more patients needing hemodialysis than there was equipment available to treat them. It was partly in response to this situation that Section 299-1 of Public Law 92-603 was passed by Congress in 1972. Those with end-stage renal disease who require hemodialysis or kidney transplants are now guaranteed treatment under Medicare.

Dialysis Costs and Decisions

More than 500,000 patients are now receiving dialysis paid for by Medicare. Present costs are more than $15 billion per year, and the patient load is increasing by about 70,000 per year. Dialysis saves lives, but the cost is high.

Although the average cost of each treatment session has dropped from $150 in 1973 to the current $120, many more groups of patients now have dialysis than were treated earlier. In particular, the treatment population now includes many more elderly and diabetic people than was envisioned when the dialysis program was established.

Quite apart from the cost, which is about four times higher than originally expected, dialysis continues to present moral difficulties. Resources are still finite, so, although virtually everyone needing dialysis can be accomodated, physicians face the problem of deciding whether everyone should be referred. If a physician believes a patient isn't likely to gain benefits from dialysis sufficient to justify the expense or isn't likely to show up for appointments, should she recommend the patient for dialysis anyway? Not to do so may mean death for the patient in the near future, yet the social cost (measured in terms of the expense of equipment and its operation, the cost of hospital facilities, and the time of physicians, nurses, and technicians) may be immense—$100,000 or more per year for a single person.

Nor does dialysis solve all problems for patients with end-stage kidney disease. Although time spent on the machine varies, some patients spend five hours, three days a week, attached to the machine. Medical and psychological problems are typical even when the process works at its most efficient. Prolonged dialysis can produce neurological disorders, severe headaches, gastrointestinal bleeding, and bone diseases. Psychological and physical stress is always present, and particularly before dialysis treatments, severe depression is common. One study showed that five percent of dialysis patients take their own lives, and "passive suicide," resulting from dropping out of treatment programs, is the third most common cause of death among older dialysis patients. (The overall death rate for those on dialysis is about twenty-five percent per year. The worst outlook is for diabetics starting dialysis at age 55 or older. After one year, only eighteen percent are still alive.) For these reasons, strong motivation, psychological stability, age, and a generally sound physical condition are factors considered important in deciding whether to admit a person to dialysis.

The characteristics required to make someone a "successful" dialysis patient are to some extent "middle-class virtues." Not only must a patient be motivated to save his life, but he also must understand the need for the dialysis, be capable of adhering to a strict diet, show up for scheduled dialysis sessions, and so on. As a consequence, where decisions about whether to admit a patient to dialysis are based on estimates of the likelihood of the patient's doing what is required, members of the white middle class appear to have a definite edge over others. Selection criteria that are apparently objective may actually involve hidden class or racial bias.

Various ways of dealing with both the costs and the personal problems presented by dialysis are currently under discussion. In the view of some, increasing the number of kidney transplants would do the most to improve the lives of patients and to reduce the cost of the kidney program. (This would have the result of increasing the demand for transplant organs even more. See the Social Context "Acquiring and Allocating Transplant Organs," in this chapter for a discussion of proposals for realizing this objective.) Others have pressed for training more patients to perform home dialysis, which is substantially cheaper than dialysis performed in clinics or hospitals. However, those who are elderly, live alone, or lack adequate facilities are not likely to be able to use and maintain the complicated equipment involved. Other things being equal, should such people be given priority for transplants?

Microallocation vs. Macroallocation

Some critics have questioned the legitimacy of the dialysis program and pointed to it as an example of social injustice. While thousands of people have benefited from the program, why should kidney disease be treated differently from other diseases? Why should the treatment of kidney disease alone be federally funded? Why shouldn't society also pay for the treatment of those afflicted with cancer, heart diseases, or neurological disorders? Perhaps only the development of a new national health care policy will render this criticism irrelevant.

The problems of transplants and dialysis involve decisions that affect individuals in a direct and immediate way. For example, a person either is or is not accepted into a dialysis program. As we will see in the next chapter, there are a number of broader social issues connected with providing and distributing medical resources. But our concern here is with decisions involving the welfare of particular people in specific situations in which demand exceeds supply. The basic question becomes, Who shall get it and who shall go without?

Any commodity or service that can be in short supply relative to the need for it raises the issue of fair and justifiable distribution. Decisions that control the supply itself—that determine, for example, what proportion of the federal budget will be spent on medical care—are generally referred to as macroallocation decisions. These are the large-scale decisions that do not involve individuals in a direct way. Similarly, deciding what proportion of the money allocated to health care should be spent on dialysis is a macroallocation decision.

By contrast, microallocation decisions directly impinge on individuals. Thus, when one donor heart is available and six people in need of a transplant make a claim on it, the decision as to who gets the heart is a microallocation decision. In Chapter 9, in discussing paying for health care, we will focus more on macroallocation, but here we will be concerned mostly with microallocation. (The distinction between macroallocation and microallocation is often less clear than the explanation here suggests. After all, decision-making occurs at many levels in the distribution of resources, and the terms "macro" and "micro" are relative ones.)

The examples we have considered have been restricted to transplant organs and dialysis machines, but, as mentioned earlier, the question of fair distribution can be raised just as appropriately about other medical goods and services. These include cardiac resuscitation teams, microsurgical teams, space in burn units or intensive-care wards, hospital beds, drugs and vaccines, medical-evacuation helicopters, operating rooms, physicians' time, and all other medical commodities that are in limited supply with respect to the demand for them. (See the Case Presentation "The Drug Lottery: The Betaseron Shortage," in this chapter.)

Earlier, in connection with transplants, we considered some of the more specific questions that have to be asked about distribution. The questions generally fall into two categories: Who shall decide? and What criteria or standards should be employed in making the allocation decision? These are questions that must be answered whenever there is scarcity relative to needs and wants.

Ethical Theories and the Allocation of Medical Resources

Discussions of the distribution of limited medical resources frequently compare such a situation to the plight of a group of people adrift in a lifeboat. If some are sacrificed, the others will have a much better chance of surviving. But who should be sacrificed?

One answer to this question is that no one should be. Simply by virtue of being human, each person in the lifeboat has an equal worth.

Thus, any action that involved sacrificing someone for the good of the others in the boat would not be morally defensible. This tenet suggests that the only right course of action would be simply to do nothing.

This point of view may be regarded as compatible with Kant's ethical principles. Because each individual may be considered to have inherent value, considerations such as talent, intelligence, age, social worth, and so on are morally irrelevant. Accordingly, there seem to be no grounds for distinguishing those who are to be sacrificed from those who may be saved. In the medical context, this would mean that when there are not enough goods and services to go around, then no one should receive them.

This is not a result dictated by Kant's principles, however. One might also argue that the fact that every person is equal to every other in dignity and worth does not require the sacrifice of all. A random procedure—such as drawing straws—might be used to determine who is to have an increased chance of survival. In such a case, each person is being treated as having equal value, and the person who loses might be regarded as exercising autonomy by sacrificing himself.

The maxim underlying the sacrifice would, apparently, be one that would meet the test of the categorical imperative. Any rational person might be expected to sacrifice himself in such a situation and under the conditions in which the decision was made. In the case of medical resources, a random procedure would seem to be a morally legitimate procedure.

Both the natural law view and Ross's view would seem to support a similar line of argument. Although we all have a duty, on these views, to preserve our lives, this does not mean that we do not sometimes have to risk them. Just such a risk might be involved in agreeing to abide by the outcome of a random procedure to decide who will be sacrificed and who saved.

Utilitarianism does not dictate a specific answer to the question of who, if anyone, should be saved. It does differ radically in one respect, however, from those moral views which ascribe an intrinsic value to each human life. The principle of utility suggests that we ought to take into account the consequences of sacrificing some people rather than others. Who, for example, is more likely to make a contribution to the general welfare of the society, an accountant or a nurse? This approach opens the way to considering the "social worth" of people and makes morally relevant such characteristics as education, occupation, age, record of accomplishment, and so on.

To take such an approach would require working out a set of criteria to assign values to various properties of people. Those to be sacrificed would be those whose point total put them at the low end of the ranking. Here, then, a typical "calculus of utilities" would be relied on to solve the decision problem. The decision problem about the allocation of medical resources would follow exactly the same pattern.

This approach is not one required by the principle of utility, however. Some might argue that a policy formulated along those lines would have so many harmful social consequences that some other solution would be preferable. Thus, a utilitarian might argue that a better policy would be one based on some random process. In connection with medical goods and services, a "first-come, first-served" approach might be superior. (This is a possible option for rule utilitarianism. It could be argued that an act utilitarian would be forced to adopt the first approach.)

Rawls's principles of justice seem clearly to rule out distributing medical resources on the criterion of "social worth." Where special benefits are to be obtained, those benefits must be of value to all and open to all. It is compatible with Rawls's view, of course, that there should be no special medical resources. But if there are, and they must be distributed under conditions of scarcity, then some genuinely fair procedure, such as random selection, must be the procedure used.

No ethical theory that we have considered gives a straightforward answer to the question of who shall make the selection. Where a procedure is random or first come, first served, the decision-making process requires only establishing the right kind of social arrangements to implement the policy. Only when social worth must be judged and considered as a relevant factor in decision-making does the procedure assume importance. (This is assuming that medical decisions about appropriateness—decisions that establish a class of candidates for the limited resources—have already been made.)

A utilitarian answer as to who shall make the allocation decision might be that the decision should be made by those who are in a good position to judge the likelihood of an individual's contribution to the welfare of the society as a whole. Since physicians are not uniquely qualified to make such judgments, leaving decisions to an individual physician or a committee of physicians would not be the best approach. A better one would perhaps be to rely on a committee composed of a variety of people representative of the society.

Many more questions of a moral kind connected with the allocation of scarce resources arise than have been mentioned here. We have not, for example, considered whether an individual should be allowed to make a case for receiving resources. Nor have we examined any of the problems associated with employing specific criteria for selection (such as requiring that a person be a resident of a certain community or state; the Case Presentation "Playing God with Dialysis," in this chapter, illustrates such a selection process). We have, however, touched upon enough basic issues to make it easy to see how other appropriate questions might be asked.

Chapter **9**

Distributing Health Care

CASES AND CONTEXTS

The Way It Was: Robert Ingram Can't Afford to Be Sick

Robert Ingram (as we will call him) was fifty-two years old and very worried about himself, a result of two months of having episodes of sharp, stabbing pains on the left side of his chest. When the pains came, he felt cold and sweaty, and although he tried to ignore them, he found that he had to stop what he was doing and wait until they passed.

He hadn't mentioned the pains to Jeri, his wife, right at first. He half expected and half hoped that they would simply go away, but they hadn't. Eventually, he'd had to tell her, when the stabbing came at home while he was moving a large upholstered chair with a broken frame out to the trash. She'd seen him put the chair down and put his hand on his chest.

When he told her how long he'd been having the pains, she'd made him call up Lane Clinic for an appointment. He hadn't wanted to miss most of a day's work. He operated Bob's Express, which picked up car and truck parts from the smaller supply houses and delivered them to mechanics and garages within a twenty-mile radius. He'd founded the business only a year ago, after working as a mechanic himself for almost thirty years.

He had hoped to be able to expand, but there weren't as many deliveries to make as he'd counted on. The big supply houses had their own distribution system, and he had to scramble to get business from the wrecking yards and the rebuilders.

He was making enough money to pay the operating expenses and the rent, but not much more. All he had to show for his work was one Chevy Silverado pickup and a ten-year-old Ford station wagon. He had one part-time employee, Phil Archer. Jeri took the phone orders from their home office, and he and Phil made the rounds. He was his own boss, and that's what he and Jeri most liked about the business. He worked hard, but he didn't have to answer to anybody.

On Wednesday, the day of his appointment, he asked Phil to work the whole day. He drove the Ford to the clinic, so he'd be able to go directly from there to Ace Distributors and pick up the shirttail full of parts he knew he had

to deliver. If anybody called with more orders for Ace, he could get them, too.

Dr. Tran was a short, thin Asian man who looked young enough to be a teenager. But he seemed to know exactly what he was doing. He moved the stethoscope over Robert's chest, listening to his heart. He had him walk across the room, then listened to it again.

Dr. Tran asked about Robert's parents and grandparents. Robert told him that both grandfathers had died of heart attacks in their late fifties. One of his grandmothers was still alive, but the other had also died of a heart attack.

Then Dr. Tran asked questions about the chest pain. How long had he had it? What did it feel like? How long did it last? Did anything in particular seem to bring it on? Did he ever get it while sleeping? Did it start when he was carrying grocery bags or simply walking? Did the pain seem to radiate down his left arm? Did his arm feel numb? Did the last two fingers tingle?

Robert did his best to answer all the questions, but he didn't see the point to them. He was almost sorry he'd come. It was easy to believe that nothing was seriously wrong with him while he was sitting on the edge of the examining table talking to Dr. Tran. He needed to be making his deliveries. Otherwise, Phil would get hopelessly behind. Late deliveries could lose customers.

Dr. Tran finished his examination and asked Robert to get dressed and have a seat in the chair beside the small built-in desk. Dr. Tran left the room for ten minutes or so, then returned. He took the swivel chair beside the desk.

"I'm worried that you may be on the verge of a heart attack," Dr. Tran told Robert. "You may already have had one or more small attacks."

"Wouldn't I have known it?" Robert could hardly believe what he was hearing.

"Not necessarily," Dr. Tran said. "The blood gets blocked for a moment, some tissue dies. You feel pain, and then it's over." He paused. "But what concerns me most is that your coronary arteries may be significantly blocked by plaque, and if that's so, the outcome could be devastating."

"You mean I could die."

"Exactly," Dr. Tran said. "We need to know what shape your heart's in, so I want you to have a coronary angiogram. I'm going to refer you to a cardiologist, and she may want you to have ultrasound as well."

Seeing Robert's blank look, Dr. Tran explained what was involved in the angiogram, then talked about the images sonography could produce.

"Do you really need to take a look at my heart like that?" Robert asked. "Couldn't you just let it go at listening?"

"We need to find out if you've got some blocked coronary arteries," Dr. Tran said. "We also need to get some sense of how your valves are working and what size your heart is. Otherwise, we'd just be guessing and basing a treatment on what we *thought* was happening. Technology lets us go beyond that."

Dr. Tran leaned forward and touched Robert's knee. "Don't worry. Angiography is quite safe, really. And the ultrasound amounts to nothing at all."

"But what will they *cost*?"

"I'm not sure exactly," Dr. Tran said. "Probably in the neighborhood of five to seven thousand dollars. Maybe more if Dr. Goode needs for you to spend the night at the hospital."

"Then it's all out of the question," Robert said. "I don't have the money."

"Your insurance will cover both procedures."

"I don't have insurance, Doctor." Robert shook his head. "I run my own business, and I put all my money into keeping it going. I can't even mortgage my house, because it's rented."

"You're not old enough to qualify for Medicare," Dr. Tran said. "Do you own some property or jewelry? Something you can sell?"

"All I own is a broken-down station wagon and part of a pickup truck. I still owe money on the truck. Maybe I could sell it for enough to pay it off and pay for those tests you want me to have."

"If the tests show what I think they might," Dr. Tran said, "you'll need coronary artery bypass surgery. That will cost in the neighborhood of thirty thousand dollars—perhaps as much a fifty, depending on complications and hospital stays."

"That's just laughable," Robert said. "No way I could raise $30,000. Not even if my life depended on it."

"I suspect it does," Dr. Tran said. "But selling your truck would have the advantage of qualifying you for Medicaid. In this state, if you have assets under $3000, you qualify."

"But if I sold my truck, I'd have to go out of business," Robert said. "I wouldn't have any way to earn a living, and my wife's sickly. She can't work a regular job, because of her headaches."

"Don't you have some family you could borrow from?"

"Maybe I could borrow a thousand from Jeri's mother, but she lives on Social Security. And there's nobody else. The few friends we have haven't got any more money than we do."

"I don't know what to say."

"Can't you just give me some pills?"

"I don't see any alternative," Dr. Tran said. "But I'm uncomfortable doing it, because I don't know exactly what we're up against. As I told you, you could be on the verge of having a heart attack. We could help you with the right tests and, if necessary, the right sort of surgery. But as it is, ..."

"I'll just have to take my chances," Robert said, "until I'm either rich enough or poor enough to get the right treatment."

SOCIAL CONTEXT

The Affordable Care Act: The New Health Care Law

In March 2010, the U.S. Congress passed the Patient Protection and Affordable Care Act, which was then signed into law by President Barack Obama. The debate surrounding the legislation was both heated and partisan, and despite various attempts at arriving at a compromise on some of the provisions, when the ACA (as it is usually called) came to a vote, it failed to secure the support of a single Republican.

Despite the lack of bipartisanship displayed in the vote, the need for a plan to reform the way health care was distributed and funded in the society had long been recognized by members of both major parties. Some thirty-seven to forty-seven million people lacked the insurance or the money needed to pay for their health care, and hundreds of thousands of people attempting to get insurance were turned down by insurers because of some preexisting medical condition (e.g., being diabetic or having been treated for cancer). Hundreds of thousands more individuals and their families were plunged into despair and bankruptcy by having their insurance canceled after they fell ill with a serious and expensive disease or by discovering that they had exceeded the cost limit allowed by their insurance company. Furthermore, the cost of medical care was continuing to rise, even after various attempts to slow it, and economists and politicians alike saw the need to try to find a way to provide medical care to more citizens while also "bending down the cost curve" so that the society would have the resources to meet other pressing needs such as defense, education, retirement, and environmental protection.

The ACA is a complex piece of legislation with provisions scheduled to become operational at different times. Also, some of its provisions contain requirements stated in general terms that must be interpreted and turned into specific rules by the Department of Health and Human Services (HHS). Similarly, the ACA requires the states to set up organizations like insurance exchanges (to serve as competitive marketplaces for insurance policies), but these organizations have not yet been established. Nor have the specific rules governing their operation been formulated by HHS.

The information presented here on the ACA is both incomplete and sketchy about even very important provisions and explicit aims. Many of the provisions don't take effect until 2014, and even then it is likely to take a number of years for the health care reforms and rules introduced by the act to become fully operational. What is offered next, accordingly, is hardly more than a fuzzy photograph of a large and indistinct body of legislation still shrouded in fog.

Getting Insurance

Starting in 2014, almost everyone in the United States will be required to have medical insurance: Those who fail to get insurance will be penalized, and those who are unable to afford

it will be eligible for subsidized coverage. Those too poor to pay anything will be eligible for coverage under the Medicaid program. How the scheme is supposed to work is presented in outline here.

Immediate Help for People with Preexisting Conditions

Starting in 2014, insurance companies will no longer be able to turn down applicants for health insurance on the grounds that they have a preexisting medical condition. (See the discussion to follow.) Insurers are eager to avoid insuring such people, because their medical costs are likely to be greater than average, and of course, this will have an impact on the company's earnings. (Most insurance companies in the United States are for profit businesses, and the few that are not see a need to reduce their expenses, avoid losses, and maintain a surplus to support their operation—i.e., make a profit.) Thus, people who have been treated for diseases that are chronic and expensive (such as Crohn's disease, colon cancer, Parkinson's disease, and rheumatoid arthritis) are routinely turned down when they apply for insurance coverage. Many people with a serious ailment who have insurance coverage through their employers often stay with jobs they don't like, because they fear that if they quit and lose their insurance, they will not be able to replace it.

The situation for such people changed in June 2010. Someone with a preexisting medical condition who has been without health insurance for at least six months is now eligible to buy a policy from a high-risk insurance pool. Until 2014, when insurance companies will no longer be able to discriminate against those with preexisting conditions, anyone eligible to buy a high-risk policy will receive a federal subsidy to pay for it. The premiums the individual must pay will be based on those for a standard population, and the annual out-of-pocket medical costs will be capped at $5,950 for an individual and $11,900 for a family.

Insurance Required

By 2014, virtually everyone will be required to have health insurance or else pay a penalty. The penalty starts at one percent of the violator's income (or $95, whichever is higher), then climbs to 2.5% (or $695 if that is higher) by 2016. Families will never be required to pay more than $2,085.

The list of those who are not required to have insurance includes American Indians (who are eligible to receive care from the federal Indian Health Service), as well as those who object to insurance on religious grounds. People who have incomes "so low that they are not required to file an income tax return ($9,350 for an individual) are not required to buy insurance," nor are those who would have to pay more than eight percent of their income for the cheapest plan that meets ACA coverage requirements.

Insurance Exchanges

People who are self-employed, have no need to work for money, are neither poor enough to qualify for Medicaid nor old enough to qualify for Medicare, or work for an employer that doesn't offer medical insurance will be able to buy it from an insurance exchange that the states are required to establish.

The exchanges are part of the plan to reduce health care costs while also increasing access to insurance. The idea behind reducing costs is that people who are insured are more likely to get preventive care and, when they do fall ill, are more likely to seek treatment when their disease is in an earlier and more treatable stage. Increasing access is supposed to result by requiring everyone to have insurance and establishing the insurance exchanges so that insurers will be motivated to compete for customers by offering the most comprehensive policies for the least cost.

The best example of a successful insurance exchange is the fifty-year-old Federal Employee Health Benefits program. Some eight million employees of the federal government are offered an array of over 250 medical plans to cover them and their dependents.

The exchange works because all federal employees must get their health care coverage through the plan. When exchanges have been attempted on a smaller scale and individuals were free to go outside the exchange to choose a policy, they were unsuccessful. Young and healthy people were given better rates by insurers who were not part of the exchange, leaving only older, sicker (and thus more expensive to treat) people as clients of the exchange. The state-operated exchanges should be able to avoid this difficulty. Even though insurance companies will be required to offer policies that pay for what the ACA defines as basic coverage, enough people of all sorts will be seeking coverage so that they will constitute a balanced risk pool.

People with an income less than four times the poverty level (i.e., an income of about $43,000) can qualify for tax credits to defray the costs of their insurance premiums. Premiums for individual health care policies (as distinct from group policies) are expected to be ten to thirteen percent higher than the average premium by 2016. This means that individual policies will cost more than now, but the amount people pay will be offset by subsidies. Thus, they may end up paying less for the same insurance than they pay now.

Medicaid as Insurance for the Poor

Medicaid is a joint program of the federal and state government that was designed initially to provide access to medical care for families and children who fall below the poverty line. The federal government matches funds appropriated by state governments, and partly for this reason, the success of the program has been limited.

Although federal laws require that children receive support for their medical care, similar rules have not applied to parents. In 2009, only about a dozen states offered care for parents who fall below the poverty level. Parents not eligible to receive care often don't know that their children are eligible, and the result is that the entire family goes without medical care.

THE 2009 POVERTY GUIDELINES FOR THE 48 CONTIGUOUS STATES AND THE DISTRICT OF COLUMBIA

Persons in family	Poverty guideline
1	$10,830
2	14,570
3	18,310
4	22,050
5	25,790
6	29,530
7	33,270
8	37,010

For families with more than 8 persons, add $3,740 for each additional person.

Source: Department of Health and Human Services, 2010.

The ACA will make everyone under the age of sixty-five with earnings less than 133% of the federal poverty level eligible for subsidized medical care under the Medicaid program. For the first time, people without children will be eligible for Medicaid. An individual with an income of about $14,400 would qualify for Medicaid help, as would a family of four with an income of around $29,327.

Changes in Medicare

Medicare is a federally funded and operated medical insurance plan for people age 65 or older. It is supported by payroll deductions, and under the program, everyone enrolled is entitled to the same benefits. Medicare determines the goods and services it is willing to pay for, and within those limits, an individual's medical need, not his income, determines what he receives. The ACA will have to be integrated with Medicare (as well as Medicaid, the federal–state program for the poor and disabled), and the process will result in a variety of changes. (Some probably cannot now be anticipated.)

Payment Advisory Board

Perhaps the largest change the ACA will introduce will have only an indirect impact on individual recipients. The act will establish an Independent Payment Advisory Board for Medicare. The board will be a commission of outside experts who will be responsible for reviewing Medicare spending. If spending exceeds the rate of growth predicted by the Congressional Budget Office (i.e., if spending becomes "out of control"), the Advisory Board will make recommendations to Congress about what steps should be taken to bring spending under control. Congress must then either accept the panel's recommendations and act on them or come up with its own plan to reduce spending.

The introduction of a Medicare Advisory Board was a deliberate effort to (1) find a mechanism to resist the political pressures that are likely to drive up Medicare spending and (2) keep health care costs in general from continuing to increase. In the language of the Obama administration, the panel was introduced to help "bend down the cost curve."

High Earners Pay More

Starting in 2013, people who make more than $200,000 a year will be required to increase their payroll tax contributions to the Medicare program. The current contribution of 1.45% will rise to 2.35%. Investment income, now exempt from payroll taxes, will be taxed at a 3.8% rate.

Free Preventive Care

Medicare will be required to provide enrollees with the same range of preventive medical care that private and group plans will be required to provide. Thus, the fees and co-payments for vaccinations, annual checkups, and blood tests will be discontinued. The thinking behind this change is that costs may be reduced by encouraging people to monitor their health and take steps to avoid preventable diseases such as pneumonia.

Improved Drug Benefits

By 2020, the Affordable Care Act will alter the way in which Medicare recipients pay for prescription drugs. The system is currently structured so that someone in a Medicare drug plan must pay a $310 deductible, after which the plan will pay seventy-five percent of the costs of drugs until the total drug cost of $2,830 is reached. The recipient is then in the "doughnut hole," in which there is no Medicare contribution to drug costs. Once the recipient has spent up to the amount of $4,550 (including deductible and co-payments) annually on drugs, the recipient has crossed to the other side of the doughnut hole. He then qualifies for "catastrophic coverage" and has to pay only $2.40 for each refill of a generic drug and $6.00 (or five percent of the cost if higher) for a proprietary drug.

This payment scheme has been denounced as ill conceived and unfair. It forces the sickest people, critics say, to pay the most for the drugs they need. The result has often been that people who reach the doughnut hole either stop taking their medications or take them less often, thus reducing or even eliminating the therapeutic effects of those medications.

The ACA will eventually close the doughnut hole. For the immediate future, it will reduce its consequences for Medicare recipients by providing them with rebates on the money they have spent for prescription drugs and with discounts of fifty percent on proprietary drugs.

Rewarding Doctors in Underserved Areas

Physicians tend to cluster in major urban areas and, within those areas, in more affluent neighborhoods. This tendency makes it difficult for people living in rural areas or the inner city of metropolitan areas to gain access to health care.

The result is that a substantial segment of the population may not receive the preventive care that is one of the strategies for lowering health care costs. Also, one aim of the ACA is to extend health care to those who have lacked access to it.

To encourage more physicians to practice in underserved areas, from 2011 to 2015 the ACA will authorize Medicare to pay a ten percent premium to physicians who see patients in rural areas or in the inner city.

Employment-based Health Insurance

Most people in the United States get their health insurance through their employer. The ACA will not necessarily change this arrangement, although for some employees, it will open up the possibility of going to the insurance exchange and getting a private plan.

No Lifetime Limit

The most important immediate change is that the act requires existing insurance plans to comply with the new rule against setting a lifetime limit on coverage. Other than this, existing plans don't have to meet any of the coverage standards in the act, unless the insurer makes significant changes in the benefits package or in the way the insurance is paid for. What counts as a "significant change" has not yet been determined, and determining it may require a court ruling or a decision by HHS.

Insurance from the Exchange

If an employee has to pay sixty percent or more of the costs of the insurance plan offered by his employer or if the plan costs the employee more than 9.5% of his income, he may choose to go to the insurance exchange and buy his own medical coverage. There is no guarantee that the employee will be able to get a better or cheaper plan, but because the exchange will be a competitive marketplace, he has a chance of doing better.

If an employee's income is less than four times the poverty level and the insurance premiums for the plan offered by his employer cost more than eight percent of his income, he is eligible to get an insurance voucher from his employer. He can then use the voucher to buy a medical insurance plan from the exchange.

These somewhat elaborate rules are designed to continue support for employer-based insurance and allow employees to keep their present plan if that is what they want. Yet the rules introduce an element of competition to encourage employers to offer reasonably priced, good-quality insurance plans, because if they don't, employees can go to the exchange and buy their own insurance.

Small-Business Tax Credits

To continue to support and encourage the current systems of employer-based medical coverage, a provision of the ACA will provide subsidies in the form of tax credits to small businesses that offer coverage to their employees during the period 2010–2013.

If an employer pays up to half the premium for its employees, the employer can receive up to thirty-five percent of the amount as a tax credit. Because the employer has to pay only fifteen percent of the premium, chances are good that the current system will suffer little or no disruption and that employees will continue to have access to insurance that is as good as or better than that available to them before. Also, given the value of the tax credit, small businesses that offered their employees no insurance before may be inclined to introduce an employee health plan. This would have the effect of extending health coverage to people who previously may not have had access to it.

Rules for Insurance Companies

Insurance companies will continue to play a major role in the reforms introduced by the ACA act. Some critics believe that this is likely to produce a health care system that falls far short of what could have been achieved.

A single-payer system like the Canadian system, some argue, would have been more successful in reducing the costs of care and making it available to all citizens. Because insurance companies are committed to making a profit for their shareholders, they have an incentive to deny care to patients and to avoid accepting as clients people who are likely to suffer from costly illnesses. (Indeed, the ideal medical insurance client for a company is someone who pays premiums for decades, is never sick or injured, and then drops dead, without ever having been

treated or hospitalized.) Also, the administrative costs (including high salaries of executives) of operating insurance plans (costs for reviewing treatment plans and hospitalizations, billing and collecting, etc.) will always be much higher than the costs in a single-payer system.

Whatever the merits of a single-payer system, the adoption of one was probably not a political possibility. The ACA takes into account many of the more important limitations of a health care system in which insurance companies continue to play a major role. The provisions of the act discussed next are intended to prevent companies from restricting access to care in ways that may be good for the company's bottom line, but are incompatible with extending access to affordable health care to a much large number of people in society.

No Denial of Coverage for Preexisting Conditions

Traditionally, insurance companies have been able to decide which applicants for medical coverage they are willing to insure. They cannot legally discriminate on the basis of race or gender, but they can decide to deny insurance to someone they believe is a bad risk—that is, someone who is likely to develop a disease requiring the company to pay out a lot of money in medical costs. Thus, women treated for breast cancer at some point in their lives most likely would be rejected as clients, and so would people with chronic ailments such as rheumatoid arthritis, diabetes, or ulcerative colitis, as well as those who are HIV positive or infected with hepatitis C.

Applications for medical insurance require the applicant to supply information about her medical history and authorize the company to examine all her medical records. Applications are also typically required to provide information about their family medical history (causes of death of parents or grandparents, diseases diagnosed in parents and siblings). Insurance companies use this information to assess the risk that an applicant will develop a serious and expensive disease. Failure to provide the information, omitting relevant facts, or lying about a medical condition or treatment can be grounds for a company to refuse to insure an applicant or for canceling the policy of someone the company has already insured.

Starting in 2014, although insurance companies will continue to be allowed to seek information about an individual's medical history, they will no longer be permitted to use this information as grounds for refusing coverage. The advocacy group Families USA estimates that about fifty-seven million Americans have been diagnosed with diseases that could result in their being refused insurance coverage. (This is equivalent to about one in five people under the age of sixty-five.) When family history is considered as a risk factor, this number might become closer to one hundred million.

Insurers also cannot charge people with preexisting medical conditions higher premiums. Nor can they, in general, deny coverage because of a person's race, gender, or current health status. Thus, someone with colon cancer who has lost his job and his insurance with it must be able to get health insurance coverage. Most likely, this would be accomplished by buying a policy through a state-run insurance exchange. (See the following discussion.)

No Policy Cancellations for Illness

A 2009 Congressional investigation found that three large insurance companies had canceled the policies of more than 19,000 people after they became ill. Insurance companies routinely review the policies of clients who develop medical problems that incur high costs (e.g., breast cancer) and look for a reason to "rescind" (cancel) the policy.

The congressional investigation showed that the grounds companies used to cancel policies were often flimsy (e.g., the client had failed to mention being treated for acne as a teenager). Also, even if a client whose policy was canceled went to court to attempt to get the insurance company to pay for medical care already provided, companies tended to prolong the proceedings. Thus, a client without enough resources might be forced to go without the additional treatment needed or might even be dead before the case came to trial.

Under provisions of the ACA, insurance companies can no longer cancel policies retroactively when patients develop serious and expensive illnesses.

No Lifetime Benefits Cap

Medical care is expensive, and before the ACA insurance policies typically placed an upper limit on the amount of money a policy would pay out for an individual patient or a family. The lifetime amount was frequently one million dollars. Although this seemed like a lot of money to most people, a million dollars can easily be exceeded when someone is being treated for a serious illness requiring repeated surgery and frequent or long-term hospitalization. The care provided at a major medical center to a newborn with a serious heart defect, for example, can exceed a million in costs before the child is even one year old. Where are the parents supposed to get the money to pay for the additional care required?

Similarly, the cumulative costs of treating a patient for a chronic incurable disease like diabetes can easily exceed the lifetime limit of an insurance policy. Someone with diabetes must follow a daily medication schedule and receive frequent medical checkups, including a panel of laboratory tests. Despite such efforts, he may develop life-threatening complications that require hospitalization and surgery, followed in some cases by rehabilitation regimens.

Many disorders, diseases, and injuries require treatments that cost so much that a million dollars may fall far short of the amount needed to pay for a lifetime of care. Thus, under the old health care system, at some point the patient might find himself in the position of still needing care, but having exhausted the money allocated to him under the conditions of his insurance policy. What a patient might do at this point depended on the resources available to him, his legal options, and his personality.

Almost never, however, did a story about such a patient have a happy ending.

In the case of married couples, when one spouse was sick and ran up medical bills insurance wouldn't pay, they were forced to sell off their assets—houses, cars, and even household goods—to raise the money. Such a couple might get divorced so that the sick one could qualify for Medicaid and avoid forcing the other into bankruptcy. If, however, Medicaid could show that this was the motive behind the divorce, the agency could lay claim to the assets of the well spouse.

Once individuals had expended their resources, they might have to declare bankruptcy to escape the unbearable burden of hundreds of thousands of dollars in medical expenses. David Himmelstein, one of the founders of Physicians for a National Health Program, conducted a study that showed that medical bills are a leading cause of personal bankruptcy in the United States. He estimated that around 900,000 cases of medical bankruptcy occurred in 2009, and each bankruptcy had an impact on the personal lives (children, spouse, other dependents) of an average of 2.7 people. Thus, about twenty-four million people a year in the United States suffer the consequences of not being able to pay their medical bills.

Not all of the people forced to declare bankruptcy were without insurance. An estimated seventy-five percent of the 2009 group had medical insurance at the time they became sick, but either it was canceled at a certain point (rescinded) or the patients' medical costs exceeded the amount their policies would pay. The ACA is intended to make it impossible for an insurance company to refuse to pay the legitimate medical expenses of a client, no matter what the cumulative costs. Under the act, medical bankruptcies should dwindle to a small number of unusual cases.

Preventive Care Without Additional Cost

One aim of the ACA is to improve the health of the nation by requiring insurers to cover,

without any additional cost to clients, a range of services (e.g., mammograms, flu shots, and HIV testing) that will either prevent disease or identify it at an early stage, when it is usually more effectively and more cheaply treated.

Promoting the health of citizens is a legitimate aim of a government, but the motivation behind the requirement that insurance companies provide clients with preventive-care services is to lower the overall costs of health care. The ACA sees insurance as a tool that can be used to help people avoid disease and stay healthy. If people are told they have certain risk factors for a disease, the information may allow them to change their habits and diets and reduce the chance that they will develop the disease. Reducing the disease burden in the society should lead to a decrease in the amount spent for medical treatment.

The provision of the ACA requiring insurance companies to offer their clients preventive-care services went into effect in September 2010, but the provision applies only to new insurance policies. Anyone buying a new policy will be guaranteed preventive care without paying additional fees, but anyone keeping an insurance policy (or signing up to renew one) that doesn't already include preventive care is not likely to get it. The situation is fluid for private insurance, however, because the Department of Health and Human Services (HHS) has not yet written rules that specify when a continuing insurance plan must pay for preventive care.

The matter is settled for Medicare, the insurance plan covering those over the age of sixty-five. Starting in 2011, anyone enrolled in Medicare will be entitled to a free annual medical examination, free screenings when appropriate (e.g., mammograms and colonoscopies), and free immunizations (such as flu shots and pneumonia vaccinations).

Eventually, HHS will issue specific rules for implementing the ACA requirement that insurers provide their clients with preventive-care services. It is possible now, however, to indicate in a general way what the HHS will require. The preventive services will be ones that the U.S. Preventive Services Task Force (an independent panel of experts) has determined to be of high value in the prevention or early detection of diseases. The tests endorsed by the Task Force include screening for HIV, hepatitis, depression, osteoporosis, colorectal cancer, and breast cancer. Tests endorsed for children include screening for sickle-cell anemia, iron deficiency, and hypothyroidism.

To decide which immunizations must be paid for by insurers, HHS will rely on the findings of the Centers for Disease Control and Prevention. Only those immunizations that are highly effective and will substantially reduce the amount of disease in the society will have to be offered. Among these are immunizations against tetanus, diphtheria, pertussis, measles, mumps, polio, flu, and hepatitis A and B.

Eventually, as experiences in other countries show, the provision of effective preventive care should reduce the disease burden in the United States Because the cost of treatment is usually many times more than the cost of prevention, preventive services should, over time, lower the cost of health care in the nation.

Basic Package of Benefits

Insurance policies can vary, and one aim of the state-operated insurance exchanges is to encourage insurance companies to compete to offer the best package of benefits at the lowest price. The general rule should be "The more you pay, the more you get," but the ACA will spell out a package of basic benefits that must be included in any health insurance policy.

The requirement will have the effect of establishing a floor that will give a policy holder access to basic health care. A so-called Cadillac plan may include provisions allowing a client to go anywhere in the world to receive care, but a basic plan may specify where the client must go to be treated. Similarly, someone with an expensive plan may be able to qualify for a heart transplant, while someone with a basic plan may not.

Exactly what kinds of conditions insurance plans will be required to cover has not yet been established. We know that insurers will have to provide a variety of preventive services without additional cost (see earlier), but other than that, we don't yet know what will constitute a basic package of medical benefits.

Envoi

The sketch of the ACA presented here does little more than capture some of its more prominent features. The legislation is complicated and extensive. Also, we have yet to see what sort of rules the Department of Health and Human Services is going to come up with to implement some of the more important provisions. (What will the free preventive services be? What will be the basic package of benefits that insurance policies must offer?) How the provisions are implemented by rules will do much to define the character of the system.

The act will also be implemented over a long period. Although some changes are immediate, most will not become operational until 2014, and still others will not be introduced into practice until 2016. No one knows here at the beginning exactly what sort of health care system we are going to have in the next five to ten years.

Many can already point to flaws in the system, and even when it is fully operational, it will no doubt be easy to imagine how it can be improved. Yet even its severest critics acknowledge that in specific respects the system now emerging is significantly better than the system that it is replacing. Millions of Americans in need of medical care will now, for the first time, have a reasonable chance of gaining access to it.

That alone is an improvement over the old system.

In Crisis Mode: Background to Health Care Reform

A crisis exists in a social institution when factors are present that tend to destroy the institution or render it ineffective in achieving its goals. Two major factors present in the American health care system at the beginning of the 21st century put it in a state of crisis: the increasing cost of health care and the failure to deliver a decent minimum of health care to everyone in needs of it.

These factors became crucial when the cost of care continued to spiral upward while the number of people unable to pay for care steadily grew. By 2010, it was clear to politicians, economists, the business community, and the public that the health care system needed to be changed in substantial ways to bring costs under control and to extend medical care to those needing it but lacking resources to obtain it. It was against the background sketched below that the debates over health care reform took place in 2009 and 2010.

Cost of Health Care

In 1960, health spending in the United States was $27 billion. In 1970 it rose to $75 billion, and in 1983 it increased to $356 billion. Around 1994 managed care plans were widely instituted to bring down costs, but although they slowed down spending, it continued to grow. By 1996, health care costs had climbed to an astounding $1 trillion. This was 4.4% more than in 1995; even so, it was the smallest increase in thirty-seven years. By 2000, spending on health care rose to $1.3 trillion, a 7% increase over 1993, the year major health care reform was first proposed. The most recent data put 2009 spending at $2.5 trillion, which amounts to an average of $8,160 per person, regardless of age.

Health care costs now make up about 18% of the nation's gross domestic product. In 1970, it was about 7% of gross domestic product (GDP). Since then, health care spending has risen 2.4% faster than the GDP has grown. By 2018, health care costs are projected to be over $4.3 trillion ($13,100 per person) and to account for more than 20% of the nation's GDP.

The Uninsured

Medical spending had stopped increasing at a double-digit rate by 2005, but it was still rising at a rate greater than the growth in the earnings of individuals. This meant that if the system was not reformed, most people would be required to spend a greater proportion of their income on medical care, but it also meant that, in the absence of reform, both medical care and medical insurance would climb beyond the financial reach of many people.

The number of people without medical insurance in 2010 was estimated to be between thirty-seven and forty-five million (as much as sixteen percent of the population). These figures are misleading, however, because people often lose their insurance when they lose their jobs and may go for a while before they get coverage from a new employer. At that time health care reforms were being debated, analysts estimated that sixty million people were uninsured for at least some of the time during the year. Half of those without insurance were children or families with children. Children themselves made up about twenty-five percent of the uninsured.

Until provisions of the ACA become operative in 2014, employers are not required by law to offer health insurance, and often they do so only as a fringe benefit to attract the workforce they want. Given a need to cut costs to compete with companies in other companies that employ lower wage workers, many U.S. companies stopped offering health insurance to their employees. (In 2006, there were eight million fewer jobs with health insurance than in 2000.) Some employers justified their decision on the ground that employees tend to prefer higher wages to health insurance.

Even when employers offer health insurance, employees usually have to contribute to paying premiums in a group plan. Workers in low-wage jobs frequently said they couldn't afford to pay their proportion of the cost. A worker making $800 a month who has to pay even as little as $75 a month for insurance coverage is left with a substantially reduced income. Finally, even if an employee was in a group health plan, the plan might not cover the employee's spouse or children. If it didn't, the family was then faced with paying for private policies that most of them couldn't afford.

So many people doing without health care and so many people having no health insurance made the passage of the ACA in 2010 timely. In the view of many critics, health care reform to address these issues had been long overdue.

Why Are Costs of Medical Care So High?

Various factors help explain why American health care costs so much. Economists point out, in general, that in medicine a surplus of services does not drive prices down. Rather, it may drive up demand. The availability of powerful drugs, laboratories, high-technology equipment, hospital beds, trauma centers, and a variety of medical services increases the probability that they will be used. Yet there are also specific reasons that explain why medical care is so costly.

- **Drug Costs.** From 1995 to 2000, the cost of drugs doubled, and from 1990 to 2000, it tripled. Starting in 1996, the increase became about ten percent a year. Even though the percentage increase slowed, the cost of drugs in 2006 (the year with the most recent data) was more than $217 billion. This is more than five times the $40 billion that drugs cost in 1990.

  Drug manufacturers justify high prices by citing the costs of research for producing new and effective drugs. Critics, however, point to new "me-too" drugs that are no more than expensive variations on older, cheaper drugs that are equally effective. That people want the new drugs is due to intensive consumer advertising. Thus, Xela, which costs $15.00 a dose, is perceived as being superior to Zola, which costs $2.00, merely because of heavy promotion. Consequently, health care costs are being driven up with little or no improvement in anybody's health.

- **Competitive Limits on Managed Care.** At the time the ACA was passed, the majority of insurance coverage involved managed care. Managed care can exert some control over the demand for medical services, but the control cannot be total. Managed-care plans must compete for contracts, and the plan that offers the employees of a company the most services at the lowest prices has a competitive advantage. Also, with hospitals, laboratories, and physicians' groups at the negotiating table, insurers and their business clients cannot dictate terms to health care providers.

- **Aging Population.** Children born during the baby boom of the 1940s are beginning to reach middle and old age, so the median age of the population has increased. An aging population requires more—and more expensive—medical care than a younger population.

- **Advanced Technology.** Advances in medical technology now make it possible to provide a greater number of services to hospitalized patients. Hence, more people are likely to be hospitalized in order to receive the services. Similarly, while sophisticated medical tests, such as CT scans, MRIs, sonograms, and endoscopic examinations can now be done on an outpatient basis, that very fact may increase the likelihood of their use.

- **Improved Therapies.** Improvements in medicine and surgery now make it possible to provide therapies for diseases that once would not have been treated. The availability of such treatments means increasing the hospital population, and the success of such treatments means that more people will be alive who can benefit from additional care.

New treatments are also likely to be expensive. Surgery, radiation, chemotherapy, and bone-marrow transplants may all be used in treating cancer, for example. When drugs, biopsies, laboratory tests, examinations, and hospitalizations are added to these treatments, the cost may rise to $300,000 or more. A liver transplant alone may cost $250,000, and the drug therapy used to treat HIV/AIDS can cost from $12 thousand to $20 thousand a year.

■ **Aggressive Medicine.** Americans take an interventionist attitude toward dealing with disease, and most people, when faced with a serious illness, choose an aggressive approach to treatment. It usually costs more money to attack a disease than to wait to see how it responds to less aggressive treatments.

The very success of medicine creates, in a sense, the need for more medicine. Americans have traditionally refused to accept less effective medical treatments when more effective ones are available, even though, more often than not, the best treatments come with a higher price tag.

■ **Antirationing.** Americans are typically unwilling to accept the explicit rationing of resources that would involve, for example, denying heart transplants to people in their seventies or mammograms to women in their forties. No doubt, the whole complex of American attitudes about health care is responsible to a large degree for the amount spent on care in our society. This is not likely to change when most of the provisions of the ACA take effect in 2014, but the act aims to lower overall health care costs by stressing preventive medicine. Also, increasing the number of people who receive basic care may mean that people who wouldn't have received medical care until their disease was at an advanced stage and expensive to treat may now receive care that is both better and cheaper.

■ **Administrative Costs.** Health care in the United States is paid for mostly by individuals through their medical insurance, and this way of paying for care has a costly overhead. (The ACA will not change this feature of U.S. health care.) A 2003 study by researchers from the Harvard Medical School and the Canadian Institute for Health Information found that 31 cents of every dollar spent on health care in the United States goes to pay administrative costs. This is nearly double the amount spent by the Canadian government-run system.

In administrative costs alone, Americans spend $752 per person more than Canadians do. This money supports the large bureaucracy required by insurers to assess risks, set premiums, design and market benefit packages, review claims, and decide whether to pay them. U.S. health care costs could be reduced by almost a third, according to some estimates, by adopting a system administered by the federal government (a "single-payer" system).

In 2010, the Congressional Budget Office estimated that 26 cents of every insurance dollar goes toward administrative expenses. The Budget Office also found that, in large businesses (those with over a thousand employees), administrative costs were seven percent although in businesses with fewer than twenty-five employees, administrative costs were twenty-six percent. The lesson here, some reformers believe, is that even if a single-payer system is not adopted, insurance should be administered by large agencies to lower the costs of administration.

Effectiveness

The United States spends more on health care than any other country in the world. For example (to take the most recent comparative figures, available in 2006), the United States spent $5,267 per person in 2002, Canada $2,931, France $2,736, Germany $2,817, and Britain only $2160. It's reasonable to ask, then, is American health care better than it is in other industrialized countries?

Despite the fact that U.S. per capita spending on health care is so much more than that of the other nations, the usual ways of measuring the health status of nations don't show that the United States is getting more for its money. Indeed, that it seemed to be getting less was one of the arguments used to support the need for health care reform when the question was debated in 2009–2010.

A 2005 study in the journal *Health Affairs* showed that Americans were far more likely to go without medical treatment than Europeans. Because of their worry about the cost, a third of Americans in the survey failed to consult a doctor when they were sick, failed to get a test recommended by their doctor, or failed to see a doctor for a follow-up visit after an initial treatment. Forty percent of those in the survey failed to fill a prescription because of the cost.

The survey also showed that sicker adults in the other countries generally did not wait longer for treatment than in the United States Americans typically had shorter waits for elective surgery (e.g., hip replacements) than people in Canada or Britain, but the waits in Germany were even shorter.

Statistics collected by the World Health Organization rank the United States 31st in life expectancy (tied with Kuwait and Chile), 37th in infant mortality, and 34th in maternal mortality. A child in the United States is 2.5 times as likely to die by age 5 as a child in Singapore or Sweden, and an American woman is eleven times as likely to die in childbirth as a woman in Ireland. A 2009 Robert Wood Johnson Foundation report cited a study showing that when nineteen developed countries were compared with respect to their success in avoiding preventable deaths among their citizens, the United States ranked in last place.

Also, various studies show that Americans find it more difficult to see a doctor when they need one than do people in other countries. One reason for this seems to be that the United States spends a larger proportion of its budget on high technology (MRIs, endoscopies, etc.) than on doctors' visits and hospitalizations.

Also, medical insurers have traditionally been more likely to pay for more expensive forms of intervention (e.g., foot amputations needed by diabetics) than for patient education, monitoring, and preventive care.

Need for a Change

The ACA was passed by the U.S. Congress and signed into law by President Obama in March 2010. The Obama administration emphasized repeatedly two major aims of the legislation. First, the ACA will extend health insurance coverage to virtually every American. Although everyone will be required to have insurance, those who cannot afford it will be given a voucher to allow them to obtain a policy that will provide them with basic coverage. Those who are too poor to pay anything toward an insurance policy will receive their coverage though the Medicaid program, and those over age 65 will be insured by the Medicare program.

Second, the ACA aims to slow the growth of health spending in the society. The hope is that it can do so, in part, by seeing to it that more people receive preventive care. When people are able to avoid developing a disease, the cost of care falls, and even when a disease is unavoidable, treating it at an early stage is less expensive than treating it at later stage.

Some provisions of the ACA have now been implemented, but the legislation will not become fully operational until 2014–2016. It is thus much too early to say whether the ACA will be successful in achieving its goals. Will it lead to an increase in life expectancy? Reduce infant and maternal mortality? Lower the overall cost of health care in the society?

The one certain thing is that the millions of Americans who were unable to afford even basic health care for themselves and their children will now be able to get it. For the first time, the richest nation in the history of the world has committed itself to making sure that even its poorest and most vulnerable citizens receive a decent minimum of medical care.

BRIEFING SESSION

Some historians of medicine estimate that it was not until the middle 1930s that the intervention of a physician in the treatment of an illness was likely to affect its outcome in a substantial way. The change was brought about by the discovery and development of antibiotic agents such as penicillin and sulfa drugs. They made it possible, for the first time, both to control infection and to provide specific remedies for a variety of diseases. Additional advances in treatment modalities, procedures, and technology have helped establish contemporary medicine as an effective enterprise.

Before these dramatic advances occurred, there was little reason for anyone to be particularly concerned with the question of access to medical care within society. The situation in the United States has changed significantly,

and over the decades, many physicians, philosophers, political theorists, and politicians have argued that everyone ought to be guaranteed at least a basic amount of medical care. In part, this view is a reflection of the increased effectiveness of contemporary medicine, but it is also due to the growing awareness of the serious difficulties faced by disadvantaged groups within society.

The previous chapter focused on one aspect of the problem of the distribution of medical resources—that of allocating limited resources among competing individuals in a particular situation. In the current chapter, we need to call attention to some of the broader social issues—issues that transcend moral decisions about particular people and raise questions about the basic aims and obligations of society.

Recognizing a Need, Not a Right

For more than thirty years, a variety of observers (ranging from economists and religious leaders to philosophers and physicians) argued that the United States was in the midst of a health care crisis. Some of the reasons they mentioned in support of this belief are outlined in the Social Context "In Crisis Mode: Background to Health Care Reform," in this chapter, and we need not repeat them here. But one element of the crisis that was invariably cited was the absence of any program to provide health care for everyone in the society. That people should be forced to do without even basic health care for primarily financial reasons seemed to some a morally intolerable state of affairs. During the political debates over health care reform in 2009 and 2010, the failure of the society to extend needed care to its citizens was often mentioned as a reason to support the adoption of particular health care plans.

The view that a society has a duty to see to the health care needs of its citizens is frequently

based on the claim that everyone has a right to health care. Thus, it is often argued, society has a duty to provide that care; if it does not, then it is sanctioning a situation that is inherently wrong. To remedy the situation requires redesigning the nation's health care system and present practices, to see to it that all who need health care have access to it.

This was not, in the end, an argument that played a substantial role in persuading Congress to pass the ACA. Making health care affordable so that millions of more people might secure the health insurance needed to pay for it was one of the major arguments offered to support the legislation. (Another major argument was that extending health care to those without it would have the effect of lowering the overall cost of care to the society.) Thus, an aim of the legislation was to help more people pay for basic medical care.

The legislation itself mentioned no right to care, nor does it change the basic market-based economic model: those needing medical care must have a way to pay for it. They will need either insurance or money, and if they lack both, the society will step in and offer basic care. (Exactly what this basic care is has yet to be spelled out.) Those who need more than basic care (e.g., a heart transplant) and are unable to find a way to pay for it probably will not be able to get it.

Some critics of the ACA criticize it on the ground that it doesn't recognize a right to health care. Thus, although the act will cover basic care for more people than before, it will still tolerate the large gap between those who need very expensive care and can pay for it and those who need the same care but cannot afford it. If a right to health care were recognized, some argue, the society would take responsibility for closing this gap and erasing the inequality it represents.

The language of "rights" is very slippery. To understand and evaluate arguments that involve claiming (or denying) rights to health care, it is important to understand the nature of the claim. The word "rights" is used in several distinct ways, and a failure to be clear about the use in any given case leads only to unproductive confusion.

The following distinctions may help capture some of the more important sorts of things that people have in mind when they talk about rights.

Claim Rights, Legal Rights, and Statutory Rights

Suppose I own a copy of the book *Fan Mail*. If so, then I may be said to have a right to do with the book whatever I choose. Other people may be said to have a duty to recognize my right in appropriate ways. Thus, if I want to read the book, burn it, or sell it, others have a duty not to interfere with me. If I lend the book to someone, then he or she has a duty to return it.

Philosophers of law generally agree that a *claim right* to something serves as a ground for other people's duties. A claim right, then, always entails a duty or duties on the part of someone else.

Generally speaking, legal rights are claim rights. Someone has a legal right when someone else has a definable duty, and legal remedies are available when the duty is not performed. Either the person can be forced to perform the duty, or damages of some sort can be collected for failure to perform. If I pay someone to put a new roof on my house by a certain date, she has contracted a duty to perform the work we have agreed to. If the task is not performed, then I can turn to the legal system for enforcement or damages.

Statutory rights are claim rights that are explicitly recognized in legal statutes or laws. They impose duties on certain classes of people under specified conditions. A hospital contractor, for example, has a duty to meet certain building codes. If he fails to meet them, he is liable to legal penalties. But not all legal rights are necessarily statutory rights. Such considerations as "customary and established practices" may sometimes implicitly involve a legally enforceable claim right.

Moral Rights

A *moral right*, generally speaking, is a right that is stated in or derived from the principles of a moral theory. More specifically, to say that someone has a moral right to certain goods or a certain manner of treatment is to say that others have a moral duty to see to it that she receives what she has a right to. A moral right is a certain kind of claim right. Here, though, the source of justification for the right and for the corresponding duty lies in moral principles and not in the laws or practices of a society.

According to W. D. Ross, for example, people have a duty to treat other people benevolently. This is a duty that is not recognized by our legal system. We may, if we wish, treat others in a harsh and unsympathetic manner and, in doing so, violate no law. (See the discussion of Ross in Part VI, "Foundations of Bioethics.")

Of course, many rights and duties that are based upon the principles of moral theories are also embodied in our laws. Thus, to take Ross again as an example, we have a prima facie duty not to injure or kill anyone. This duty, along with its correlative right to be free from injury or death at the hands of another, is reflected in the body of statutory law and common law that deals with bodily harm done to others and with killing.

The relationship between ethical theories and the laws of a society is complicated and controversial. The fundamental question is always the extent to which laws should reflect or be based upon an ethical theory. In a society such as ours, it does not seem proper that an ethical theory accepted by only a part of the people should determine the laws that govern us all. It is for this reason that some object to laws regulating sexual activity, pornography, and abortion. These are considered best regarded as a part of personal morality.

At the same time, however, it seems that we must rely upon ethical theories as a basis for evaluating laws. Unless we are prepared to say that what is legal is, in itself, what is right, we must recognize the possibility of laws that are bad or unjust. But what makes a law bad? A possible answer is that a law is bad when it violates a right derived from the principles of an ethical theory. Similarly, both laws and social practices may be criticized for failing to recognize a moral right. A moral theory, then, can serve as a basis for a demand for the reform of laws and practices.

Clearly, there is no sharp line separating the moral and the legal. Indeed, virtually all of the moral theories discussed in Part VI have been used by philosophers and other thinkers as the basis for principles applying to society as a whole. Within such frameworks as utilitarianism, natural law theory, and Rawls's theory of a just society, legal and social institutions are assigned roles and functions in accordance with more general moral principles.

Political Rights

Not everyone attempts to justify claims to rights by referring such claims directly to a moral theory. Efforts are frequently made to provide justification by relying on principles or commitments that are generally acknowledged as basic to our society. (Of course, to answer how these are justified may force us to invoke moral principles.) Our society, for example, is committed to individual autonomy and equality, among other values. It is by reference to commitments of this sort that we evaluate proposals and criticize practices.

From this point of view, to recognize health care as a right is to acknowledge it as a political right. This means showing that it is required by our political commitments or principles. Of course, it may also mean resolving any conflicts that may arise from other rights that seem to be demanded by our principles, too. But this is a familiar state of affairs. We are all aware that the constitutional guarantee of freedom of speech, for example, is not absolute and unconditional: it can conflict with other rights or basic commitments, and we look to the courts to provide us with guidelines to resolve the conflicts.

Health Care as a Right

With the distinctions that we have discussed in mind, let's return to the question of a general right to health care. What can those who make such a claim be asserting?

Obviously, everyone in our society is free to seek health care and, when the proper arrangements are made, to receive it. That is, health care is a service available in society, and people may avail themselves of it. At the same time, however, no physician or hospital has a duty to provide health care that is sought. The freedom to seek does not imply that others have a duty to provide what we seek.

In our society, there is no legally recognized claim right to health care. Even if I am sick, no one has a legal duty to see to it that I receive treatment for my illness. (Hospitals receiving federal money have a legal duty to treat people faced with life-threatening emergencies until they are stabilized.) I may request care, or I may attempt to persuade a physician that it is his or her moral duty to provide me with care. But I have no legal right to health care, and if someone refuses to provide it, I cannot seek a legal remedy.

I may, of course, contract with a physician, clinic, or hospital for care, either in general or for a certain ailment. If I do this, then the other party acquires a legally enforceable duty to provide me the kind of care that we agreed upon. Contracting for health care, in this respect, is not relevantly different from contracting for a new roof on my house.

Those who assert that health care is a right cannot be regarded as making the obviously false claim that there is a legal right to care. Their claim, rather, must be interpreted as one of a moral or political sort. They might be taken as asserting something like "Everyone in our society ought to be entitled to health care, regardless of his or her financial condition."

Anyone making such a claim must be prepared to justify it by offering reasons and evidence in support of it. The ultimate source of the justification is most likely to be the principles of a moral theory. For example, Kant's principle that every person is of inherent and equal worth might be used to support the claim that every person has an equal right to medical care simply by virtue of being a person.

Justification might also be offered in terms of principles that express the aims and commitments of the society. A society that endorses justice and equality, one might argue, must be prepared to offer health care to all if it offers it to anyone.

However justification is offered, to claim that health care is a right is to go beyond merely expressing an attitude. It is to say more than something like "Everyone would like to have health care" or "Everyone needs health care."

A consequence (and aim) of the ACA is to increase the number of people who can make a claim right for health care. Those with low incomes who, before the act went into effect, would have to do without medical care because they had no insurance or money to pay for it, will now have insurance. (Those with some money will receive vouchers to make up the difference between the cost of a basic policy

and what they can pay; those too poor to pay anything will have a Medicare plan, and those sixty-five or older will have Medicare.) Thus, they can claim the right to get a certain amount of care from doctors and hospitals. They can claim only basic care (whatever this turns out to be), and if they need expensive surgery, they will not be able to claim the right to it. Doctors and hospitals will thus have no duty to provide it.

Health care reform could have gone beyond the right recognized in the ACA. It could have endorsed the notion that every citizen has a right to as much health care as is needed and available (e.g., a liver transplant) or is entitled to receive as much needed care as anyone else (including the rich). Instead, the act recognizes only a claim right to basic care, and even gaining that right requires having a way (cash, insurance, or public program) to pay for the care sought.

The language of "rights" is frequently used in a rhetorical way to encourage us to recognize the wants and needs of people—or even other organisms, such as animals and trees. This is a perfectly legitimate way of talking. But, at bottom, to urge that something be considered a right is to make a claim requiring justification in terms of some set of legal, social, or moral principles. Those unhappy about the ACA believe that the Obama administration passed over the opportunity to make the argument that the principles of U.S. society, as embodied in the Constitution, require that we recognize a right to health care.

Objections

Why not recognize health care for all as a right? Virtually everyone would admit that in the abstract it would be a good thing. If this is so, then why should anyone wish to oppose it? Briefly stated, arguments against a right to health care are most frequently of two kinds.

First, some argue that we live in a market economy and medical care is simply a commodity like cars, houses, or vacations on tropical islands. For people to receive medical care, it is perfectly legitimate for us to ask for them to find a way to pay for it. They may compete for jobs that offer health insurance, establish savings accounts to accumulate funds needed for medical care, pay cash for drugs and treatments, or use earnings from their jobs to buy the insurance they decide they need. If they decide to use their income to make mortgage payments on a house instead of buying an insurance policy, then they must accept the consequences. We shouldn't, as a society, provide for the improvident at the expense of those who spend their money wisely. It violates the principles of the marketplace to give away a commodity—medical care—that should be purchased, and the market will punish the improvident.

Conservative critics of the ACA object strenuously to its requirement that (virtually) everyone in the society be required to purchase health insurance. They regard this as an unwarranted intrusion of the state into the affairs of individuals. People are being required, critics say, to spend their money in ways that they have not chosen. This means that they are forced to accept restrictions on the exercise of their autonomy.

Second, some critics have pointed out that, although it is possible to admit health care to the status of a right, we must also recognize that health care is only one social good among others. Education, defense, environmental protection, housing, legal assistance, and so on are other goods that also sought and needed by members of our society. It is impossible to admit all of these (and perhaps others) to the status of rights, for the society simply cannot afford to pay for them.

The first line of argument fails to recognize that it is contrary to basic moral commitments of our society to treat everything as a commodity. We do not, for example, buy and sell slaves, rent children to pedophiles, or allow transplant organs to be sold in public auctions.

Some argue that medical care, unlike golf lessons or even a painting by Degas, is not a commodity in the ordinary sense. People who do not receive health care suffer pain,

lose functions like the ability to walk, and even die. Health, some argue, is a condition necessary to enjoy the goods of the world, and because medical care is often essential to preserve or restore health or (at least) relieve suffering, medical care is not an ordinary commodity. A society committed to protecting the autonomy of individuals (or, in the language of the Declaration of Independence, promoting "life, liberty, and the pursuit of happiness") has a moral duty to see to it that its citizens receive the medical care needed to make this possible.

The second line of argument does not necessarily lead to the conclusion that we should not recognize a right to health care. It does serve to warn us that we must be careful to specify exactly what sort of right—if any—we want to support. Do we want to claim, for example, that everyone has a right to a certain minimum of health care? Or do we want to claim that everyone has a right to equal health care? Whatever anyone can get, everyone can demand. Rights can have scope, and we may not be able to fulfill claims of the broadest sort.

Furthermore, this line of argument warns us that we have to make decisions about what we, as a society, are willing to pay for. Would we, for example, be willing to give up all public support for education in order to use the money for health care? Probably not. But we might be willing to reduce the level of support for education in order to increase that for health care. Whatever we decide, we have to face up to the problem of distributing our limited resources. This is an issue that is obviously closely connected with what sort of right to health care (or, really, the right to what sort of health care) we are prepared to endorse.

The need for health care calls attention to fundamental issues about rights, values, and social goals. If we are to recognize a right to health care, we must be clear about exactly what this involves. Are we prepared to offer only a "decent minimum"? Does justice require that we make available to all whatever is available to any? Are we prepared to restrict the wants of some people in order to satisfy the basic needs of all people?

Such questions are of more than academic interest. How they are resolved will affect us all, directly and indirectly, through the character of our society. For the first time in U.S. history, the country has made a commitment to providing basic health care to its citizens. We don't yet know how the provisions of the ACA will play out in practice. The act may be the country's first step toward recognizing at least a limited amount of health care as a right.

READINGS

Section 1:   The Right to Health Care

An Ethical Framework for Access to Health Care

President's Commission for the Study of Ethical Problems in Medicine

The commission claims that the role played by health care in enabling people to live full and satisfying lives gives it a special importance. The crucial role of health care explains why it ought to be accessible in an equitable fashion to everyone in the society. After reviewing various meanings of "equitable access," the commission concludes that fairness is satisfied if everyone has access to "an adequate level of care."

The commission stops short of endorsing a "right" to health care. It holds, rather, that society has a moral obligation to provide everyone with access to adequate care. The government, as one social institution among others, is not solely or even primarily responsible for providing the access. It might be achieved by a pluralistic approach that relies on both the private and public sectors. Ultimately, though, it is the government that has a duty to see to it that society's moral obligation to provide care is satisfied.

. . . Most Americans believe that because health care is special, access to it raises special ethical concerns. In part, this is because good health is by definition important to well-being. Health care can relieve pain and suffering, restore functioning, and prevent death; it can enhance good health and improve an individual's opportunity to pursue a life plan; and it can provide valuable information about a person's overall health. Beyond its practical importance, the involvement of health care with the most significant and awesome events of life—birth, illness, and death—adds a symbolic aspect to health care: it is special because it signifies not only mutual empathy and caring but the mysterious aspects of curing and healing.

Furthermore, while people have some ability—through choice of life-style and through preventive measures—to influence their health status, many health problems are beyond their control and are therefore undeserved. Besides the burdens of genetics, environment, and chance, individuals become ill because of things they do or fail to do—but it is often difficult for an individual to choose to do otherwise or even to know with enough specificity and confidence

From President's Commission for the Study of Ethical Problems in Medicine and Biomedical and Behavioral Research, "An Ethical Framework for Access to Health Care," *Securing Access to Health Care*, Vol. 1 (1983): 11–12, 16–21, 22–23, 30–32, 34–37 (Notes and references omitted).

what he or she ought to do to remain healthy. Finally, the incidence and severity of ill health is distributed very unevenly among people. Basic needs for housing and food are predictable, but even the most hardworking and prudent person may suddenly be faced with overwhelming needs for health care. Together, these considerations lend weight to the belief that health care is different from most other goods and services. In a society concerned not only with fairness and equality of opportunity but also with the redemptive powers of science, there is a felt obligation to ensure that some level of health services is available to all.

There are many ambiguities, however, about the nature of this societal obligation. What share of health costs should individuals be expected to bear, and what responsibility do they have to use health resources prudently? Is it society's responsibility to ensure that every person receives care or services of as high quality and as great extent as any other individual? Does it require that everyone share opportunities to receive all available care or care of any possible benefit? If not, what level of care is "enough"? And does society's obligation include a responsibility to ensure both that care is available and that its costs will not unduly burden the patient?

The resolution of such issues is made more difficult by the spectre of rising health care costs and expenditures. Although the finitude of national resources demands that trade-offs be made between health care and other social goods, there is little agreement about which choices are most acceptable from an ethical standpoint. In this chapter, the Commission attempts to lay an ethical foundation for evaluating both current patterns of access to health care and the policies designed to address remaining problems in the distribution of health care resources. . . .

The Special Importance of Health Care

Although the importance of health care may, at first blush, appear obvious, this assumption is often based on instinct rather than reasoning. Yet it is possible to step back and examine those properties of health care that lead to the ethical conclusion that it ought to be distributed equitably.

Well-Being

Ethical concern about the distribution of health care derives from the special importance of health care in promoting personal well-being by preventing or relieving pain, suffering, and disability and by avoiding loss of life. The fundamental importance of the latter is obvious: pain and suffering are also experiences that people have strong desires to avoid, both because of the intrinsic quality of the experience and because of their effects on the capacity to pursue and achieve other goals and purposes. Similarly, untreated disability can prevent people from leading rewarding and fully active lives.

Health, insofar as it is the absence of pain, suffering, or serious disability, is what has been called a primary good, that is, there is no need to know what a particular person's other ends, preferences, and values are in order to know that health is good for that individual. It generally helps people carry out their life plans, whatever they may happen to be. This is not to say that everyone defines good health in the same way or assigns the same weight or importance to different aspects of being healthy, or to health in comparison with the other goods of life. Yet though people may differ over each of these matters, their disagreement takes place within a framework of basic agreement on the importance of health. Likewise, people differ in their beliefs about the value of health and medical care and their use of it as a means of achieving good health, as well as in their attitudes toward the various benefits and risks of different treatments.

Opportunity

Health care can also broaden a person's range of opportunities, that is, the array of life plans that is reasonable to pursue within the conditions obtaining in society. In the United States equality of opportunity is a widely accepted value that is reflected throughout public policy. The effects that meeting (or failing to meet) people's health needs have on the distribution of opportunity in a society become apparent if diseases are thought of as adverse departures from a normal level of functioning. In this view, health care is that which people need to maintain or restore normal functioning or to compensate for inability to function normally. Health is thus comparable in importance to education in determining the opportunities available to people to pursue different life plans.

Information

The special importance of health care stems in part from its ability to relieve worry and to enable patients to adjust to their situation by supplying reliable information about their health. Most people do not understand the true nature of a health problem, when it first develops. Health professionals can then perform the worthwhile function of informing people about their conditions and about the expected prognoses with or without various treatments. Though information some-times creates concern, often it reassures patients either by ruling out a feared disease or by revealing the self-limiting nature of a condition and, thus, the lack of need for further treatment. Although health care in many situations may thus not be necessary for good physical health, a great deal of relief from unnecessary concern—and even avoidance of pointless or potentially harmful steps—is achieved by health care in the form of expert information provided to worried patients. Even when a prognosis is unfavorable and health professionals have little treatment to offer, accurate information can help patients plan how to cope with their situation.

The Interpersonal Significance of Illness, Birth, and Death

It is no accident that religious organizations have played a major role in the care of the sick and dying and in the process of birth. Since all human beings are vulnerable to disease and all die, health care has a special inter-personal significance: it expresses and nurtures bonds of empathy and compassion. The depth of a society's concern about health care can be seen as a measure of its sense of solidarity in the face of suffering and death. Moreover, health care takes on special meaning because of its role in the beginning of a human being's life as well as the end. In spite of all the advances in the sci-entific understanding of birth, disease, and death, these profound and universal experiences remain shared mysteries that touch the spiritual side of human nature. For these reasons a society's commitment to health care reflects some of its most basic attitudes about what it is to be a member of the human community.

The Concept of Equitable Access to Health Care

The special nature of health care helps to explain why it ought to be accessible, in a fair fashion, to all. But if this ethical conclusion is to provide a basis for evaluat-ing current patterns of access to health care and pro-posed health policies, the meaning of fairness or equity in this context must be clarified. The concept of equi-table access needs definition in its two main aspects: the level of care that ought to be available to all and the extent to which burdens can be imposed on those who obtain these services.

Access to What?

"Equitable access" could be interpreted in a number of ways: equality of access, access to whatever an individual needs or would benefit from, or access to an adequate level of care.

Equity as Equality

It has been suggested that equity is achieved either when everyone is assured of receiving an equal quan-tity of health care dollars or when people enjoy equal health. The most common characterization of equity as equality, however, is as providing everyone with the same level of health care. In this view, it follows that if a given level of care is available to one individual it must be available to all. If the initial standard is set high, by reference to the highest level of care presently received, an enormous drain would result on the resources needed to provide other goods. Alternatively, if the standard is set low in order to avoid an excessive use of resources, some beneficial services would have to be withheld from people who wished to purchase them. In other words, no one would be allowed access to more services or services of higher quality than those available to everyone else, even if he or she were willing to pay for those services from his or her personal resources.

As long as significant inequalities in income and wealth persist, inequalities in the use of health care can be expected beyond those created by differences in need. Given people with the same pattern of prefer-ences and equal health care needs, those with greater financial resources will purchase more health care. Conversely, given equal financial resources, the differ-ent patterns of health care preferences that typically exist in any population will result in a different use of health services by people with equal health care needs. Trying to prevent such inequalities would require interfering with people's liberty to use their income to purchase an important good like health care while leaving them free to use it for frivolous or inessential ends. Prohibiting people with higher incomes or stron-ger preferences for health care from purchasing more care than everyone else gets would not be feasible, and would probably result in a black market for health care.

EQUITY AS ACCESS SOLELY ACCORDING TO BENEFIT OR NEED   Interpreting equitable access to mean that everyone must receive all health care that is of any benefit to them also has unacceptable impli-cations. Unless health is the only good or resources are unlimited, it would be irrational for a society—as for an individual—to make a commitment to provide whatever health care might be beneficial regardless of cost. Although health care is of special importance, it is surely not all that is important to people. Pushed to an extreme, this criterion might swallow up all of society's resources, since there is virtually no end to the funds that could be devoted to possibly beneficial care for diseases and disabilities and to their prevention.

Equitable access to health care must take into account not only the benefits of care but also the cost in comparison with other goods and services to which those resources might be allocated. Society will reasonably devote some resources to health care but reserve most resources for other goals. This, in turn, will mean that some health services (even of a lifesaving sort) will not be developed or employed because they would produce too few benefits in relation to their costs and to the other ways the resources for them might be used.

It might be argued that the notion of "need" provides a way to limit access to only that care that confers especially important benefits. In this view, equity as access according to need would place less severe demands on social resources than equity according to benefit would. There are, however, difficulties with the notion of need in this context. On the one hand, medical need is often not narrowly defined but refers to any condition for which medical treatment might be effective. Thus "equity as access according to need" collapses into "access according to whatever is of benefit."

On the other hand, "need" could be even more expansive in scope than "benefit." Philosophical and economic writings do not provide any clear distinction between "needs" and "wants" or "preferences." Since the term means different things to different people, "access according to need" could become "access to any health service a person wants." Conversely, need could be interpreted very narrowly to encompass only a very minimal level of services—for example, those "necessary to prevent death."

Equity as an Adequate Level of Health Care

Although neither "everything needed" nor "everything beneficial" nor "everything that anyone else is getting" are defensible ways of understanding equitable access, the special nature of health care dictates that everyone have access to *some* level of care: enough care to achieve sufficient welfare, opportunity, information, and evidence of interpersonal concern to facilitate a reasonably full and satisfying life. That level can be termed "an adequate level of health care." The difficulty of sharpening this amorphous notion into a workable foundation for health policy is a major problem in the United States today. This concept is not new; it is implicit in the public debate over health

policy and has manifested itself in the history of public policy in this country. In this chapter, the Commission attempts to demonstrate the value of the concept, to clarify its content and to apply it to the problems facing health policymakers.

Understanding equitable access to health care to mean that everyone should be able to secure an adequate level of care has several strengths. Because an adequate level of care may be less than "all beneficial care" and because it does not require that all needs be satisfied, it acknowledges the need for setting priorities within health care and signals a clear recognition that society's resources are limited and that there are other goods besides health. Thus, interpreting equity as access to adequate care does not generate an open-ended obligation. One of the chief dangers of interpretations of equity that require virtually unlimited resources for health care is that they encourage the view that equitable access is an impossible ideal. Defining equity as an adequate level of care for all avoids an impossible commitment of resources without falling into the opposite error of abandoning the enterprise of seeking to ensure that health care is in fact available for everyone.

In addition, since providing an adequate level of care is a limited moral requirement, this definition also avoids the unacceptable restriction on individual liberty entailed by the view that equity requires equality. Provided that an adequate level is available to all, those who prefer to use their resources to obtain care that exceeds that level do not offend any ethical principle in doing so. Finally, the concept of adequacy, as the Commission understands it, is society-relative. The content of adequate care will depend upon the overall resources available in a given society, and can take into account a consensus of expectations about what is adequate in a particular society at a particular time in its historical development. This permits the definition of adequacy to be altered as societal resources and expectations change.

With What Burdens?

It is not enough to focus on the care that individuals receive; attention must be paid to the burdens they must bear in order to obtain it—waiting and travel time, the cost and availability of transport, the financial cost of the care itself. Equity requires not only that adequate care be available to all, but also that these burdens not be excessive.

If individuals must travel unreasonably long distances, wait for unreasonably long hours, or spend most of their financial resources to obtain care, some will be deterred from obtaining adequate care, with adverse effects on their health and well-being. Others may bear the burdens, but only at the expense of their ability to meet other important needs. If one of the main reasons for providing adequate care is that health care increases welfare and opportunity, then a system that required large numbers of individuals to forgo food, shelter, or educational advancement in order to obtain care would be self-defeating and irrational.

The concept of acceptable burdens in obtaining care, as opposed to excessive ones, parallels in some respects the concept of adequacy. Just as equity does not require equal access, neither must the burdens of obtaining adequate care be equal for all persons. What is crucial is that the variations in burdens fall within an acceptable range. As in determining an adequate level of care, there is no simple formula for ascertaining when the burdens of obtaining care fall within such a range. Yet some guidelines can be formulated. To illustrate, since a given financial outlay represents a greater sacrifice to a poor person than to a rich person, "excessive" must be understood in relation to income. Obviously everyone cannot live the same distance from a health care facility, and some individuals choose to locate in remote and sparsely populated areas. Concern about an inequitable burden would be appropriate, however, when identifiable groups must travel a great distance or long time to receive care—though people may appropriately be expected to travel farther to get specialized care, for example, than to obtain primary or emergency care. . . .

A Societal Obligation

Society has a moral obligation to ensure that everyone has access to adequate care without being subject to excessive burdens. In speaking of a societal obligation the Commission makes reference to society in the broadest sense—the collective American community. The community is made up of individuals, who are in turn members of many other, overlapping groups, both public and private: local, state, regional, and national units; professional and workplace organizations; religious, educational, and charitable organizations; and family, kinship, and ethnic groups. All these entities play a role in discharging societal obligations.

The Commission believes it is important to distinguish between society, in this inclusive sense, and government as one institution among others in society. Thus the recognition of a collective or societal obligation does not imply that government should be the only or even the primary institution involved in the complex enterprise of making health care available. It

is the Commission's view that the societal obligation to ensure equitable access for everyone may best be fulfilled in this country by a pluralistic approach that relies upon the coordinated contributions of actions by both the private and public sectors.

Securing equitable access is a societal rather than a merely private or individual responsibility for several reasons. First, while health is of special importance for human beings, health care—especially scientific health care—is a social product requiring the skills and efforts of many individuals; it is not something that individuals can provide for themselves solely through their own efforts. Second, because the need for health care is both unevenly distributed among persons and highly unpredictable and because the cost of securing care may be great, few individuals could secure adequate care without relying on some social mechanism for sharing the costs. Third, if persons generally deserved their health conditions or if the need for health care were fully within the individual's control, the fact that some lack adequate care would not be viewed as an inequity. But differences in health status, and hence differences in health care needs, are largely undeserved because they are, for the most part, not within the individual's control. . . .

In light of the special importance of health care, the largely undeserved character of differences in health status, and the uneven distribution and unpredictability of health care needs, society has a moral obligation to ensure adequate care for all. Saying that the obligation is societal (rather than merely individual) stops short, however, of identifying who has the ultimate responsibility for ensuring that the obligation is successfully met.

Who Should Ensure That Society's Obligation Is Met?

A Role for Government

The extent of governmental involvement in securing equitable access to care depends on the extent to which the market and private charity achieve this objective. . . . Although it is clear that—even for those with adequate resources—the purchase of health care differs from other market transactions, the market (which includes private health insurance) is capable of providing many people with an adequate level of health care. However, when the market and charity do not enable individuals to obtain adequate care or cause them to endure excessive burdens in doing so, then the responsibility to ensure that these people have equitable access to health care resides with the local, state, and Federal governments.

LOCATING RESPONSIBILITY   Although it is appropriate that all levels of government be involved in seeing that equitable access to health care is achieved, the *ultimate* responsibility for ensuring that this obligation is met rests with the Federal government. The Commission believes it is extremely important to distinguish between the view that the Federal government ought to provide care and the view that the Federal government is ultimately responsible for seeing that there is equitable access to care. It is the latter view that the Commission endorses. It is not the purpose of this Report to assign the precise division of labor between public and private provision of health care. Rather, the Commission has attempted here only to locate the ultimate responsibility for ensuring that equitable access is attained.

A view that has gained wide acceptance in this country is that the government has a major responsibility for making sure that certain basic social goods, such as health care and economic security for the elderly, are available to all. Over the past half-century, public policy and public opinion have increasingly reflected the belief that the Federal government is the logical mechanism for ensuring that society's obligation to make these goods available is met. In the case of health care, this stance is supported by several considerations. First, the obligation in question is society-wide, not limited to particular states or localities; it is an obligation of all to achieve equity for all. Second, government responsibility at the national level is needed to secure reliable resources. Third, only the Federal government can ultimately guarantee that the burdens of providing resources are distributed fairly across the whole of society. Fourth, meeting society's obligation to provide equitable access requires an "overview" of efforts. Unless the ultimate responsibility has been clearly fixed for determining whether the standard of equitable access is being met, there is no reason to believe it will be achieved.

THE LIMITATIONS OF RELYING UPON THE GOVERNMENT   Although the Commission recognizes the necessity of government involvement in ensuring equity of access, it believes that such activity must be carefully crafted and implemented in order to achieve its intended purpose. Public concern about the inability of the market and of private charity to secure access to health care for all has led to extensive government involvement in the financing and delivery of health care. This involvement has come about largely as a result of ad hoc responses to specific problems: the result has been a patchwork of public initiatives at the local, state, and Federal level. These efforts have done much to make health care more widely available to all citizens, but . . . they have not achieved equity of access.

To a large extent, this is the result of a lack of consensus about the nature of the goal and the proper role of government in pursuing it. But to some degree, it may also be the product of the nature of government activity. In some instances, government programs (of all types, not just health-related) have not been designed well enough to achieve the purposes intended or have been subverted to serve purposes explicitly not intended.

In the case of health care, it is extremely difficult to devise public strategies that, on the one hand, do not encourage the misuse of health services and, on the other hand, are not so restrictive as to unnecessarily or arbitrarily limit available care. There is a growing concern, for example, that government assistance in the form of tax exemptions for the purchase of employment-related health insurance has led to the overuse of many services of only very marginal benefit. Similarly, government programs that pay for health care directly (such as Medicaid) have been subject to fraud and abuse by both beneficiaries and providers. Alternatively, efforts to avoid misuse and abuse have at times caused local, state, and Federal programs to suffer from excessive bureaucracy, red tape, inflexibility, and unreasonable interference in individual choice. Also, as with private charity, government programs have not always avoided the unfortunate effects on the human spirit of "discretionary benevolence," especially in those programs requiring income or means tests.

It is also possible that as the government role in health care increases, the private sector's role will decrease in unforeseen and undesired ways. For example, government efforts to ensure access to nursing home care might lead to a lessening of support from family, friends, and other private sources for people who could be cared for in their homes. Although these kinds of problems do not inevitably accompany governmental involvement, they do occur and their presence provides evidence of the need for thoughtful and careful structuring of any government enterprise.

A Right to Health Care?

Often the issue of equitable access to health care is framed in the language of rights. Some who view health care from the perspective of distributive justice argue that the considerations discussed in this chapter show not only that society has a moral obligation to provide equitable access, but also that every individual has a moral right to such access. The Commission has chosen not to develop the case for achieving equitable access through the assertion of a right to health care. Instead it has sought to frame the issues in terms of the special nature of health care and of society's moral obligation to achieve equity, without taking a position on whether the term "obligation" should be read as entailing a moral right. The Commission reaches this conclusion for several reasons: first, such a right is not legally or Constitutionally recognized at the present time; second, it is not a logical corollary of an ethical obligation of the type the Commission has enunciated; and third, it is not necessary as a foundation for appropriate governmental actions to secure adequate health care for all. . . .

Moral Obligations and Rights

The relationship between the concept of a moral right and that of a moral obligation is complex. To say that a person has a moral right to something is always to say that it is that person's due, that is, he or she is morally entitled to it. In contrast, the term "obligation" is used in two different senses. All moral rights imply corresponding obligations, but, depending on the sense of the term that is being used, moral obligations may or may not imply corresponding rights. In the broad sense, to say that society has a moral obligation to do something is to say that it ought morally to do that thing and that failure to do it makes society liable to serious moral criticism. This does not, however, mean that there is a corresponding right. For example, a person may have a moral obligation to help those in need, even though the needy cannot, strictly speaking, demand that person's aid as something they are due.

The government's responsibility for seeing that the obligation to achieve equity is met is independent of the existence of a corresponding moral right to health care. There are many forms of government involvement, such as enforcement of traffic rules or taxation to support national defense, to protect the environment, or to promote biomedical research, that do not presuppose corresponding moral rights but that are nonetheless legitimate and almost universally recognized as such. In a democracy, at least, the people may assign to government the responsibility for seeing that important collective obligations are met, provided that doing so does not violate important moral rights.

As long as the debate over the ethical assessment of patterns of access to health care is carried on simply by the assertion and refutation of a "right to health care," the debate will be incapable of guiding policy. At the very least, the nature of the right must be made

clear and competing accounts of it compared and evaluated. Moreover, if claims of rights are to guide policy they must be supported by sound ethical reasoning and the connections between various rights must be systematically developed, especially where rights are potentially in conflict with one another. At present, however, there is a great deal of dispute among competing theories of rights, with most theories being so abstract and inadequately developed that their implications for health care are not obvious. Rather than attempt to adjudicate among competing theories of rights, the Commission has chosen to concentrate on what it believes to be the more important part of the question: what is the nature of the societal obligation, which exists whether or not people can claim a corresponding right to health care, and how should this societal obligation be fulfilled?

Meeting the Societal Obligation

How Much Care Is Enough?

Before the concept of an adequate level of care can be used as a tool to evaluate patterns of access and efforts to improve equity, it must be fleshed out. Since there is no objective formula for doing this, reasonable people can disagree about whether particular patterns and policies meet the demands of adequacy. The Commission does not attempt to spell out in detail what adequate care should include. Rather it frames the terms in which those who discuss or critique health care issues can consider ethics as well as economics, medical science, and other dimensions.

CHARACTERISTICS OF ADEQUACY   First, the Commission considers it clear that health care can only be judged adequate in relation to an individual's health condition. To begin with a list of techniques or procedures, for example, is not sensible: A CT scan for an accident victim with a serious head injury might be the best way to make a diagnosis essential for the appropriate treatment of that patient; a CT scan for a person with headaches might not be considered essential for adequate care. To focus only on the technique, therefore, rather than on the individual's health and the impact the procedure will have on that individual's welfare and opportunity, would lead to inappropriate policy.

Disagreement will arise about whether the care of some health conditions falls within the demands of adequacy. Most people will agree, however, that some conditions should not be included in the societal obligation to ensure access to adequate care. A relatively uncontroversial example would be changing the shape of a functioning, normal nose or retarding the normal effects of aging (through cosmetic surgery). By the same token, there are some conditions, such as pregnancy, for which care would be regarded as an important component of adequacy. In determining adequacy, it is important to consider how people's welfare, opportunities, and requirements for information and interpersonal caring are affected by their health condition.

Any assessment of adequacy must consider also the types, amounts, and quality of care necessary to respond to each health condition. It is important to emphasize that these questions are implicitly comparative: the standard of adequacy for a condition must reflect the fact that resources used for it will not be available to respond to other conditions. Consequently, the level of care deemed adequate should reflect a reasoned judgment not only about the impact of the condition on the welfare and opportunity of the individual but also about the efficacy and the cost of the care itself in relation to other conditions and the efficacy and cost of the care that is available for them. Since individual cases differ so much, the health care professional and patient must be flexible. Thus adequacy, even in relation to a particular health condition, generally refers to a range of options.

THE RELATIONSHIP OF COSTS AND BENEFITS The

level of care that is available will be determined by the level of resources devoted to producing it. Such allocation should reflect the benefits and costs of the care provided. It should be emphasized that these "benefits," as well as their "costs," should be interpreted broadly, and not restricted only to effects easily quantifiable in monetary terms. Personal benefits include improvements in individuals' functioning and in their quality of life, and the reassurance from worry and the provision of information that are a product of health care. Broader social benefits should be included as well, such as strengthening the sense of community and the belief that no one in serious need of health care will be left without it. Similarly, costs are not merely the funds spent for a treatment but include other less tangible and quantifiable adverse consequences, such as diverting funds away from other socially desirable endeavors including education, welfare, and other social services. There is no objectively correct value that these various costs and benefits have or that can be discovered by the tools of cost/benefit analysis. Still, such an analysis, as a recent report of the Office of Technology Assessment noted, "can be very helpful to decision makers because the process

of analysis gives structure to the problem, allows an open consideration of all relevant effects of a decision, and forces the explicit treatment of key assumptions." But the valuation of the various effects of alternative treatments for different conditions rests on people's values and goals, about which individuals will reasonably disagree. In a democracy, the appropriate values to be assigned to the consequences of policies must ultimately be determined by people expressing their values through social and political processes as well as in the marketplace.

APPROXIMATING ADEQUACY The intention of the Commission is to provide a frame of reference for policymakers, not to resolve these complex questions. Nevertheless, it is possible to raise some of the specific issues that should be considered in determining what constitutes adequate care. It is important, for example, to gather accurate information about and compare the costs and effects, both favorable and unfavorable, of various treatment or management options. The options that better serve the goals that make health care of special importance should be assigned higher value. As already noted, the assessment of costs must take two factors into account: the cost of a proposed option in relation to alternative forms of care that would achieve the same goal of enhancing the welfare and opportunities of the patient's and the cost of each proposed option in terms of foregone opportunities to apply the same resources to social goals other than that of ensuring equitable access.

Furthermore, a reasonable specification of adequate care must reflect an assessment of the relative importance of many different characteristics of a given form of care for a particular condition. Sometimes the problem is posed as: What *amounts* of care and what *quality* of care? Such a formulation reduces a complex problem to only two dimensions, implying that all care can readily be ranked as better or worse. Because two alternative forms of care may vary along a number of dimensions, there may be no consensus among reasonable and informed individuals about which form is of higher overall quality. It is worth bearing in mind that adequacy does not mean the highest possible level of quality or strictly equal quality any more than it requires equal amounts of care; of course, adequacy does require that everyone receive care that meets standards of sound medical practice.

Any combination of arrangements for achieving adequacy will presumably include some health care delivery settings that mainly serve certain groups, such as the poor or those covered by public programs. The fact that patients receive care in different settings or from different providers does not itself show that some are receiving inadequate care. The Commission believes that there is no moral objection to such a system so long as all receive care that is adequate in amount and quality and all patients are treated with concern and respect. . . .